PHYSICS OF THE UPPER ATMOSPHERE

PHYSICS
of the
UPPER ATMOSPHERE

Edited by

J. A. RATCLIFFE

Cavendish Laboratory
University of Cambridge

1960

ACADEMIC PRESS
NEW YORK AND LONDON

Academic Press Inc.
111 Fifth Avenue
New York 3, New York

U.K. Edition, Published by
Academic Press Inc. (London) Ltd.
17 Old Queen Street
London, S.W.1

Library of Congress Catalog Card Number : 60–8053

PRINTED IN GREAT BRITAIN AT
THE UNIVERSITY PRESS
ABERDEEN

161301

CONTRIBUTORS

D. R. BATES, Department of Applied Mathematics, The Queen's University of Belfast, Northern Ireland

HENRY G. BOOKER, School of Electrical Engineering, Cornell University, Ithaca, New York

SYDNEY CHAPMAN, Geophysical Institute, University of Alaska, and High Altitude Observatory, Boulder, Colorado

HERBERT FRIEDMAN, U.S. Naval Research Laboratory, Washington, D.C.

J. S. GREENHOW, University of Manchester, Jodrell Bank Experimental Station, Cheshire, England

A. C. B. LOVELL, University of Manchester, Jodrell Bank Experimental Station, Cheshire, England

HOMER E. NEWELL, Jr., National Aeronautics and Space Administration, Washington, D.C.

M. NICOLET, Service du Rayonnement, IRM., Uccle, Belgium

J. A. RATCLIFFE, Cavendish Laboratory, University of Cambridge, Cambridge, England

E. H. VESTINE, Engineering Division, The Rand Corporation, Santa Monica, California

K. WEEKES, Cavendish Laboratory, University of Cambridge, Cambridge, England

PREFACE

This book is concerned with that part of the atmosphere above a height of about 60 km. The experimental techniques employed, and the theories involved, in this field of investigation are varied and cover a wide range of subjects. The book has therefore been written by a team of workers, each of whom has contributed a chapter, in the form of a monograph, on his own speciality.

Workers in one branch of the subject will find a detailed authoritative account, well supported by references, in the chapters with which they are most closely concerned. The other chapters will provide the background of allied knowledge which is so difficult to acquire from the ordinary scientific literature of a subject as wide as the present one. For those not working on the physics of the upper atmosphere the book as a whole will provide a survey of a part of physics which has made rapid advances in recent years.

The physics of the upper atmosphere was being intensively studied during the period (July 1957 to December 1958) of the IGY, when the book was being written. A final chapter is therefore included in which the individual authors bring their accounts up to date by inclusion of information available up to December 1959 when the book finally went to press.

The bibliographical notes appended to each chapter are intended to present a full set of references to the most important papers on the subject, complete up to December 1959.

J. A. RATCLIFFE,
Editor

Cavendish Laboratory,
Cambridge, January 1960

CONTENTS

CONTRIBUTORS.. v
PREFACE.. vii

Chapter 1. The Thermosphere—The Earth's Outermost Atmosphere
SYDNEY CHAPMAN

1.1 Outline Description of the Earth's Atmosphere............................. 1
1.2 The Boundary between the Earth's Atmosphere and the Solar Corona.......... 7
References.. 16

Chapter 2. The Properties and Constitution of the Upper Atmosphere
M. NICOLET

2.1 The Atmospheric Regions.................................... 17
2.2 Interrelation between Pressure, Temperature, and Composition................ 22
2.3 Composition of the Homosphere............................... 25
2.4 The Dissociation of Molecular Oxygen......................... 29
2.5 The Problem of Diffusion.................................... 35
2.6 Thermal Conductivity in the Thermosphere..................... 48
2.7 Constitution of the Upper Atmosphere......................... 54
References... 69

Chapter 3. The Upper Atmosphere Studied by Rockets and Satellites
HOMER E. NEWELL, Jr.

3.1 Introduction... 73
3.2 Atmospheric Structure...................................... 74
3.3 Winds.. 97
3.4 Charge Densities in the Ionosphere........................... 102
3.5 Earth's Magnetic Field...................................... 108
3.6 Chemical and Ion Composition of the Upper Atmosphere.......... 111
3.7 Atmospheric Contamination Experiments...................... 118
3.8 Night Airglow... 119
3.9 Auroral Particles.. 120
3.10 Cosmic Rays.. 122
3.11 Micrometeors... 123
3.12 Discussion.. 125
References... 129

Chapter 4. The Sun's Ionizing Radiations
HERBERT FRIEDMAN

Introduction.. 133
4.1 Solar Levels... 135
4.2 Rocket Measurements of the Quiet Solar Spectrum.............. 151
4.3 Interaction of Solar Radiation with the Atmosphere............ 178
4.4 Formation of the Ionosphere................................. 186
4.5 Solar Flares... 193
4.6 X-Ray and Ultraviolet Radiation in the Night Sky.............. 202

4.7 Atmospheric Densities and Composition from Radiation Measurements.......... 208
4.8 Auroral X-Rays.. 214
    References.. 215

Chapter 5. The Airglow
D. R. BATES

5.1 Nightglow... 219
5.2 Twilightglow.. 251
5.3 Dayglow... 260
    References.. 261

Chapter 6. General Character of Auroras
D. R. BATES

6.1 Appearance.. 269
6.2 Classification of Auroral Forms... 271
6.3 Altitude... 272
6.4 Other Features of the Geometry... 278
6.5 Geographical Distribution.. 280
6.6 Temporal Distribution.. 284
6.7 Relation with Other Geophysical Phenomena............................... 288
6.8 Motion of Aurora along Lines of Latitude.................................. 293
    References.. 294

Chapter 7. The Auroral Spectrum and its Interpretation
D. R. BATES

7.1 Identifications... 298
7.2 Absolute Intensity... 304
7.3 Relative Intensities.. 307
7.4 Variations in the Auroral Spectrum....................................... 310
7.5 Theory of the Auroral Spectrum.. 316
7.6 Temperature... 339
7.7 Electric Fields... 343
    References.. 348

Chapter 8. Radar Studies of the Aurora
HENRY G. BOOKER

8.1 Introduction... 355
8.2 Pulse Radar Experiments.. 356
8.3 Analysis of Observations in Terms of Azimuth............................ 359
8.4 The Distribution of Auroral Echoes with Range.......................... 360
8.5 Analysis of Auroral Echoes in Terms of Height.......................... 360
8.6 Diurnal, Seasonal, and Sunspot Cycle Variations of Auroral Echoes........... 362
8.7 Motion Associated with Auroral Echoes.................................. 362
8.8 Frequency Dependence of Auroral Echoes................................ 366
8.9 Polarization of Auroral Echoes.. 366
8.10 The Importance of Approximate Perpendicularity between the Earth's Magnetic
     Field and the Radius from the Radar to the Aurora........................ 366
8.11 Theories of Auroral Radar Echoes....................................... 369
8.12 The Cause of Movement in the Location of Auroral Echoes................. 373
     References.. 374

Chapter 9. The Ionosphere
J. A. RATCLIFFE AND K. WEEKES

9.1 Introduction 378
9.2 Theory of the Origin and Shape of Layers of Electrons....................... 380
9.3 The Ionosphere as a Dynamo and a Motor.................................... 392
9.4 Theory of Wave Propagation through the Ionosphere......................... 397
9.5 The Undisturbed D Region... 403
9.6 The Undisturbed E Layer.. 414
9.7 The Undisturbed $F1$ Layer (or Ledge)...................................... 425
9.8 The Undisturbed $F2$ Layer... 427
9.9 The Collision Frequency of Electrons....................................... 441
9.10 Horizontal Irregularities and Movements................................... 445
9.11 Disturbances and Storms in the Ionosphere................................. 450
     References.. 456

Chapter 10. The Upper Atmosphere and Geomagnetism
E. H. VESTINE

10.1 Solar Daily Variation, S_q 471
10.2 Lunar Daily Magnetic Variation... 490
10.3 Magnetic Storms.. 495
10.4 Minor Magnetic Disturbances.. 506
10.5 Magnetic Pulsations.. 508
10.6 Geomagnetism in Relation to other Geophysical Phenomena.................. 509
     References.. 511

Chapter 11. The Upper Atmosphere and Meteors
J. S. GREENHOW AND A. C. B. LOVELL

11.1 Introduction... 513
11.2 Techniques of Measurement.. 514
11.3 Evaporation of Meteors in the Upper Atmosphere........................... 515
11.4 Scattering of Radio Waves from Meteor Trails............................. 518
11.5 Total Meteor Influx 520
11.6 Determination of Scale Heights and Densities............................. 528
11.7 Winds in the Upper Atmosphere: Determination by Meteor Techniques.......... 536
11.8 Recombination and Diffusion of Ionization in Meteor Trails................... 544
     References.. 548

Chapter 12. Advances during the IGY 1957/58
By AUTHORS OF PREVIOUS CHAPTERS

12.1 The Van Allen Radiation Belts That Surround the Earth..................... 551
12.3 The Upper Atmosphere Studied by Rockets and Satellites.................... 555
12.4 The Sun's Ionizing Radiations.. 556
12.8 Radar Studies of the Aurora.. 558
12.9 The Ionosphere... 558
12.11 The Upper Atmosphere and Meteors.. 561

AUTHOR INDEX... 565
SUBJECT INDEX.. 579

Chapter 1

The Thermosphere—
The Earth's Outermost Atmosphere*

SYDNEY CHAPMAN

1.1 Outline Description of the Earth's Atmosphere............................ 1
   1.1.1 Progress of our Conceptions of the Atmosphere...................... 1
   1.1.2 The Mesopause and the Thermosphere............................. 3
   1.1.3 Dissociation, Chemical Reactions, and Luminous Emission in the
      Atmosphere.. 4
   1.1.4 The Ionosphere... 5
   1.1.5 The Hypothetical Isothermal Exosphere........................... 6
1.2 The Boundary between the Earth's Atmosphere and the Solar Corona 7
   1.2.1 The Sun.. 7
   1.2.2 Heat Flow into the Earth's Atmosphere from the Interplanetary Gas.. 11
   1.2.3 The Solar and Coronal "Constants" of Energy Supply............... 11
   1.2.4 The Nature of the Earth's Outermost Atmosphere................... 13
   References... 16

1.1 Outline Description of the Earth's Atmosphere

1.1.1 *Progress of our Conceptions of the Atmosphere*

The primary properties of the atmosphere are its density, temperature, pressure, composition, and motion. The last of these was perhaps the first to be studied, by wind vanes that give the direction of the motion; such vanes date back at least to the time of the ancient Greeks. The wind speed was not reliably measured until much later. The barometer and thermometer came into use in the seventeenth century. Pascal realized that the air pressure measures the weight of overlying air, and confirmed his conclusion by showing that the reading on Torricelli's barometer decreased when this was taken up a mountain. The air temperature, T, measured on mountains and later on balloons and kites, was also found to decrease with increasing height. At first it was thought that this decrease continued indefinitely to the "top" of the atmosphere. If so, the atmosphere would have a limited height, of the order of only about 50 km—forming an aerial mantle round the earth of relatively very small thickness.

This conception of the atmosphere was overthrown when de Bort, about 1900, using registering thermometers carried on kites, found that T ceases to decrease at a height of about 10 km; there, rather abruptly, the temperature gradient falls to a low value, or may even be reversed. Napier Shaw gave

* A brief bibliography will be found at the end of the chapter.

1

convenient names for the level of this transition, and for the regions below and above it. The lower region, of changing weather, he called the *troposphere*; the upper region, of nearly uniform T, he called the *stratosphere*; the boundary between them he called the *tropopause*. He also gave the name *lapse rate* to the temperature gradient (about 6°C km^{-1}) in the troposphere.

It is convenient to use the verb *lapse* to signify an *upward decrease* of any property of the atmosphere, and to use the verb *mount* for an *upward increase*. For example, the air pressure, p, and density, ρ, lapse at all heights, but the lapse of T in the troposphere ceases at the tropopause; in the overlying stratosphere, indeed, T may even mount slightly.

After the discovery of the stratosphere, it was widely thought that T remained constant (at about 220°K) at all greater heights. Calculations of p and ρ were made on this basis. It was also supposed that the stratosphere was a calm region in which the different chemical constituents of the air were in diffusive equilibrium. Air samples taken from heights of around 20 km were thought to reveal a slight increase of the proportion of helium, and even of nitrogen, relative to the heavier constituent, oxygen. According to these conceptions, the atmosphere above about 150 km would consist mainly of molecular hydrogen.

These ideas also were soon overthrown, by several lines of evidence incompatible with them. Meteor trails, occasionally seen at levels of 80 to 100 km, sometimes endure for minutes, or even for an hour or more: in such cases they almost always become distorted, sometimes even tangled— revealing the presence at such levels of strong winds, varying rapidly and irregularly with height. This must hinder the process of atmospheric diffusion, which is slow at such levels. During the last few years, samples of air collected by rockets have confirmed that the air composition is almost the same at 60 km as at the ground.

About 1922 Lindemann * and Dobson inferred from a theory of the more commonly observed very transient meteor trails that the air density at 80 to 100 km exceeds that which is calculated, assuming a uniform value of T at all levels above the tropopause. Hence they concluded that T at some intermediate levels must be greater than was then assumed. This would explain also the occasional observation of loud sounds (from gunfire or explosions) up to the distance of 150 km or so, beyond a zone of silence surrounding the area in which the sound was normally heard. The abnormal propagation came from sound waves that had traveled upward and been refracted down again, from a region of mounting values of T and of the speed of sound.

The presence of such a region of mounting T was later confirmed by thermometric measures on balloons, and especially from rockets. The latter revealed also that above about 50 km, where T attained a maximum of the

* Later Lord Cherwell.

order of 280° to 300°K, it lapsed again to a low minimum at about 80 km. The value of this minimum T is still rather uncertain—estimates range from 150° to 220°K. Above this level T mounts again.

1.1.2 *The Mesopause and the Thermosphere*

By analogy with the nomenclature troposphere, tropopause, and stratosphere, based on the distribution of air temperature, the names stratopause, mesosphere, mesopause, and thermosphere have been proposed for the overlying regions and the boundaries between them. The *thermosphere* is defined as the region of mounting T above the *mesopause*, which is the level of minimum T at about 80 km. The *stratopause*, or upper boundary of the

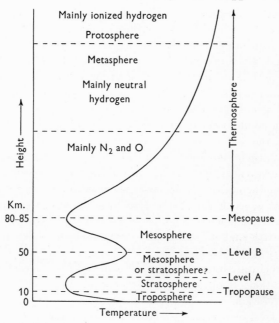

FIG. 1. Schematic diagram of air temperature, T, as a function of height, to illustrate atmospheric nomenclature. Neither the height scale above 80 km, nor the temperature scale above 500°K, is uniform. According to a definition given by Chapman in 1950 level A is called the stratopause and level B the mesopeak, and the mesosphere extends from the level A to the mesopause. Nicolet prefers to name level B the stratopause and to include the region between levels A and B as part of the stratosphere (see p. 18).

stratosphere, has been variously defined as the upper limit of the *isothermal* stratosphere (Fig. 1), where T first begins to mount at a rate of about 2°C km^{-1}, or (as recently defined by Nicolet) as the level of maximum T, at about 50 km. In the former case this maximum level was called the *mesopeak*.

In either case, the region between the stratopause and mesopause is called the *mesosphere*. The diversity of usage concerning the stratopause and the mesosphere will doubtless be eliminated in time—perhaps by international agreement reached through consultation between Associations of the International Union of Geodesy and Geophysics and the World Meteorological Organization. It does not affect the main subject of the present article, which is the atmospheric region above the mesopause.

1.1.3 *Dissociation, Chemical Reactions, and Luminous Emission in the Atmosphere*

The conceptions of the atmosphere prevailing until nearly 1930 envisaged the air as merely a *mixture* of different constituents. It became known, however, through the work of Fabry, Fowler and Rayleigh, Dobson, Götz, and others that the air contains a small amount of the chemically active gas ozone, and that this is relatively more abundant in the stratosphere than in the troposphere. The explanation of its continued presence opened up a new subject—aeronomic chemistry. (*Aeronomy* is the science of the upper region of the atmosphere, where dissociation and ionization are important.) Even as low as 20 or 30 km, the sun's radiation, in the ultraviolet, begins to affect the nature of the air. A very small fraction of the oxygen molecules are broken up into their component atoms, by the relatively intense electrical forces in the ultraviolet light rays from the sun. The oxygen atoms mostly quickly attach themselves to an adjacent molecule of oxygen, to form a triatomic *ozone* molecule. The ozone thus formed, though an extremely rare constituent, absorbs much of the ultraviolet radiation of rather longer wavelength. The earth and its inhabitants are thereby shielded from harmful effects of such rays. The absorbed radiation heats the air, producing the increased temperature inferred by Lindemann and Dobson and confirmed by rocket observations. Some of the ozone is carried downward into the troposphere by convection.

Above the level of maximum relative concentration of ozone its proportion lapses; also its heating effect lapses toward the mesopause. On the contrary, the proportion of unattached oxygen atoms mounts, and above about 100 km the oxygen exists more in the atomic than in the molecular form.

The sun's ultraviolet radiation also dissociates other types of molecule. Nitrogen (N_2) is partly dissociated to atomic nitrogen, though to a far less extent than in the case of oxygen; water vapor (H_2O) is dissociated into atomic hydrogen (H) and hydroxyl (OH), and carbon dioxide (CO_2) into atomic oxygen (O) and carbon monoxide (CO). These dissociations open the way to a numerous set of chemical reactions, leading, *inter alia*, to the formation of oxides of nitrogen—although only nitric oxide (NO) can exist undissociated, to any significant extent, at levels around 100 km. The chemical reactions transform some of the energy, originally imparted by absorption of ultraviolet solar radiation, into luminous energy characteristic of the atoms and molecules involved—particularly O and Na (sodium) and OH. The transformation proceeds throughout the night as well as by day, and gives rise to the *airglow*—the intrinsic luminous emission of the upper atmosphere, more easily observable by night than by day. Much has been learned about the nature of the upper atmosphere from the study of the airglow. This has been advanced not only by observation and theory, but also by experiment. After an initial suggestion by Bates in 1950, gases such as sodium vapor, nitric oxide, and ethylene have been introduced at high levels by means of rockets; luminous effects and additional ionization have been observed as a consequence.

1.1.4 *The Ionosphere*

The shorter-wave ultraviolet solar radiation, extending into the X-ray region, acts still more violently on the molecules and atoms of the upper atmosphere—by detaching one of their electrons, leaving behind a molecular or atomic (positive) ion. Some of the electrons will attach themselves to an atom or molecule of oxygen to form a negative ion. These actions lead to several others—particularly charge transfer and three-body or radiative recombinations. The region in which there are free electrons in significant number is called the *ionosphere* (as proposed by Watson Watt). It extends even below the mesopause (80 km), but the electron density is greatest above 100 km. It rises to a maximum (of the order of 10^5 cm^{-3}) at the peak of the E layer (at about 120 km), and to a greater maximum (of the order of 10^6 cm^{-3}) at the peak (about 300 km) of the F_2 layer. The existence of the ionosphere, as an electrically conducting region, was first glimpsed in 1883 by Balfour Stewart. He inferred it from a study of the small daily geomagnetic variation observed at the earth's surface. In the opening years of this century, after Marconi had transmitted radio waves across the Atlantic, the presence of an ionized region of the upper atmosphere was invoked as the explanation, by Kennelly and Heaviside independently. This region can prevent the passage of radio waves of wavelength below a certain limit into outer space; instead, it reflects or bends them round the curved surface of the earth. Since about 1920 the ionosphere has been energetically explored by radio scientists, among whom Appleton, and Breit and Tuve, were early pioneers. Appleton recognized the presence of more than one ionized layer, and to him are due the names E and F (and the parts $F1$ and $F2$); later electrons were detected in the D region extending below the E layer into the mesosphere.

There is still much to be learned about the ionosphere, but in recent years our understanding of it has greatly advanced. At the low densities there encountered, diffusive transport is far more rapid than in the regions below the mesopause. The importance of diffusion in the ionosphere, in addition to the photochemical and photoelectric action of sunlight, has been shown by Nicolet. Though oxygen is mainly dissociated above 100 km, diffusion maintains some molecular oxygen, as well as nitrogen, even as high as the $F2$ peak. There, however, atomic oxygen seems likely to be a main constituent.

The spectrum of the aurora has added to our knowledge of the ionosphere; atomic oxygen and molecular nitrogen are the chief contributors to the spectrum, but molecular oxygen and atomic nitrogen also reveal their presence thereby. The spectrum shows, in addition, the lines of atomic hydrogen. But these lines have a special character—Doppler broadening and displacement—indicating that the hydrogen atoms have come into the atmosphere with great speed from outside. They are thought to come from the sun. The polar situation of the aurora is a consequence of the deflecting influence of the geomagnetic field on the hydrogen atoms, which enter not as complete neutral particles but as separate nuclei (protons) and electrons. The auroral light from the main region of emission—90 to 130 km—indicates that the gas there is at a low temperature. At times, when the air that emits the auroral light is sunlit, this light is visible up to very great heights, such as 1000 km. This, even more than the existence of the $F2$ layer with its peak at 300 km, is evidence of the great extension of the atmosphere. This great extension is due partly to the reduced mean molecular weight of the air (by reason of dissociation and ionization); even more it is due to the mounting temperature at high levels. The temperature at the $F2$ peak is still not at all accurately known, but reasonable estimates suggest a value of at least 1000°K.

1.1.5 *The Hypothetical Isothermal Exosphere*

Until recently the atmospheric temperature above the $F2$ peak was commonly thought to mount further for another few hundred kilometers. The thermosphere—the region of mounting T extending upward from the mesopause at about 80 km—was then supposed to end, at a level which might naturally be called the thermopause. Above this level T was supposed to remain constant, with a value of about 1500°K. This isothermal region was called the *exosphere*. In this region the air atoms and molecules that happened to be moving upward after their last collision were supposed to suffer no further collision at a higher level. If their upward speed was sufficient, they would escape altogether from the gravitational attraction of the earth— hence the name exosphere. Those with less speed would rise to a maximum height and then fall back again into the atmosphere. The lightest atoms would have the greatest average speeds—which would also depend on the temperature, T; these gases would therefore tend to be lost from the earth's atmosphere, at a slower or faster rate. The atmosphere is supposed to have lost the major part of the helium emitted during the decay of radioactive elements in the solid earth during the course of its long existence. The loss of atomic hydrogen must have been still more rapid.

The possibility and the interest of this process of escape from the atmosphere were first recognized around 1890 by Stoney. The theory of it was later developed by Jeans, Milne, Lennard-Jones, Spitzer, and others. Stoney realized that, although the faster upward-moving molecules in the outer levels of the atmosphere could escape from the earth's attraction, most of them would still remain subject to the attraction of the sun. They would therefore not escape from the solar system but would remain in interplanetary space. Hence this space must have become pervaded to some extent by particles that had escaped from the control of the earth and other planets. On this account, if on no other, these bodies would from time to time—or, more exactly, continuously—*gain* particles from this pervasive gas through which they move in their orbits. Ultimately a fairly steady state must have been reached, in which the escape and inflow at least partly balance. The theories of escape, however, took no account of any such return flow.

But the interplanetary gas may not come only from the planetary atmospheres—indeed these may be only a minor source of it. May not the sun make an appreciable, perhaps even the major, contribution to it? To answer this question it is natural to proceed to consider the atmosphere of the sun.

1.2 The Boundary between the Earth's Atmosphere and the Solar Corona

1.2.1 *The Sun*

The sun is a vast all-gaseous body, near whose center the pressure and temperature permit nuclear transformations. These release energy, somewhat as in a hydrogen bomb or nuclear reactor. The temperature of the generating region is of the order of 15 million degrees C. The energy released streams, mainly as radiation, through the overlying layers. As it travels upward and outward, through regions of ever-lapsing temperature, the spectral constitution of the radiant energy is continually changed. Finally the radiation emerges as sunlight, across what to us looks like a rather sharply defined "edge" of the sun—the photosphere. This region has a temperature of about 6000°K, and the spectrum of sunlight corresponds approximately to that of light emitted by an incandescent solid at this temperature. The lapse rate of temperature from the sun's center to the photosphere is of the order of 20°C km^{-1}. The relatively cool photosphere imposes some absorption lines on the solar spectrum.

Many complicated phenomena occur in and above the photosphere. These are nowadays closely observed by solar physicists. There are sunspots, with their strong and changing magnetic fields. There are "sunstorms," in which intensely bright "flares" may occur, while jets of luminous gas are vigorously thrown upward—to heights of tens or hundreds of thousands of kilometers, or even with speeds that allow complete escape from the sun's attraction. Often also luminous gas is seen streaming downward from invisible sources, along curved paths whose form suggests lines of magnetic force. The lower part of the region above the photosphere is called the *chromosphere*; this is a region of mounting temperature. It is surmounted by a still more tenuous region called the solar corona. In the corona T continues to mount, until at a height of about 50,000 km it attains a maximum whose average value, T_0, is estimated to be of the order of two million degrees. The average mount rate of T from the photosphere up to this coronal peak level is therefore of the order of 40°C km^{-1}.

The corona is composed mainly of ionized atomic hydrogen, that is, of hydrogen broken up into protons and electrons. There is also a small proportion of helium, also fully ionized into nuclei (α-particles) and electrons. In addition there are other elements in much smaller proportions—to be reckoned in parts per million protons. Those with the smaller atomic numbers, such as carbon and oxygen, are also almost completely ionized. But the emission spectrum of the corona contains lines due to heavier elements, like argon, nickel, iron, and calcium, that are highly but incompletely ionized; they have lost from nine to fifteen of their electrons. This high state of ionization is one indication of the high temperature of the corona. Another indication is the absence of the Fraunhofer absorption lines in the continuous spectrum of the major part of the light by which the inner hottest layer of the corona reveals its presence. This light is sunlight scattered by the coronal electrons, and the Doppler effect on this light blurs out the absorption lines, because of the high random speeds of the electrons. Yet another indication of the high coronal temperature is the short-wave radio emission from it.

The main physical properties of the coronal gas are determined by its principal constituent, ionized atomic hydrogen—protons and electrons. The thermal conductivity, K, for such a gas can be calculated fairly exactly; it depends little on the number density, and greatly on T—in fact K varies as $T^{5/2}$.

The corona loses some heat by its own emission of light from the comparatively few atoms in it that retain some electrons. It loses more heat by thermal conduction, mainly downward to the photosphere, but also outward into interplanetary space. Above the coronal peak level, conduction is an important process of heat loss, but the main process may be eddy conduction associated with turbulence.

A first approximation to the thermal state of the outer corona, above this level, can be inferred from calculations based on an idealized model of the corona. The corona is not static, constant, and spherically symmetrical; it is irregular in form and often disturbed by gas projected into or through it from below. Still it is of interest and value to consider what its state would be if these disturbing influences were absent; and at least at periods of low sunstorm activity such influences are much reduced.

In the model corona the total outflow of heat, F, conducted across any concentric sphere of radius r must be independent of r—otherwise there would be depletion or accumulation of heat in particular layers, and hence a changing temperature. Thus, if K refers to combined "molecular" and eddy conduction,

$$F = -4\pi r^2 K \, dT/dr = \text{Constant.} \tag{1.1}$$

In this expression we may write

$$K = K_0 \, (T/T_0)^s \tag{1.2}$$

where $s = 5/2$ if conduction is only "molecular"; if eddy conduction is also operating, s is unknown and may not be constant; K_0 refers to the coronal peak level at radius r_0 and temperature T_0. The combination of equations (1.1) and (1.2) gives a very simple differential equation connecting T and r; its solution is

$$T_0^q - T^q = C(1/r_0 - 1/r) \tag{1.3}$$

where $q = 1 + s$, and

$$C = qFT_0^s/4\pi \, K_0 = -qr_0^2 T_0^s T_0' \tag{1.4}$$

where T' denotes dT/dr, and T_0' its value at radius r_0.

If T is taken to be zero, or small compared with T_0, at infinity or at a radius large compared with r_0, equation (1.3) indicates that

$$C = r_0 T_0^q \tag{1.5}$$

either exactly or approximately. Hence also

$$F = 4\pi r_0 K_0 T_0/q \tag{1.6}$$

and

$$T = T_0(r_0/r)^{1/q}. \tag{1.7}$$

Thus T varies inversely as a small fractional power of r. At the earth's distance, if eddy conduction is absent, this indicates a temperature, T_E, of the order of 200,000°K if $T_0 = 10^6$, and proportionately for any smaller or larger value of T_0. The lapse rate of T radially outward from the sun at this distance is below 10°C per 10,000 km. Thus the earth is moving through a very hot gas of nearly uniform temperature, at least if eddy conduction is absent.

Having inferred the relation between T and r in the model outer corona, we can calculate rather simply the number density, N, of protons and electrons in it, at any distance up to and beyond the earth (until T sinks below 30,000°K, after which there is appreciable recombination to form neutral hydrogen atoms). The calculated relation between N and r does not determine the value of N_0 at the coronal peak radius, r_0. But when N_0 in the theoretical formula is taken equal to the value determined for that level by the astronomer's eclipse observations, and T_0 is taken to be of the order of 10^6, then the values of N at other radii agree fairly well with the observed values; these have been determined to a distance of over 25 solar radii, by observations from balloons and aircraft.

The corresponding density N_E at the earth's distance is sensitive to the value of T_0; if T_0 is 10^6, N_E is about 340; if T_0 is 1.2 million, N_E is 4100.

However, an analysis of the values of N inferred by Blackwell from the coronal observations he made from an aircraft during the eclipse of June 30, 1954, suggests a less simple "model" of the outer corona and solar atmosphere. The value I deduced from them for the temperature T_0 is about two million degrees instead of one million—and this agrees with the current opinion of the solar physicists who study the coronal spectrum. Also s is less than $5/2$, and decreases outward. This decrease is ascribed to the influence of eddy conduction. Extrapolation to obtain the value of T at the earth's distance is uncertain, but values of 100,000° to 50,000° seems not unlikely. Owing to our ignorance of the rate of the rotation of the outer atmosphere of the sun (indicated by the elliptical form of the zodiacal light) no certain deduction of N_E at the earth's distance is yet possible, in the plane of the sun's equator or the ecliptic.

At this distance the value of N_E may be more uncertain than the value of T_0. This is because the model steady state may be disturbed by the gas that appears to stream from active solar areas, with speeds of the order of 1000 km sec $^{-1}$. There may also be a general slower outward streaming from all over the sun. The study of the zodiacal light has led to an estimate $N_E = 600$ for the space around the earth, but this seems rather uncertain. But whatever the value of N_E may be, it seems not unlikely that the coronal temperature at the earth's distance will be of order 50,000°K or more.

Thus the earth's orbital motion proceeds through a space filled with a rare but very hot gas, composed mainly of protons and electrons. The zodiacal light reveals that dust also is present. The mean free path is very long, namely a moderate fraction of the distance between the sun and the earth. The interplanetary gas is a part of the sun's atmosphere—far more extensive than was formerly supposed. It also receives contributions from gas that escapes from the planetary atmospheres. Conversely, some of the solar interplanetary gas is captured by the planets—there is a balance, not necessarily complete, between the processes of escape from and gain to the atmospheres of the planets.

1.2.2 Heat Flow into the Earth's Atmosphere from the Interplanetary Gas

The earth is a cold object moving through the hot interplanetary gas. Heat must be conveyed from this gas to the earth's atmosphere. There must be a gradual transition from the temperature, T_E, of the coronal gas at the earth's distance to that of the ionosphere. Hence the conception of an isothermal exosphere must be given up. Instead one must conclude that the thermosphere, the region of mounting temperature extending upward from the mesopause, includes all the overlying part of the earth's atmosphere. At least we know of no cause that would indicate a region of inversion, where T again lapses. The past history of conceptions of the atmosphere shows how likely one is to err in picturing the state of unknown upper regions not yet explored. But on the basis of present knowledge it would seem that the thermopause, the upper limit of the thermosphere, is the ill-defined level at which our atmosphere merges with the interplanetary gas. Below that level T decreases, though not uniformly, down to the mesopause. The merging level, the thermopause, will also be that at which the density begins to increase downward toward the earth, under its gravitational attraction.

Thus the earth must gain heat from the sun by *conduction*, trapping some of the convective heat flowing outward through the far-spreading corona above its peak level. This gain of heat is additional to the energy of sunlight intercepted by the earth. The radiant energy of sunlight streams almost unaffected through the gas-filled interplanetary space, and only a small fraction of that which the earth receives is absorbed at various levels in our atmosphere.

1.2.3 The Solar and Coronal "Constants" of Energy Supply

The radiative energy flux in the solar rays at the earth's distance is a quantity of prime concern to meteorology and climatology. The part of this flux that falls on (one hemisphere of) the earth drives the great atmospheric " engine" and energizes the variations of weather. The name " solar constant" is given to the magnitude of this flux, just outside the earth's atmosphere. Meteorologists usually express it in calories cm^{-2} min^{-1} (the value so expressed is about 1.95); in ergs cm^{-2} sec^{-1} its value is approximately 1.36×10^6. Most of it reaches ground level, but some is absorbed, scattered, or reflected (as by clouds) in the atmosphere. Except at the subsolar point the flux per square centimeter of the earth's surface is reduced because of the obliquity of the beam to the vertical. The total flux falling on the illuminated hemisphere is about 3.5×10^{24} ergs sec^{-1}.

The heat imparted to the earth's atmosphere from the interplanetary coronal gas flows inward over the whole sphere. Its distribution is unlikely to be uniform, because of the orbital motion through the corona, and because of the geomagnetic field. The total inward flux, F_E, over the whole earth may also vary with time, as the corona near the sun is observed to do, both irregularly, and in the course of the 11-year sunspot cycle. It seems appropriate to give the name *coronal constant* (by analogy with *solar constant*) to the flux intensity, f_E, given by F_E/S, where S denotes the area of the earth's surface (5.1×10^{18} cm^2)—though it might be better to divide F_E by the area of the surface of a concentric sphere at a height of (say) 500 km above the earth. This coronal constant, f_E, is likely to vary more with time than does the solar constant, whose changes so far appear ever smaller, the more accurate is the measurement.

It does not seem possible at present to calculate F_E or f_E reliably from coronal data. One factor that must complicate the calculation is the orbital motion of the earth. Another is the influence of the geomagnetic field, which in an ionized gas reduces the thermal conductivity for heat flow across the field. I have attempted to estimate F_E, on crude assumptions, and obtained the value 2.4×10^{19} ergs sec^{-1}, giving f_E as 4.7 ergs cm^{-2} sec^{-1}. But I place little reliance on this estimate—which, be it noted, gives the ratio of the solar to the coronal constant as about 3 parts in a million. It certainly seems likely that the coronal constant has no significance for the main thermal and dynamical processes of the earth; but its influence on the outermost atmosphere is profound. The ever-mounting temperature above the mesopause greatly reduces the density lapse rate, so that the atmosphere extends to far greater distances than would correspond to the older conception of an isothermal exosphere.

But F_E and f_E may be determinable in due time from observations of the thermal gradient, dT/dh, in the atmosphere, and from a knowledge of the thermal conductivity, K. The downward-conducted heat flux is $K\, dT/dh$. In 1949 Spitzer drew attention to this downward flux; he estimated K (using a rigid-sphere formula) to be 4.1×10^3 ergs cm^{-1} sec^{-1} deg^{-1}. He estimated the radiant energy absorbed in the F layer, and the temperature gradient that would enable conduction downward to dispose of this energy. Bates later wrote two important papers on the same general subject. He used a formula for K that took account of its variation with T—at a greater rate than according to the rigid-sphere formula used by Spitzer. For $T = 1000°$K his value of K was 5.9×10^3 ergs cm sec^{-1} deg^{-1}. In his second paper (Bates, 1956) he concluded that the probable downward heat flow below the F_2 peak was decidedly greater than could be explained by solar radiant energy absorbed in the F layer, unless rather improbable assumptions are made. These may be unnecessary if, as here indicated, heat flows *through* the F layer from the coronal gas surrounding the earth. If this is the *main* part of the heat flux below the $F2$ peak, and if, for the present tentative discussion, dT/dh there is taken to be uniform over the earth, then F_E will be given approximately by

$$F_E = 4\pi R^2 K \, dT/dh$$

where $R = a + h$ (and a denotes the earth's radius).

At present neither K nor dT/dh is accurately known for the region between the mesopause and the $F2$ peak. For an order-of-magnitude calculation one may use the values $h = 200$ km, $K = 5 \times 10^3$, $dT/dh = 5$ deg km^{-1} or 5×10^{-5} deg cm^{-1}. The estimate of F_E so obtained is 1.36×10^{18} ergs sec^{-1}; the corresponding downward flux intensity, $K \, dT/dh$, is 0.25 erg cm^{-2} sec^{-1} —about a nineteenth of the doubtfully estimated value of f_E earlier mentioned. If the picture of the outermost atmosphere here presented is essentially true, the heat flux may exceed 0.25 erg cm^{-2} sec^{-1}.

1.2.4 *The Nature of the Earth's Outermost Atmosphere*

In an isothermal atmosphere in diffusive equilibrium, each constituent is distributed with density varying exponentially with height, if we may ignore the curvature of the level layers and the upward decrease of gravity. That is, the density of constituent n varies as exp $(-h/H_n)$, where H_n denotes the scale height $RT/W_n g$; R is the gas constant 8.3×10^7 ergs deg^{-1}, and W_n is the (chemical) molecular or atomic weight. Alternatively the variation is expressible as $10^{(-h/H'_n)}$, where $H'_n = 2.30 \, H_n$; H'_n denotes the decimal scale height.

Nicolet has recently concluded that at the $F2$ peak the principal constituent of the air is atomic oxygen, for which $W_n = 16$. There must, however, also be some atomic hydrogen at that level, partly produced by dissociation of water vapor at lower levels; for this gas, $W_n = 1$. If, as Nicolet concludes, diffusion at and above the $F2$ peak far overpowers any mixing tendencies that are present, and if the atmosphere were isothermal and exponential in those regions, the proportion of O to H would decrease upward in the ratio $1 : 10^{-15}$ in a distance of one decimal scale height of atomic hydrogen. For the actual atmosphere, of mounting T and lapsing g, the same general conclusion can be drawn, that at some height above the $F2$ peak the atomic oxygen (and other elements) must become negligible compared with atomic hydrogen, which will there be effectively the sole constituent of the "air." The height at which this will occur cannot, however, be calculated at present

—because we do not know the ratio of H to O at the $F2$ peak, nor the values of dT/dh and K there and above. Likewise we cannot yet estimate reliably the value of T at the level where H becomes the main constituent—nor the proportion of the atomic hydrogen that is ionized into protons and electrons. This proportion depends partly on T, and partly on the photoionizing influence of sunlight of wavelength less than about 1000 A. At levels where T is 30,000°K or more, however, the hydrogen will be almost completely ionized by thermal ionization, apart from any contribution by photoionization. Thus, in the outer part of the thermosphere, where T mounts from 30,000°K to the temperature (50,000°K or more?) of the interplanetary gas, the "air" consists almost entirely of protons and electrons. Hence its nature is the same as that of the surrounding interplanetary gas. The source of this air is twofold. Some of it has come from below by diffusion from levels where water vapor and molecular hydrogen were dissociated by sunlight. Some has come from the coronal gas, "captured" by the earth's gravitational pull. It is unnecessary here to inquire what are the relative contributions from these two sources.

It may be worth while to give special names to the two parts of the outer atmospheric region where atomic hydrogen is effectively the sole constituent. The fully ionized upper part may be called the *protosphere*,* and the lower, partly neutral layer may be called the *metasphere* (from *meta*, between). The division between the two (the *metapause*) is naturally rather indefinite, as it depends on the significance of the words *fully* and *partly*.

In the protosphere the thermal conductivity for the flow of heat along the geomagnetic lines of force may be estimated rather accurately—perhaps within 10 %—as $5 \times 10^{-7} T^{5/2}$ erg sec^{-1} cm deg^{-1}. But for heat conduction across the lines of force K is reduced by a factor of the order of $\nu^2/(\nu^2 + \omega^2)$, where ν denotes the collision frequency of the electrons, and ω their gyromagnetic frequency, eB/m; here e denotes the charge (emu) and m the mass of an electron, and B the magnetic induction.

There are reasons for thinking that B and ω do not diminish simply according to the law $1/R^3$ for a dipole field; and we do not yet know how ν varies with R. Hence we cannot yet estimate the degree of reduction of K and of the heat flow from the coronal gas, for example in the geomagnetic equatorial plane, as compared with K and the heat flow along the geomagnetic axis. It seems likely, however, that the top of the metasphere receives more conducted heat per square centimeter in polar than in low latitudes. This may set up a general circulation in the metasphere; naturally it will differ in character from the general circulation of lower regions of the atmosphere,

---

* From *protos*, first—this being the first part of our atmosphere when approached from outside. The same root occurs also, of course, in proton, and this may be a reminder that the protosphere consists of protons (and electrons).

where the heating is greater in low than in polar latitudes. It is not clear at present how these processes will affect the temperature distribution and the extension of the metasphere and protosphere—for example, whether or not the outer atmosphere will be markedly ellipsoidal rather than spherical.

In the metasphere and at lower levels the air is a mixture. Calculations of K must take account of this. The contribution to K from the neutral part of the air is not affected, at least directly, by the presence of the geomagnetic field. In the metasphere and below, the distribution of the downward heat flux may tend toward uniformity over the earth—that is, K and dT/dh may be independent of the latitude, or nearly so, though they will vary with height.

In such a region, so long as its composition is *uniform*, equations (1.1) to (1.4) already given for the model solar corona would be approximately applicable to the earth's atmosphere, because K varies approximately as T^s. The value of s for a nearly neutral simple or mixed gas, however, is much less than $5/2$—it probably lies between $1/2$ and 1. Equations (1.5) to (1.7) obtained by taking T to be zero for infinite R, are of course not valid here.

But in a region in which the composition and the mean molecular weight, W, change with height, equations (1.1) to (1.4) are not applicable, because K depends on W (as $1/W^{\frac{1}{2}}$, for a simple gas) as well as on T.

It is certain that if the general ideas here outlined are correct, so that except at very high levels $R^2K\, dT/dh$ is constant, the temperature gradient, dT/dh, must continually decrease upward, as R increases, and as K increases because of its dependence on T and W. In passing from the metasphere to the protosphere, however, K may conceivably at first decrease. The value of K for neutral atomic hydrogen is not known, but it may be estimated as

$$K = 1.5 \times 10^3\, T^{\frac{1}{2}}\ \text{ergs sec}^{-1}\,\text{cm}^{-1}\,\text{deg}^{-1} \qquad \text{(metasphere)}.$$

That of fully ionized atomic hydrogen, of the densities and temperatures concerned, is approximately

$$K = 5 \times 10^{-7}\, T^{5/2}\ \text{ergs sec}^{-1}\,\text{cm}^{-1}\,\text{deg}^{-1} \qquad \text{(protosphere)}.$$

These are equal at $T = 55{,}000°\text{K}$—a temperature perhaps attained at a level above the metapause. Hence at the metapause, in polar regions where the effective K in the protosphere is uninfluenced by the geomagnetic field, there may possibly be an upward increase of dT/dh by a factor of about 3 —which is the ratio of the above two expressions for K when T is $30{,}000°\text{K}$. Actually, however, any such increase is likely to be gradual, as the hydrogen approaches practically complete ionization. In fact there may be no lapse of K near the metapause, but only a reduction in its mount rate.

It is hardly possible at present to estimate the heights of the metapause and the thermopause. Even if we knew the constants involved in the calculation, on the simplest lines that are consistent with the above ideas, the calculation would be very difficult. But it is likely that there are significant features of the upper thermosphere of which as yet we have no conception. One pointer to such features is the discovery of the intense rays revealed by Van Allen's cosmic-ray counters carried by the first and third satellites of the United States, at a height of about 1000 km. (See § 12·1)

It does seem highly probable, however, that the extent of the earth's atmosphere far exceeds what was formerly thought. This can be crudely inferred as follows.

The value of dT/dh seems unlikely to exceed 20 deg km^{-1} at the level in the F layer (at or below the $F2$ peak) where T is 1000°K. The main constituent there may be atomic oxygen; hence W will be at least 16. At the unknown higher level where T has attained the value 25,000°K, one may suppose that W has fallen to 1, corresponding to atomic hydrogen. If the minimum value of s is taken to be $\frac{1}{2}$, the value of K will have increased twentyfold. Hence, as R has also increased, dT/dh will have become less than 1 deg km^{-1}. It seems rather unlikely that at greater heights it will increase—rather the opposite, at least along the geomagnetic lines of force. Hence if T is to rise from 25,000°K to perhaps 50,000°K, a distance of the order of 100,000 km may be required. Thus one may infer that the earth's atmosphere extends outward to distances that are a considerable fraction of the distance to the moon, at least along the direction of the geomagnetic axis.

Within this atmosphere, perhaps below the metapause, doubtless many electromagnetic phenomena of great interest take place. Among these one may mention whistlers and other radio events, and phenomena associated with cosmic rays, magnetic storms, and the aurora.

References

Bates, D. R., *Proc. Phys. Soc.* B**64**, 805 (1951).

Bates, D. R. and Nicolet, M., *J. Geophys. Res.* **55**, 301 (1950).

Bates, D. R., *Proc. Roy. Soc.* A**236**, 206 (1956).

Chapman, S., *Proc. Phys. Soc.* B**64**, 833 (1951).

Chapman, S., *Smithsonian Contrib. Astrophys.* **2**, 1 (1957).

Chapman, S. *in* "The Threshold of Space" (M. Zelikoff, ed.). Pergamon, London, 1958.

Chapman, S., *Astrophys. J.* **120**, 151 (1954).

Chapman, S., *Proc. Roy. Soc.* A**253**, 462 (1959).

Havens, R. J., Knoll, R. T., and Lagow, H. E., *J. Geophys. Res.* **57**, 59 (1952).

Mange, P., *J. Geophys. Res.* **62**, 279 (1957).

Nicolet, M., *J. Atmos. Terr. Phys.* **5**, 132 (1954).

Nicolet, M., and Mange, P., *J. Geophys. Res.* **59**, 16 (1954).

The Rocket Panel, *Phys. Rev.* **84**, 1027 (1952).

Spitzer, L., *in* "The Earth as a Planet" (G. Kuiper, ed.), Univ. of Chicago Press, Chicago, 1949.

Chapter 2

The Properties and Constitution of the Upper Atmosphere

M. NICOLET

2.1 The Atmospheric Regions... 17
2.2 Interrelation between Pressure, Temperature, and Composition.............. 22
2.3 Composition of the Homosphere... 25
2.4 The Dissociation of Molecular Oxygen...................................... 29
2.5 The Problem of Diffusion.. 35
2.6 Thermal Conductivity in the Thermosphere................................. 48
2.7 Constitution of the Upper Atmosphere..................................... 54
    References.. 69

2.1 The Atmospheric Regions

In a general description of its physical constitution and chemical composition, the earth's atmosphere may be considered as a perfect gas composed of molecules and atoms of which only a small fraction is represented by charged particles, ions, and electrons, influenced by the geomagnetic field.

It is not possible, however, to determine the behavior of the neutral particles, and finally to obtain a physical picture of the upper atmosphere, without determining whether vertical distribution depends on mixing or diffusion, or on a chemical or photochemical equilibrium. In particular, it is extremely important to determine how dissociation and recombination of molecular and atomic oxygen and nitrogen are distributed with height. Furthermore, the structure of the upper atmosphere deduced from pressure or density measurements is related to the variations of the mean molecular mass, depending on diffusion effects. In addition, it is necessary to know which are the most important processes of heat propagation, that is to say, convection, conduction, or radiation.

Before describing the atmosphere above 50 km it is best to summarize our knowledge of the regions below (Fig. 1).

The lower region, called the *troposphere* (*tropos* = turn or change), can be defined, in a static atmosphere, by the pressure and the temperature if the molecular mass is assumed to be constant. Meteorological soundings have shown that the temperature decreases with altitude in the troposphere, reaching a temperature of about 220°K in the polar regions and about 190°K at the equator. These lower limits of the temperature are representative of the *tropopause* (*pausis* = end, cessation). The latter, however, varies

2 17

in height as a function of latitude, from below 10 km in the polar regions to more than 15 km in the equatorial belt. The variations in the level of the

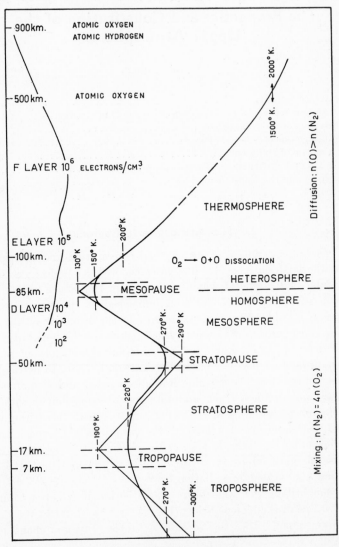

Atmospheric Nomenclature.

FIG. 1. The main names of the atmospheric regions, from *troposphere* to *thermosphere*, are based on a thermal classification. When the classification is given according to composition, the term *homosphere* means that the mean molecular mass is constant, and *heterosphere* means that the mean molecular mass varies. Names such as *ionosphere*, *chemosphere*, and *ozonosphere* are descriptive of regions where particular processes take place.

tropopause (about 5 km) in the middle latitudes show that the changes in its structure are dependent on such atmospheric phenomena as high and low pressures. One of the essential characters of the troposphere is that the geographic equator is, to a certain extent, a "barrier" differentiating and separating the northern and southern hemispheres.

The *stratosphere* is essentially that region where the temperature increases, or at least does not decrease, with altitude. The stratosphere * extends from the tropopause to an altitude of about 50 km (stratopause *), where the temperature reaches a peak of the order of 270°K. The seasonal variation in atmospheric ozone and the fall-out of radioactive products artificially introduced into the stratosphere show that, if the mass exchange in the stratosphere is sufficient to maintain mixing, the transport is certainly carried out from each side of the equator. In other words, one of the characteristic properties of the stratosphere is that meridional transport must be added to zonal transport. Since the eruption of Krakatoa in 1883, it has been known that the mean speed of deplacement around the earth is about 120 km per hour. In addition, the spread of matter northward or southward indicates that the meridional circulation in the stratosphere is different from that of the troposphere.

The *mesosphere* (*mesos* = middle) is a region situated above the stratopause (50 ± 5 km) where the temperature decreases rapidly with altitude. The temperature may reach a minimum, as low as 150° ± 10°K, at about 85 ± 5 km, where the mesosphere ends at a level called the mesopause. Photochemical action is very important in the mesosphere; the chemical reactions affecting minor constituents in the air play an important role in determining atmospheric behavior. As a result of photochemical actions, airglow emissions are observed in the mesosphere. As a result not only of atmospheric motions, but also of atomic and molecular processes, the mesopause must have a tendency toward variation in height just as have the tropopause and the stratopause. The mesosphere is particularly important for the study of aeronomic processes because in it one may still follow fluctuations arising from atomic and molecular processes which manifest themselves as day-to-day variations in the hydrodynamic variables.

The essential feature of these three lower regions is that the hydrodynamical problems are practically identical. The differences are made clear at the

---

* Because of possible ambiguity in the terminology, S. Chapman found it preferable to use the word stratosphere to mean not the whole region above the troposphere but only a layer between the tropopause and an upper boundary called the stratopause. We propose that the stratosphere represents a region differing from the regions below (troposphere) and above (mesosphere), and in which there are positive temperature gradients in contrast to the negative gradients in the neighboring regions.

limits. Thus the conditions in the troposphere are dependent on the conditions at the surface of the earth. In the heat budget of the stratosphere the effects of radiation have to be added to those of convection. Nevertheless, the characteristic common to these three regions is that the mean molecular mass of the principal constituents of the air remains constant, which implies that mixing is always maintained. Because the composition remains the same, it is said that the *homosphere* (*homos* = same) extends from ground level to the mesopause.

The vertical distribution of ozone makes it possible to understand the different roles of these three regions of the homosphere. In the mesosphere, atmospheric ozone is less abundant than atomic oxygen, in an atmosphere illuminated by the sun, and there is a considerable variation between day and night. In the stratosphere, ozone, the presence of which depends on photochemical reactions, has a very long life, and as its residence time is of the order of a year its seasonal variations are due to meridional transport. Finally, in the troposphere, ozone is a permanent element of the air mass, and its variations are intrinsically associated with the advective and dynamic transports of air. Thus, the ozonosphere is a term which cannot be associated with a definitive altitude region.

Above the mesopause there is a change in the composition and the structure of the air concurrent with the large height gradient of temperature. Because the composition of the atmosphere changes with height, this region * is called the *heterosphere* (*heteros* = other). This variation is due, first to the partial dissociation of oxygen and, second, to diffusion.

If, however, the temperature, which is an important parameter in this region, is considered, then this region above the mesopause is called the thermosphere, because the temperature in the thermosphere increases with altitude. The height at which this temperature gradient should cease could be called the thermopause, but, as we shall see later, it is possible to state that there is no thermopause if, for example, there is heat flow by conduction from the solar corona.

This height gradient of temperature in the thermosphere results from absorbed energy. Above the mesopause all ultraviolet radiation with a wavelength less than 1750 A is gradually absorbed, and an important fraction of the energy obtained may be used for heating the thermosphere. As there is only one possible means of transfer of energy by radiation [the line at 63 μ of atomic oxygen (see §2.4)], the principal processes of heat transport are convection in the lower thermosphere and conduction in the upper thermosphere.

---

* The heterosphere may begin at the mesopause. It is not yet possible, however, to determine the exact altitude at which the mean molecular mass is sufficiently affected by the dissociation of O_2 and diffusion, and in any case this altitude can be expected to be variable owing to latitudinal and seasonal effects.

Above a certain altitude simple laws deduced from the statical equation and the equation of state (2.2) no longer apply because dynamic processes modify the statical picture. In this region, the *metasphere* (*meta* = between), the behavior cannot be explained by a static representation, although the medium is still mainly un-ionized.

The outermost part of the atmosphere, which is almost fully ionized and where protons are more abundant than neutral hydrogen, should be called the *protosphere*.* The satellites have played an important part in the exploration of these regions, which were originally called the *exosphere* (*exo* = outside) because it was thought that in this region the laws of gas kinetics no longer applied.

To a certain extent, the study of the exosphere was concerned with the escape of neutral particles and the level at which this escape began (the beginning of the exosphere). The processes affecting charged particles are involved, however, in the dynamics of the upper atmosphere, which should be studied in relation to the geomagnetic field.

For several years we have placed limits on the ionosphere (that region where ions and electrons play a role). Conventional definitions of the ionosphere include that part of the atmosphere which comprises the D, E, and F regions, that is to say, roughly the atmospheric region between 80 and 400 km. Even in certain old and unsatisfactory systems of nomenclature the word ionosphere was used to represent an atmospheric layer between other layers, such as the layer between a "stratosphere" and a "mesosphere." Today, after observations obtained from whistlers, rockets, and satellites, this can no longer be accepted because the total electron content of the atmosphere is several times the electron content below the $F2$ peak. Thus the term ionosphere covers several atmospheric regions. Furthermore the fact that the word ionosphere is associated with the properties of charged particles requires that the geomagnetic field be taken into account. In addition, the dynamic processes are more important in the ionosphere than in that part of the ionosphere which is neutral. Finally, there is an association of the ionospheric phenomena with the geographic distribution of the aurora, and for this reason it is possible to make the appropriate distinctions when using the terminology of Chapman. Thus, the *auroral regions* include those of geomagnetic latitudes greater than 60°; there is a northern auroral and a southern auroral region. The *subauroral belts* lie between geomagnetic latitudes 60° and 45° and are the geographical regions where auroras are occasionally seen in mean latitudes, especially near and during a sunspot maximum. In the same way, it is possible to consider a *minauroral belt* lying between geomagnetic latitudes 45° N and S where only exceptional auroras

* According to a private communication from S. Chapman; according to Shlovsky's nomenclature, the metasphere and protosphere should be called the geocorona.

are visible. In the analysis of geomagnetic and ionospheric observations one
also speaks of the *equatorial belt* situated within the minauroral belt and
lying between geomagnetic latitudes 20° N and S.

In finishing this brief description it should be said that in aeronomy,
where particular importance is attached to the study of physical and chemical
properties, and where dissociation and ionization play a primary role, the
minor constituents should be considered to be of the same importance as the
major constituents, nitrogen and oxygen.

2.2 Interrelation between Pressure, Temperature, and Composition

In the air the height (z) distribution of the atmospheric pressure is obtained
from the differential equation relating the density, ρ, to the hydrostatic
pressure, p:

$$dp/dz = - g\rho \tag{2.1}$$

where g denotes the acceleration of gravity. The density, ρ, is a function of
the molecular masses of the various constituents, m_i, and the number densities
or concentrations of the constituents, n_i. Thus,

$$\rho = \Sigma n_i m_i \equiv nm \tag{2.2}$$

with the mean molecular mass defined by

$$m = \Sigma n_i m_i / \Sigma n_i \tag{2.3}$$

and the total concentration by

$$n = \Sigma n_i. \tag{2.4}$$

The statical equation (2.1) indicates that there is no variation in height
and in time of the mean mass transport velocity. If there is some variation,
a more complicated equation, i.e., the conservation equation of momentum,
must be considered and generally does not correspond to a steady state.

Since air behaves like a perfect gas, the equation of state is written as
follows:

$$p = nkT \tag{2.5}$$

in which $k = 1.38 \times 10^{-16}$ ergs deg^{-1} denotes Boltzmann's constant, and T
is the absolute temperature.

On combining the equation of state (2.5) with the statical equation (2.1),
the general law governing a neutral atmosphere is obtained:

$$dp/p = dn/n + dT/T = - dz/H \tag{2.6}$$

where

$$H = kT/mg \tag{2.7}$$

is a quantity having the dimension of length that Chapman has termed the
(local) scale height.

Since the scale height depends on three parameters (temperature, mean molecular mass, and gravitational acceleration) the interrelation between pressure, temperature, and composition will depend on the height variation of these three parameters. The variation of g is given by the known law of gravitation:

$$\frac{g}{g_0} = \left(\frac{R + z_0}{R + z}\right)^2 \tag{2.8}$$

where g denotes the acceleration of gravity at an altitude z, g_0 the acceleration at $z = z_0$, and $R + z$ is the appropriate distance from the earth's center. For example, g being about 980 cm sec^{-2} at ground level, g is about 950 at 100 km, 900 at 280 km, 850 at 475 km, and 800 near 700 km. To a first approximation, when computations are made for a sufficiently thin layer, it is possible to use a mean value of g. If the mean molecular mass, m, remains constant, as in the homosphere, there is a direct relation between the pressure and the temperature. Thus, in an atmosphere with perfect mixing, a knowledge of how the pressure varies with height leads to a knowledge of the vertical distribution of the temperature and also of the concentrations.

On considering sufficiently thin layers where g and the temperature gradient are kept constant, it is possible to write

$$dH/dz = \beta = \text{Constant} \tag{2.9}$$

and therefore, by integration of (2.6),

$$p/p_0 = (H/H_0)^{-1/\beta} \tag{2.10}$$

and

$$n/n_0 = (H/H_0)^{-(1 + \beta)/\beta}. \tag{2.11}$$

When the layer is isothermal, (2.10) and (2.11) can be written

$$p/p_0 = n/n_0 = e^{-z/H} \tag{2.12}$$

which expresses the conventional exponential decrease of pressures and concentrations.

The vertical distribution of the temperature in the whole homosphere has been determined from direct measurements of the height distribution of pressure made by means of rockets. In the heterosphere the temperature cannot be deduced directly from measurements of pressure, since there is a simultaneous variation of the mean molecular mass. Since this variation is due to a dissociation effect, there is a decrease of the mean molecular mass, so that temperatures deduced on the assumption of constant mass would lead to too high temperatures. On the other hand, any hypothesis about how the molecular mass varies would imply a particular vertical distribution of the temperature.

When there is a steady state of diffusion, formula (2.6) must be written

$$dp_i/p_i = dn_i/n_i + dT/T = - dz/H_i \qquad (2.13)$$

to indicate that each constituent has a concentration or pressure gradient associated with its own mass. The vertical distribution in a diffusion equilibrium depends, however, on the thermal diffusion, and equation (2.13) should be acceptable as a first approximation for almost all aeronomic purposes.* Integration of (2.13) to give

$$n_i/n_{i,0} = (H_i/H_{i,0})^{-(1+\beta_i)/\beta_i} \qquad (2.11a)$$

shows that each constituent is vertically distributed according to its own scale height gradient, β_i. In any atmosphere in diffusive equilibrium, the height variation of one constituent (n_i, m_i) is known directly in terms of the corresponding quantities from another constituent (n_a, m_a), since one can write

$$\beta_i m_i = \beta_a m_a. \qquad (2.14)$$

It follows that an analysis of the pressure data can lead to a determination of the temperature when there is a complete mixing which keeps the ratios of all constituents constant. Any diffusion large enough to modify the value of the mean molecular mass precludes the possibility of using pressure † data to deduce an exact vertical distribution of temperature. Furthermore, states of simple mixing and diffusion are not the only possible ones. Suppose, in a system in either of these two steady states, a constituent (in fact, there will be oxygen) undergoes dissociation in a binary or ternary mixture (in fact, atomic and molecular oxygen and molecular nitrogen); there would then be a possibility of a change of the mean molecular mass which would modify in a very complicated manner the interrelation between pressure, temperature, and composition. It has been shown (see § 2.4) that such a situation does exist in the thermosphere, where transition from molecular oxygen to atomic oxygen occurs. In photochemical equilibrium conditions (2.11a) is replaced by

$$n_i/n_{i,0} = (H/H_0)^{-3(1+\beta)/\beta} \qquad (2.11b)$$

where β is the gradient of the atmospheric scale height.

The several distributions (2.11) may be represented by means of a convenient parameter, X, which is called the vertical distribution factor.

---

* It is necessary to add to unity a thermal diffusion factor which in certain circumstances may be of the order of 0.3, i.e., atomic hydrogen and helium, but it can be neglected for oxygen and nitrogen. See K. E. Grew and T. L. Ibbs, "Thermal Diffusion of Gases", Cambridge Univ. Press, Cambridge, 1952.

† At the time of writing, no measurements of pressure have been made above 120 km. Only measurements of density have been published for regions above 140 km.

Thus if n_i refers to a minor constituent, it may be written in terms of the mixed main atmosphere according to the representation

$$n_i/n_{i,0} = (H/H_0)^{-X(1+\beta)/\beta} \qquad (2.15)$$

where X has the following values:

Mixing	1
Diffusion	$[(m_i/m) + \beta]/(1 + \beta)$
Photochemical equilibrium	
Two-body	2
Three-body (constant temperature)	3
(varying temperature)	$3 - (\beta/2)(1 + \beta)$

The vertical distribution factor clearly indicates that, the greater the disparity between the molecular masses of a constituent and the atmosphere, the more the diffusion equilibrium distribution deviates from the mixing distribution. The temperature variation is seen to play also a role in fixing the various concentration distributions.

2.3 Composition of the Homosphere

In the study of aeronomic problems, the application of theoretical considerations will be greatly simplified in considering a subdivision between major and minor constituents. Nitrogen (about 78 %) and oxygen (about 21 %) are the major constituents of the dry air, even if argon and CO_2 represent 0.9 % and 0.03 % of the mean molecular mass of the air, respectively.

Data for the permanent constituents of the air are listed in Table I. From this table, it is easy to deduce that in perfect mixing the constant ratio of oxygen and nitrogen concentration is

$$n(O_2)/n(N_2) = 0.2683 \qquad (2.16)$$

and, when there is a dissociation of oxygen,

$$\frac{n(O) + 2n(O_2)}{n(N_2)} = 0.5365 \qquad (2.17)$$

which, for the law of vertical distribution of the mass density, leads to

$$\rho = 1.34n(N_2)m(N_2) \qquad (2.18)$$

Since the molecular mass of molecular nitrogen ($M = 28.02$) almost corresponds to the mean molecular mass of air ($M = 28.97$), the vertical distribution of N_2 is almost the same in any atmosphere subject to mixing or to diffusion. A knowledge of the concentration of molecular nitrogen should therefore give fairly good estimates of the atmospheric temperature even at high levels.

Among the minor constituents, it is also useful to distinguish between the inert gases and chemically active gases in order to discuss separately the constituents which are involved in chemical or photochemical reactions.

TABLE I

Principal Constituents of the Air at Ground Level

Molecule	Mass[a]	Percentage	Concentration[b]	Total[c]
N_2	28.022	78.084 $\pm$ 0.004	2.098×10^{19}	1.678×10^{25}
O_2	32.009	20.946 $\pm$ 0.002	5.629×10^{18}	4.501×10^{24}
A	39.960	0.934	2.510×10^{17}	2.007×10^{23}
CO_2	44.024	0.33	8.87×10^{15}	7.09×10^{21}
Air	28.973	100.00	2.687×10^{19}	2.148×10^{25}

[a] Physical mass with Avogadro's number: 6.025×10^{23} gm mole^{-1}.

[b] Number of molecules per cubic centimeter at standard pressure (760 mm Hg) and standard temperature (273.16°K). Loschmidt's number: 2.687×10^{19} cm^{-3}.

[c] Number of molecules per square centimetre column, with a reduced height or scale height defined by $H = kT/mg$, where $k = 1.38 \times 10^{-16}$ erg deg^{-1}, $T = 273.16$°K, $m = 48.08 \times 10^{-24}$ gm, and $g = 980.665$ cm sec^{-2}.

Data for the inert gases are given in Table II, from which it is easy to see that the abundance ratios differ considerably from the cosmic abundance ratios.

TABLE II

Inert Gases at Ground Level

Atoms	Ratio by volume	Number (cm^{-3})	Number (cm^{-2})
He	$(5.24 \pm 0.004) \times 10^{-6}$	1.41×10^{14}	1.13×10^{20}
Ne	$(1.818 \pm 0.004) \times 10^{-5}$	4.89×10^{14}	3.89×10^{20}
A	$(9.34 \pm 0.01) \times 10^{-3}$	2.51×10^{17}	2.01×10^{23}
Kr	$(1.14 \pm 0.01) \times 10^{-6}$	3.06×10^{13}	2.45×10^{19}
Xe	$(8.7 \pm 0.1) \times 10^{-8}$	2.34×10^{12}	1.87×10^{18}

The low concentrations of helium are due to its continuous escape at the top of the earth's atmosphere. It has been shown[1] that the generation of α-particles by the disintegration of uranium and thorium in the mantle and crust of the earth is of the order of 1 or 2 million particles per second and per square centimeter of surface.

On considering the present amount of helium in the earth's atmosphere (see Table II), it is easy to deduce[1] that only 2 million years are necessary to produce this total.* It is appropriate, therefore, to ask how escape processes

* The total generation rate of α-particles is 1.75×10^6 cm^{-2} sec^{-1}. Therefore 1.13×10^{20} He^4 atoms cm^{-2} are produced in about 2,100,000 years.

have appeared to transport the helium from ground level to the outside of the atmosphere since the formation of the earth more than 4 billion years ago. If the escape velocity is attributed, as in the kinetic theory, to the peculiar speeds related to the temperature, it may be deduced[1] that at high levels in the thermosphere the kinetic temperature cannot be less than 2000°K.

Most of the argon, which is not the normal argon of mass $M = 36$ but is an isotope of mass $M = 40$, is of radiogenic origin. It is a result of the transformation of radioactive potassium, which is more than sufficient to have produced the present amount of atmospheric argon since the beginning of the formation of the earth. Argon, being a gas which is simultaneously an inert, permanent, and minor constituent of the atmosphere, is a perfect tracer for the study of diffusion, and particularly for the detection of the beginning of diffusion. For that purpose, the measurement of the ratio between the concentrations of argon and molecular nitrogen is certainly the best procedure, since, as was pointed out earlier, the molecular mass of N_2 does not differ very much from the mean molecular mass of the air.

TABLE III

Molecular Content of Minor Constituents

Molecule	Ratio by volume	Remarks
H_2O	10^{-5} to 10^{-2}	Variable, particularly in troposphere. Decrease in stratosphere. Dissociation in mesosphere.
O_3	10^{-7} to 10^{-8}	Increase with height, maximum in stratosphere and diurnal variation in mesosphere.
CH_4	1.5×10^{-6}	Mixed in troposphere, oxidized in stratosphere. Dissociation in mesosphere.
N_2O	5×10^{-7}	Mixed in troposphere. Continuous dissociation in stratosphere and mesosphere.
CO	6×10^{-8} to 2×10^{-7}	Variable.
H_2	5×10^{-7}	Mixed. Dissociation in mesosphere.
NO_2 / NO	5×10^{-10} to 2×10^{-8}	Industrial origin in troposphere. Photochemical origin in mesosphere and thermosphere.

As far as the minor constituent molecules are concerned, it is difficult to be certain that no variation occurs. Several of these were discovered by spectroscopic identifications of absorption bands in the infrared solar spectrum, but no systematic study of them has been made at high levels. Several others are essentially variable, as shown in Table III, but all of them present variations with height. The height distributions of all these molecules differ from those of the main atmospheric constituents partly because changes occur due to chemical and photochemical actions, and partly because changes may also occur in the physical state of substances such as water. A chemical reaction is certainly the cause of the variation of ozone at ground level, whereas in the mesosphere the principal reaction is a photochemical one.

Atmospheric methane (CH_4) probably plays a part in the production of atomic hydrogen in the thermosphere even if H_2O is involved in the photochemistry of the mesosphere. CH_4 has a biological origin, since C^{14} has the normal percentage present in a biological product.[2] It is oxidized in the stratosphere and in the mesosphere, and, according to Bates,[3] it is possible to consider oxidation rates of the order of 10^{-6} per second at the stratopause level. In order to replace the dissociated methane, an upward transport of CH_4 from the troposphere to the stratosphere must therefore occur, and the flow is subject to the law of exchange of mass between these two atmospheric regions. Thus, atomic hydrogen and its various compounds should have in the mesosphere a value of the order 5×10^{-6} of the main atmospheric gases, if there is a steady state.

The loss rate of CH_4 could be as large as 10^{10} to 10^{11} molecules cm^{-2} sec^{-1}, which would imply that the whole atmospheric methane content would be replaced in about 10 to 100 years. In any event, it is certain that atomic hydrogen must exist in the lower thermosphere in quantities which depend on processes affecting methane and water vapor in the mesosphere.

If the vertical distribution of N_2O above the tropopause followed the same atmospheric distribution as in the troposphere, about 10^{11} N_2O molecules cm^{-2} sec^{-1} would be dissociated. Since the association of N_2 and O is a very slow process, depending on three-body collisions, there is a deflection with height of the concentration of that molecule which can be neglected at mesospheric levels.

On the other hand, nitric oxide and nitrogen dioxide, which are not generally considered in the lower atmosphere, are produced in the mesosphere and thermosphere.

Twenty-five years ago it was generally accepted that the composition of the stratospheric air varied with altitude, because helium and oxygen samples taken from heights above 20 km showed departures from a mixing distribution toward partial diffusive separation. Comparison of oxygen and nitrogen percentages in the stratosphere showed that the relative amount of oxygen decreased with height. Paneth[4] has suggested as a probable explanation that oxygen overreacts with collecting chambers. Although early helium analysis showed an increase in the relative content in the stratosphere (16 to 25 km), Gluckauf and Paneth[5] now believe that the percentage of helium remains constant in the stratosphere just as it does in the troposphere. A relative upward increase of helium and neon and a decrease of argon have been deduced from the analysis of rocket samplings in the mesosphere from 60 to 90 km. This does not, however, necessarily imply an effect of diffusive separation but may be explained by mass discrimination in the sampling system.* First mass spectrometric observations[6] taken at altitudes up to the thermosphere (137 km) showed that there was practically no change in the ratio of argon to molecular nitrogen. More recent observations, however, by Meadows and Towsend[7] in the winter nighttime show that diffusive separation of argon and nitrogen exists in the region 110 to 150 km and may begin at about 105 km. Thus, it is possible to conclude that gases which are sufficiently inert chemically do not exhibit changes in relative abundance below 100 km.

Friedman and his collaborators[8] have used photon counters in a series of rocket flights to measure solar radiation near 1500 A. These measurements showed how the molecular oxygen absorption varied with height, and consequently the vertical distribution of O_2 between 110 and 180 km is known. The results show that partial dissociation of O_2 occurs above 100 km, but it is possible to show that the observed concentrations are larger than those deduced from photochemical equilibrium and in fact correspond to an upward diffusive transport of molecular oxygen. This point will be discussed in detail later with the general subject of diffusion.

In conclusion, information on the composition of the atmosphere up to 100 km indicates that the homosphere extends certainly to the mesopause. A constant ratio of molecular oxygen and nitrogen concentrations is maintained by mixing. Beyond the mesopause—that is to say, in the thermosphere —a varying mean molecular mass must be taken into account even though there is still mixing, for partial dissociation of oxygen must occur. Nevertheless, the effect of mixing will decrease with height compared to the increasing power of diffusive separation. Finally, the mean of the molecular mass will decrease in the thermosphere according to the vertical distribution of oxygen and nitrogen in diffusive equilibrium.

2.4 The Dissociation of Molecular Oxygen

Since Chapman's study † in 1930, it has been supposed that oxygen dissociates at a height of about 100 km, and in all subsequent theories ‡ the

---

* A fuller account will be found in "Rocket Exploration of the Upper Atmosphere" (R. L. F. Boyd and M. J. Seaton, eds.), Pergamon, London, 1954.

† See a general account by S. Chapman, "The photochemistry of atmospheric oxygen" *Repts. Prog. in Phys.* **9**, 92 (1943).

‡ For a fuller account of the various theories by M. Nicolet and P. Mange, see "The dissociation of oxygen in the high atmosphere", *J. Geophys. Res.* **50**, 15 (1954).

problem was attacked from the standpoint of an assumed photochemical equilibrium where the photodissociation and recombination processes are considered to yield the same number of processes cm^{-3} sec^{-1} (statistical equilibrium) or the same energy (ergs cm^{-3} sec^{-1}, radiative equilibrium). In other words, the times of dissociation (τ_{diss}) or of recombination (τ_{rec}) were assumed to be small compared with the time of diffusion (τ_{diff}) or the time of mixing (τ_{mix}). General conditions, however, such as

$$\tau_{\text{rec}} < \tau_{\text{mix}} \tag{2.19}$$

or

$$\tau_{\text{diss}} < \tau_{\text{diff}} \tag{2.20}$$

cannot be accepted, so that there are serious departures from photochemical equilibrium, and condition (2.17) cannot be used in the problem of the transition region of oxygen dissociation.

Inasmuch as the dissociation of molecular oxygen begins to occur, for increasing height levels, in the lower thermosphere, one is no longer free to assume a constant molecular mass at these levels, so that, as stated before, there is no simple relation between the measured pressure and the temperature. In fact, vertical transport can carry molecular oxygen upward while the atomic oxygen resulting from dissociation is carried downward by diffusion. The process is as follows: one dissociated O_2 molecule is replaced by another through upward diffusion while oxygen atoms are forced downward until they reach a region in which the pressure is sufficient to cause them to recombine.

Let us consider first the general equation[9] for the photochemical and recombination effects influencing molecular oxygen:

$$dn(O_2)/dt + n(O_2)J = an^2(O) \tag{2.21}$$

in which J denotes the rate coefficient for dissociation of O_2 (per molecule sec^{-1}), and a is the recombination coefficient. At sufficiently high levels $n(O_2) < n(O)$, and any variations of $n(O_2)$ hardly affect the magnitude of $n(O)$. When the optical depth is negligible, J may be taken as a constant. Thus, the solution of (2.21) is

$$n(O_2) = n_0(O_2)e^{-Jt} + \frac{an^2(O)}{J}(1 - e^{-Jt}) \tag{2.22}$$

where $n_0(O_2)$ is the O_2 concentration at time $t = 0$.

The time necessary to reach 50 % of the photochemical equilibrium value (or of any initial value) is called the time, $\tau_{\text{diss}}(O_2)$, of dissociation of molecular oxygen and is thus

$$\tau_{\text{diss}}(O_2) = 0.7/J \tag{2.23}$$

A calculation of the dissociation rate coefficient, J, requires the computation of the dissociation in the Schumann-Runge continuum of O_2 by solar radiation of wavelengths shorter than 1750 A. Numerical results[9] lead to a value of J of the order of 10^{-6} sec^{-1} at zero optical depth, so that the dissociation time of molecular oxygen in the solar radiation field is of the order of 15 days. In the actual atmosphere with finite optical depth the times of dissociation of molecular oxygen correspond to not less than 15 days, and if diffusion times are shorter than that there is an upward vertical transport of oxygen molecules.[10]

The long time required for the dissociation of molecular oxygen is due to the low radiation temperature observed on the spectral range of the Schumann-Runge continuum. In order to show how much the dissociation rate coefficient is affected by the radiation temperature, various values calculated by Nicolet and Mange[9] are presented in Table IV. The temperature

TABLE IV

Oxygen Dissociation Rate Coefficients (sec^{-1})

Molecules cm^{-2}	Black-body temperature:				
	4000°K	4500°K	5000°K	5500°K	6000°K
10^{15}	1.24×10^{-7}	1.57×10^{-6}	1.28×10^{-5}	6.64×10^{-5}	2.76×10^{-4}
10^{16}	1.18×10^{-7}	1.47×10^{-6}	1.15×10^{-5}	6.19×10^{-5}	2.56×10^{-4}
10^{17}	7.34×10^{-8}	8.63×10^{-7}	6.43×10^{-6}	3.34×10^{-5}	1.34×10^{-4}

This table shows the rates at which O_2 would be dissociated if it were irradiated with black-body radiation having the different temperatures listed and subject to preliminary absorption by columns of 10^{15}, 10^{16}, and 10^{17} O_2 molecules cm^{-2}.

dependence shows that the radiation energy is the most important parameter, which leads to different conclusions. The time of dissociation is less than 1 hour for a radiation from a black body at 6000°K, less than 1 day for 5000°K, of the order of 10 days for 4500°K, and about 4 months for 4000°K. Thus, it is easy to understand why no departure from photochemical equilibrium was considered to be possible when radiation temperatures greater than 5000°K were adopted.

As far as atomic oxygen is concerned, the equation may be written as follows:

$$dn(O)/dt + 2an^2(O) = 2n(O_2)J \qquad (2.24)$$

During dark hours $J = 0$, and the solution of (2.24) is

$$n(O) = \frac{n_0(O)}{1 + 2an_0(O)t} \qquad (2.25)$$

so that $n(O)$ is reduced to 50 % of its initial value, $n_0(O)$, in a time, τ_{rec} (O), given by

$$\tau_{rec}(O) = \tfrac{1}{2}an_0(O). \tag{2.26}$$

The value

$$a = 5 \times 10^{-34}n(M)T^{\frac{1}{2}} \text{ cm}^6 \text{ sec}^{-1} \tag{2.27}$$

has been deduced[11] from a theory in which molecules are formed by three-body collisions involving a third particle with concentration $n(M)$. Such a value is obtained when the collision probability for molecular formation is about 50 %. In order to obtain orders of magnitude, we adopt for T an arbitrary value 400°K, and we obtain

$$\tau_{rec}(O) = \frac{5 \times 10^3}{n(M)n_0(O)} \text{ sec.} \tag{2.28}$$

In Table V the lifetimes of an oxygen atom are given corresponding to different values of the concentration of the third particle (total number

TABLE V

Lifetimes of Oxygen Atoms

$n(O)$ (cm^{-3})	$n(M)$(cm^{-3})			
	10^{15}	10^{14}	10^{13}	10^{12}
10^{13}	> 1 day	< 1 day	1 week	
10^{12}	< 1 day	1 week	> 1 month	> 1 year
10^{11}	1 week	> 1 month	> 1 year	> 10 years
10^{10}	> 1 month	> 1 year	> 10 years	

This table shows how the time for the formation of molecules from oxygen atoms, by a recombination process involving a third particle (M), depends on the concentration of M and of the original concentration of O.

density) and of the initial concentration of atomic oxygen. Since we know that at altitudes above 120 km both concentrations are certainly less than 10^{12} particles cm^{-3}, the lifetimes of oxygen atoms are more than a year. There is therefore downward transport of all oxygen atoms produced in a sunlit atmosphere. At 100 km, where the total concentration can reach 10^{13} cm^{-3}, the recombination time is not less than a month, so that even there transport processes are allowed to act and, finally, to modify the whole structure of the transition region of oxygen dissociation which would be obtained under photochemical equilibrium conditions.

The introduction of atmospheric data concerning pressure and temperature makes it possible to consider numerical magnitudes[12] and to reach interesting conclusions.* First, the production peak of atomic oxygen, caused by photo-dissociation of molecular oxygen in the Schumann-Runge continuum at wavelengths shorter than 1750 A, occurs between 90 and 95 km with a rate coefficient of about 1.5×10^5 atoms cm^{-3} sec^{-1}. The concentration peak should be observed near 110 km under conditions of photochemical equilibrium and would have a value of the order of 1.7×10^{12} atoms cm^{-3}. Such a concentration would be of the order of the nitrogen concentration and would lead to a total pressure greater than that measured at 110 km. Therefore, $n(O) = 1.7 \times 10^{12}$ cm^{-3} may be considered as the maximum value which can be reached at 110 km.

Second, the production of oxygen atoms at a rate of about 4×10^{11} oxygen atoms cm^{-2} sec^{-1} must be balanced by the same total number of recombinations. By writing

$$\int_z^\infty n(O_2)J \, dz = \int_z^\infty an(M)n^2(O) \, dz \tag{2.29}$$

it is possible, by adopting a mean value for $n(O)$, to conclude that

$$\left[\overline{n(O)}\right]^2 an(M)H = 2 \times 10^{11} \, cm^{-2} \, sec^{-1} \tag{2.30}$$

in which H denotes the atmospheric scale height, and $\overline{n(O)}$ will be the maximum concentration of atomic oxygen in an altitude range of the order of the peak height. Concentrations obtained from (2.30), which cannot be applied above the production peak, show that the maximum concentration of a layer formed by continuous transport, and for which the thickness is of the order of one scale height, varies between 7×10^{11} cm^{-3} at 85 km and 1.7×10^{12} cm^{-3} at about 95 km. Figure 2 represents the vertical distribution of atomic and molecular oxygen in the lower thermosphere. By comparing the possible concentrations of atomic oxygen between 100 and 110 km, the two extreme limits can be determined. The downward transport leads almost to

$$n(N_2) = 10n(O) \tag{2.31}$$

and the photoequilibrium conditions to

$$n(O) = 2n(N_2) \tag{2.32}$$

instead of the constant ratio defined by (2.17), which is approximately

$$n(O) = \tfrac{1}{2}n(N_2) - 2n(O_2). \tag{2.33}$$

A constant mixing ratio (2.33) as a result of perfect mixing would lead to a concentration peak of atomic oxygen just below 90 to 95 km and, therefore, a vertical distribution above that peak following the atmospheric distribution of O_2 and N_2. Such a low value for the concentration of atomic oxygen

---

* It is not possible to consider precise values of pressure, since observational data are very different at 100 km. An error of 5 km may be possible.

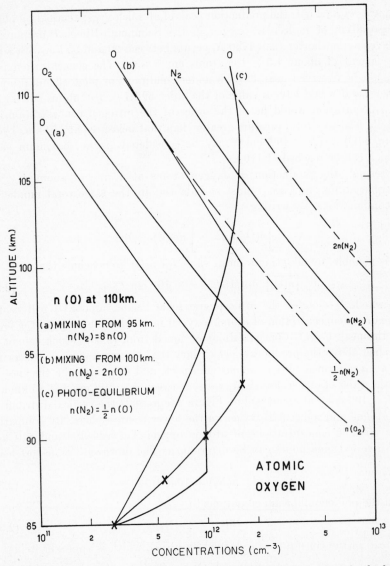

FIG. 2. Possible vertical distributions of atomic and molecular oxygen in the lower thermosphere. Because the times involved in the recombination of oxygen increase rapidly with height above the mesopause, photoequilibrium cannot be maintained. The altitude of the peak of atomic oxygen is not determined by photochemical equilibrium conditions but by the effect of a downward transport depending on mixing conditions. The figure shows how the conditions at the atomic oxygen peak vary from photoequilibrium to strong mixing. It must be pointed out that in this figure the altitude of 100 km corresponds to a pressure of 10^{-4} mm Hg. Such a pressure may correspond to 105 km in the atmosphere described in Tables VI and VII, and the concentrations indicated in the figure between 90 and 110 km can therefore represent conditions between 95 and 115 km when the pressure at 100 km is 3×10^{-4} mm Hg.

$[n(N_2) \simeq 10n(O_2)]$ in the lower thermosphere would prevent this atom from playing an important role except at sufficiently high altitudes.

After considering the extreme conditions it is difficult to define the normal conditions, although it is possible to say that the concentration of atomic oxygen between 90 and 110 km is of the order of $(1.0 \pm 0.5) \times 10^{12}$ cm^{-3}. The curves in Fig. 2 show the vertical distributions of atomic oxygen for vertical transport downward to below the production peak [between curves (a) and (b)] and for photochemical equilibrium [curve (c)].

Since the peak of atomic oxygen is situated in the lower thermosphere, it is safe to conclude that the heterosphere begins above the mesopause. The mesopause may be considered as the extreme lowest border of the homopause, where a change in the mean molecular mass occurs. Because the mesopause is the level where a temperature minimum is reached, the physical conditions will vary with temperature, with changes of the order of 70°K involved. In the mesosphere, atomic oxygen is subject to photochemical and chemical actions, leading to different aeronomic conditions between day and night, such as increase of the mesospheric ozone at night, whereas its vertical distribution in the thermosphere depends on the downward transport and its maximum concentration is related to a balance between the total production and total recombination. Because the absolute concentration is varied by atmospheric motions, fluctuations in some aeronomic processes, such as the emission of the green line of atomic oxygen, can be understood.

2.5 The Problem of Diffusion

Before discussing the effect of diffusion in the thermosphere it is useful to introduce certain velocities by which one-dimensional diffusion motions only may be described.

Suppose each molecule has a velocity, c, with respect to an arbitrary reference frame; then the mean velocity of the molecules, $\bar{c}$, in an infinitesimally small region is obtained by summing all the individual velocities and dividing by the number, n, of molecules. Since $\bar{c}$ is in fact a point function and may vary in space, $n\bar{c}$ is the number of molecules per unit time passing through unit cross section of a plane at rest with respect to the reference frame. If the gas consists of several types of molecules, the mean velocity, $\bar{c}$, is defined by the total particle transport at a given point through the expression

$$n\bar{c} \equiv \Sigma n_i \bar{c}_i \tag{2.34}$$

where $\bar{c}_i$ denotes the mean velocity associated with molecules of the ith type. Summing the mass transport, $n_i m_i \bar{c}_i$, the mean mass transport velocity, c_0, is defined at a given point by

$$\Sigma n_i m_i \bar{c}_i = \Sigma \rho_i c_i \equiv c_0 \rho. \tag{2.35}$$

The velocity $\bar{c}_i$ is not the same as $\bar{c}$, when one constituent is moving relative to the general motion of the gas at a specified point. The peculiar velocity, or the mean thermal velocity, $\bar{C}_i$, is then defined by

$$\bar{C}_i \equiv \bar{c}_i - \bar{c}.$$

If two kinds of molecules are considered, (2.34) leads to

$$\bar{C}_1 - \bar{C}_2 = \bar{c}_1 - \bar{c}_2$$

a quantity which is not altered by the reference velocity.

In a physical situation the conservation equations of mass, momentum, and energy are involved. They are, according to Chapman and Cowling,[13]

$$\frac{\partial \rho}{\partial t} + \frac{\partial(\rho c_0)}{\partial z} = 0 \tag{2.36}$$

$$\frac{\partial c_0}{\partial t} + c_0 \frac{\partial c_0}{\partial z} + \frac{1}{\rho} \frac{\partial p}{\partial z} + g = 0 \tag{2.37}$$

$$\frac{\partial p}{\partial t} + \frac{\partial(c_0 p)}{\partial z} + \frac{2}{N} p \frac{\partial c_0}{\partial z} + \frac{2}{N} \frac{\partial q}{\partial z} = 0 \tag{2.38}$$

where q represents the vertical component of the heat flow vector, and N denotes a factor depending on the internal energy of molecules; $N = 3$ for monoatomic gases, and $N = 5$ for diatomic molecules considered as rigid and elastic spheres.

For a two-constituent gas, q is given by

$$q = - \lambda_c \frac{\partial T}{\partial z} + k n T \alpha_T \frac{n_1 n_2}{n^2} (\bar{C}_1 - \bar{C}_2) + \frac{5}{2} kT (n_1 \bar{C}_1 + n_2 \bar{C}_2) \tag{2.39}$$

in which λ_c is the coefficient of thermal conductivity, and α_T the thermal diffusion factor, which is almost a constant.

The first term represents the thermal flux by ordinary conduction in a gas consisting of a single kind of molecule.

The second term represents the heat transport by diffusion. The mean relative velocity of the two constituents $(\bar{C}_1 - \bar{C}_2)$ is given by

$$\bar{C}_1 - \bar{C}_2 = \frac{n^2}{n_1 n_2} D \left[\frac{\partial(n_1/n_2)}{\partial z} + \frac{n_1 n_2 (m_2 - m_1)}{n \rho} \frac{\partial \log p}{\partial z} + \frac{n_1 n_2}{n^2} \alpha_T \frac{1}{T} \frac{\partial T}{\partial z} \right] \tag{2.40}$$

in which D denotes the diffusion coefficient. This term will disappear when there is no mutual diffusion, i.e., when the steady state has been obtained.

The third term is associated with the general motion of the gas, for each molecule carries an average quantity of heat energy equal to $(5/2)kT$. When this term is neglected, that is, when the mean velocity is zero, the total number of molecules per unit volume remains constant, so that

$\partial n/\partial t = 0$, and molecules pass equally frequently in each direction through a plane moving with the gas. The mass velocity may, however, differ from zero, i.e., $\partial \rho/\partial t \neq 0$.

For a discussion of dynamic processes the statical equation (2.1) is modified as indicated in (2.37) to take account of diffusion effects. These are certainly small, however, compared with the effects of gravitational acceleration, and the law of conservation of momentum (2.37) may be considered identical, to a good degree of approximation, with the statical law relating the mass density, ρ, to the hydrostatic pressure, p.

The conservation of mass for each constituent is governed by the expressions

$$\partial n_1/\partial t + \partial(n_1 c_1)/\partial z = 0 \qquad (2.41)$$

and

$$\partial n_2/\partial t + \partial(n_2 c_2)/\partial z = 0. \qquad (2.42)$$

The change of pressure with time is due essentially to the mass velocity, whereas the variation of the heat flux with height is due to the variation of the mass velocity; that is, (2.38),

$$\partial p/\partial t = -g\rho c_0 \qquad (2.43)$$

and

$$\partial q/\partial z = \frac{5}{2} p \, \partial c_0/\partial z. \qquad (2.44)$$

In equation (2.43) products of derivatives of first-order quantities in the integration of the momentum equation (2.37) have been neglected.

If the mass velocity had been neglected, there would be [see equation (2.43)] no variation of pressure. In other words, when an aeronomic problem is considered, it is necessary to know whether or not the total pressure is affected. If the constituents are major constituents, the variation of pressure with time is a direct result of diffusion and cannot be neglected. Application of the theory to atomic oxygen and molecular nitrogen shows that the pressure increases markedly when diffusion equilibrium replaces mixing equilibrium.

In the study of the behavior of a minor constituent the problem of diffusion is much simpler. In effect, the total pressure remains practically constant in a mixed atmosphere, while the minor constituent diffuses upward or downward. The following conditions can therefore be applied for a minor constituent:

(*i*) $$\partial p/\partial t = 0 \qquad (2.45)$$

showing that the main atmospheric distribution is fixed in time;

(*ii*) $$n = n_1 + n_2 \simeq n_2 \qquad (2.46)$$

indicating the difference between concentrations of major and minor constituents; and

(iii)
$$n_1 c_1 + n_2 c_2 = 0 \qquad (2.47)$$

on the assumption that there is no net particle flow across any surface.

Then, if the velocity, c_1, of the minor constituent is denoted by w for convenience, (2.40) becomes, after use of conditions (2.45), (2.46), and (2.47),

$$w = - D \left[\frac{1}{n_1} \frac{\partial n_1}{\partial z} + \frac{m_1 g}{kT} + (1 + \alpha_T) \frac{1}{T} \frac{\partial T}{\partial z} \right] \qquad (2.48)$$

Using relations (2.7) and (2.9), we write for the main constituent[14]

$$\beta/H = (1/T)\, \partial T/\partial z = (1/H)\, \partial H/\partial z \qquad (2.49)$$

$$(1 + \beta)/H = - (1/n)\, \partial n/\partial z \qquad (2.50)$$

and for the minor constituent (2.15)

$$X(1 + \beta)/H = - (1/n_1)\, \partial n_1/\partial z \qquad (2.51)$$

where X is the vertical distribution factor introduced in (2.15). When $X = 1$, the constituent follows a mixing distribution.

The vertical velocity, w, of the minor constituent given by (2.48) takes the following form, from (2.49) and (2.51):

$$w = \frac{D}{H} \left[X(1 + \beta) - \beta(1 + \alpha_T) - \frac{m_1}{m} \right] \qquad (2.52)$$

The vertical velocity, w, increases almost exponentially with altitude and is upward if

$$X > X_D = \frac{\beta(1 + \alpha_T) + (m_1/m)}{1 + \beta} \qquad (2.53)$$

and downward if

$$X < X_D \qquad (2.54)$$

Although the direction of diffusive transport is naturally dependent on the relative mass (m_1/m) of the constituent, it must be pointed out that the concentration gradient may change the whole picture. For example, any photochemical equilibrium of molecular oxygen corresponds to (2.53), and there is a continuous upward transport. Any production of oxygen atoms in the thermosphere corresponds to (2.54), and there is a continuous downward transport.

The continuity equation of diffusion for vertical motion, according to (2.41) and (2.47), is

$$\partial n_1/\partial t = \partial(n_1 w)/\partial z \qquad (2.55)$$

in which the right side is the one-dimensional counterpart of the usual divergence term. With the use of (2.52), the neglect of thermal diffusion $(\alpha_T = 0)$, and an expression for the diffusion coefficient, D, it is possible to explain the continuity equation (2.55). Here, we describe molecules as elastic spheres with a collision diameter, σ, and D is written *

$$D = (3/32n\pi\sigma^2)\,(1 + m_1/m)^{\frac{1}{2}}\,(8kT/\pi m_1)^{\frac{1}{2}} \qquad (2.56)$$

where $(8kT/\pi m_1)^{\frac{1}{2}}$ is the mean molecular velocity of gas molecules of mass m_1 at temperature T, and $(1 + m_1/m)^{\frac{1}{2}}\,(8kT/\pi m_1)^{\frac{1}{2}}$ is the mean relative velocity for two constituent gases.

Thus, (2.55) is written, from (2.52) and (2.56),

$$\frac{\partial n_1}{\partial t} + n_1 w\left[\frac{2+\beta}{2(1+\beta)} - X\right]\frac{1+\beta}{H} + n_1\frac{(1+\beta)D}{H}\frac{\partial X}{\partial z} = 0 \qquad (2.57)$$

or

$$\frac{\partial n_1}{\partial t} = n_1\frac{D(1+\beta)}{H^2}\left\{\left[\beta + \frac{m_1}{m_2} - X(1+\beta)\right]\left[\frac{2+\beta}{2(1+\beta)} - X\right] - \frac{\partial X}{\partial z}\right\} \qquad (2.58)$$

Stationary-state solutions are obtained for values of the vertical distribution factor, X, which are solutions of the appropriate Riccati equation. The equilibrium distribution is obtained by equating the first bracket of equation (2.58) to zero.

The solution of (2.58) has been worked out by Epstein[15] for an isothermal atmosphere and by Mange[16] for the more general case of an atmosphere with varying scale height. A still more general solution which takes account of sources and sinks due to photochemical action or atomic production by meteors has also been obtained by Mange.[17] An important result of Mange's work is that diffusion times deduced directly from expressions of diffusion velocities differ from those obtained by detailed consideration of equations such as (2.58). In fact, it is possible to deduce the time necessary to change the concentration by a fixed percentage, when diffusion proceeds from an initial X state at any specified level. In fact, the times to reach diffusion equilibrium strongly depend on initial and final concentration gradients. Furthermore, the variation of the concentration at a given altitude is a function of the concentration at lower altitudes.

In order to obtain a sufficiently precise estimate of the situation, it is necessary to adopt a working model of the thermosphere in the form of a primary model in which conditions of pressure and temperature are not too far from the final and actual conditions.

Let us consider an atmosphere in which the scale height at a given reference level is $H = 10$ km and has a constant gradient $\beta = dH/dz = 0.2$. Adopting

* The diffusion coefficient is proportional to $T^{\frac{1}{2}}/n$. In fact, the temperature exponent may be between the two extreme values $\frac{1}{2}$ and 1, corresponding to elastic spheres and Maxwellian molecules, respectively. Furthermore, interactions which can occur between certain atoms may modify the absolute value of the coefficient. See, for example, A. Dalgarno, "The mobilities of ions in their parent gases," *Phil. Trans.* **250**, 426 (1958).

an average molecular mass $M = 24$, which lies between those of atomic and molecular oxygen, we define the atmospheric model by taking the total concentration $n(M) = 1.25 \times 10^{12}$ cm^{-3} at $H = 10$ km.

Such an atmospheric model may correspond to an initial thermosphere in which the temperature is 273°K between 110 and 115 km. Since $M = 24$, atomic oxygen concentration must be 4.2×10^{11} cm^{-3}, and molecular nitrogen concentration 8.3×10^{11} cm^{-3}. Since at the start the mean molecular mass is constant, the equivalent height can be found, and an atmospheric model such as that shown in Table VI may be used for describing diffusion phenomena. It may be pointed out that slight modifications are possible to fit observational data in the region of 100 to 120 km, but they will not modify the whole argument.

TABLE VI

Working Atmospheric Model for the Study of Diffusion

Scale height (km)	Altitude (km)	Temperature (°K)	Pressure (mm Hg)	Concentration (cm^{-3})
8	100–105	220	1.1×10^{-4}	4.8×10^{12}
10	110–115	272	3.5×10^{-5}	1.25×10^{12}
12	120–125	326	2.2×10^{-5}	4.2×10^{11}
14	130–135	379	9.4×10^{-6}	1.7×10^{11}
16	140–145	432	3.3×10^{-6}	7.5×10^{10}

This table corresponds to an atmospheric model in which the gradient of the scale height $dH/dz = 0.2$ and the mean molecular mass $M = 24$; i.e., $n(N_2) = 2n(O)$. Observations show that a pressure of the order of 10^{-4} mm Hg corresponds to altitudes between 100 and 105 km.

Let us consider first the departure from conditions under which molecular oxygen is in photochemical equilibrium. Starting from conditions of photochemical equilibrium, we find an increase in the molecular oxygen concentration according to the continuity equation

$$\partial n(O_2)/\partial t = - n(O_2)J - \partial[n(O_2)w]/\partial z \qquad (2.59)$$

which expresses the loss of oxygen molecules by photodissociation and transport by diffusion. The recombination is neglected, since it always has the same sign as the diffusion term and is, moreover, always small compared with it.

The final result is shown in Fig. 3, in which the continuous curves represent the effect of diffusion overcoming the effect of photodissociation. It has been assumed that solar radiation is present for 12 hours each day, and it can be seen that the concentration changes are extremely rapid, several orders of magnitude in a few days in regions above 140 km.

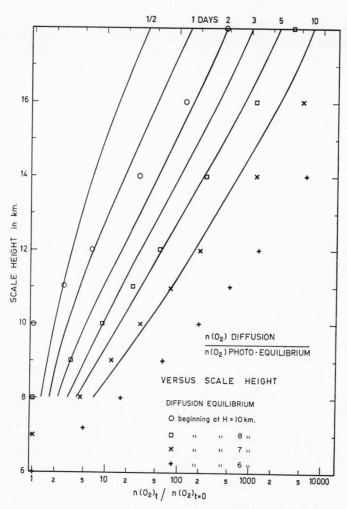

FIG. 3. Photoequilibrium of molecular oxygen changed into diffusive equilibrium by upward transport of O_2. Height is represented by the scale height appropriate to each level in the atmosphere described in Table VI. The abscissae represent the factor by which the initial concentration, $n(O_2)_{t=0}$, appropriate to photoequilibrium alone, is increased to give a concentration $n(O_2)_t$, after a time, t, which is different for each of the curves. The points $\bigcirc$, $\square$, $\times$, and $+$ represent characteristic distributions of O_2 in diffusive equilibrium for four different boundary conditions. For example, if diffusion begins at $H = 10$ km (symbol $\bigcirc$ and corresponding to altitudes between 100 and 105 km), a diffusion distribution of O_2 will be reached above this reference level in not more than 2 days.

By comparing these changes (Fig. 3) in the molecular oxygen concentrations with arbitrary diffusion equilibrium distributions, it is possible to determine the rapidity with which a particular diffusion equilibrium is reached. For example, let us assume that below $H = 10$ km a photochemical equilibrium can be maintained, and that above this level diffusion can take place. Figure 3 shows that for the whole thermosphere above $H = 10$ km a vertical distribution of oxygen in diffusive equilibrium is produced in about 2 days. Under the same conditions but with $H = 8$ km, a distribution of O_2 in diffusive equilibrium will take less than 10 days. Since $H = 8$ km may represent an altitude between 100 and 105 km, photochemical equilibrium is replaced by diffusive equilibrium because the diffusion time is shorter than the dissociation time for molecular oxygen.

It is clear that no other atmospheric transport process can oppose the upward diffusion of molecular oxygen. If mixing is effective, its action will reinforce the upward motion and may lead to a vertical distribution following the general atmosphere for which the height gradient is less steep than that for diffusion. Therefore, it is necessary to consider the other aspect of diffusion, i.e., the conditions of diffusive separation of constituents in an atmosphere in which initial conditions are represented by mixing.

The effect of diffusion on the distribution of molecular oxygen originally in mixing equilibrium is shown in Fig. 4. The different curves represent the effect of diffusion for successive days during one week.

The changes in the concentration of O_2 ($M = 32$), a *minor* constituent in an atmosphere of atomic oxygen, and molecular nitrogen ($M = 24$), are extremely rapid. Figure 4 shows that only 1 day is necessary to reach a diffusion distribution above the level where $H = 12.5$ km. In the atmospheric model used for the calculation (see Table VI) this corresponds to an altitude at which the total concentration would be less than 3×10^{11} cm^{-3} or the density would be of the order of 10^{-11} gm cm^{-3}. Another interesting level corresponds to $H = 10$ km, because this may be the level at which diffusive equilibrium begins, if diffusion is possible in 3 days. Figure 3 shows how, above $H = 10$ km, or an altitude of 110 to 115 km according to data of Table VI, a diffusive distribution of O_2 results after 3 days. If the two distributions of O_2 (Figs. 3 and 4) are compared with their limits for photochemical and mixing conditions, it can be said that the diffusion conditions beginning at $H = 10$ km (an altitude of 110 to 115 km) should represent the mean of the two extreme possibilities. In other words, if the diffusion times (2 to 3 days) necessary for photochemical or mixing conditions are the same, a diffusive equilibrium represents the normal condition when dissociation and mixing require more than 3 days.

When making measurements of the variation of the concentration of a constituent with altitude, at lower altitudes, it is necessary to specify the vertical distribution as a function of time and concentration, because the mixing time determines the lower boundary condition of the continuity

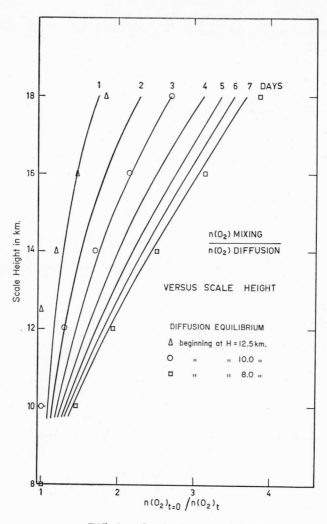

Diffusion of molecular oxygen.

FIG. 4. Mixing distribution of molecular oxygen changed into diffusive equilibrium by downward transport of O_2. Height is represented by the scale height appropriate to each level in the atmosphere described in Table VI. The abscissae represent the factor by which the initial concentration, $n(O_2)_{t=0}$, appropriate to mixing alone, is *decreased* to give the final concentration, $n(O_2)_t$ after a time, t, which is different for each of the curves. The points $\triangle$, $\bigcirc$, and $\square$ represent characteristic distributions of O_2 in diffusive equilibrium for three different boundary conditions. For example, if diffusion begins at $H = 10$ km (symbol $\bigcirc$) and is prevented below this reference level, molecular oxygen will reach a vertical diffusive distribution above the reference level in not more than 3 days.

equation related to the transport by diffusion. Argon compared with molecular nitrogen is such an example which can be used to determine the transition from the mixing to diffusion states.

If the working model is the same as that used for discussing the diffusion of molecular oxygen (Table VI), it is possible to obtain a sufficiently precise estimate of the situation. It must be pointed out, however, that "diffusion times" may have different meanings according to the conditions involved.

If diffusion time is defined as the time necessary to increase concentrations by a certain factor at a certain height when diffusion is upward (helium),

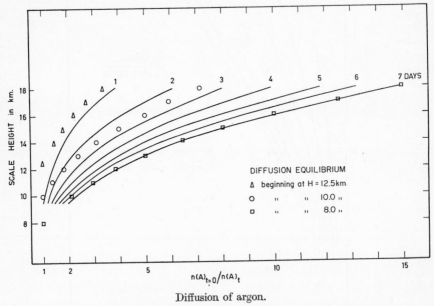

Diffusion of argon.

n(A) Mixing/n(A) diffusion *versus* scale height.

Fig. 5. Diffusion of argon in the thermosphere. Mixing distribution of argon changed into diffusive equilibrium by downward transport. Height is represented by the scale height appropriate to each level in the atmosphere described in Table VI. The abscissae represent the factor by which the initial concentration, $n(A)_{t=0}$, appropriate to mixing alone, is decreased to give the final concentration, $n(A)_t$, after a time, t, which is different for each of the curves. The points $\triangle$, $\bigcirc$, and $\square$ represent characteristic distributions of argon in diffusive equilibrium for three different boundary conditions, namely $H = 12.5$ km, 10 km, and 8 km. These distributions indicate that diffusive equilibrium distributions of argon can be obtained above reference levels $H = 12.5$ km, 10 km and 8 km in not more than 1, 3, and 7 days, respectively. Since the reference level $H = 10$ km corresponds to altitudes in the range 100 to 105 km in which observational data show diffusive separation of A and N_2, the time of mixing is more than 3 days, and less than 7 days at $H = 10$ km.

or decrease it by the same factor when it is downward (argon), absolute times can be defined by using the continuity equation. In that case, the shortest times are found for constituents with masses which differ greatly from the mean molecular mass, and the longest times for constituents having masses comparable with the mean molecular mass. In an aeronomic problem, however, another criterion for diffusion is necessary, one in which a direct comparison is made above a certain altitude between a mixing distribution and a diffusion distribution. In such a case, the diffusion times have a completely different meaning and are directly related to the absolute values of the concentrations in a definite atmospheric region.

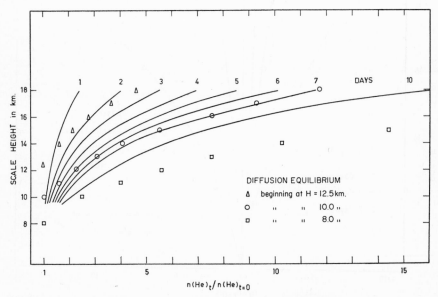

FIG. 6. Diffusion of helium in the thermosphere. Mixing distribution of helium changed into diffusive equilibrium by upward transport. The abscissae represent the factor by which the initial concentration, $n(\mathrm{He})_{t=0}$, appropriate to mixing alone, is increased to give the final concentration, $n(\mathrm{He})_t$, after a time, t, which is different for each of the curves. The symbols have the same meaning as those of Fig. 5. By comparing results of Figs. 5 and 6, it can be seen that the times required for the diffusion of helium are about twice those for the diffusion of argon.

Figures 5 and 6 show the results for argon and helium, respectively. The initial vertical distributions are represented by the principal constituent of mass $M = 24$, and diffusion occurs for minor constituents of mass $M(\mathrm{A}) = 40$ and $M(\mathrm{He}) = 4$. The final states are vertical diffusion distributions corresponding to three starting levels $H = 8$ km, 10 km, and 12.5 km.

In this way characteristic times are derived for redistribution of a minor constituent originally completely mixed and are related to different diffusion distributions beginning at a series of different levels.

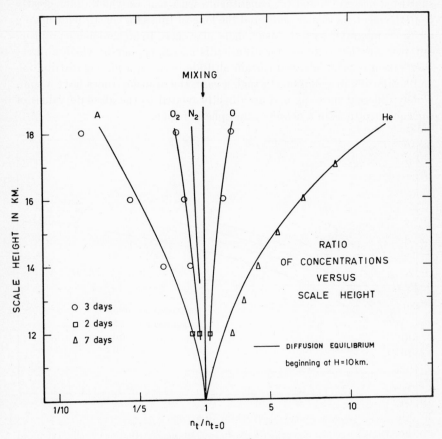

Diffusion in the thermosphere.

FIG. 7. Change of mixing distribution of various minor constituents into diffusive distribution by upward or downward transport. Height is represented by the scale height appropriate to each level in the atmosphere as described in Table VI; $H = 10$ km is the reference level corresponding to altitudes between 100 and 105 km. Below the reference level mixing prevents any separation of the constituents, and diffusion exists above this level. Such conditions are obtained in less than 3 days for all minor constituents (symbol ◯) except for helium, which requires 7 days (symbol △).

One feature of Figs. 5 and 6 is immediately apparent: the rapidity with which a diffusion equilibrium is reached depends on the altitude. For example, if diffusion is not counteracted by mixing above $H = 8$ km (between 100 and 105 km), 7 days (see Fig. 5) is necessary to reach a diffusion equilibrium for argon in the thermosphere above that altitude. During the same time (Fig.6) diffusion will have no important effect on helium below $H = 10$ km (between 110 and 115 km). In other words, diffusion transport produces an equilibrium distribution above $H = 10$ km in about 3 days for argon and in about 7 days for helium. Finally, above $H = 12.5$ km the shortest times of diffusion are involved: less than 1 day is required to reach diffusion equilibrium for argon, and less than 3 days for helium.

These various criteria describe clearly how concentration changes occur in the thermosphere under the continuous effect of diffusion and finally lead to a clear conclusion that, above a certain level in the lower thermosphere, mixing must ultimately be replaced by diffusion. If the time of mixing is introduced, the discussion may be limited by arbitrary conditions, since we do not yet know the coefficient of mass exchange at altitudes of 100 km. Thanks to observations of Meadows and Townsend,[7] it is possible to assume that the mixing times for argon are not less than 1 day and not more than 1 week between 100 and 110 km, altitudes which are represented (Table VI) by $H = 8$ km and 10 km in our working atmospheric model. There is therefore no doubt that in any atmospheric model using diffusion equilibrium at 110 km the concentrations of all constituents will be correct to a factor of 2.

Figure 7 shows the distribution of the different gases in the thermosphere when diffusion equilibrium has been set up above the level where $H = 10$ km, i.e., between 110 and 115 km. The times necessary to achieve such an equilibrium from a state of complete mixing are also shown, and it can be seen that more than 1 day but not more than 1 week is required.

In the light of these results, it is safe to consider that in the thermosphere above 110 km all *minor* constituents which are sufficiently inert and neutral to be free from rapid chemical reactions are distributed according to a height gradient corresponding to a diffusion equilibrium. Thus, the density in the thermosphere above a certain altitude depends on the varying molecular mass of the *principal* constituents. It decreases with height according to the increasing ratio of the concentrations of atomic oxygen and molecular nitrogen, which are the principal constituents.

It may be important to point out that the problem of diffusion of the free charged particles in the ionospheric $F2$ layer is different from that considered here. The behavior depends not only on the absolute value of the diffusion coefficient,[18] but also on several factors[19] such as recombination, ionization, and magnetic field, for which values must be known as a function of real heights. Atomic oxygen should be an important constituent in the $F2$ layer, and, according to Dalgarno's data[18] for the diffusion coefficient (D) of O^+ in O (about four times the coefficient for neutral particles[19]), diffusion is certainly less marked than previous deductions have indicated.

2.6 Thermal Conductivity in the Thermosphere

Convection is the major process of heat transport in the homosphere, particularly in the troposphere, and radiation also becomes important in the stratosphere; but in the thermosphere conduction is of predominant importance. Ionospheric data, rocket results, and more recently satellite observations have shown that the temperature gradient must be very large in the thermosphere. It is therefore important to consider the conduction of heat in that part of the atmosphere.

Spitzer[20] has drawn attention to the effect of thermal conductivity in the thermosphere as compared with the heating from absorbed solar radiation. Bates[21] has made an investigation of the thermal equilibrium by considering the rate at which energy is gained from ionizing photons, and lost through conduction and radiation.

Since practically no polyatomic molecule exists in the thermosphere, and since molecular oxygen and nitrogen have no dipole moment, the principal radiation of heat is from atomic oxygen, by virtue of its magnetic dipole emission[21] from the two upper levels of the ground state. Direct application of the heat-transfer equation by Bates[22] shows that a large temperature gradient can be maintained only if the heat supplied by photoionization and subsequent energy transformation is sufficiently important. These results do not, however, lead one to expect a gradient of temperature above the $F2$ peak because no ultraviolet radiation absorption processes occur there. A discussion by Johnson[23] has shown that, if solar electromagnetic radiation is the sole predominant heat source, the temperature cannot increase with height above about 300 km.

Any gradient of temperature above 300 km requires the introduction of heat at higher levels and therefore a transport by conduction throughout the upper thermosphere. Such a source of heating may be supplied by particles entering the atmosphere in various forms. For example, protons of velocities of about 1000 km sec^{-1} having charge-transfer cross sections greater than 10^{-16} cm^2 in nitrogen, i.e., between ten and fifty times the photo-ionization cross section of ultraviolet radiation, would lead by the ionization process and subsequent dissociative recombination to some heating at heights greater than that by solar radiation.* More evidence on the properties of these particles is needed, however. Interstellar particles entering the atmosphere could provide a source of heating in the region where their kinetic energy can be transformed into heat by adequate collisions with atmospheric particles.†

* $\Delta z \simeq 4H$, about four times the scale height, for a ratio 50 of the cross sections since $n/n_0 = \exp(-z/H)$.

† For example, G. A. Harrower, in *Canad. J. Phys.* **35**, 792 (1957), has made an analysis of radio star scintillations in which he considers that the atmosphere would receive about 6×10^{12} hydrogen atoms cm^{-2} sec^{-1} with a velocity of the order of 3×10^6 cm sec^{-1}.

Other suggestions * may be made, and Chapman[24] has suggested that the conduction of heat from the ionized coronal gas to the terrestrial atmosphere could lead to temperature gradients above the ionospheric $F2$ peak. In a conservative model of the solar corona he has shown that the heat available is 2.4×10^{19} ergs sec^{-1} at a distance of five earth's radii. If the total energy were trapped, not less than 4 ergs cm^{-2} sec^{-1} would be available at an altitude of 500 km. The energy carried down into the thermosphere, however, is only a fraction of the total energy, since a concentrative process would be needed. Instead of this, Chapman[24] has indicated that the geomagnetic field would have a hindering effect. It may nevertheless be considered that for the polar regions the magnetic field does not preclude the possibility of the heat transport, nor, therefore, the subsequent transport due to the existence of an horizontal temperature gradient.

In conclusion, it appears that sufficient energy may be supplied to the thermosphere from two sources; at the lowest levels up to the $F2$ peak by electromagnetic solar radiation, and throughout the whole thermosphere by the conduction of heat resulting from far and wide sources such as the coronal gas. Of the processes (convection, radiation, and conduction) available for heat loss, convection has its major effect in the lower part of the thermosphere, radiation has an effect which decreases with altitude, almost directly in proportion to the atomic oxygen concentration, and conduction remains as the only important process at the highest altitudes. Furthermore, since thermospheric conditions change from the sunlit to the dark atmosphere, it must be pointed out that daily variations are unavoidable. Such a variation was discussed by Lowan,[25] who made a numerical estimation of the rate of cooling of the thermosphere with a specific temperature gradient after the cessation of the external heating. The calculation showed that the assumed initial height distribution of the temperature begins to shift immediately after the incoming radiation ceases, and the effect is particularly important in the ionospheric $F2$ layer. In the heat budget of the thermosphere, it is therefore necessary to consider that in addition to a steady state in its upper part, maintained by the heat received by the Chapman process, there is a daily variation depending on the variation of the incident ultraviolet radiation and on the heat capacity of the thermosphere. In other words, the boundary conditions change between day and night. Since the heating due to solar radiation is caused by processes such as a recombination releasing heat, a night effect cannot be neglected.

If convection is neglected, the heat balance in the thermosphere is a function of the thermal flux arriving at a certain level, the heat production

* According to Van Allen (*J. Geophys. Res.* **64**, 271 (1959)), there is a possibility that the radiation belt is the source of a leakage of energetic particles contributing to the general heating of the atmosphere.

P, per unit volume, and the heat, R, radiated per unit volume. Thus, the transfer equation is

$$dE/dz + P = R. \tag{2.60}$$

At the lowest heights in the thermosphere P represents absorption of solar radiation by O_2 molecules undergoing dissociation and transformation of the energy involved in the X-ray spectral region; in the ionospheric F layers, it corresponds to the energy available in the ultraviolet region, for example in the helium lines which, according to Oster,[26] may lead to more than 10^{10} photons cm^{-2} sec^{-1}. Above the peak of the $F2$ layer, it is not possible to maintain an active source of heat production by electromagnetic radiation.

The symbol R represents the energy transformed in the Bates atomic oxygen emission process which is prevalent throughout the thermosphere. It decreases exponentially with height as it follows the vertical distribution of atomic oxygen. The maximum value of R is*

$$R = 1.65 \times 10^{-18} n(O) \text{ erg cm}^{-3} \text{ sec}^{-1}. \tag{2.61}$$

When sufficient energy is supplied by an external heat flow, R is negligible at the highest levels in the thermosphere, and, therefore, the transfer equation is simply

$$dE/dz = 0. \tag{2.62}$$

Conduction related to an energy flux, E, is expressed by

$$E = -\lambda_c \, dT/dz \tag{2.63}$$

where λ_c is the conductivity coefficient.

If we consider a sphere of radius r, the total flux, F, is

$$F = 4\pi r^2 \lambda_c \, dT/dz \tag{2.64}$$

and, instead of (2.62), the transfer equation in the atmosphere must be written

$$dF/dz = 0. \tag{2.65}$$

The coefficient, λ_c, of heat conduction is connected, according to Chapman and Cowling,[13] with the coefficient of viscosity, μ, by an equation

$$\lambda_c = f\mu c_v \tag{2.66}$$

in which c_v denotes the specific heat at constant volume, and f is a pure number equal to 2.52 for rigid elastic spheres and to 2.50 for Maxwellian

* $R = 0.67 \times 10^{-18} n(O)$ at $T = 250°K$;
  $1.05 \times 10^{-18} n(O)$ at $T = 500°K$; $1.34 \times 10^{-18} n(O)$ at $T = 1000°K$,
  and $1.44 \times 10^{-18} n(O)$ at $T = 1500°K$

molecules. Thus, for a monatomic gas λ_c can be represented with sufficient accuracy by

$$\lambda_c = \frac{5}{2}\mu c_v = \frac{5}{2}\left\{\frac{0.1792(kmT)^{\frac{1}{2}}}{\sigma^2}\right\}\frac{3k}{2m} \tag{2.67}$$

in which σ is the collision diameter. It is customary, however, to represent the temperature variation of viscosity by the empirical expression

$$\mu/\mu_0 = (T/T_0)^s \tag{2.68}$$

where s denotes an empirical constant ranging from 0.5 to 1. But, if we consider that in the thermosphere the range of temperature is different from the range used for the adoption of (2.68), it is easy to see, according to Kestin,[27] that (2.66) is more precise for thermospheric application. In fact, empirical relations of Keyes[27] show that:

$\mu(O_2) = 1.5 \ \times 10^{-5}T^{\frac{1}{2}}$ within $\pm$ 5 % between 600° and 1200°K
$\mu(N_2) = 1.25 \times 10^{-5}T^{\frac{1}{2}}$ within $\pm$ 5 % between 600° and 1500°K
$\mu(air) = 1.3 \ \ \times 10^{-5}T^{\frac{1}{2}}$ within $\pm$ 5 % between 600° and 1500°K
$\mu(A) \ \ = 1.66 \times 10^{-5}T^{\frac{1}{2}}$ within $\pm$ 6 % between 500° and 1500°K
$\mu(He) = 1.45 \times 10^{-5}T^{\frac{1}{2}}$ within $\pm$ 10 % between 500° and 1750°K

From these numerical values it may be concluded that (2.66) is applicable in the thermosphere, and thus

$$\lambda_c = AT^{\frac{1}{2}} \tag{2.69}$$

giving

$$\lambda_c(air) = 1.8 \times 10^2 T^{\frac{1}{2}} \tag{2.70}$$
$$\lambda_c(O) = 3.6 \times 10^2 T^{\frac{1}{2}} \tag{2.71}$$
$$\lambda_c(H) = 2.1 \times 10^3 T^{\frac{1}{2}} \tag{2.72}$$

if $\sigma(O) = 2.4$ A and $\sigma(H) = 2.0$ A.

Equation (2.65) can be written, by using (2.64) and (2.69), as

$$4\pi A\frac{d(r^2T^{\frac{1}{2}}\,dT/dr)}{dr} = 0 \tag{2.73}$$

and integration between reference levels z and $z = 0$, corresponding to $r = (a + z)$ and a, the respective distances from the center of the earth. leads to

$$F = 4\pi a(a + z)\frac{2}{3}A\frac{T^{3/2} - T_a^{3/2}}{z} \tag{2.74}$$

or

$$E_{a+z} = \frac{a}{a + z}\frac{2}{3}A\frac{T^{3/2} - T_a^{3/2}}{z} \tag{2.75}$$

and

$$E_a = E_{a+z}[(a + z)/a]^2 \tag{2.76}$$

If the heat flow is known at a certain distance, $a + h$, from the center of the earth, (2.74) by means of (2.76) leads to

$$\frac{T^{3/2} - T_a^{3/2}}{T_h^{3/2} - T_a^{3/2}} = \frac{z}{h}\frac{a + h}{a + z} \tag{2.77}$$

which gives the vertical distribution of the temperature; (2.77) can be also written as follows:

$$T^{3/2} = \frac{(a + h)^2}{a(a + z)}\frac{3E_{a+h}}{2A}z + T_a^{3/2} \tag{2.78}$$

which shows that the temperature depends on the boundary condition through the term $T_a^{3/2}$.

If x represents a certain distance below or above the height h, (2.78) leads to

$$T_{h+x}^{3/2} - T_{h-x}^{3/2} = x[1 + (x/a + h)^2]\,3E_{a+h}/A \tag{2.79}$$

which shows how temperatures are related to the heat flow arriving at a certain specific level.

Expression (2.79) can be applied to a region where atomic oxygen should be the principal constituent, i.e., the thermospheric region above the $F2$ peak. If we consider the heat flow arriving at 500 km and boundary conditions at 300 km, the temperatures at 700 km are as follows:

$E_{500\ km}$ (ergs cm^{-2} sec^{-1})		0.1	0.2	0.5
$T_{700\ km}$, if $T_{300\ km}$	$= 400°K$	850	1300	2000
	$= 900°K$	1250	1550	2300
	$= 1600°K$	1850	2100	2900

It can be seen that very high temperatures can easily be obtained if a significant fraction of the energy available at the top of the earth's atmosphere is trapped in the thermosphere. The temperature also depends, however, on the lower boundary condition, i.e., the conditions below 300 km, where absorption of solar radiation is possible. For example, if the temperature is of the order of 1600°K at 300 km, a heat flow of 0.1 erg cm^{-2} sec^{-1} will only lead to a temperature of 1850°K at 700 km, i.e., an increase of only 250°K for a range of 400 km, which is not yet detectable.

At such heights, the heat production, P, per unit volume by ultraviolet radiation is

$$P = n(O)K(\lambda)E_0(\lambda) \tag{2.80}$$

in which $K(\lambda)$ denotes the absorption coefficient, and $E_0(\lambda)$ the ultraviolet energy available at the top of the earth's atmosphere. Since the absorption coefficient for constituents in the F layer is of the order of 10^{-17} cm^2, the transfer equation (2.60) may be written

$$dE(\lambda)/dz = n(O)[10^{-17}\,E_0(\lambda) - 1.65 \times 10^{-18}]. \tag{2.81}$$

This shows that the effect of the radiant heat may be neglected when $E_0(\lambda)$ is more than 1 erg cm^{-2} sec^{-1}. Because the energy available in the helium lines should be not less than 1 erg cm^{-2} sec^{-1}, integration of (2.81) leads to

$$E(\lambda) = E_0(\lambda)[1 - e^{-n(0)H10^{-17}}] \qquad (2.82)$$

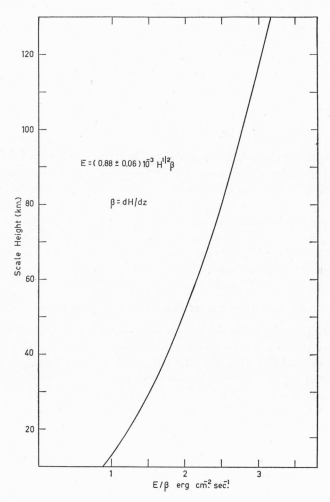

FIG. 8. Heat flow and scale height. The effect of thermal conductivity in the thermosphere is shown by a curve relating the scale height and the energy necessary to maintain the gradient $\beta = dH/dz$. From the abscissae representing E/β, it may be deduced that any gradient, β, of the order of unity, requires energy flows from 1 to 3 ergs cm^{-2} sec^{-1} in the whole thermosphere, since thermospheric scale heights are between 10 and 100 km. It must be pointed out that the distribution of E with height must follow a distribution given by an equation of a type described by (2.82).

which must be compared with the energy supplied by external flow. A vertical column of less than 10^{16} oxygen atoms cm^{-2} will be easily subject to an external heat flow since, according to (2.82),

$$E(\lambda) < 0.1E_0(\lambda). \tag{2.83}$$

It may be concluded, therefore, that the gradient of the scale height in the thermospheric region, where only the external heat flow plays a role, depends on the conditions prevailing at lower altitudes where the ultraviolet radiation is absorbed.

In the F layer where ultraviolet radiation is absorbed, atomic oxygen and molecular nitrogen are the principal constituents. By using equations (2.70) and (2.71) and taking $g = 900$ cm sec^{-2}, equation (2.63) can be written as

$$E = (0.88 \pm 0.06)10^{-3} \, H^{\frac{1}{2}} \, dH/dz. \tag{2.84}$$

Figure 8 shows the relationship between heat flow and scale height. For example, a gradient of the order of unity for a scale height of about 50 km corresponds to a heating of 2 ergs cm^{-2} sec^{-1} resulting from absorption of ultraviolet radiation above the reference level $H = 50$ km. Ionospheric observations require that the degree of heating should be less than this, and it is therefore necessary to introduce a constituent which is instrumental in absorption but which does not contribute to the electron concentration as detected by radiotechniques.

2.7 Constitution of the Upper Atmosphere

The first direct determinations of pressures at altitudes up to 120 km and densities up to 160 km were reported in 1952 by Havens et al.[28] on the basis of about twelve rocket flights. In the same year a conventional atmospheric model combining all available rocket results was adopted by the Rocket Panel.[29] A temperature distribution between 30 and 80 km was deduced which took into account the temperatures observed by all the different groups of observers in the United States. The temperature distribution for the thermosphere up to 220 km was obtained from rocket measurements of the mass densities at about 160 km and 220 km, and the temperature gradient adopted for the region between 110 and 220 km was about 6 deg km^{-1}. The final model was based,[30] however, on the assumption of a uniform gradient for the dissociation of oxygen in the 80- to 120-km range, and for the dissociation of nitrogen in the 120- to 220-km range. Since the actual height distribution of the oxygen dissociation does not have a uniform gradient and since total dissociation of nitrogen does not occur, the Rocket Panel atmospheric model is not suitable for studying the behavior of the thermosphere.

Table VII shows an atmospheric model for the *homosphere* between 50 km and 100 km. The temperature at the stratopause is of the order of

TABLE VII
Atmospheric Data between 50 and 100 km

Altitude (km)	Temperature[a] (°K)	Pressure (mm Hg)	Concentration (cm⁻³)	Density (gm cm⁻³)
50.0	274	6.7×10^{-1}	2.4×10^{16}	1.1×10^{-6}
52.5	274	4.9×10^{-1}	1.7×10^{16}	8.3×10^{-7}
55.0	274	3.6×10^{-1}	1.3×10^{16}	6.1×10^{-7}
57.5	263	2.7×10^{-1}	9.7×10^{15}	4.7×10^{-7}
60.0	253	1.9×10^{-1}	7.3×10^{15}	3.5×10^{-7}
62.5	242	1.4×10^{-1}	5.4×10^{15}	2.6×10^{-7}
65.0	232	9.6×10^{-2}	4.0×10^{15}	1.9×10^{-7}
67.5	221	6.6×10^{-2}	2.9×10^{15}	1.4×10^{-7}
70.0	210	4.5×10^{-2}	2.1×10^{15}	9.9×10^{-8}
72.5	197	3.0×10^{-2}		7.0×10^{-8}
	207	3.0×10^{-2}	1.4×10^{15}	6.7×10^{-8}
75.0	183	1.9×10^{-2}		4.9×10^{-8}
	203	2.0×10^{-2}	9.5×10^{14}	4.6×10^{-8}
77.5	170	1.2×10^{-2}		3.3×10^{-8}
	200	1.3×10^{-2}	6.4×10^{14}	3.1×10^{-8}
80.0	156	7.2×10^{-3}		2.1×10^{-8}
	197	8.7×10^{-3}	4.3×10^{14}	2.1×10^{-8}
82.5	143	4.1×10^{-3}		1.3×10^{-8}
	193	5.7×10^{-3}	2.8×10^{14}	1.4×10^{-8}
85.0	130	2.2×10^{-3}		8.0×10^{-9}
	190	3.7×10^{-3}	1.9×10^{14}	9.0×10^{-9}
87.5	143	1.2×10^{-3}		3.9×10^{-9}
	193	2.4×10^{-3}	1.2×10^{14}	5.7×10^{-9}
90.0	156	7.0×10^{-4}		2.1×10^{-9}
	197	1.6×10^{-3}	7.6×10^{13}	3.7×10^{-9}
92.5	170	4.2×10^{-4}		1.1×10^{-9}
	200	1.0×10^{-3}	4.9×10^{13}	2.4×10^{-9}
95.0	183	2.6×10^{-4}		6.6×10^{-10}
	203	6.8×10^{-4}	3.2×10^{13}	1.5×10^{-9}
97.5	197	1.7×10^{-4}		4.0×10^{-10}
	207	4.5×10^{-4}	2.1×10^{13}	1.0×10^{-9}
100.0	210	1.1×10^{-4}		2.5×10^{-10}
	210	3.0×10^{-4}	1.4×10^{13}	6.6×10^{-10}

[a] Between 70 and 100 km, two distributions of temperature are given for atmospheres in which the temperatures at 85 km are 130°K and 190°K.

273°K, and at the mesopause 190°K or 130°K. At 100 km, the temperature is 210°K. After comparison of the data of Table VII with observational data, it can be said that 273°K is an average value at the stratopause, since variations[31] observed there indicate T(stratopause) $= 273° \pm 20°$K.

Various methods have been used for measuring the density. The results of LaGow *et al.*[32] seem to indicate that the arctic densities coincide practically with those at 33° N; i.e., they do not vary by more than 10 to 20 %. But according to Jones *et al.*,[33] there is a trend for the density at 50 km to decrease with increasing latitude, and for the density at latitude 58° N in the neighborhood of 70 km to vary by a factor of 2, namely between 5×10^{-8} and 10^{-7} gm cm^{-3}.

Observational data for 100 km are very different.* The Rocket Panel[29] adopted 4.5×10^{-4} mm Hg, whereas Havens *et al.*[28] gave a determination of 4.2×10^{-4} mm Hg. Horowitz and LaGow,[34] however, after correcting the pressures measured with Viking 7, have obtained data leading to a value of 1.1×10^{-4} mm Hg, and Byram *et al.*[35] indicate from measurements on the incident X-ray flux that the Rocket Panel values were too high by a factor of 3. There is a variation of a factor of 4 for all these values, which are for White Sands (33° N). The data (U.S.S.R.) published by Michnevitch[36] indicate a relatively low pressure: 1.8×10^{-4} mm Hg at 100 km. But data obtained at Fort Churchill (58° N) show that the pressure[37] is not less than 3×10^{-4} mm Hg and that density data[38] for molecular oxygen must lead to a total density of not less than 9×10^{-10} gm cm^{-3}. Thus, there is a broad range of a factor of 4 in the pressure and density data at 100 km. This cannot be attributed to a permanent latitudinal effect, since the variation at White Sands corresponds to the difference between the White Sands minimum value and the average values obtained at Fort Churchill. In other words, the pressure at 100 km can be of the order of $(3 \pm 1) \times 10^{-4}$ mm Hg, but it is not yet possible to determine the exact range of real variations.

Since any atmospheric model, even at such low heights as 100 km, is subject to uncertainty, we have introduced (Table VII) between 70 and 100 km the variation of temperature which is required to lead to a low pressure at 100 km. Because large variations of the temperature may occur near the mesopause, the layer between 70 and 100 km is divided into two parts, 15 km thick, in order to obtain the minimum temperature near 85 km. In any case, with a pressure of 4.5×10^{-2} mm Hg corresponding to a density of 10^{-7} gm cm^{-3} at 70 km (see Table VII), and if the pressure at 100 km varies by a factor of about 3, there would be a variation of about 60°K at 85 km. If the temperature at 70 km and at 100 km is 210°K, the general trend should be as follows:

Temperature at 85 km (°K)

130	140	150	160	170	180	190	200	210

Pressure at 100 km (10^{-4} mm Hg)

1.1	1.4	1.7	2.0	2.3	2.6	3.0	3.4	3.8

* Only pressure measurements were made. There is no direct measurement of density.

If there is a possibility of a very large variation of the pressure at 100 km, any atmospheric model to be used for the thermosphere above 100 km will be affected to the same extent. For example, a density at 200 km of the order of 6×10^{-13} gm cm^{-3} (deduced from satellite observations) requires a completely different structure of the atmosphere between 100 and 200 km if the density at 100 km varies by a factor of 3.

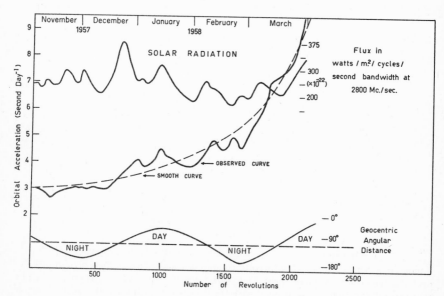

Fig. 9. Orbital acceleration in seconds per day of Satellite 1957 β1 (Sputnik II) during 5 months, according to Jacchia.[46] The perigee, which was about 225 km during the first revolution, changed slowly from 50° N to the equator. The fluctuations of the acceleration around an average value, which are less than 20 %, may be explained by the variations in the solar heating, reaching a maximum near 150 km. A first analysis may be made in considering the position of the perigee in a sunlit or dark atmosphere. According to Jacchia (Harvard College Observatory, Announcement Card 1423, January 16, 1959), however, a comparison can be made between the solar radiation represented by its emission at 2800 Mc/sec and the variation of the orbital acceleration of the satellites. Solar radiation data are taken from the Bulletin of the National Research Council, Ottawa, Canada.

The data available on atmospheric density, obtained by means of rockets and of satellites, must be compared even if sufficient data are still lacking. Present rocket information[37, 39] on densities at 200 km (59° N) indicates a variation by a factor greater than 10 between a summer day (6×10^{-13} gm cm^{-3}) and a winter night (4×10^{-14} gm cm^{-3}). Analysis of satellite observations made by several authors[40-58] shows that in general the density at such altitudes does not vary by more than a factor 2.

Figure 9 shows the variations in the density[46] at the altitude of the perigee of Sputnik II. The period of revolution may be affected by complex phenomena, such as the orientation of the object and particular drag coefficients.

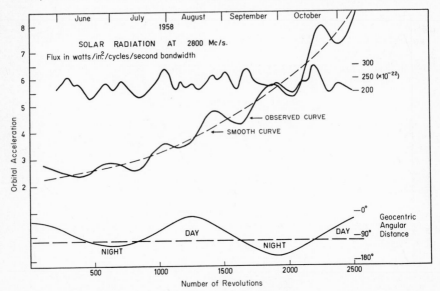

FIG. 10a. Orbital acceleration in days per day of Satellite 1958 δ_1 (Sputnik III) during 5 months, according to Jacchia (private communication). During 2500 revolutions the orbital acceleration is subject to rhythmic variations of less than 20 %. There is evidence that these fluctuations are associated with the principal variations of the solar radiation represented by the solar flux at 2800 Mc/sec. The associations between variations of the atmospheric density and the solar heating is more apparent in Fig. 10b.

Irregularities due to these effects, however, do not seem to be the most important, for they can be explained by variations in the atmospheric density at the altitude of the perigee. Furthermore, these irregularities in the deceleration (Fig. 9), which are within ± 20 % of the average value, show that in the range of altitudes covered by the perigree of Sputnik II (initial perigee, 240 km) the actual value of the density is always equivalent to the average value ± 20 %. A certain variation in the indicated limits may result from a difference due to the position of the perigee in the night side or the day side of the earth, but it is clear that the most obvious association must be made with the variation of the solar radiation which causes the heating of the thermosphere.

Figures 10a and 10b show the variation of density[48] at the altitudes of the perigees of Sputnik III and the Vanguard satellite. The simultaneous variations in the densities of the atmosphere near 650 km (± 50 %) and 250 km (± 20 %) must result from a change in the atmospheric conditions below 150 km, to which the heat is conducted from higher levels where the ultraviolet radiation is absorbed, and perhaps in addition from a variation in the heat flow coming from the top of the atmosphere.

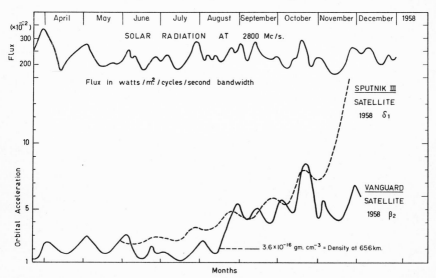

FIG. 10b. Comparison between the variations of the orbital acceleration of satellites Vanguard and Sputnik III in association with the solar heating, according to Jacchia's data. During 1500 revolutions (about 5 months) the fluctuations of the acceleration of the Satellite 1958 β_2 (Vanguard) lead, near the perigee, at an altitude of 656 km, to variations of about 50 % in the density, namely $\rho = (3.6 \pm 1.8) \times 10^{-16}$ gm cm^{-3}. A sharp increase in the acceleration in August corresponds to an increase by a factor of 2.5 in the average density between the two periods April–July and September–December. The fluctuations are related, however, to variations of the solar radiation. As an example, the principal peak in October is well represented in the three curves, indicating that the accelerations of both satellites varied almost in unison with the solar heating.

Analysis of satellite observations such as those made by Sterne,[40] Harris and Jastrow,[45] Jacchia,[47] Schilling and Whitney,[49] and Siry[55] shows that densities between 200 and 800 km may have the vertical distribution given in the tabulation (see Fig. 11).

Such a vertical distribution of thermospheric densities must be interpreted by an increase of the atmospheric scale height between 200 and 800 km. According to formula (2.6)

$$d\rho/\rho = - (1 + 1/\beta) \, dH/H - dg/g \qquad (2.85)$$

in which

$$\beta = dH/dz \qquad (2.86)$$

and

$$dH/H = dT/T - dm/m - dg/g \qquad (2.87)$$

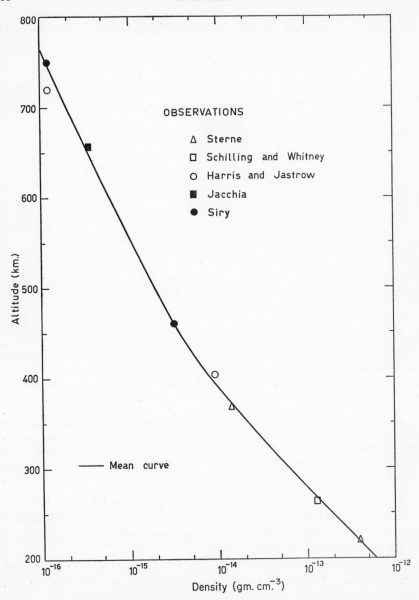

Thermospheric densities.

FIG. 11. Density-altitude relations deduced from satellite observations.* The observational values are taken from Sterne[40] for Sputnik II (1957 α_2) and Explorer I (1958 α), from Schilling and Whitney[49] for Explorer IV (1958 ϵ), from Harris and Jastrow[45] for Explorer I and Vanguard (1958 β_2), from Jacchia [47] for Vanguard, and from Siry[55] for Explorer I and Vanguard.

* Approximate values since variations are observed.

Altitude (km)	Density (gm cm^{-3})	Density (gm cm^{-3})
200	6×10^{-13}	
250		2×10^{-13}
300	6×10^{-14}	
350		2×10^{-14}
420	6×10^{-15}	
500		2×10^{-15}
600	6×10^{-16}	
700		2×10^{-16}
800	6×10^{-17}	

If the variation of the scale height were due only to the variation of temperature,* the gradient, β, should be given, according to (2.80), by

$$\beta \simeq 10^3 E/H^{\frac{1}{2}}. \tag{2.88}$$

The heat flow, E, depends on the absorption processes of the ultraviolet radiation below 300 km and on the transport by conduction in the upper part of the thermosphere.

If the variation of the scale height were due only to the variation of the mean molecular mass,† m, the gradient, β, should be

$$\beta \simeq -(1/m^2)\, dm/dz \tag{2.89}$$

depending on the level at which diffusion begins.

Thus, when a complete interpretation of the thermospheric densities is required, it is necessary to consider the simultaneous variations of four parameters, z, T, m, and g, in the following expression:

$$d\rho/\rho = -dz/H - dT/T + dm/m + dg/g. \tag{2.90}$$

It is clear that an exact knowledge of the composition and constitution of the thermosphere cannot be obtained without knowing the simultaneous variations of T and m. In other words, there are many possibilities for thermospheric models leading to the densities obtained from satellite measurements. Among these models a few can be selected by lower boundary conditions, namely by assumptions made on temperature and mean molecular mass between 100 and 200 km.

In order to show how different interpretations can be obtained, we shall discuss various conditions which can be introduced between 100 and 200 km and then adopt two extreme models.

In Table VII two pressures, 1.1×10^{-4} and 3.0×10^{-4} mm Hg, are obtained at 100 km according to conditions required at the mesopause.

* This is the case when, if the variation of g is neglected, no diffusion is considered: $m =$ constant.

† This is the case when, the variation of g being neglected, diffusion plays a role in an isothermal atmosphere.

These pressures were computed for the homosphere in which no dissociation of molecular oxygen occurs. From the following assumptions:

Model A	Model B
Strong dissociation of O_2: 80 %	Low dissociation of O_2: 25 %
$n(O) \simeq n(N_2)$	$n(N_2) + n(O_2) = 10n(O)$

the conditions at 100 km are:

$p = 1.4 \times 10^{-4}$ mm Hg	$p = 3 \times 10^{-4}$ mm Hg
$T = 200°K$	$T = 200°K$
$\rho = 2.9 \times 10^{-10}$ gm cm^{-3}	$\rho = 6.6 \times 10^{-10}$ gm cm^{-3}
$M = 25.5$	$M = 27.4$

Between 100 and 150 km various conditions can be adopted. We choose the following ones:

Model A			Model B		
Diffusion from 110 km			No diffusion		
Temperature at 150 km:			Temperature at 150 km:		
(a)	(b)	(c)	(d)	(e)	(f)
450°K	575°K	700°K	1180°K	1650°K	2100°K

leading to the following values at 150 km.

(a)	(b)	(c)	(d)	(e)	(f)
$\rho = 2.0 \times 10^{-12}$	2.9×10^{-12}	3.2×10^{-12}	1.55×10^{-12}	1.5×10^{-12}	1.4×10^{-12}
$M = 18.0$	18.9	19.2	27.4	27.4	27.4

These two extreme cases show how the density depends on the mean molecular mass and temperature. It is clear, however, that the variation of density is not very sensitive to the variation of temperature in the lower thermosphere, since $\rho = (2.3 \pm 0.9) \times 10^{-12}$ gm cm^{-3} in all circumstances. As an example, Fig. 12 exhibits the density-altitude relation for model B above 120 km for three different large gradients of the scale height, namely $\beta = 1$, 1.5, and 2.0, corresponding at 150 km to heat flows of the order of 1.7, 2.0, and 2.5 ergs cm^{-2} sec^{-1}, respectively. It is found by the procedure adopted that solutions can be obtained which are close to observed values but which relate to an aeronomic problem impossible to resolve. The procedure leads, however, at higher altitudes to different solutions such as the following ones at 200 km:

Model A			Model B		
(a)	(b)	(c)	(d)	(e)	(f)
$\rho = 2.1 \times 10^{-13}$	4.3×10^{-13}	6.1×10^{-13}	3.8×10^{-13}	5.2×10^{-13}	6.1×10^{-13}

Here one can exclude one or another possibility if the atmospheric density at 200 km does not vary between 2×10^{-13} and 6×10^{-13} gm cm^{-3}.

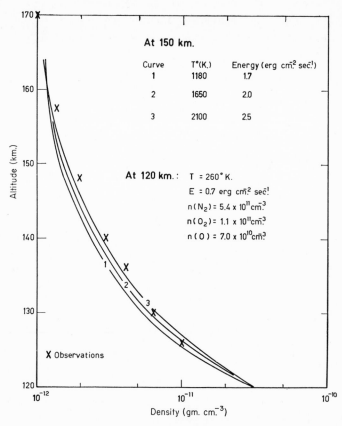

At 150 km.

Curve	T°(K.)	Energy (erg cm^2 sec^1)
1	1180	1.7
2	1650	2.0
3	2100	2.5

At 120 km. : T = 260° K.

E = 0.7 erg cm^2 sec^1

n(N$_2$) = 5.4 x 10^{11}cm^3

n(O$_2$) = 1.1 x 10^{11}cm^3

n(O) = 7.0 x 10^{10}cm^3

X Observations

Thermospheric densities.

FIG. 12. Density-altitude relations above 120 km for various heat flows at 150 km and constant scale height gradients. The symbol (x) represents the data from a rocket flight at Fort Churchill (59° N) published by LaGow et al.[37] The height variation of the density shows that any solution for a too-short range of altitudes is highly arbitrary.

For the sake of simplicity we shall now discuss each model separately, since model A requires a heat flow conducted from the top of the earth's atmosphere, and model B is based on the assumption of heating due only to photoionization and subsequent dissociative recombination.

Figure 13 shows the variation of density in the thermosphere up to the 800-km level, the heat flow being between 0.1 and 1.0 erg cm^{-2} sec^{-1}. The basic boundary conditions are taken to be $T = 700°K$ at 150 km, and the particle concentrations are deduced from model A at 100 km, where $n(O) \simeq n(N_2)$. Attention must be drawn to the portion of Fig. 13 which refers to the region between 200 and 300 km, since it shows that the density is not very sensitive to variations of the heat flow. But great significance must be attached to the behavior of the atmosphere below 150 km, i.e., to boundary conditions. In the region above 300 km the variation of the density

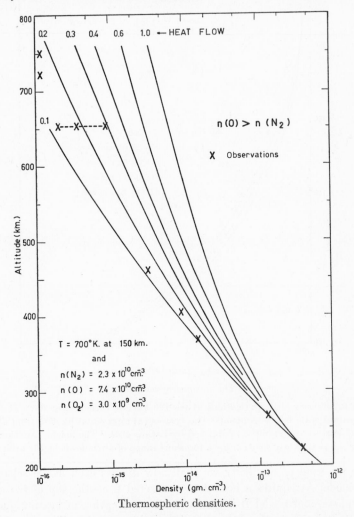

Thermospheric densities.

FIG. 13. Effect of heat flows, conducted from the top of the earth's atmosphere, on thermospheric densities. If one adopts at 500 km a rate of conduction of energy in the range from 0.1 to 1.0 erg cm^{-2} sec^{-1}, it can be seen that the thermospheric densities are very sensitive to the energy input. The absolute values of density depend on the lower boundary condition at 150 km, where $T = 700°K$ and $n(O) > n(N_2)$. The crosses indicate the satellite data. Between 200 and 300 km the density is not very sensitive to the energies which are involved in the heat flow. Variations observed at 650 km would correspond to a variation of a factor of 2 in the heat flow. This figure corresponds to model A discussed in the text.

is more pronounced and depends primarily on the importance of the heat flow. Data from satellites applied to such a working model suggest a heat flow of the order of 0.15 erg cm^{-2} sec^{-1}. A variation of a factor of 5 in the density at 650 km corresponds to fluctuations between 0.15 and 0.3 erg cm^{-2} sec^{-1}.

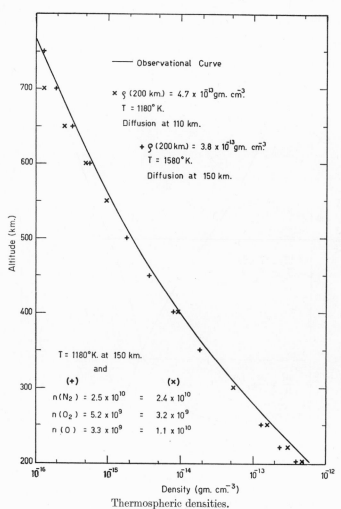

Thermospheric densities.

FIG. 14. Densities in an isothermal atmosphere. The observational curve can be followed when certain conditions are assumed below 200 km. If large gradients of the temperature between 120 and 160 km are assumed [see (Fig. 12)], the effect of diffusion will be to lead to a decrease with altitude of the mean molecular mass corresponding to an increase of the scale height. It is possible to fit the satellite observations of density above 200 km to this curve. This figure corresponds to model B discussed in the text.

5

To return to model B, it can be shown that temperatures of the order of 1650°K and 2100°K at 150 km lead to densities at 600 km which are normally

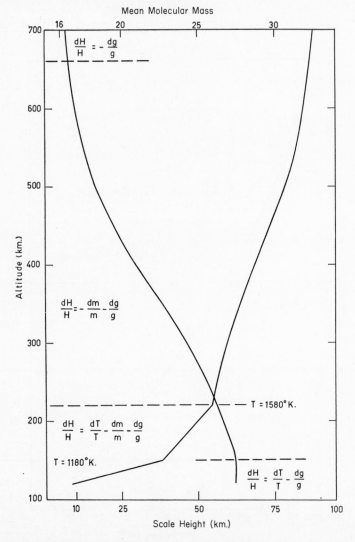

FIG. 15. Variations of the scale height and of the mean molecular mass with altitude. When no gradient of the temperature is assumed above a certain altitude (here 220 km), the vertical distribution of density deduced from satellite observations (see Fig. 11) can be explained only if the scale height increases with height. Thus, the variation of the scale height must be associated with a variation of the mean molecular mass depending on diffusion. In this figure the relation between scale-height and mean molecular mass must be associated with the density shown in Fig. 14.

too high, namely more than 10^{-15} gm cm^{-3}. Attention is therefore directed to the analysis of the model for which the temperature is not more than 1200°K at 150 km.

Figure 14 shows the variation of density with diffusion beginning at 110 km or 150 km, when the temperature is constant above 150 km or 220 km, respectively. In the atmospheric region covered by satellite observations the fit is close over the major part of the curve if a constant temperature is assumed. The lower part, below 250 km, is, however, not adequately represented. Nevertheless, since information on absolute values is lacking, differences of 50 % may be accepted. Figure 15 exhibits the relations between scale height and mean molecular mass between 100 km and 700 km in order to show how the basic parameters vary with height. In the region below 150 km the variation of H is related to the variation of T, whereas above 220 km the two parameters H and m are closely related. Since reliable information on the variation of the scale height with altitude is lacking, several solutions for the vertical distribution of the density are possible, depending on conditions below 200 km.

The discussion of the two atmospheric models concerns physical conditions which are completely different, and the observed values of the density in the thermosphere can be approached without difficulty, under either assumption. Any attempt to distinguish between heating due only to ultra-violet radiation (i.e. T constant at high altitudes) and heating from an external source (i.e. T increasing with height) meets with several difficulties. From energies which are involved in both cases it is, however, apparent that the total heating rate near $F1$ peak is strongly dependent on the heating due to solar radiation. This leads to a temperature gradient which must be greater than 20 deg km^{-1}.

If the number of photons available in the resonance line of HeII, at $\lambda = 304$ A, is of the order of 10^{11} photons cm^{-2} sec^{-1}, i.e., an energy of about 4 ergs cm^{-2} sec^{-1} available for heating, the rate of ionization, $\mathscr{H}$, at the absorption peak is, according to Nicolet's formula,[14]

$$\mathscr{H} = (1 + \beta) e^{-(1 + \beta)} Q_\infty / H \qquad (2.91)$$

in which Q_∞ is the number of photons available at the top of the earth's atmosphere. A local scale height $H \geqslant 50$ km and a gradient $\beta = 1.5$ leads to a production rate of electrons at the $F1$ peak of the order of

$$\mathscr{H} = 3000 \pm 1000 \text{ electrons cm}^{-3} \text{ sec}^{-1} \qquad (2.92)$$

which is not less than ten times the production rate deduced from ionospheric observations. The conventional method used in the analysis of ionospheric data gives

$$q = \alpha n_e^2 \simeq 300 \text{ electrons cm}^{-3} \text{ sec}^{-1} \qquad (2.93)$$

at the peak of the $F1$ layer.

As has been pointed out before,[22] it is necessary that at least two species of ion are formed and recombine with different recombination coefficients. Here, molecular nitrogen and atomic oxygen are involved. Since the time of recombination of N_2^+ is certainly less (100 to 1000 times) than that of O^+, the following conditions must be adopted near the $F1$ peak:

$$n(N_2) \geqslant 10n(O) \tag{2.94}$$

in order to reconcile (2.92) with (2.93). Hence one can exclude the possibility that atomic oxygen * is the principal constituent of the thermosphere below 200 km, for according to the above the percentage of dissociation of molecular oxygen should be less than 20 %. In other words, if condition (2.94) must be applied, the fraction of dissociated oxygen is small, and at 150 km

$$n(O_2) \geqslant 2n(O). \tag{2.95}$$

The discussion in the two preceding paragraphs concerns steady conditions in the atmosphere. Since the heat transfer is governed by the differential equation

$$\frac{\partial T}{\partial t} = \frac{5}{2nm} \operatorname{div}\left[\mu \left(\operatorname{grad} T\right)\right] \tag{2.96}$$

or, in one-dimensional conduction transport (2.67 and 2.69),

$$\frac{\partial T}{\partial t} = \frac{\overline{AT^{\frac{1}{2}}}}{(5/2)kn} \frac{\partial^2 T}{\partial x^2} \tag{2.97}$$

it is necessary to determine the periods of time involved in the heat transport as a function of the concentrations and distances.

As an example, let us consider an atomic oxygen atmosphere with two regions in which the temperatures, T_0 and T_1 are such that $T_0 = 2T_1$. The time, $\tau_{\text{conduction}}$, necessary to increase T_1 to $T = 0.9\,T_0$ can be deduced from (2.97). The solution† of (2.97) is

$$\tau_{\text{conduction}} = 2 \times 10^{-19} x^2 n. \tag{2.98}$$

According to (2.98) a temperature equilibrium to a distance of 10,000 km would be reached in 2×10^4 sec with a concentration, n, of the order of 10^5 cm^{-3}. This shows that it is not possible to maintain a difference of temperature with latitude at very high altitudes. At altitudes below 200 km,

* In the $F2$ layer the production of electrons due to atomic oxygen should increase compared with that resulting from molecular nitrogen, for the ratio $n(O)/n(N_2)$ increases with height. Such an effect should be introduced in the analysis of the behavior of the $F1$ and $F2$ layers.

† The solution would be the same if $T_1 = 0.9\,T_0$ and $T = 0.98\,T_0$ or $T_1 = 0.8\,T_0$ and $T = 0.96\,T_0$.

however, where $n > 10^{10}$ cm^{-3} a temperature equilibrium would only be obtained to a maximum distance of 30 km in the same time (2×10^4 sec).

It is therefore clear from the times involved in the conduction of heat in the thermosphere that densities at very high altitudes must depend primarily on the temperature near 200 km. Since it has been shown that the density at 200 km is not very sensitive to the gradient of temperature, the variations at such an altitude should be relatively small, but the magnitude of the variations should increase with altitude. The analysis of satellite observations made by Jacchia [59] shows that the oscillations of the solar radiations are amplified from 200 km to 700 km, and therefore demonstrates the direct effect of ultraviolet radiation in heating the thermosphere. On the other hand, the importance of these variations compared with the variations [60] resulting from a possible latitude effect leads us to the conclusion that there is a strong tendency to isothermy with latitude at the highest altitudes. Similarly, a variation between day and night will be related to this tendency to isothermy at the highest latitudes but should depend on the temperature near 200 km, because the density above that altitude depends essentially on the absolute value of the temperature.

In conclusion, valuable information on the vertical structure of the thermosphere would be obtained from a complete study of the whole region above 100 km. Additional data from rockets for the region between 100 km and 200 km are essential to know the exact composition. Between 200 and 1000 km, continuous observations from the variation of the acceleration of satellites ($\propto \rho H^{\frac{1}{2}}$) would indicate how $\rho H^{\frac{1}{2}}$ varies with solar radiation in sunlit and dark atmospheres. Using these methods, an important parameter of the thermosphere, i.e. the temperature, will be determined, with its daily variation and its vertical distribution. Such a determination is essential to avoid explanations of the composition and constitution of the thermosphere based only on working atmospheric models.

References

1. M. Nicolet, *Ann. Géophys.* **13**, 1 (1957).
2. E. Gluckauf *in* "Compendium of Meteorology," p. 1, American Meteorological Society, Boston, Massachusetts, 1951.
3. D. R. Bates *in* "The Earth as a Planet" (G. P. Kuiper, ed.), Chapter 12, Univ. Chicago Press, Chicago, 1954.
4. F. A. Paneth, *J. Chem. Soc.* Part 3, 3651 (1952).
5. E. Gluckauf and F. A. Paneth, *Proc. Roy. Soc.* A**185**, 69 (1946).
6. J. W. Townsend, Jr., E. B. Meadows, and E. C. Pressly, *in* "Rocket Exploration of the Upper Atmosphere" (R. L. F. Boyd and M. J. Seaton, eds.), p. 169, Pergamon, London, 1954.
7. E. B. Meadows and J. W. Townsend, Jr., *Ann. Géophys.* **14**, 80 (1958).

8. E. T. Byram, T. A. Chubb, and H. Friedman, *in* "The Proceedings of the Conference on Chemical Aeronomy" (M. Zelikoff, ed.), p. 211, Pergamon, London, 1957.
9. M. Nicolet and P. Mange, *J. Geophys. Res.* **59**, 16 (1954).
10. M. Nicolet, *J. Atmos. Terr. Phys.* **5**, 132 (1954).
11. D. R. Bates and M. Nicolet, *J. Geophys. Res.* **55**, 301 (1950).
12. M. Nicolet, *Ann. Géophys.* **15**, 1 (1959).
13. S. Chapman and T. G. Cowling, "The Mathematical Theory of Non-Uniform Gases," Cambridge Univ. Press, London, 1939 and 1952.
14. M. Nicolet, *in* "The Earth as a Planet" (G. P. Kuiper, ed.), Chapter 13, Univ. Chicago Press, Chicago, 1954.
15. P. S. Epstein, *Beitr. Geophys.* **35**, 153 (1932).
16. P. Mange, *Ann. Géophys.* **11**, 153 (1955).
17. P. Mange, *J. Geophys. Res.* **62**, 279 (1957).
18. A Dalgarno, *J. Atmos. Terr. Phys.* **12**, 219 (1958).
19. V. C. Ferraro and I. Ozdogan, *J. Atmos. Terr. Phys.* **12**, 140 (1958).
20. L. Spitzer, Jr., *in* "The Atmospheres of the Earth and Planets" (G. P. Kuiper, ed.), p. 211, Univ. Chicago Press, Chicago, 1952.
21. D. R. Bates, *Proc. Phys. Soc.* B**64**, 805 (1951).
22. D. R. Bates, *Proc. Phys. Soc.* A**236**, 206 (1956).
23. F. S. Johnson, *J. Geophys. Res.* **61**, 71 (1956).
24. S. Chapman, *Smithsonian Contrib. Astrophys.* **2**, 1 (1957).
25. A. N. Lowan, *J. Geophys. Res.* **60**, 421 (1955).
26. L. Oster, *Z. Astrophys.* **40**, 28 (1956).
27. J. Kestin, *in* "American Institute of Physics Handbook" (D. E. Gray, ed.), Section 2, p. 201, McGraw-Hill, New York, 1957.
28. R. J. Havens, R. T. Koll, and H. E. LaGow, *J. Geophys. Res.* **57**, 59 (1952).
29. The Rocket Panel, *Phys. Rev.* **88**, 1027 (1952).
30. F. L. Whipple, *in* "The Earth as a Planet" (G. P. Kuiper, ed.), Chapter 10, Univ. Chicago Press, Chicago, 1954.
31. W. G. Stroud, W. Nordberg, and J. R. Walsh, *J. Geophys. Res.* **61**, 45 (1956).
32. H. E. LaGow, R. Horowitz, and J. Ainsworth, *Ann. Géophys.* **14**, 131 (1958).
33. L. M. Jones, F. F. Fischbach, and J. W. Peterson, *IGY Rocket Rept. Ser.* **No. 1**, 47 (1958).
34. R. Horowitz and H. E. LaGow, *J. Geophys. Res.* **62**, 57 (1957).
35. E. T. Byram, T. A. Chubb, and H. Friedman, *J. Geophys. Res.* **61**, 251 (1956).
36. V. V. Michnevitch, *Prog. Phys. Sci., Acad. Sci. USSR* **63**, 197 (1957).
37. H. E. LaGow, R. Horowitz, and J. Ainsworth, *IGY Rocket Rept. Ser.* **No. 1**, 38 (1958).
38. J. E. Kupperian, Jr., E. T. Byram, H. Friedman, and A. Unzicker, *IGY Rocket Rept. Ser.* **No. 1**, 203 (1958).
39. J. W. Townsend, Jr., and E. B. Meadows, *Ann. Géophys.* **14**, 117 (1958).
40. T. E. Sterne, *Science*, **128**, 420 (1958).
41. T. E. Sterne, *Phys. Fluids*, **1**, 165 (1958).
42. T. E. Sterne and G. F. Schilling, *Smithsonian Contrib. to Astrophys.* **2**, 207 (1958).
43. G. F. Schilling and T. E. Sterne, *J. Geophys. Res.* **64**, 1 (1959).
44. I. Harris and R. Jastrow, *Science*, **127**, 471 (1958).
45. I. Harris and R. Jastrow, *Science*, **128**, 421 (1958).
46. L. G. Jacchia, *Smithsonian Astrophys. Observ., Spec. Rept.* **No.13**, 1 (1958).
47. L. G. Jacchia, *Smithsonian Astrophys. Observ. Spec. Rept.* **No. 12**, 30 (1958).
48. L. G. Jacchia and R. E. Briggs, *Smithsonian Astrophys. Observ. Spec. Rept.* **No. 18**. 9 (1958).

49. G. F. Schilling and C. A. Whitney, *Smithsonian Astrophys. Observ. Spec. Retd.* **No. 18,** 13 (1958).
50. H. K. Paetzold and H. Zschörner, *Naturwissenschaften* **45,** 485 (1958).
51. G. V. Groves, *Nature* **181,** 1055 (1958).
52. D. G. King-Hele and D. C. Leslie, *Nature* **182,** 860 (1958).
53. C. H. Bosanquet, *Nature* **182,** 1533 (1958).
54. G. V. Groves, *Nature* **182,** 1533 (1958).
55. J. W. Siry, *Ann. IGY* to be published.
56. M. Nicolet, *Science* **127,** 1317 (1958).
57. R. M. Merson, D. G. King-Hele, and R. N. A. Plimmer, *Nature* **183,** 239 (1959).
58. J. W. Townsend, Jr., *Science* **129,** 80 (1959).
59. L. G. Jacchia, *Nature,* **183,** 1662 (1959).
60. D. G. King-Hele, *Nature,* **183,** 1224 (1959).

Chapter 3

The Upper Atmosphere Studied by Rockets and Satellites

HOMER E. NEWELL, JR.

3.1 Introduction 73
3.2 Atmospheric Structure... 74
3.3 Winds.. 97
3.4 Charge Densities in the Ionosphere.................................. 102
3.5 Earth's Magnetic Field... 108
3.6 Chemical and Ion Composition of the Upper Atmosphere.......... 111
3.7 Atmospheric Contamination Experiments........................... 118
3.8 Night Airglow... 119
3.9 Auroral Particles... 120
3.10 Cosmic Rays... 122
3.11 Micrometeors.. 123
3.12 Discussion.. 125
    References 129

3.1 Introduction

The field of ionizing radiations discussed in Chapter 2 is only one of many that can be studied profitably by means of rockets and satellites. Those quantities that are absorbed in the high atmosphere or otherwise obscured from the observer on the ground must be studied by means of high-altitude vehicles. Included in this category are the ionizing radiations already mentioned, the chemical and ion composition of the upper atmosphere, auroral particles, low-energy cosmic rays, and micrometeors. Even in the case of quantities that can be deduced from ground-based observations, such as pressures, temperatures, densities, winds, ionospheric charge densities, airglow, and the aurora, it is often much better to take advantage of the rocket's ability to make direct *in situ* measurements.

The rocket technique has been applied to the research of the upper atmosphere and the sun now for over a decade, particularly in the United States and the Soviet Union, and a considerable body of information has accrued.[1-6] Measurements have been made from the ground out to several hundred kilometers. Research firing locations range from the Arctic to the Antarctic. Launchings have been carried out in all seasons, both during the day and at night. Under the impetus of the International Geophysical Year (IGY), the rocket-sounding activity has expanded until now the roster of countries instrumenting rockets for high-altitude research includes Australia, Canada, England, France, Japan, the United States, and the U.S.S.R.

At the start of rocket probing of the high atmosphere, the rocket's behavior and especially its effect on the measurements being made were little understood. Now, after a dozen years of experience, the situation has changed. Reliable techniques have been worked out for radio telemetering of measured data, for automatic recording in flight, for recovery of equipment, specimens, and film after flight, and for measuring in flight the atmospheric, ionospheric, and solar parameters of interest to the physicist. The motions and behavior of the rocket are well understood, as are the requirements placed by the vehicle on the research instrumentation. Most important, the rocket experimenter now has sufficient familiarity with the rocket vehicle to evaluate its influence on accuracy of measurement. He is able to quote results with a reasonable degree of assurance that his estimates of error are correct.

The purpose of this chapter is to take up the discussion of rocket sounding of the upper atmosphere where Chapter 2 left it, and to present major results obtained on: atmospheric temperatures, pressures, densities, winds, and composition; the ionosphere and the earth's magnetic field; auroral particles; airglow; and meteors.

3.2 Atmospheric Structure

Knowledge of the pressure, density, and temperature of the atmosphere is fundamental to an understanding of the atmosphere, of its dynamics, and of the ionosphere. In an effort to obtain such knowledge numerous techniques have been employed throughout the past half-century. Among the indirect, ground-based approaches are included the study of the anomalous propagation of sound from large explosions, observations of meteors, ionospheric soundings, and auroral radiation studies. For the past dozen years sounding rockets have afforded a direct means of measurement, and most recently artificial earth satellites have begun to contribute.

In a large number of cases, the basic rocket data were pressures measured at the nose or along the sides of the flying vehicle. It was then necessary to deduce the ambient atmospheric conditions from the measurements. For this purpose the theories of Taylor and Maccoll, of Kopal, and of Stone[7-10] have proved useful below roughly 100 km. Above the 100-km level the mean free paths of the air molecules become sufficiently large to require the application of kinetic theory in the reduction of the rocket data.

One class of rocket experiments sought to measure the local speed of sound in the ambient air. The most successful of this class has been that in which grenades were ejected from the flying rocket and exploded. From the measured times and angles of arrival of the sound wave front at suitably placed listening stations on the ground it was possible to deduce the speed of the wave front in the upper air. This speed could then be separated into two components, one due to local winds, the other being the local speed of sound. Since the latter is given by $\sqrt{\gamma\,RT/\mu}$, where T is absolute air temperature, γ the ratio of specific heats, R the universal gas constant, and μ the average molecular mass of the air, the temperature could be deduced.

Mass spectrometer measurements, although directed primarily toward identifying the different chemical and ionic constituents of the high atmosphere, also give the partial pressures of the individual constituents. Combining these partial pressures yields the total atmospheric pressure.

The drag, D, on an object moving at high speed through air is given by

$$D = \tfrac{1}{2}\rho\,V^2 C_D A \tag{3.1}$$

where ρ is the air density, V the speed of motion relative to the air, C_D the drag coefficient of the body, and A its cross-sectional area normal to the direction of motion. The drag is seen to be proportional to the ambient air density. By observing the motions of the body in question, its speed and the deceleration due to the air drag can be measured. From the latter the drag force can be determined. With these data, and with C_D and A for the body known, the air density, ρ, can be calculated. This technique has been used on spherical test bodies ejected from flying rockets, and most recently in connection with orbiting satellites.

In still another method, the measured absorption of solar X-rays as a function of altitude has been used to give atmospheric density in and above the E region of the ionosphere.

There are two relationships among the three atmospheric structure parameters—pressure p, density ρ, and temperature T—that can be used to pass from measured values of one parameter to deduced values of another. First there is the equation of state

$$p = \rho RT/\mu \tag{3.2}$$

The form given assumes that the atmosphere behaves as a perfect gas. This assumption is quite reasonable for the regions above the troposphere, in the high atmosphere where the water vapor content is very small.

Second, there is the barometric equation

$$dp = -\,\rho g\,dh \tag{3.3}$$

where h is altitude and g is the acceleration of gravity. This relation assumes the atmosphere to be in static equilibrium under gravity. This is probably a good assumption, although errors can be introduced by atmospheric motions such as pronounced turbulence.

The equation of state gives any one of p, ρ, or T in terms of the other two. It does, however, require knowledge of the average molecular mass, μ.

TABLE I

Rocket Methods for Determining Atmospheric Structure

Basic measurement	Method of measurement	Theory	Final atmospheric quantities		Altitude range (km)	Non-instrumental sources of error
			Primary	Secondary		
Pressure on side of rocket	Pressure gages	Ambient pressure ring exists on flying rocket	Pressure	Density Temperature	30–120	Wind; yaw; outgassing
Pressure on nose cone of rocket	Pressure gages	Taylor-Maccoll; Stone	Pressure	Density Temperature	30–120	Wind; yaw; outgassing
Pressure at nose tip of rocket	Pressure gages	Rayleigh pitot-tube formula	Density	Pressure Temperature	> 30	Wind; yaw; outgassing
Pressure at nose tip and on nose cone	Alphatrons	Taylor-Maccoll; Stone; Kopal	Temperature	Pressure Density Density	30–120	Wind; out-gassing
Absorption of solar X-rays in atmosphere	Photon counters	X-ray absorption function of intervening air mass	Air mass			
Partial densities of atmospheric constituents	RF mass spectrometer	Sum of partial densities equals total density	Density	Pressure Temperature	> 95	Outgassing
Ratio of argon to nitrogen	RF mass spectrometer	Variation of A/N_2 gives measure of diffusive separation	Estimate of mixing		> 95	Outgassing
Absorption of solar ultraviolet light in atmosphere	Spectrograph	Solar ultraviolet heats atmosphere	Daily temperature variation		20–70	

Observed quantity	Instrument	Principle	Measured quantity	Height (km)	Sources of error
Pressure modulations on rolling rocket	Pressure gages	Modulation proportional to density	Density	> 30	Wind; yaw; outgassing
Pressure modulations; trajectory and missile attitude	Pressure gages; magnetometer; cameras; radar	Displacement of relative wind gives atmospheric wind	Wind	> 30	
Transit times of sound wave	Grenades; geophones	Transit times depend on air temperatures and winds	Temperature Winds	30–90	
Shock wave angle	Pressure gage probe	Shock wave angle gives Mach number	Temperature		Diffuseness of wave; yaw
Trajectory of falling sphere	DOVAP	Drag on sphere gives air density	Density	50–70	Winds; spin
Orbit of satellite	Optical and radio tracking	Drag on satellite gives density	Density	> 160 [a]	Solar-induced fluctuations in the atmosphere; variations in geographic position of perigee; electric charging of satellite

[a] At present this method gives density at perigee only.

Up to the E region the atmosphere is apparently well mixed, and whatever photochemical changes do occur have little effect on μ. Hence, the sea level value of 28.966 can be used. Within the E region and above, marked photochemical effects, such as dissociation of oxygen, plus diffusive separation of the different constituents alter the value of μ and must be taken into account.

The barometric equation gives pressure versus altitude once density versus altitude is known, or vice versa. Moreover, to make such a conversion does not require knowledge of the average molecular mass, μ. By introducing the gas law into the barometric equation, a temperature-altitude curve can be derived from either a pressure-altitude or a density-altitude curve, and conversely. But in these operations it is necessary to know the value of μ.

If the barometric equation is used over large height ranges it is necessary to take into account variations in g. In general the effects of the earth's rotation and non-sphericity may be neglected, and it suffices to use

$$g = g_0\left(\frac{a}{a+h}\right)^2 \tag{3.4}$$

where g_0 is the sea level value of g, a is the radius of the earth, and once again h is height above sea level.

In the lower atmospheric levels pressure, density, and temperature all have clearly understood meanings. With increasing height, however, the meaning of temperature becomes less and less clear physically. Generally, rocket measurements give pressures and densities, from which temperatures must be calculated. The nearest one comes to making a direct measurement of temperature is the measurement of sound speed which is proportional to the square root of temperature, such measurements being successful only at levels below the E region of the ionosphere. For the purposes of the present discussion it will be agreed that temperature will be what falls out of the gas equation when values of p and ρ are inserted together with the proper value of μ. Thus T will be a measure of the mean kinetic energy of random motion of the air molecules.

Table I lists a number of different rocket techniques for determining atmospheric structure parameters. With such techniques, a considerable body of information about the structure of the high atmosphere has been accumulated.

The knowledge of upper atmospheric structure that existed when rocket-sounding experiments began in the United States in 1946 is reflected in the tentative standard atmosphere published in 1947 by the National Advisory Committee for Aeronautics.[11] The data on which the tentative standard was based came from ground-based observations of meteors, sound propagation, the ionosphere, the aurora and airglow, and from numerous theoretical studies.

It soon became apparent from the early rocket results that the NACA standard departed considerably from the facts at the higher altitudes. At the same time, the rocket measurements pointed up systematic errors that crept into the ground-based techniques of estimating upper atmospheric structure. By 1952, enough rocket results had accumulated for the Upper Atmosphere Rocket Research Panel to issue a summary, now often referred to as the "Panel Atmosphere."[12]

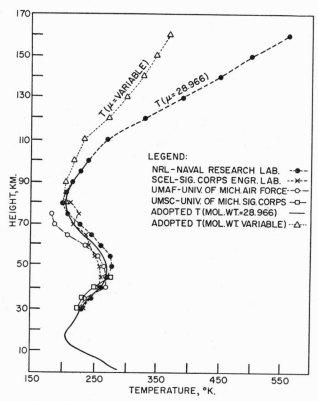

FIG. 1. Comparison of rocket atmospheric temperature data with curves adopted by the Rocket Panel. From The Rocket Panel, *Phys. Rev.* **88**, 1027 (1952); reproduced by courtesy of *The Physical Review*.

The Panel assembled all available rocket data in the form of atmospheric temperatures, assuming an average molecular mass of 28.966. A suitably weighted average of the data was constructed, after which the average temperatures were smoothed and interpolations made so that functions of T, $\log_{10}p$, and $\log_{10}\rho$ would be numerically integrable to an accuracy of about three significant figures for steps of 2 km in height. Then $\log_{10}p$ and $\log_{10}\rho$ were deduced from equations (3.2) to (3.4).

Table II gives the final smoothed data. Inasmuch as average molecular mass, μ, changes from the sea level value in and above the E region, the Panel then computed a second set of temperatures based on a variable μ. The new temperatures were obtained simply by multiplying those of column 2, Table II, by $\mu/28.966$, where μ is listed in column 2 of Table III. The new

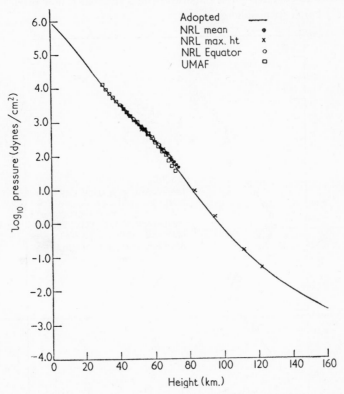

FIG. 2. Comparison of rocket atmospheric pressures with the curve adopted by the Rocket Panel. From The Rocket Panel, *Phys. Rev.* **88**, 1027 (1952); reproduced by courtesy of *The Physical Review*.

values of μ were chosen to reflect the best estimate at the time of the effect of changes in composition. The corresponding temperatures are listed in column 3 of Table III, which also gives scale heights, $H = RT/\mu g$ (column 4), g (column 5), and mean free path (column 6).

A graphical comparison of the Panel atmosphere with the rocket data on which it is based appears in Figs. 1 to 3. Some of the rocket data used may be found in Tables IV and V.

The rocket results underlying the Panel atmosphere were all obtained at

White Sands, New Mexico, except for a single Viking firing from the equator. Key conclusions from these early data are the following:

1. Up to about 110 km, both the pressure and the density of the atmosphere fall off by a factor of 10 for roughly every 10 miles of increase in altitude.

2. Above 150 km, the rate of decrease with altitude of both pressure and density is markedly less than at lower altitudes.

3. The density at 220 km above White Sands was found to be within 20 % of 10^{-7} gm/m³.

TABLE II
Panel Summary of Rocket Atmospheric Data

From The Rocket Panel, *Phys. Rev.* **88**, 1027 (1952), reproduced by courtesy of *The Physical Review.*

Height above sea level (km)	Temperature ($M = 28.966$) (°K)	Pressure ($\log_{10}$ of dynes/cm²)	Density ($\log_{10}$ of gm/cm³)
1.216	291.0	5.945	− 2.977
2	282.0	5.905	− 3.003
4	272.6	5.799	− 3.095
6	260.0	5.688	− 3.185
8	245.0	5.571	− 3.276
10	230.8	5.446	− 3.375
12	219.5	5.315	− 3.484
14	211.6	5.178	− 3.606
16	208.0	5.037	− 3.739
18	209.0	4.895	− 3.883
20	212.8	4.755	− 4.030
22	216.7	4.618	− 4.176
24	220.9	4.484	− 4.318
26	225.1	4.352	− 4.458
28	228.5	4.222	− 4.594
30	231.7	4.095	− 4.728
32	235.7	3.969	− 4.861
34	241.2	3.846	− 4.994
36	248.1	3.726	− 5.126
38	255.6	3.610	− 5.256
40	262.5	3.497	− 5.380
42	267.6	3.386	− 5.499
44	270.5	3.278	− 5.612
46	271.7	3.170	− 5.722
48	271.6	3.062	− 5.829
50	270.8	2.955	− 5.936
52	269.7	2.847	− 6.042
54	267.6	2.738	− 6.147
56	263.7	2.629	− 6.250
58	258.6	2.517	− 6.353
60	252.8	2.404	− 6.457

TABLE II (continued)

Panel Summary of Rocket Atmospheric Data

Height above sea level (km)	Temperature ($M = 28.966$) (°K)	Pressure ($\log_{10}$ of dynes/cm^2)	Density ($\log_{10}$ of gm/cm^3)
62	246.5	2.287	− 6.563
64	239.0	2.167	− 6.669
66	231.0	2.044	− 6.778
68	223.2	1.916	− 6.891
70	218.0	1.784	− 7.012
72	213.6	1.650	− 7.138
74	210.5	1.513	− 7.268
76	207.9	1.375	− 7.401
78	205.8	1.235	− 7.536
80	205.0	1.094	− 7.676
82	205.8	0.953	− 7.818
84	207.7	0.814	− 7.962
86	210.3	0.675	− 8.105
88	213.5	0.539	− 8.248
90	217.0	0.405	− 8.389
92	220.7	0.274	− 8.528
94	225.0	0.144	− 8.666
96	230.0	0.018	− 8.802
98	235.0	− 0.106	− 8.935
100	240.0	− 0.227	− 9.065
102	245.0	− 0.345	− 9.192
104	250.0	− 0.461	− 9.317
106	255.0	− 0.575	− 9.440
108	261.0	− 0.686	− 9.561
110	270.0	− 0.794	− 9.684
115	300.0	− 1.045	− 9.981
120	330.0	− 1.273	− 10.249
125	360.0	− 1.480	− 10.495
130	390.0	− 1.670	− 10.720
135	419.0	− 1.845	− 10.927
140	447.0	− 2.009	− 11.119
145	475.0	− 2.163	− 11.299
150	503.0	− 2.308	− 11.468
155	531.0	− 2.445	− 11.629
160	560.0	− 2.574	− 11.781
170	618.7	− 2.813	− 12.062
180	676.9	− 3.030	− 12.318
190	734.9	− 3.228	− 12.552
200	792.5	− 3.411	− 12.768
210	849.8	− 3.580	− 12.968
220	906.6	− 3.738	− 13.154

Table III

Atmospheric Data

From The Rocket Panel, *Phys. Rev.* **88**, 1027 (1952), reproduced by courtesy of *The Physical Review.*

Height above sea level (km)	Adopted molecular weight (gm/mole)	Temperature (°K)	Scale height (km)	Acceleration of gravity (cm/sec^2)	Mean free path (cm)
1.216	28.97	291.0	8.53	979.2	8.6×10^{-6}
5	28.97	276.8	7.83	978.0	1.2×10^{-5}
10	28.97	230.8	6.78	976.5	2.1×10^{-5}
15	28.97	209.1	6.16	974.9	4.2×10^{-5}
20	28.97	212.8	6.28	973.4	9.7×10^{-5}
25	28.97	223.0	6.59	971.9	2.2×10^{-4}
30	28.97	231.7	6.85	970.4	4.8×10^{-4}
35	28.97	244.5	7.24	968.9	1.0×10^{-3}
40	28.97	262.5	7.79	967.3	2.2×10^{-3}
45	28.97	271.3	8.06	965.8	4.2×10^{-3}
50	28.97	270.8	8.06	964.3	7.8×10^{-3}
55	28.97	265.8	7.93	962.8	1.4×10^{-2}
60	28.97	252.8	7.55	961.3	2.6×10^{-2}
65	28.97	235.0	7.03	959.8	4.8×10^{-2}
70	28.97	218.0	6.53	958.4	9.3×10^{-2}
75	28.97	209.1	6.27	956.9	2.0×10^{-1}
80	28.97	205.0	6.16	955.4	4.3×10^{-1}
85	28.23	203.6	6.29	953.9	9.5×10^{-1}
90	27.52	206.2	6.54	952.4	2.1×10^{0}
95	26.86	210.9	6.87	951.0	4.5×10^{6}
100	26.22	217.3	7.26	949.5	9.5×10^{0}
110	25.03	233.3	8.19	946.6	3.8×10^{1}
120	23.95	272.8	10.04	943.6	1.3×10^{2}
130	22.50	302.9	11.90	940.7	3.7×10^{2}
140	21.21	327.3	13.68	937.9	8.7×10^{2}
150	20.06	348.4	15.44	935.0	1.8×10^{3}
160	19.34	368.0	17.24	932.1	3.6×10^{3}
170	18.10	386.7	19.11	929.3	6.1×10^{3}
180	17.26	403.4	20.97	926.4	1.0×10^{4}
190	16.50	418.5	22.84	923.6	1.8×10^{4}
200	15.79	432.1	24.70	920.8	3.0×10^{4}
210	15.15	444.4	26.57	918.0	5.1×10^{4}
220	14.55	455.5	28.43	915.2	8.7×10^{4}

TABLE IV

Rocket Data on Atmospheric Pressures

(Except where noted, the probable errors in pressure, including an estimate of systematic effects, is less than 10 % for heights below 75 km; but it may be as much as a factor of 2 at the higher altitudes.)

Winter Data—Pressure (mm Hg)

Height above sea level (km)	White Sands, New Mexico (32° 24' N, 106° 22' W)						Fort Churchill, Canada (58° 46' N, 94° 10' W) 17 Nov. '56 1100 CST (Probable error 3 %)
	10 Oct. '46 1102 MST	7 Mar. '47 1123 MST	22 Jan. '48 1313 MST	28 Jan. '49 1020 MST	6 Sept. '49 0957 MST	12 Dec. '50 0015 MST	
1.2			655	662			
10			205	200			
20							38.2
42		2.2		1.8			
43		1.7	1.6	1.57			
44			1.30	1.37			
45		1.5	1.21	1.19			
46				1.08			
47		1.00	1.00	0.93			
48		0.86	0.87	0.85			

49						0.74	
50		0.66	0.76			0.66	
51			0.65			0.57	
52			0.60			0.51	0.57 ± 0.04
54		0.49	0.49				
55			0.43				
61.3				0.17 ± 0.03			
63	0.140						
64		0.144					
64.7							0.109 ± 0.004
65	0.112	0.124	0.107				
66	0.098						
67	0.092	0.100	0.086				
68		0.086	0.074				
69	0.067	0.074	0.060				
70	0.061		0.047				
71	0.052	0.050					
72	0.045	0.042	0.033				
73		0.033	0.030				
94			1.2×10^{-3}				
112		1.0×10^{-4}	1.4×10^{-4}				
120			1.4×10^{-5}				
122	3.5×10^{-5}	3.5×10^{-5}	3.5×10^{-5}				

The data in this Table were obtained by U. S. Naval Research Laboratory and are reproduced by courtesy of H. E. LaGow.

TABLE IV

Rocket Data on Atmospheric Pressures

Summer Data—Pressure (mm Hg)

Height above sea level (km)	White Sands, New Mexico (32° 24' N, 106° 22' W)			Equator (160° W)	Arctic		Fort Churchill, Canada (58° 46' N, 94° 10' W)
	5 Aug. '48 1837 MST	3 May '49 0914 MST	7 Aug. '51 1100 MST	11 May '50 1600 LCT	(62° 04' N, 63° 55' W) 5 Aug. '53 2154 Z	(74° 34' N, 94° 29' W) 11 Aug. '53 1709 Z	29 July '57 1600 CST (Probable error: < 10 %)
0	662	656		760			
1.2	218	213		222			
10				130			
13.7							
20					43.5	43.7	
24					23.8	23.8	
28					13.3	13.7	
32					7.65	8.65	
36					4.67	5.55	
40					2.95	3.26	
41		2.10					
42	2.00	1.70					
43	1.70	1.50					
44						1.84	
45	1.38	1.21					
46		1.06					
47	1.10	0.97					
48		0.83		0.90			
49	0.85	0.72					
50	0.74	0.64					
51	0.65	0.52					
52		0.48					

Altitude (km)						Pressure	Density
53	0.52	0.43					
54	0.45	0.40					
55	0.41	0.35					
56	0.33	0.30	0.31				
57		0.26					
59		0.20	0.23				
62		0.114	0.15				
63		0.106					
64		0.086					
65		0.079	0.100				
66		0.072					
67		0.066	0.070				
68		0.062					
69		0.058					
70		0.052					
71.0		0.042					
72.0		0.038					
73.0		0.033					
78.0			0.034	0.038			
82.4				0.014	$(7 \pm 2) \times 10^{-3}$		
96.0					2.0×10^{-4}		
100.0					1.0×10^{-4}	$3.0 \times 10^{-4} (\pm 20\%)$	0.197
110.0					2.4×10^{-5}	$6.5 \times 10^{-5} (\pm 20\%)$	0.133
120*						2.1×10^{-5}	0.118
130						1.3×10^{-5}	0.104
140						9.9×10^{-6}	0.0910
150						8.2×10^{-6}	0.0693
160						7.1×10^{-6}	0.0610
170						6.3×10^{-6}	0.0545
180						5.7×10^{-6}	0.0480
190						5.1×10^{-6}	0.0420
200						4.6×10^{-6}	0.0377
210						4.1×10^{-6}	0.0332

*Pressures at altitudes of 120 km and up were computed from density data. Table values are estimated to be within a factor of 2 of true values.

TABLE V

Rocket Data on Atmospheric Densities

(Except where noted, the probable error is less than 20 %.)

The data were obtained by the U. S. Naval Research Laboratory and are published by courtesy of H. E. LaGow.

Density (gm/m³)

Height above sea level (km)	White Sands, New Mexico (32° 24′ N, 106° 22′ W)			Equator (160° W)	Arctic		Fort Churchill, Canada (58° 46′ N, 94° 10′ W)		
	7 Mar. '47 1123 MST	5 Aug. '48 1837 MST‡	7 Aug. '51 1100 MST	11 May '50 1600 LCT	(62° 04′ N, 63° 55′ W) 5 Aug. '53 2154 Z	(74° 34′ N, 94° 29′ W) 11 Aug. '53 1709 Z	17 Nov. '56 1100 CST Probable error 3 %	29 July '57 1600 CST Probable error < 5 %	24 Feb. '58 0100 CST
20					88.0	90.0	82.0	90.0	
24					48.3	49.5	43.7	49.5	
28					26.2	26.5	23.9	27.0	
32					13.9	14.3	12.7	14.7	
36					7.60	7.80	6.78	8.20	
39				5.9				5.32	
40					4.30	4.34	4.28	4.63	
43				2.5	2.52	2.46		3.07	
44								2.68	
46				2.0				2.08	
48								1.62	
52								0.990	
56								0.610	
60								0.385	
61		0.39						0.337	

Altitude (km)			
62	0.296	0.35	
64	0.227	0.26	
65	0.199	0.24	
66	0.175	0.21	0.20
67	0.152	0.19	
68	0.132	0.17	
69	0.113	0.14	0.151
70	0.097		0.129
71			0.114
73			0.090
75			0.063
76			0.057
78			0.042
79			0.035

Altitude (km)		
100*	7.2×10^{-4}	2.5×10^{-4}
110	1.3×10^{-4}	5.0×10^{-5}
120	2.6×10^{-5}	1.2×10^{-5}
130	6.4×10^{-6}	3.3×10^{-6}
140	3.0×10^{-6}	1.2×10^{-6}
150	1.9×10^{-6}	6.6×10^{-7}
156		$(2.0 \pm 0.5) \times 10^{-6}$
160	1.4×10^{-6}	4.3×10^{-7}
170	1.1×10^{-6}	3.0×10^{-7}
180	8.9×10^{-7}	2.3×10^{-7}
190	7.9×10^{-7}	1.8×10^{-7}
200	7.0×10^{-7} $\left(3.6 {}^{+3.0}_{-1.5}\right) \times 10^{-7}$	1.4×10^{-7}
202†	$(1.3 \pm 0.6) \times 10^{-7}$	
210	6.2×10^{-7}	1.1×10^{-7}
220		9.0×10^{-8}

* Density data from 100 km and up have an estimated error of ± 30 %.
† The results from Churchill are provisional.
‡ Data are average of ascent and descent and are accurate to within a factor of 2.

4. The atmospheric temperature-versus-height curve shows a maximum of about 270°K in the neighborhood of 50 km, a deep minimum of around 200°K near 80 km, and a steadily rising temperature above 80 km.

5. The pressure drop from sea level to 100 km was found to be that which would occur in an isothermal atmosphere of about 240°K. In this sense it may be said that the "average" temperature of the atmosphere below the E region is 240°K.

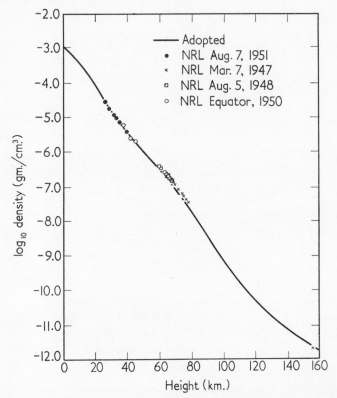

Fig. 3. Comparison of rocket atmospheric densities with the curve adopted by the Rocket Panel. From The Rocket Panel, *Phys. Rev.* **88**, 1027 (1952); reproduced by courtesy of *The Physical Review*.

6. No significant diurnal variations in pressure or density were found.

7. Between 30 and 70 km, the daily temperature variation is small, the maximum total swing being of the order of 5° at around 48 km.

8. No significant seasonal variations in pressure, density, or temperature were found.

9. There was no marked difference between the atmosphere above 30 km observed over the equator in mid-Pacific Ocean and that over White Sands.

References 13 through 24 present rocket and satellite atmospheric structure measurements and derived results published since the issuance of the Panel atmosphere. Tables IV and V include such data obtained by the U.S. Naval Research Laboratory. Table VI gives temperatures obtained at White Sands

TABLE VI

Temperatures and Winds in the High Atmosphere above White Sands, New Mexico

From W. G. Stroud, W. Nordberg, and J. R. Walsh, *J. Geophys. Res.* **61**, 45 (1956), reproduced by courtesy of the *Journal of Geophysical Research*.

Date of firing	Altitude (km)	Temperature (°K)	Probable error (°K)	Wind speed (m/sec)	Probable error (m/sec)	Wind direction (deg)	Probable error (deg)	Layer thickness (km)
14 July '50	35.4	260.7	1.4	19	3	79	9	6.6
0137 MST	41.6	251.4	1.4	33	4	102	7	5.9
	47.3	267.5	1.5	46	5	72	6	5.3
	56.0	249.7	3.8	63	2	75	2	12.1
16 Oct. '50	50.0	264.7	3.0	46	7	272	9	8.5
2100 MST	57.8	261.1	3.6	58	9	277	9	7.1
	64.4	233.5	4.0	42	11	256	16	6.1
	70.1	224.4	4.8	35	14	234	24	5.2
	75.4	225.5	5.0	47	14	217	18	5.6
	80.3	211.5	7.2	53	20	260	22	4.2
11 Dec. '50	35.9	234.9	1.4	44	3	269	4	6.5
2106 MST	41.8	261.5	1.6	64	4	270	4	5.4
	48.1	266.0	1.4	83	4	265	2	7.2
	54.7	251.5	1.7	104	5	272	3	5.9
	60.1	249.0	2.1	83	7	273	5	4.8
	64.5	244.7	2.3	68	8	284	7	4.1
12 Dec. '50	33.3	231.5	4.5	43	1	263	2	12.7
0210 MST	43.5	266.5	1.1	74	3	267	2	7.8
	53.1	261.0	5.9	87	2	286	2	11.3
	61.2	211.6	1.4	92	6	204	4	4.9
8 June '51	29.6	234.6	3.0	12	6	59	29	6.7
2311 MST	38.7	253.0	1.4	23	5	96	11	11.5
	46.9	264.2	2.3	15	13	55	53	4.9
	51.5	260.4	1.7	61	16	113	16	4.3
	55.4	265.6	4.6	89	21	66	14	3.6
	58.7	258.9	7.2	73	22	158	18	3.0
	61.9	252.2	1.3	30	23	109	46	3.5

TABLE VI (continued)

Temperatures and Winds in the High Atmosphere above White Sands, New Mexico

Date of firing	Altitude (km)	Temperature (°K)	Probable error (°K)	Wind speed (m/sec)	Probable error (m/sec)	Wind direction (deg)	Probable error (deg)	Layer thickness (km)
1 Nov. '51	33.7	229.0	2.1	13	6	258	27	7.4
0246 MST	40.5	253.4	2.3	71	8	262	7	6.2
	46.3	265.0	2.7	66	11	268	10	5.4
	53.3	263.4	1.7	87	8	274	6	8.5
	60.5	241.8	5.8	64	13	255	12	5.9
24 Sept. '52	42.1	266.5	3.2	23	6	317	133	6.3
2050 MST	48.2	270.0	3.6	14	8	259	33	5.8
	54.0	274.1	4.0	35	10	314	16	5.6
	59.6	254.3	3.8	18	10	328	32	5.6
	67.3	222.1	1.8	23	6	357	15	9.8
	76.5	204.3	2.8	17	8	201	26	8.6
22 Oct. '52	47.3	255.6	3.1	33	7	228	13	6.1
2045 MST	53.3	278.2	3.7	77	10	277	7	6.0
	59.0	263.9	4.2	63	11	278	10	5.3
	66.6	223.4	1.8	15	6	178	13	9.8
17 Feb. '53	48.3	262.6	1.4	48	4	290	5	12.1
2350 MST	59.3	246.2	1.8	64	5	283	5	9.9
	69.0	235.3	1.8	54	7	219	7	9.4
	77.8	214.5	1.8	41	8	335	12	8.2
24 April '53	47.1	257.3	0.4	30	2	93	4	7.9
0319 MST	54.7	262.5	0.4	7	2	61	20	7.3
	61.8	244.6	0.4	28	3	145	6	6.7
	68.1	222.6	0.4	43	3	95	5	5.9
31 Aug. '53	49.9	283.7	2.2	48	6	340	7	8.5
2205 MST	58.1	239.9	1.9	57	7	193	7	7.8
	65.7	236.0	1.9	22	9	340	22	7.3
	72.7	240.6	4.4	44	5	327	7	6.7
4 Sept. '53	58.5	259.0	1.6	7	5	46	38	7.7
2236 MST	65.8	224.5	1.4	8	6	353	41	7.0
	72.5	207.1	2.1	30	10	51	20	6.4
	78.7	203.4	3.0	25	16	344	36	5.8

by the U. S. Army Signal Research and Development Laboratory (formerly Signal Corps Engineering Laboratories).[15] Similar data for Fort Churchill, Canada, are given graphically in Fig. 4. Figure 5 shows density values for Fort Churchill obtained by mass spectrometer measurements by Townsend and co-workers.

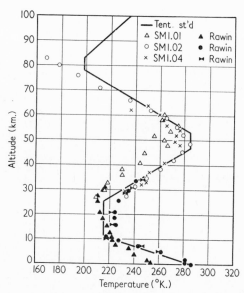

FIG. 4. Temperature results from the grenade experiment at Fort Churchill, Canada. The lower, solid points are the corresponding radiosonde data taken at the time of each firing. SM1.01 is a winter firing; SM1.02 and SM1.04 are summer firings. From W. G. Stroud, W. R. Bandeen, W. Nordberg, F. L. Bartman, J. Otterman, and P. Titus, "Temperatures and Winds in the Arctic as Obtained by the Rocket-Grenade Experiment," V CSAGI; reproduced by courtesy of the authors.

Significant conclusions from the most recent work are:

1. Above Fort Churchill, 59° N latitude, at an altitude of 200 km, the summer daytime atmospheric density is 6.6×10^{-7} gm/m³, which is two times the winter daytime value.

2. At 200 km above Fort Churchill the summer daytime atmospheric density is five times the corresponding White Sands value of 1.4×10^{-7} gm/m³.

3. At 200 km above Fort Churchill the summer daytime scale height is 95 km; the maximum scale height gradient occurs in the upper E region and is 2 km/km.

4. The upper air densities measured with IGY vertical sounding rockets are consistent with the densities determined from satellite drag computations.

5. At heights between 30 and 45 km, arctic density measurements indicate that seasonal and latitude variations are less than 15 %, and summer

pressure measurements show arctic temperatures and pressures to be significantly higher than values for White Sands.

6. Between 30 and 80 km above Fort Churchill, atmospheric temperatures show a significant variation from winter to summer, the spread being about 20°C at 50 km.

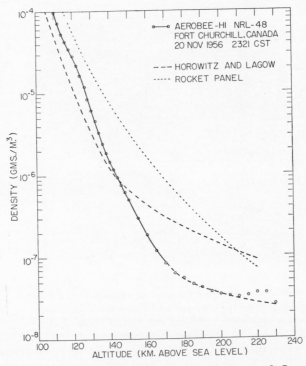

FIG. 5. Density versus altitude, NRL–48. From J. W. Townsend, Jr., and Edith B. Meadows, *IGY Rocket Rept. Ser.* **No. 1,** 22 (1958); reproduced by courtesy of the National Academy of Sciences.

7. Summer temperature at 80 km above Fort Churchill was found to be 165°K.

8. The density of the atmosphere at 150 km above Fort Churchill on a winter night was measured by a radiofrequency mass spectrometer at 5×10^{-7} gm/m³.

In Fig. 6 LaGow compares sounding rocket results with satellite results. Curves 1 and 2 of the figure are maxima and minima indicated by the rocket measurements, the former corresponding to a summer day at White Sands, the latter to a summer day at Fort Churchill. In each case the solid portion is based on actual measurement. The dashed portion, on the other hand, is an extrapolation using a constant scale height (43 km for the lower curve and 95 km for the upper one) equal to the scale height corresponding to the 200 km point at the end of the solid portion of the curve. Indicated by WD and WN are winter day and winter night points near 200 km obtained from rocket measurements at Fort Churchill, 59° N latitude. The remaining points shown in the figure are from satellite drag measurements which give air density at the perigee point of the satellite orbit. Some of the satellite points were provided by Jastrow of the U. S. Naval Research Laboratory;[25]

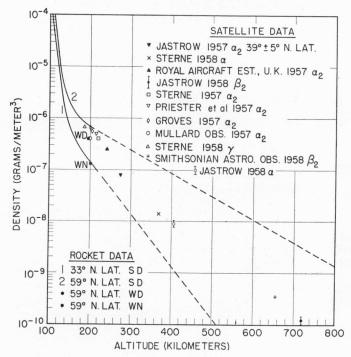

Fig. 6. Extrapolated rocket density data compared with satellite data. Reproduced by courtesy of H. E. LaGow.

the remaining were reported by the Smithsonian Astrophysical Laboratory.[26] It can be seen that there is close agreement between the 1957 α_2 points and the rocket curve for 59° N latitude, and also that all the satellite density points fall between the two rocket curves. It should further be noted that the density data from the Soviet satellites tend to favor curve 2, which was derived from rocket measurements in the auroral zone; this tendency is consistent with the high inclination of the orbits of the Soviet satellites, and with the fact that their perigees were located at high latitude. The density points obtained from the U. S. satellites lie midway between the extreme curves of Fig. 6, which is consistent with the low latitudes of the perigees of the U. S. satellites. From the data set forth in the figure, the average scale heights for the high atmosphere appear to lie between 43 and 95 km, with some indication that they are closer to the higher value.

Soviet data on atmospheric structure show good general agreement with the results listed above. For the lower altitude studies the U.S.S.R. has used the so-called "Meteorological Rocket" during the IGY at Mirny in the Antarctic, at Franz Josef Land in the Arctic, and from shipboard at many latitudes.[27] The data cover the seasons and show definite seasonal variations in temperature between 25 and 50 km. For the northern hemisphere, below 40 km the temperature varied in sinusoidal fashion with a total excursion of about 25°C. The maximum temperature came in late June. Above 40 km

TABLE VII

Comparison of U. S. and U.S.S.R. Data on Atmospheric Densities

Height (km)	Density (gm/m³)		
	U.S.S.R. Rocket (middle latitudes)	Viking 7 (U. S.) (33° N)	U.S.S.R. satellites (northern latitudes)
100	4×10^{-4}	2.5×10^{-4}	—
150	1.7×10^{-6}	6.6×10^{-7}	—
200	2.7×10^{-7}	1.4×10^{-7}	—
220	1.6×10^{-7}	9.0×10^{-8}	—
228	1.3×10^{-7}	—	$(2.4 \text{ to } 3.2) \times 10^{-7}$
260	6.9×10^{-8}	—	1×10^{-7}
355	—	—	8.8×10^{-9}

the temperature variation was again sinusoidal but with a larger excursion of about 35°C. Also, the maximum temperature occurred earlier at the higher altitudes, coming in late May. The data showed a temperature minimum at 26 km, where the December value was 200°K; and a maximum at 50 km, where the May value was 290°K.

On the higher altitude rocket flights pressure gage measurements turned out results that agree well with the U. S. data, particularly when latitude differences are taken into account.[28] Table VII gives a comparison of Soviet and U. S. rocket data on atmospheric densities. The U. S. data correspond to White Sands, New Mexico, and the Soviet data were placed at "middle latitudes" (45° N?). The last column also shows densities obtained by means of artificial earth satellites. The point at 228 km was obtained from satellite drag measurements,[29] the points at 260 and 355 km by means of pressure gages mounted in Sputnik III. In the case of the last two points, it was stated that difficulties of analysis arose because of the satellite's motion and because of outgassing, the residual gage pressure amounting to 10^{-7} mm Hg on the first day, to 10^{-8} mm Hg on the second day, and to 10^{-9} mm Hg on the third day.

Taken together, the Soviet and U. S. data show the latitude dependence pointed out earlier. Seasonal variations are also indicated, and one U.S.S.R. paper[29] suggests a strong diurnal variation of density at about 225 km.

3.3 Winds

Note. Throughout this section the direction of a wind is considered to be that *from which* it comes. This nomenclature is usual in meteorology, but in ionosphere studies, and in other chapters of this book, the direction is considered to be that *toward which* it is moving.

A powerful rocket method for the determination of upper atmosphere winds is the grenade experiment mentioned above in connection with the determination of temperatures. It will be recalled that the basic idea behind the rocket grenade experiment is to explode a series of grenades in the upper atmosphere and to measure the times required for the sounds from the explosions to reach observing stations on the ground. In the absence of upper air winds, the difference in transit times for the sound waves from two consecutive explosions can be taken as a measure of the speed of sound in the region between the two bursts. Knowing the speed of sound, one can then immediately deduce the temperature of the ambient air.

When upper winds are present, however, they affect the apparent speed of sound, and unless corrected for they lead to false estimates of the temperatures. It is possible, however, in the analysis to correct for the winds, and in the process to determine the winds themselves. The method is described by Stroud and co-workers in their publications.[14,15,23,30] Their results are summarized in Table VI and Fig. 7. Note the seasonal effect in the wind direction, the winds being easterly in the summer and westerly in winter. At Fort Churchill in particular, the summer winds were relatively weak, and the winter winds quite strong, a velocity of 150 meters per second having been recorded at a 58-km altitude.

A second method of determining upper winds by means of rockets is to measure the relative wind experienced by the rocket during its flight, and subtract out that part due to the motion of the vehicle. What remains is the true wind. The actual measurements required are the velocity vector of the missile relative to the ground obtained by flight-path tracking, the attitude angles of the missile axis determined by means of on-board gyroscopes, and the angle of attack of the missile measured with meters at the

7

missile nose. This method has been described in detail by Reisig and used
to determine winds up to 60 km over Cape Canaveral, Florida.[31] The results
appear in Figs. 8 to 13. The wind regime seems to be quite similar to that
observed by Stroud and co-workers at White Sands. Once again the winds
are easterly in the summer, and westerly in winter.

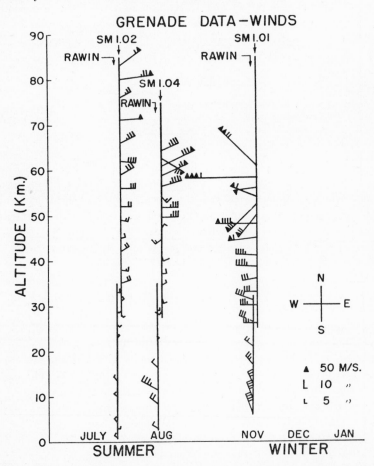

Fig. 7. Wind results from the grenade experiment at Fort Churchill, Canada. The
vectors indicate the magnitudes of the winds and the *directions from which they come.**
North is at the top; thus the summer winds are from the east; winter winds from the
west. The lower altitude data, displaced to the left, are the corresponding RAWIN
data. From W. G. Stroud, W. R. Bandeen, W. Nordberg, F. L. Bartman, J. Otterman,
and P. Titus, "Temperatures and Winds in the Arctic as Obtained by the Rocket-
Grenade Experiment," V CSAGI (1958); reproduced by courtesy of the authors.

* The nomenclature is different from that used in ionosphere work where the vector
is drawn in the direction in which the wind is travelling.

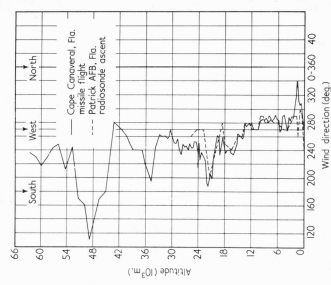

Fig. 9. Wind direction versus altitude, case 1, January, 1954. From G. H. R. Reisig, J. Meteorol. 13, 448 (1956); reproduced by courtesy of the Journal of Meteorology.

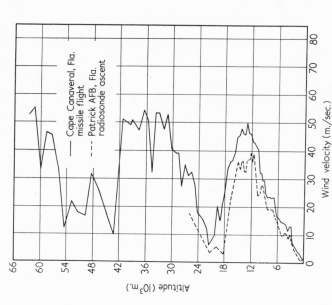

Fig. 8. Wind speed versus altitude, case 1, January, 1954. From G. H. R. Reisig, J. Meteorol. 13, 448 (1956); reproduced by courtesy of the Journal of Meteorology.

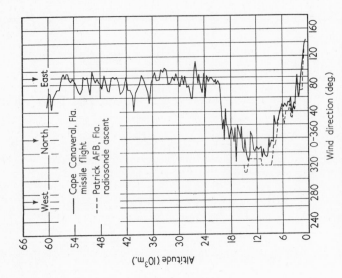

FIG. 11. Wind direction versus altitude, case 2, April, 1955. From G. H. R. Reisig, *J. Meteorol.* **13**, 448 (1956); reproduced by courtesy of the *Journal of Meteorology.*

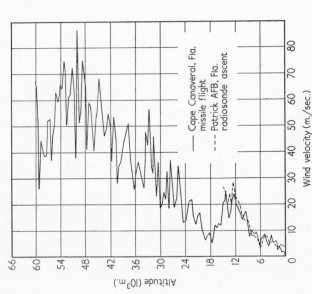

FIG. 10. Wind speed versus altitude, case 2, April, 1955. From G. H. R. Reisig, *J. Meteorol.* **13**, 448 (1956); reproduced by courtesy of the *Journal of Meteorology.*

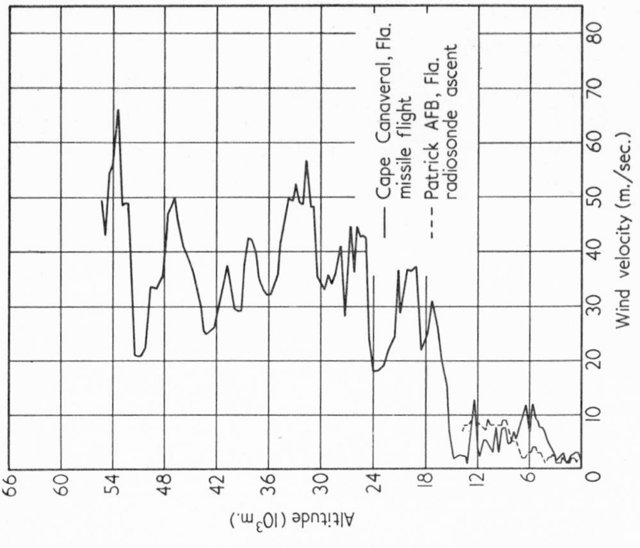

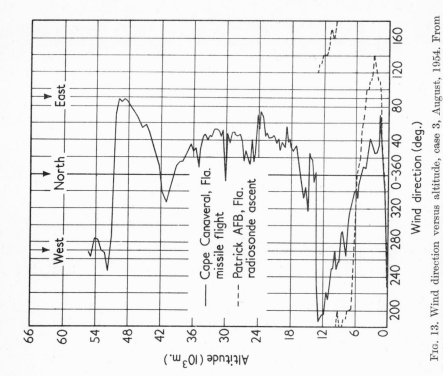

FIG. 13. Wind direction versus altitude, case 3, August, 1954. From G. H. R. Reisig, *J. Meteorol.* **13**, 448 (1956); reproduced by courtesy of the *Journal of Meteorology.*

FIG. 12. Wind speed versus altitude, case 3, August, 1954. From G. H. R. Reisig, *J. Meteorol.* **13**, 448 (1956); reproduced by courtesy of the *Journal of Meteorology.*

3.4 Charge Densities in the Ionosphere

The propagation of radio waves through the high atmosphere provides a means of studying the ionosphere. In the first two decades of ionospheric research, the probing radio signals were all sent from the ground, and the reflected signal brought back information about the ionized regions. Since the end of World War II it has been possible to use high-altitude sounding rockets to provide a platform within the ionosphere itself for the reception or transmission of the probing signals. This possibility enables one to determine the complete charge density distribution as a function of altitude. The elements of the basic theory behind the methods used are given below.

The phase speed, c, wavelength, λ, and frequency, f, of a steady-state electromagnetic signal are related by the equation

$$c = \lambda f \tag{3.5}$$

If the signal is being propagated through a material medium, then c differs from the free-space phase speed, c_0, in accordance with the relation

$$c = c_0/n \tag{3.6}$$

where n is the index of refraction of the medium.

Whenever the source of the radio signal moves relative to the observer, the frequency of the signal appears to change. In the case in which the source moves radially from or toward the observer, the change, Δf, is given by

$$\Delta f = -f(v/c) = -f(nv/c_0) \tag{3.7}$$

where the speed, v, of the source is regarded as positive if the source moves away from the observer, and negative if the source moves toward him.

The value of n in the above equation is given by Goubau's[31a] modification of the well-known Appleton-Hartree formula:

$$n^2 = \text{Re}\left[n_i^2 - \cfrac{X}{1 - jZ - \cfrac{\frac{1}{2}Y_T^2}{1 - X/n_i^2 - jZ} \pm \sqrt{\cfrac{\frac{1}{4}Y_T^4}{(1 - X/n_i^2 - jZ)^2} + Y_L^2}} \right] \tag{3.8}$$

where Re signifies the real part of the square root, and where

$X = 4\pi N e^2/\omega^2 m$.

N = number of electrons per unit volume.

e = electronic charge.

$\omega = 2\pi f$.

f = frequency of the propagated wave.

m = electronic mass.

$j = \sqrt{-1}$.

$Z = \nu/\omega$.

ν = electron collision frequency.

$Y_T = H_T e/\omega m c_0.$
H_T = magnetic-field component transverse to direction of propagation.
c_0 = speed of light in a vacuum.
$Y_L = H_L e/\omega m c_0.$
H_L = magnetic-field component along direction of propagation.
$n_i^2 = 1 - X_i/(1 - jZ_i)$
$X_i = 4\pi N_i e_i^2/\omega^2 m_i.$
N_i = number of ions per unit volume.
e_i = ionic charge.
m_i = ionic mass.
ν_i = frequency of ion collisions with neutral molecules.
$Z_i = \nu_i/\omega.$

In the formula as written, the Lorentz polarization term has been dropped, since the results of rocket measurements have shown that it should not be included for the cases we shall consider.

There are two values for n, corresponding to the plus and minus signs before the radical in the denominator. Physically this is manifested by a splitting of the wave into two components, the one corresponding to the plus sign being referred to as the Ordinary wave; the other, corresponding to the minus sign, is called the Extraordinary wave. For higher radiofrequencies, the value of n rapidly approaches unity.

It is clear from the formulas above that, when n is unity, the Doppler shift in the signal can be calculated very simply from the frequency, f, if the radial speed, v, is known. This fact permits one to use a high-frequency signal to or from a flying rocket as a reference against which to compare lower frequency signals in order to determine the effect of the ionosphere on the lower frequencies. Such a comparison leads to a determination of the value of n for the lower frequency in the neighborhood of the flying rocket. Once n has been determined as a function of height, it is then possible, though often laborious, to deduce charge densities as a function of altitude.

The analysis of the problem becomes much more complicated when the motion of the rocket is not radial from or toward the observer. Nevertheless it is sometimes necessary to use the more complicated analysis to avoid large errors in the final results. For example, on some rocket flights which departed appreciably from vertical trajectories the fuller analysis was required to avoid errors as large as 30 % in the final estimate of the charge densities.

Figures 14 to 17 summarize the results obtained by Seddon, Jackson, and co-workers at the U. S. Naval Research Laboratory, using two harmonically related signals transmitted from flying rockets.[24, 32-45] The results pertain to White Sands, New Mexico, and to Fort Churchill, Canada. Most of the curves were obtained from daytime flights, although there is one nighttime curve.

Figure 18 shows a curve of charge densities above White Sands, New Mexico, obtained by Berning of the Ballistic Research Laboratories at Aberdeen, Maryland.[46] The Berning curve was obtained from a Bumper-WAC firing, at 2222 GCT on February 24, 1949, in which a WAC Corporal rocket was

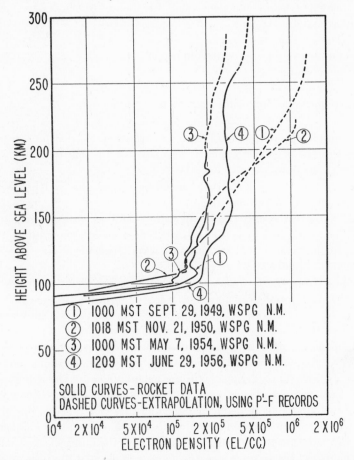

FIG. 14. Summary of U. S. Naval Research Laboratory rocket measurements of the ionosphere above White Sands, New Mexico. Reproduced by courtesy of J. E. Jackson.

fired from the nose of a flying V-2. The effect of the ionosphere on Doppler radio tracking of the WAC was used to deduce the charge densities.

Following are some specific conclusions based on rocket ionospheric measurements:

1. The daytime ionosphere appears to remain dense between the E and $F2$ regions.

2. The $F2$ maximum for middle latitudes lies in the neighborhood of 300 km and is fairly constant in altitude, even when virtual heights vary widely.

3. The lower edge of the E region commonly has a very steep electron density gradient of about 10^4 electrons/cm³ per kilometer. Other high-gradient regions occasionally appear at higher altitudes. The presence of sporadic reflections correlates well with these high-gradient regions.

4. Electron densities as low as 10^3 electrons/cm³ have been measured in the D region.

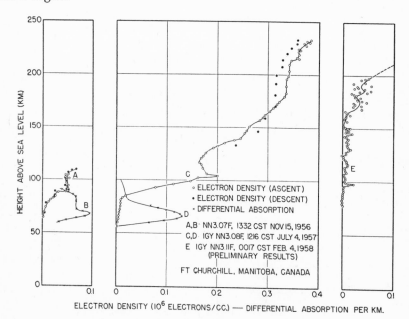

FIG. 15. Electron densities and 7.75-Mc/s differential absorption above Fort Churchill, Canada. Curves C and E show two extreme conditions, namely, summer noon and winter midnight. Presented at the Fifth Assembly of CSAGI in Moscow, August, 1958. Reproduced by courtesy of the authors, J. C. Seddon and J. E. Jackson.

5. The maximum value of differential absorption for 7.75 Mc/sec occurs at the lower edge of the E region and is negligible in the D region on undisturbed days.

6. The Lorentz polarization term should not be used in the Appleton-Hartree index formula at 4 Mc/sec.

7. The daytime electron density-versus-height profile for Fort Churchill is similar to the daytime profiles for White Sands.

8. Above Fort Churchill, at night, less than 2×10^4 electrons/cm³ were found up to a height of 170-km.

9. Curve 2 of Fig. 17 was obtained at the time of a strong polar blackout, indicating that such blackouts are caused by high absorption in the 60-to 80-km region.

10. Figure 16 shows that electron collision frequencies in the 60-to 80-km region are smaller by a factor of 3 than those previously suggested by Nicolet.

11. During the night flight above Fort Churchill, the condition known as spread F was observed above an altitude of 190 km, and the region was found to be very turbulent and irregular, according to Seddon and Jackson.

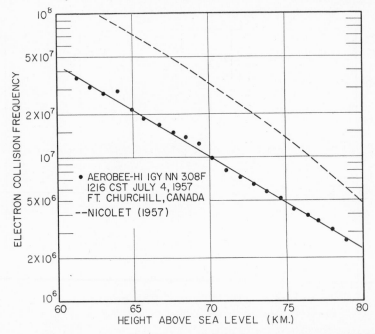

Fig. 16. Comparison between electron collision frequencies computed by Nicolet (1957) and the measurement made by the U. S. Naval Research Laboratory. Presented at the Fifth General Assembly of CSAGI in Moscow, August, 1958. Reproduced by courtesy of the authors, J. C. Seddon and J. E. Jackson.

Soviet data on charge densities in the ionosphere extend to well above the maximum of the $F2$ region. The data were obtained from observations with both Sputniks and rockets.[47,48] The results show general agreement with the U. S. results below the $F2$ maximum; above the $F2$ maximum they indicate a slower decline of electron density with increasing altitude than had hitherto been expected.

In the vertical rocket measurements, the U.S.S.R. workers used the two-frequency propagation method devised by the U. S. Naval Research Laboratory.[48] The electron density profiles obtained show an ionosphere

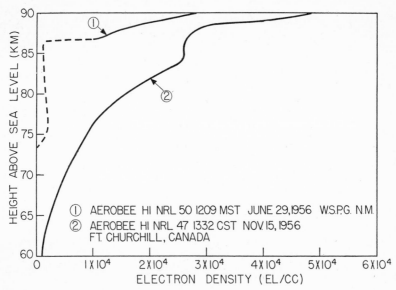

FIG. 17. Comparison of D-region ionization above Fort Churchill, Canada, during a polar blackout, with D-region ionization at White Sands, New Mexico, on a day of moderate absorption. Presented at the Fifth General Assembly of CSAGI in Moscow, August, 1958. Reproduced by courtesy of the authors, J. C. Seddon and J. E. Jackson.

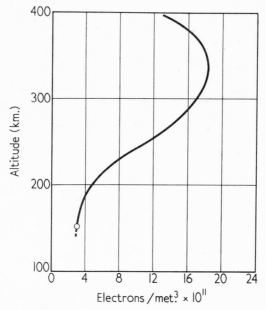

FIG. 18. Ion density in the F region at mid afternoon. The measurements were made during the flight of the Bumper-WAC launched at 1522 MST February 24, 1949, at White Sands, New Mexico. Reproduced by courtesy of W. W. Berning.

without deep indentations and agree well with those of Seddon and Jackson. In a flight of the "Geophysical Rocket," on February 21, 1958, the $F2$ maximum was found to be at 290 km, where the electron density was 1.8×10^6 electrons/cm^3. At 470 km the measured electron density was 10^6 electrons/cm^3

Observations on the radio "rise" and "set" of Sputnik I were made on both the frequencies 20 and 40 Mc/sec.[47] An electron density profile for the region above $F2$ maximum was deduced. Further such data were obtained

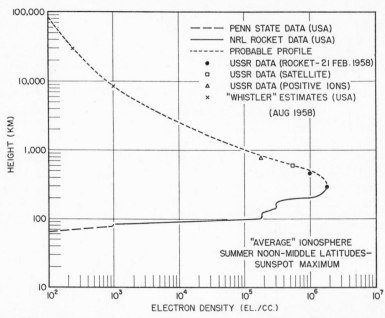

Fig. 19. Summary of ionosphere data corresponding to summer noon, middle latitudes, and sunspot maximum. The $F2$ maximum electron density drops by about one order of magnitude at sunspot minimum. Presented by courtesy of J. E. Jackson.

from an ion trap carried in Sputnik III.[48] The ion trap gave, on May 15, 1958, at middle latitudes, in the morning before noon, 5.2×10^5 ions/cm^3 at 242 km, and 1.8×10^5 ions/cm^3 at 795 km. Taking these results together with U. S. ground-based observations,[49] U. S. rocket results, and whistler data,[50] J. E. Jackson drew up the summary presented in Fig. 19. The summary curve provides a sort of "average ionosphere" for middle latitudes near summer noon during sunspot maximum.

3.5 Earth's Magnetic Field

Although not a feature of the earth's upper atmosphere, the earth's magnetic field must nevertheless be known and taken into account to understand the atmosphere and its behavior, particularly in studying the ionosphere and the effect of incoming charged particles on the atmosphere. The rocket makes it possible to carry aloft magnetometers for measuring the earth's field at high altitude. The main field is that of a dipole, and in magnitude falls off inversely as the cube of the distance from the center of the earth. This can be and has been checked with rocket experiments. Of greater interest, however, is the possibility of using rocket-borne magnetometers to detect and measure departures from the inverse cube law caused by ionospheric current flows, or by intensive streams of charged particles such as cause the aurora.

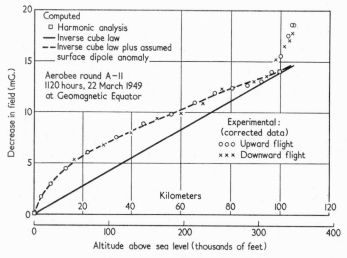

FIG. 20. Earth's magnetic field versus height above the geomagnetic equator at 1120 local time on March 22, 1949. This was near the time of maximum variation in sea level field. From S. F. Singer, *J. Geophys. Res.* **56**, 265 (1951); reproduced by courtesy of the *Journal of Geophysical Research*.

Using a total-field magnetometer carried in an Aerobee rocket, Singer *et al.* measured the earth's magnetic field as a function of altitude on two different occasions during March, 1949.[51-53] The first rocket was fired at 10° 48′ S, 89° 14′ W (geographic coordinates), at 1720, 90th meridian time, on March 17. The firing took place near the time of minimum variation in the surface field intensity, and no evidence of a current layer in the *E* region was found.

The second rocket was launched at 1120, 90th meridian time, on March 22, at 11° 06′ S, 88° 26′ 30″ W. This firing occurred near a time of maximum change in the surface field intensity, and definite evidence of a current sheet in the *E* region was found. This can be seen in the curve of Fig. 20, in which a sharp break in the field intensity curve appears at 93 km. The decrease between 93 and 105 km was put at 4 ± 0.5 milligauss and was adequate to account for the change in surface intensity.

Results similar to those obtained on the first of the above rockets have been obtained in an Aerobee rocket carrying a proton precession magneto-meter.[54] This rocket was launched at 0052 MST on July 5, 1956, at White Sands. There was no magnetic disturbance at the time of the firing and, although the earth's magnetic field fell off with altitude more rapidly than would a dipole (cf. Fig. 21), no evidence for an E region current layer was found.

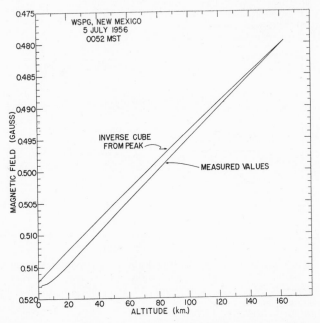

FIG. 21. Comparison of measured and calculated earth's magnetic field as a function of altitude. From J. P. Heppner, J. D. Stolarik, and L. H. Meredith, *J. Geophys. Res.* **63**, 277 (1958); reproduced by courtesy of the *Journal of Geophysical Research*.

Further magnetic-field measurements have been made by means of proton precession magnetometers flown in Rockoons, i.e., balloon-launched rockets, near the equator.[55] The measurements detected a current sheet extending from 97 to 110 km and a second sheet extending from 118 km to at least the peak Rockoon altitude of 121 km.

Flights of proton precession magnetometers have been made in Aerobee-Hi rockets in the auroral zone.[56] These measurements have confirmed the fact that electric currents flow in the upper atmosphere in the auroral zone and that at least some are directly related to the presence of visible auroras. During one aurora, currents were found to flow at an altitude of about 120 km. The measurements have also indicated that the currents can have relatively small dimensions.

Soviet rocket and satellite data on the earth's magnetic field are not yet available, although at the Fifth Assembly of CSAGI in Moscow the magnetometer carried in Sputnik III was described with full details of its construction and calibration.[57] The U.S.S.R. scientists reported that a considerable amount of information has been accumulated, including evidence for sharp jumps in magnetic-field intensity at higher altitudes. There was, however, no evidence of magnetic damping of the spin rate of the satellite, and no evidence of "electric drag" such as would be expected if there were a large charge on the orbiting body.

3.6 Chemical and Ion Composition of the Upper Atmosphere

Several methods exist for determining the composition of the high atmosphere: direct sampling, atmospheric absorption of solar radiation, and the use of mass spectrometers. The direct-sampling approach is the least tractable above the E region, but below the E region it has indicated a slight separation of the rare gases relative to nitrogen.[58-65] The separation first becomes apparent at about 60 km. For argon the change in relative concentration is not more than 15 or 20 % up to the bottom of the E region; there are indications that the change in helium may be more pronounced.

Measurement of the effect of the intervening air mass on the sun's radiation traversing the atmosphere has proved to be a powerful means of detecting and measuring the concentrations of ozone and atomic oxygen, and of locating the levels at which the various ionospheric layers are formed. This is discussed in detail in Chapter 4; supplementing that discussion we shall present here the ozone results obtained by Tousey and co-workers.

The ozone distribution was determined from a series of solar spectrograms obtained from rocket-borne spectrographs. Ultraviolet light in the wavelengths around 2550 A is strongly absorbed by ozone. This absorption is apparent on rocket spectrograms, which can accordingly be used to determine the total amount of ozone doing the absorbing. With spectra taken at varying altitudes, the total ozone between the various observing points and the sun can be determined, which in turn permits one to calculate the ozone concentration as a function of height. Three different sets of data obtained by Tousey and co-workers in the above manner are listed in Tables VIII to X.[66-69] The same information is plotted in Fig. 22 in the form of ozone concentration versus height. The measurements show that the maximum relative concentrations all appear to lie in the neighborhood of 28 km.

At 70 km the concentration is 2.5×10^{-5}, many orders of magnitude less than the maximum concentration.

Ultraviolet spectrographic techniques have also been used by Jursa of the Air Force Cambridge Research Center, to look for nitric oxide. His conclusion is that from 60 to 90 km over New Mexico the nitric oxide concentration cannot exceed 10^8 molecules/cm³.

TABLE VIII

Vertical Distribution of Ozone above New Mexico, October 10, 1946, 1103 MST

From F. S. Johnson, J. D. Purcell, and R. Tousey, *J. Geophys. Res.* **56**, 583 (1951); reproduced by courtesy of the *Journal of Geophysical Research*.

Mean altitude above sea level (km)	Vertical O_3 (mm, STP)	Estimate of accuracy (mm)
1.33	2.34	0.15
2.12	2.42	0.15
3.78	2.34	0.15
6.49	2.34	0.15
10.34	2.34	0.11
12.2	2.15	0.15
13.2	2.12	0.11
15.5	2.12	0.08
17.9	1.96	0.11
19.3	1.85	0.08
22.3	1.25	0.08
25.4	0.83	0.08
27.2	0.55	0.015
31.3	0.12	0.006
35.5	0.038	0.009
37.9	0.019	0.003
47.9	< 0.004	0.002
50.4	0	0.002
55.4	0	0.002
60.0	0	0.002
62.4	0	0.002
67.1	0	0.002

The mass spectrometer technique has proved to be a powerful approach to the study of the upper atmosphere. Townsend and co-workers at the U. S. Naval Research Laboratory have flown a specially modified version of the Bennett radiofrequency mass spectrometer to determine both the neutral and the ionic composition of the upper atmosphere.[24, 70-82] For the neutral composition studies an ion source with a four-stage analyzer having a resolution of one part in 40 atomic mass units was used. In the case of ion composition measurements, the ion source was omitted, and the air sample was admitted directly to a three-stage analyzer from the outside ionosphere. Mass numbers from about 9 to above 46 atomic mass units were covered by each instrument, the range being swept through approximately once per second.

TABLE IX

Vertical Distribution of Ozone above New Mexico, April 2, 1948, 0647 MST

From F. S. Johnson, J. D. Purcell, and R. Tousey, *J. Geophys. Res.* **56**, 583 (1951); reproduced by courtesy of the *Journal of Geophysical Research*.

Mean altitude above sea level (km)	Vertical O_3 (mm, STP)	Estimate of accuracy (mm)
11.3	1.73	0.06
12.0	1.76	0.06
12.8	1.70	0.06
13.5	1.71	0.06
14.3	1.71	0.05
15.2	1.64	0.05
16.1	1.52	0.05
17.0	1.42	0.05
17.9	1.30	0.04
19.0	1.15	0.04
20.0	1.03	0.03
21.1	0.89	0.03
22.3	0.77	0.025
23.5	0.68	0.02
24.7	0.54	0.016
26.1	0.415	0.012
27.5	0.33	0.01
28.9	0.225	0.006
30.3	0.15	0.005
32.0	0.10	0.004
33.6	0.072	0.004
35.3	0.055	0.004

In a flight at White Sands, New Mexico, Townsend and co-workers found no diffusive separation of argon relative to nitrogen below 137 km in the E region of the ionosphere. Above Fort Churchill, Canada, however, a diffusive separation of argon relative to nitrogen was detected and measured. The results from three flights are shown graphically in Fig. 23, from which it is seen that the separation was definitely in evidence in the E region.

8

The general conclusion is that above Fort Churchill separation of argon relative to nitrogen becomes effective at an altitude between 100 and 120 km, the ratio A/N_2 decreasing steadily with height.

TABLE X

Ozone Concentration above New Mexico, at sunset on June, 14, 1949

From F. S. Johnson, J. D. Purcell, R. Tousey, and K. Watanabe, *J. Geophys. Res.* **57**, 157 (1952); reproduced by courtesy of the *Journal of Geophysical Research.*

Altitude above sea level (km)	Ozone concentration (mm/km, STP)
20	9.1×10^{-2}
22	9.6
24	9.9
26	1.08×10^{-1}
28	1.03
30	8.9×10^{-2}
32	7.5
34	5.7
36	3.9
38	2.5
40	1.6
42	1.2
44	9.4×10^{-3}
46	6.4
48	3.2
50	2.2
52	1.3
54	7.4×10^{-4}
56	5.1
58	3.6
60	3.0
62	1.9
64	1.2
66	6.5×10^{-5}
68	3.8
70	2.5

Ion composition results obtained with the radiofrequency mass spectrometer are summarized in Table XI, which was kindly provided by C. Y. Johnson. Note especially the following:

1. Above Fort Churchill, on three flights covering fall, winter, and spring, and including both day and night shots, nitric oxide, although found to be a negligible neutral constituent of the high atmosphere, was found to be the predominant positive ion in the E region.

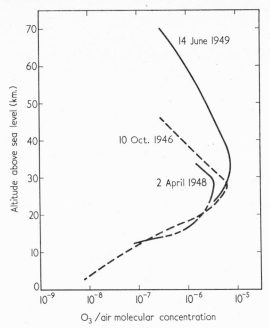

FIG. 22. Molecular concentration of ozone versus height above White Sands, New Mexico. Based on data of Johnson *et al.*, *J. Geophys. Res.* **56**, 583 (1951); **57**, 157 (1952); reproduced by courtesy of the *Journal of Geophysical Research.*

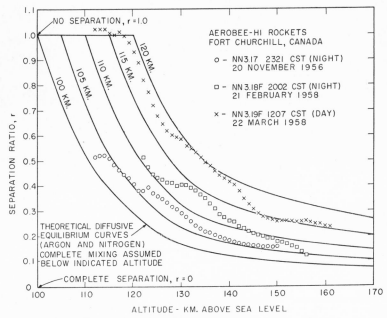

FIG. 23. Rocket measurements of diffusive separation of argon relative to nitrogen in the upper atmosphere. Presented at the Fifth General Assembly of CSAGI in Moscow, August, 1958. Reproduced by courtesy of the authors, J. W. Townsend and co-workers.

2. On the three flights of (1) above, atomic oxygen was found to be the predominant positive ion in the F region of the ionosphere above Fort Churchill.

3. Above Fort Churchill it was found that, as altitude increases from 100 km to 150 km to 200 km, the order of relative abundance of positive ions during the daytime changes from (O_2^+, NO^+) to (NO^+, O_2^+, O^+) to (O^+, NO^+, O_2^+).

4. The major negative ion detected above Fort Churchill and White Sands was NO_2^-.

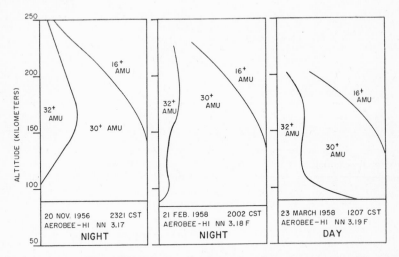

ILLUSTRATIONS FOR TABLE XI. Relative abundance data from three Aerobee-Hi rockets

It is plain from the above results that there is a special need for spectrometric measurements in the ionosphere covering the mass numbers down to that of hydrogen. It will also be of interest to extend the upper portion of the range covered.

The Soviets have flown mass spectrometers in a rocket and in Sputnik III. The instrument appears to be identical to the one used by Townsend and co-workers in the United States and permits measurement of the nature and relative abundance of positive ions in the range from 6 to 50 atomic mass units.[83] Results from the satellite show that in the region from 250 to 950 km the principal positive ion is mass 16, presumably atomic oxygen, O^+. Atomic nitrogen was also detected and found to vary with altitude, as shown in Table XII.

The rocket spectrometer data agree closely with the United States observations in showing a predominant ion of mass 30 (NO^+) along with an ion of mass 32 (O_2^+) in the E region. Above the E region and into the F region

TABLE XI

Ion Composition of the Ionosphere: Summary of Rocket Borne Ion Mass Spectrometer Experiments

Rocket	Time	Date	Location	Ion data (km)	Condition of ionosphere	Ion observed Positive	Ion observed Negative	Relative abundance	Remarks	Ref.
Viking 10	1000 MST	7 May 1954	White Sands Proving Ground New Mexico	93–219	Normal E and F region; mild storm in F-2	$16^+(O)$ $18^+(H_2O)$ $21^+(?)$ $26^+(CN?)$ $30^+(NO)$ $32^+(O_2)$		30^+, 32^+ are prominent throughout the flight; 16^+ appears above 100 km; 26^+ disappears above 124 km; 18^+ and 21^+ are minor.	Single positive ion spectrometer. Ion peaks (1) identified as masses 12^+, 23^+, 45^+, 19^+ and 38^+ are probably harmonics of 16^+ and 26^+. Rocket potential and evolution of gas from the rocket complicated this experiment.	1 6
Aerobee NRL 23	0139 MST	8 July 1955	W.S.P.G. N.M.	93–115	Sporadic E region	$28^+(N_2)$	$46^-(NO_2)$	46^- detected on 7 sweeps between 110 and 115 km		2 5
Aerobee NRL 24	1016 MST	29 Nov. 1955	W.S.P.G. N.M.	93–181	Normal E region		$46^-(NO_2)$ $32^-(O_2)$ $22^-(?)$ $16^-(O)$	46^- 97 %	Lack of positive ion spectra not satisfactorily explained. Ion peak identified as 29^-(3) is a harmonic (6).	3 5 6
Aerobee-Hi NN 3. 17 (NRL 48)	2321 CST	20 Nov. 1956	Fort Churchill, Canada	90–251		$14^+(N)$ $16^+(O)$ $18^+(H_2O)$ $28^+(N_2)$ $30^+(NO)$ $32^+(O_2)$	$46^-(NO_2)$	14^+, 18^+, and 28^+ less than 3% (see remarks). See the accompanying illustrations.	Indirect evidence (4) for ion at 63 ± 2 AMU now identified as harmonic (6).	4 5 6 7
Aerobee-Hi NN 3. 18F	2002 CST	21 Feb. 1958	Fort Churchill, Canada	85–225	Aurora				In presence of aurora the relative concentration of 32^+, 30^+, and 28^+ became approx. equal in the 100–105 km region.	
Aerobee-Hi NN 3. 19F	1207 CST	23 Mar. 1958	Fort Churchill, Canada	86–202	Polar radio blackout				Analysis of NN 3. 18F and NN3.19F partially completed at time summary compiled, 21 July 1958.	

REFERENCES

1. C. Y. Johnson and E. B. Meadows, *J. Geophys. Res.* **60**, 193 (1955).
2. C. Y. Johnson and J. P. Heppner, *J. Geophys. Res.* **60**, 533 (1955).
3. C. Y. Johnson and J. P. Heppner, *J. Geophys. Res.* **61**, 575 (1956).
4. C. Y. Johnson, J. C. Holmes, and E. B. Meadows, *Trans. Amer. Geophys. Union* **38**, 397 (1957).
5. C. Y. Johnson, J. P. Heppner, J. C. Holmes, and E. B. Meadows, *Ann. Geophys.* **14** (1958).
6. C. Y. Johnson, *J. Appl. Phys.* **29**, 740 (1958).
7. C. Y. Johnson, E. B. Meadows, and J. C. Holmes, *J. Geophys. Res.* **63**, 443 (1958).

masses 30 and 32 give way to mass 16 (O^+), which becomes the predominant ion above 250 km.*

TABLE XII

Soviet Data on the Relative Abundance of N^+ in the High Atmosphere

Height (km)	N^+/O^+
230	0.037
250	0.03
255	0.035
285	0.045
385	0.06
460	0.06
650	0.07
705	0.07
820	0.06

3.7 Atmospheric Contamination Experiments

Following a suggestion by D. R. Bates, the U. S. Air Force Cambridge Research Center undertook a series of rocket experiments to test the effect of ejecting sodium vapor into the high atmosphere.[84] A thermite mixture containing small pellets of metallic sodium, properly compounded to ensure the ejection of atomic sodium into the atmosphere, was sent aloft in a number of Aerobee rockets and burned. In two rockets launched at the beginning of evening twilight from the Holloman Air Development Center, New Mexico, one on January 21, 1955, and the other on October 12, 1955, 3 kg of sodium vapor was ejected into the atmosphere at a height between 50 and 113 km. Above 85 km. there was a definite enhancement of sodium emission at 5890 A observable on the ground; below 85 km no such emission was seen. The enhancement was attributed to resonance radiation from the sunlit sodium vapor. The emission faded away as the cloud spread, and no increase in the 5890-A nightglow was observed during the night.

Further flights took place in 1956, one of them at night. On the night time flight an unexpected strong emission was observed at 135 km, which, according to Wyckoff, was interpreted as the result of a photochemical reaction with metastable nitrogen atoms.

* An additional result of the ionosphere and ion composition measurements was that both the ion trap and the mass spectrometer indicated a satellite potential of between − 2 and − 6 volts relative to the surrounding medium during daylight, with essentially zero charge at night.

The seeding of the atmosphere with sodium vapor was followed in later rocket flights by seeding with other contaminants such as nitric oxide (NO) and ethylene. On March 14, 1956, at 0147 MST, at the Holloman Air Development Center, an Aerobee rocket released $18\frac{1}{2}$ pounds of nitric oxide gas into the atmosphere at 106 km.[85] A bright glow appeared immediately at the release point. As the cloud spread, the glow diminished in intensity, until after 10 minutes it was no longer visible on the ground. It was concluded that the nitric oxide had acted as a catalyst to bring about the recombination of atomic oxygen according to the following reactions:

$$NO + O \rightarrow NO_2 + h\nu \quad \text{(continuum)} \tag{3.9}$$

$$NO_2 + O \rightarrow NO + O_2{}^* \tag{3.10}$$

$$O_2{}^* \rightarrow O_2 + h\nu \text{ (oxygen atmospheric bands)} \tag{3.11}$$

The energy of recombination appeared as the visible glow detected on the ground.

On another flight during the daytime, 18 pounds of nitric oxide released at about 90 km produced a cloud of ionization amounting to roughly 10^6 electrons/cm^3.

In February of 1957, ethylene gas was released at night at a height between 105 and 150 km. Again a glow was produced, this time, according to Wyckoff, from energy released from atomic nitrogen.

3.8 Night Airglow

It has been known for many years that the upper atmosphere emits light during the night. This night airglow consists of a continuum on which are superimposed many atomic and molecular lines, the total radiation amounting to about five times starlight in the visible and ultraviolet. The most intense of these in the visible are the OI (λ 5577 A), Na D lines (λ 5890 to 5896 A), OI (λ 6300 to 6364 A), and Meinel OH bands.

The determination of the altitude of these emissions presents a difficult problem for ground-based measurements which has yet to be solved. Rocket determination of the emission altitudes can be made relatively easily by measuring the change in a rocket-borne photometer output as the rocket passes through the emitting regions. Such photometer measurements have been made on three Aerobee rockets.[86-88] The first of these rockets was fired from White Sands Proving Ground, New Mexico, on November 17, 1955, at 0200 MST and measured the OI (λ 5577 A) line and the continuum. The second, which essentially repeated these measurements but added the sodium D lines, was fired on December 12, 1955, at 2200 MST. The third rocket measured all the wavelengths given above and was fired at 0052 MST on July 5, 1956.

The results of these measurements are essentially in agreement and show that the altitude of emission of OI ($\lambda\,5577$ A) is centered at about 95 km, has a sharp lower boundary at about 90 km, and extends only up to an altitude of about 120 km (cf. Fig. 24). The sodium D-line emission is much less sharply defined in altitude. The emission is, however, primarily from the altitude interval 75 to 100 km and has peak luminosity at about 90 km. The OI ($\lambda\,6300$ to 6364 A) lines were found to be emitted above 163 km, and the 6257-A (9-3) Meinel OH band is emitted in the region 50 to 100 km.

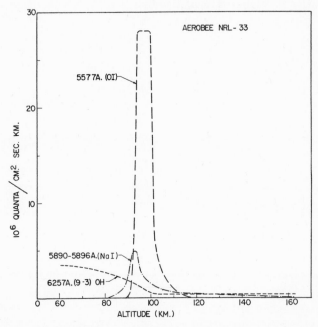

Fig. 24. Rocket night airglow results. From J. P. Heppner and L. H. Meredith, *J. Geophys. Res.* **63**, 51 (1958); reproduced by courtesy of the *Journal of Geophysical Research.*

3.9 Auroral Particles

For many years ground-based measurements have been made to determine the mechanisms responsible for the production of auroras. These investigations have not given definitive results as to the nature of the incident radiation that causes the aurora.

In a pioneering set of rocket measurements, Meridith, Van Allen, and co-workers, while seeking to trace out fully the latitude dependence of the cosmic-ray intensity, discovered that in the auroral zone the counting rate of their counters did not level off between 45 and 50 km as it had been shown to do in the lower latitudes. Instead a remarkable increase in soft-radiation intensity was observed.[89] In an effort to pin down the nature of the soft radiation, further flights were made with both shielded and unshielded Geiger tubes, scintillation counters, and photomultiplier tubes.[90] It was concluded from the later measurements that the radiation consisted of X-rays in the 10- to 100-kev range, the total intensity being from 10^3 to 10^5 photons $cm^{-2} sec^{-1}$. It was presumed that the X-rays were associated with a primary auroral radiation, but were themselves not the primary radiation.

The first direct measurement of the primary radiation was made on an Aerobee-Hi rocket fired from Fort Churchill, Canada, on January 25, 1958, at 2219 CST.[91] This rocket was fired into a visible aurora. Subsequent to this firing, two additional Aerobee-Hi rockets[91] and four Nike-Cajun rockets[92] have been fired to investigate the auroral particles directly.

The analysis of the data from the Aerobee-Hi rocket measurements is still proceeding; but they have already established that, at least in those auroras that were penetrated, the primary source of the auroral luminosity was electrons incident on the upper atmosphere. No appreciable electron flux was found outside but near a visible aurora. Energetic ions were also found to be incident on the upper atmosphere both within and outside visible auroras. On one of the three flights there were essentially no incident ions, but on the two flights on which ions were detected their spectra were markedly different. The ion flux was unaffected by the presence of a rayed auroral structure. The preliminary Nike-Cajun results[92] support these con-clusions.

Auroral electrons were detected by Soviet scientists in an experiment carried aboard Sputnik III. The detector in this experiment was a large scintillator consisting of a sodium iodide crystal, 40 × 40 mm, backed by a photomultiplier.[93] The device was apparently interior to the satellite. By scaling the output pulses using a threshold of 35 kev, by measuring the total ionization within the crystal as given by the anode current, and from the existence of a dinode current that was not linearly related to the anode current, it was possible to determine particle flux, energy flux, and energy spectrum. The information was telemetered by using modulation of the pulse length and pulse spacing on the 20-Mc/sec transmission.

A high-intensity X-radiation was observed, which was assumed to be caused by a bombardment by energetic electrons on the surface of the material surrounding the detector. Whenever Sputnik III was north of 60° N geographic latitude, in the auroral zone, a sharp increase in the measured intensity was observed. The Soviet scientists attribute this effect to auroral electrons with an energy of about 100 kev impacting on the satellite shell. Within the auroral zone, in the energy range of 200 to 300 kev, a flux of 10^4 particles per square centimeter per second was deduced as typical; in the range 20 to 60 kev a typical flux was 10^7 particles per square centimeter per second. Outside the auroral zone there were indications that the satellite may be running into corpuscular streams, probably electrons of energies less than 100 kev.

3.10 Cosmic Rays (See also § 12.1)

In addition to providing a powerful tool for the study of the earth's upper atmosphere, the rocket has proved very useful in the measurement of cosmic rays. It is not intended to review the rocket results on cosmic rays, however, but rather to point to two outcomes of the rocket program in cosmic rays that are pertinent to a study of the high atmosphere. The first of these is the discovery of the soft radiation in the auroral zone, already discussed in § 3.9.

The second concerns the discovery, in satellite experiments, of a high-intensity radiation at altitudes above 1000 km. The existence of this radiation was revealed by the U. S. satellites Explorers I and III, which were instrumented for cosmic-ray studies. After the discovery, a more elaborate installation, consisting of two small Geiger counters and two scintillation counters, with varying amounts of shielding, was sent aloft in Explorer IV. In a preliminary report, Van Allen and co-workers describe the radiation as follows:[94]

"The flux of particles with ranges greater than 1 gm per cm^2 has now been measured to be approximately 3000 per second per square centimeter per steradian at an altitude of 1900 km above the magnetic equator. At least 60 % of these particles can also penetrate 2.5 gm per cm^2. In addition to these penetrating particles there is a still higher flux of less penetrating particles. At high latitudes the shorter range particles greatly predominate. Here the flux of particles with range greater than 0.14 gm per cm^2 at 2200 km is about 100,000 per sec-cm^2-ster. with a total energy flux of particles with range greater than 0.001 gm per cm^2 of about 20 ergs per sec-cm^2-ster. This energy flux is similar to those recently measured in aurorae at Ft. Churchill, Canada, where it was found to be primarily due to electrons in the energy range 5 to 100 kev."

It is noted that the spatial distribution of the radiation remained quite stable during the first 2 weeks that Explorer IV was in orbit. Variation by a factor of 2 would certainly have been detectable. There appears to be a variation in quantity and nature with both latitude and altitude. The relative number of the high-energy particles increases as the magnetic equator is approached. Many of the higher particles have ranges exceeding 2 gm/cm^2.

Results from the Soviet satellite experiments appear to be consistent with those of Van Allen.[95] In one experiment aboard Sputnik III, detectors mounted on the outside of the satellite consisted of two photomultipliers with thin phosphor screens.[96] The screens interposed 2×10^{-3} gm/cm² of material; one was covered by aluminum foil, adding 4×10^{-4} gm/cm², the other by aluminum foil amounting to 8×10^{-4} gm/cm². Being mounted on the outside of the satellite, the screens were exposed directly to the incident radiation. Strong variations in total radiation were detected. Greatest intensities were observed at high altitudes and in the polar regions. The Soviet scientists attributed the bulk of the radiation to 10-kev electrons. The maximum energy flux detected was 4×10^3 ergs cm^{-2} ster^{-1} sec^{-1}. It was thought that these might be electrons trapped in the earth's magnetic field, oscillating from pole to pole, with absorption occurring at the northernmost and southernmost regions where the particle trajectories dip down into the atmosphere. It was pointed out that the large energy flux involved was sufficient to contribute materially to heating and ionization of the upper atmosphere.

3.11 Micrometeors

The term micrometeors is used to denote meteoric particles that are only a few microns in diameter. Widely differing estimates have been given for the total quantity of such material striking the earth per day, ranging up to 1000 tons per day. Micrometeoritic material may account for a small portion of the E-region ionization.

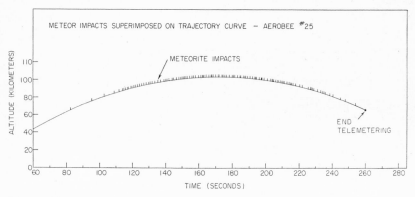

FIG. 25. Micrometeorite counts obtained during an Aerobee rocket flight. From O. E. Berg, *J. Geophys. Res.* **61**, 751 (1956); reproduced by courtesy of the *Journal of Geophysical Research.*

Rockets and satellites afford a means for studying micrometeors at first hand, above the retarding atmosphere. Early experiments, using polished metal plates or thin strips of film to record the pitting effect of the particles, succeeded in detecting their presence at rocket altitudes but did not yield quantitative measurements. Later, in an Aerobee rocket, Berg and co-workers used light flashes generated in a Lucite block thinly coated with aluminum and backed by a photomultiplier to count the number of micrometeor particles striking the detector. A plot of the counts obtained appears in Fig. 25. They correspond to a flux of one particle per square centimeter every 58 seconds on the moving exposed area. Presumably the flux across a stationary square centimeter would be much smaller, but this normalization has not been carried out.

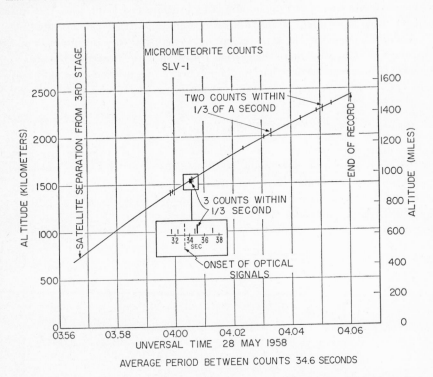

AVERAGE PERIOD BETWEEN COUNTS 34.6 SECONDS

Fig. 26. Micrometeorite counts obtained during a Vanguard satellite launching attempt. Presented at the Fifth General Assembly of the CSAGI in Moscow, August, 1958. Reproduced by courtesy of the author, H. E. LaGow.

LaGow and co-workers made measurements of micrometeor particles by means of sensitive microphones in the Vanguard satellite which was sent aloft from Florida on May 27, 1958.[98] Although the satellite failed to go into orbit, it reached an altitude of a couple of thousand miles with the research equipment working. A record of the seventeen meteor impacts detected is given in Fig. 26. The average period between counts is 34.6 seconds, but the statistics are meager, and final results must rest on more extensive collections of data such as are being obtained in various artificial earth satellites. From laboratory calibrations, which were made only for low-velocity particles and are still to be verified for high velocities, it was estimated that a particle of mass 2.5×10^{-13} gm would be detected if it impacted on the satellite with a speed of 17 km/sec. With this, one could proceed to estimate the total mass of particles striking the earth per day, but the result should be treated with caution because of the poor statistics in the count data. LaGow's estimate, based on Watson's unconfirmed estimates of particle number and size distribution, is 2.5×10^4 kg/day.

Soviet data on micrometeors differ from most of the U. S. data.[99] At the Fifth Assembly of CSAGI an average counting rate of 90 particles per second per square meter was given for a microphone carried in Sputnik III. It was stated that micrometeors of mass greater than 10^{-9} gm could be detected. This sensitivity is comparable to that of the U. S. instruments that show a much slower impact rate. When converted into mass of meteoric material falling on the earth per day, the Soviet results appear to lead to extremely high numbers.

3.12 Discussion

A fairly complete picture of the high atmosphere up to 200 km is beginning to take form. Pressures and densities have been measured directly, and temperatures deduced, giving a reasonably accurate picture of their variation with altitude. Below the E region the accuracy of measurement is generally better than 10 or 20 %. The seasonal and daily variations of the three structure parameters are quite small for the atmosphere above New Mexico. In the more northerly latitudes, there is an appreciable variation of temperature and pressure with season, and probably a much lesser one of density. A good beginning has been made in defining the wind regime for these altitudes, and it should be possible to fit the structure and wind observations together into a reasonable theoretical picture of the general circulations of the atmosphere, showing the seasonal effects.

At the higher altitudes, above the E region, the errors of measurement are larger, but generally not worse than a factor of 2. This accuracy is sufficient to reveal seasonal, diurnal, and geographic variations, which become quite pronounced above 150 km. It appears that as much as an order of magnitude change in density at 220 km may be expected in going from New Mexico latitudes to those of Fort Churchill, as suggested by the summer daytime curves 1 and 2 of Fig. 6. Almost as large a diurnal variation above Fort Churchill is indicated by actual winter day and winter night measurements. Taken together, rocket and satellite measurements give a consistent picture when the temporal and geographic variability of the structure parameters is taken into account.

Scale heights above 200 km are quite large. The smallest value indicated by the measurements is about 40 km, suggested by the summer daytime curve 1 of Fig. 6 obtained for New Mexico. Curve 2, on the other hand, corresponding to Fort Churchill, leads to the value of 95 km. The density values obtained from satellite observations at the higher altitudes give something in between these two, and once again a variation with latitude is to be noted. The scale height results are consistent with those deduced from rocket ionospheric charge density observations, which now indicate a rather slow decline in charge density above the $F2$ maximum.

It is plain that the rocket and satellite experimenters should now seek to pin down the extent of seasonal, diurnal, and geographic variations in the atmospheric structure parameters at F-region altitudes. Daily variations at White Sands latitudes should be looked for, and a repeated effort to detect seasonal changes there would be worth while. Measurements of atmospheric structure out to altitudes of 1000 km should also be pushed vigorously, exploiting both the satellite drag technique and the use of gages. Further wind measurements below the E region are required at various latitudes, and there is a need for a series of rocket measurements of wind at heights above the E region. It is to be noted that the equatorial regions have received very little attention up to now, and this omission should be corrected.

In the last several years large pieces of the ionosphere puzzle have fallen into place. At the same time it has become increasingly clear that the total picture is much larger than the early concepts of the ionosphere might have indicated. Whereas the region below the $F2$ maximum is generated primarily by ionizing photons from the sun, the higher levels may be associated with diffusion processes, and in some way with trapped particle radiations, particularly those of thermal energies, and with circulating currents about the earth, an association that doubtless becomes more and more pronounced as distance from the earth increases.

The classical picture of an ionosphere consisting of discrete layers with pronounced minima in charge density intervening between the maxima has given way to a picture of an ionosphere that remains quite dense from the bottom of the E region up to $F2$ maximum, the charge density increasing steadily for the most part, although slight indentations in the charge density curve are observed in the upper E and lower F regions. The absolute altitude of the $F2$ maximum for middle latitudes remains at about 300 km even when virtual heights shown on $P'(f)$ records vary by hundreds of kilometers. Often increases in virtual height can be correlated with pronounced increases in electron density gradient which produce a marked phase retardation in electromagnetic signals propagating vertically through the medium.

The rocket observations cover a period of time including both sunspot maximum and sunspot minimum. As seen in Fig. 14, whereas the height of

$F2$ maximum remains essentially constant, the charge density varies by about one order of magnitude between the minimum and the maximum of the sunspot cycle. The curve of Fig. 19, prepared by J. E. Jackson, gives the picture as it exists today of the ionosphere in middle latitudes around midday at the time of sunspot maximum. The D-region data are those obtained by the Pennsylvania State University. They are fitted onto an average of U. S. rocket data for White Sands, New Mexico, which extend only up to the $F2$ maximum; U.S.S.R. rocket observations show general agreement with this portion of the curve. Above the $F2$ maximum the curve is defined by U.S.S.R. rocket and satellite data and by deductions from U. S. whistler observations. The two solid circles represent measurements made in the Soviet "Geophysical Rocket." The square was obtained by deducing from the radio rise and set of Sputnik I, on 20 and 40 Mc/sec, the exponent of an assumed exponential charge density curve. The triangle stems from positive ion trap measurements on Sputnik III; Jackson made the plausible assumption that the number of electrons was equal to the measured number of positive ions.

Noting that the altitude scale in Fig. 19 is logarithmic, we see that the $F2$ maximum is quite broad, and that the decline in electron density above the maximum is considerably slower than the increase with altitude below the maximum. The crosses from whistler data at 8500 and 30,000 km certainly fit onto a reasonable enough extension of the rocket and satellite ionosphere curve. The extension moreover appears to be consistent with results obtained from radar bounces off the moon, which have indicated an appreciable amount of ionization between the $F2$ maximum and the moon.

The exciting challenge of the moment is to obtain the full story on the hitherto hidden portion of the ionosphere charge density curve, to trace it out to the distance of the moon if possible, and to determine what relationships exist between the ionosphere, incident particle radiations, and the aurora.

In the matter of atmospheric composition, the picture is also beginning to clear. Mixing processes appear to be effective in counteracting diffusive separation up to about 100 km, although a slight separation of helium may occur. One can, therefore, except for the minor though important constituent ozone, assume sea level composition of the atmosphere up to the bottom of the E region. Above 100 km more and more of the atmospheric oxygen is in atomic form, although the rate with which the molecular oxygen content decreases with altitude is slower than had once been supposed. Dissociation is only 65 % complete at 130 km; and some molecular oxygen still remains at F-region altitudes. The molecular oxygen-versus-atomic oxygen content appears to be determined by mixing and diffusion in the E region and by diffusion above; the regime is not that of photochemical equilibrium.

A marked diffusive separation of argon relative to nitrogen is apparent above the E region over Fort Churchill. As seen in Fig. 23, the separation becomes apparent at between 105 and 120 km, above which levels the ratio of argon to nitrogen decreases much as might be expected theoretically. The results suggest that an even more pronounced separation of lighter gases should be found, and it would be of particular interest to repeat the rocket experiment with equipment capable of measuring the change with height of the relative concentrations of helium, for example. In early experiments over New Mexico, no marked diffusive separation of argon relative to nitrogen was found. It would be well to repeat these measurements to check the earlier result, and also to extend them to the lighter gases.

It has become clear that nitric oxide is a negligible minor constituent of the E region and above. Otherwise its presence would have been detected quite readily in rocket solar spectrograms by its pronounced absorption in the ultraviolet. Moreover, as the NO seeding experiments show, the presence of natural neutral NO in the upper atmosphere would suppress atomic oxygen, which, however, is definitely present in large quantities.

On the other hand, NO^+ turns out to be a major positive ion in the E region. This fact, determined by direct mass spectrometric measurement, is consistent with the daytime NO seeding experiment, in which a pronounced ionization was produced. The naturally existing nitric oxide ion may very well be formed by direct reaction between molecular nitrogen and positive oxygen ions.

The U. S. rocket results had shown that O^+ becomes the predominant positive ion in the lower F region, suggesting that atomic oxygen might well be the principal positive ion at the top levels of the ionosphere. This fact is established by the Soviet observations up to almost 1000 km; at the same time it was shown that there are a few atomic nitrogen ions, N^+, varying from 3 to 7 %.

Future rocket and satellite experiments, in addition to continuing the present observations, should seek to determine the neutral composition out to 1000 km and should take a look at the light ions and molecules.

The night airglow results speak for themselves. With the rocket measurements, the altitudes of emission of some of the more important radiations have been pinned down. In many cases the ground-based estimates of these altitudes had varied by a hundred or more kilometers.

The attack on the problem of auroral particles is fully under way, although still in its early stages. It has already become apparent that cosmic-ray, ionospheric, current ring, and auroral particle observations are inter-dependent. It may be that the immediate source of auroral electrons is a flux of electrons trapped in the earth's magnetic field. This is certainly an important question to resolve. Moreover, the deeper question of the ultimate origin of the auroral particles is an even more challenging problem, one that rockets and satellites should undertake to solve.

We began this section with the remark that the picture of the atmosphere up to 200 km was becoming reasonably clear. Certainly the bewildering array of choices open to the theorist a decade ago has been whittled down to a tractable number. In the next decade it may be expected that theory and observation together can account for very nearly the full story. Furthermore, it must be plain from the data that are accumulating and from the above discussion that one can now speculate quite intelligently about the atmosphere up to 1000 km and beyond.

Acknowledgments

I am grateful to my colleagues at the U. S. Naval Research Laboratory for valuable help during the preparation of this chapter; particularly to H. E. LaGow for providing material in atmospheric structure and meteors; to J. E. Jackson on the ionosphere; to C. Y. Johnson on atmospheric composition; to L. H. Meredith on earth's magnetic field, aurora, and night airglow; and to J. W. Townsend, Jr., for assembling material on U.S.S.R. rocket and satellite results.

References

1. S. F. Singer, *J. Brit. Interplanet. Soc.* **11**, 61 (1952).
2. Clayton S. White and Otis O. Benson, Jr., "Physics and Medicine of the Upper Atmosphere," Univ. New Mexico Press, Albuquerque, 1952.
3. H. E. Newell and J. W. Siry, *J. Amer. Rocket Soc.* **23**, 7 (1953).
4. H. E. Newell, "High Altitude Rocket Research," Academic Press, New York, 1953.
5. "Rocket Exploration of the Upper Atmosphere" (R. Boyd and M. J. Seaton, eds.) Pergamon, London, 1954.
6. H. E. Newell *et al.*, "Sounding Rockets," McGraw-Hill, New York, 1959.
7. G. I. Taylor and J. W. Maccoll, *Proc. Roy. Soc.* A**139**, 278 (1939).
8. A. H. Stone, *J. Math. and Phys.* **27**, 67 (1948).
9. A. H. Stone, *J. Math. and Phys.* **30**, 200 (1952).
10. Z. Kopal (Director), Tables of Supersonic Flow around Cones, Technical Report No. 1 (1947); Tables of Supersonic Flow around Yawing Cones, Technical Report No. 3 (1947); Tables of Supersonic Flow around Cones of Large Yaw, Technical Report No. 5 (1949); by the staff of the Computing Section, Center of Analysis, Massachusetts Institute of Technology, Cambridge, Massachusetts.
11. Calvin N. Warfield, *NACA Tech. Note* No. 1200 (1947).
12. The Rocket Panel, *Phys. Rev.* **88**, 1027 (1952).
13. H. E. Newell, *Ann. Géophys.* **11**, 115 (1955).
14. M. Ference, W. G. Stroud, J. R. Walsh, and A. G. Weisner, *J. Meteorol.* **13**, 5 (1956).
15. W. G. Stroud, W. Nordberg, and J. R. Walsh, *J. Geophys. Res.* **61**, 45 (1956).
16. H. E. LaGow and J. Ainsworth, *J. Geophys. Res.* **61**, 77 (1956).
17. H. K. Kallman, W. B. White, and H. E. Newell, *J. Geophys. Res.* **61**, 513 (1956).
18. Arnold N. Lowan, *J. Geophys. Res.* **60**, 4 (1955).
19. R. Horowitz and H. E. LaGow, *J. Geophys. Res.* **62**, 57 (1957).
20. H. E. LaGow, R. Horowitz, and J. Ainsworth, *Ann. Géophys.* **14**, 131 (1958).

21. H. E. LaGow, R. Horowitz, and J. Ainsworth, "Arctic Atmospheric Structure to 250 Km," V CSAGI.*
22. R. Horowitz and H. E. LaGow, *J. Geophys. Res.*, **63**, 4 (1958).
23. W. G. Stroud, W. R. Bandeen, W. Nordberg, F. L. Bartman, J. Otterman, and R. Titus, "Temperatures and Winds in the Arctic as Obtained by the Rocket-Grenade Experiment," V CSAGI.
24. National Academy of Sciences, *IGY Rocket Rept. Ser.* **No. 1** (1958).
25. I. Harris and R. Jastrow, "An Interim Atmosphere Derived from Rocket and Satellite Data," V CSAGI.
26. *Smithsonian Astrophys. Observ., Spec. Rept.* **No. 12**, (1958).
27. E. G. Shvidkovsky, "Meteorological Rocket Research of Stratosphere," V CSAGI.
28. V. V. Michnevich, "On Pressure and Density in Upper Layers of Atmosphere," V CSAGI.
29. L. I. Sedov, "On Dynamic Effects in Artificial Earth Satellite Movement," V CSAGI.
30. Allan G. Weisner, *J. Meteorol.* **13**, 1 (1956).
31. Gerhard H. R. Reisig, *J. Meteorol.* **13**, 5 (1956).
31a. G. Goubau, *Hochfrequenztech. u. Elek. Akus.* **46**, 37 (1935).
32. J. C. Seddon, *J. Geophys. Res.* **58**, 323 (1953).
33. J. E. Jackson, *J. Geophys. Res.* **59**, 377 (1954).
34. J. C. Seddon, A. D. Pickar, and J. E. Jackson, *J. Geophys. Res.* **59**, 513 (1954).
35. J. C. Seddon, *J. Geophys. Res.* **59**, 463 (1954).
36. J. C. Seddon and J. E. Jackson, *Phys. Rev.* **97**, 1182 (1955).
37. J. C. Seddon and J. E. Jackson, *Ann. Géophys.* **11**, 169 (1955).
38. J. E. Jackson, *J. Geophys. Res.* **61**, 107 (1956).
39. J. E. Jackson and J. C. Seddon, *J. Geophys. Res.* **63**, 197 (1958).
40. J. E. Jackson, J. A. Kane, and J. C. Seddon, *J. Geophys. Res.* **61**, 749 (1956).
41. J. C. Seddon and J. E. Jackson, *Ann. Géophys.* **41**, 4 (1958).
42. J. Carl Seddon, "Ionospheric Electron Densities Above Fort Churchill," CSAGI Rocket and Satellite Symposium, Washington, D.C., September–October, 1957.
43. J. Carl Seddon, *J. Geophys. Res.* **63**, 209 (1958).
44. J. E. Jackson and J. Carl Seddon, *J. Geophys. Res.* **63**, 197 (1958).
45. J. E. Jackson and J. Carl Seddon, "Rocket Arctic Ionospheric Measurements," V CSAGI.
46. W. W. Berning, *J. Meteorol.* **8**, 175 (1951).
47. "Preliminary Results of Scientific Researches on the First Soviet Artificial Earth Satellites and Rockets." *Acad. Sci. USSR* **No. 1**, 40–108 (1958).
48. V. I. Krasovsky, "Soviet Investigations of Ionosphere through Rockets and Satellites," V CSAGI.
49. R. E. Houston, Jr., *J. Atmos. Terr. Phys.* **12**, 4 (1958).
50. "Whistlers and Related Phenomena," *IGY Bull.* **No. 6**, 5–10 (1957).
51. E. Maple, W. A. Bowen, Jr., and S. F. Singer, *Phys. Rev.* **82**, 957 (1951).
52. S. F. Singer, *J. Geophys. Res.* **56**, 265 (1951).
53. S. F. Singer, E. Maple, and W. A. Bowen, Jr., *Nature* **170**, 1093 (1952).
54. J. P. Heppner, J. D. Stolarik, and L. H. Meredith, *J. Geophys. Res.* **63**, 277 (1958).
55. L. J. Cahill, Jr., and J. A. Van Allen, *J. Geophys. Res.* **63**, 270 (1958).

* Here and henceforth in this list V CSAGI denotes a paper presented at the Fifth Assembly of the Comité Speciale pour l'Année Géophysique Internationale, held at Moscow, U.S.S.R., from July 30 to August 9, 1958. Papers presented at V CSAGI will be published in the *Annals of the International Geophysical Year*, by Pergamon Press, London, and may also appear elsewhere in the literature.

56. L. H. Meredith, L. R. Davis, J. P. Heppner, and O. E. Berg, "Rocket Auroral Investigations," V CSAGI.
57. S. S. Dolginov, "Magnetic Field Intensity Measurement," V CSAGI.
58. K. F. Chackett, F. A. Paneth, and E. J. Wilson, *Nature* **164**, 128 (1949).
59. K. F. Chackett, F. A. Paneth, and E. J. Wilson, *J. Atmos. Terr. Phys.* **1**, 49 (1950).
60. K. F. Chackett, F. A. Paneth, P. Reasbeck, and B. S. Wiborg, *Nature* **168**, 358 (1951).
61. L. M. Jones, L. T. Loh, H. W. Neill, M. H. Nichols, and E. A. Wenzel, *Phys. Rev.* **84**, 846 (1951).
62. F. A. Paneth, *J. Chem. Soc.* **1952**, 3651.
63. L. M. Jones, *in* "Rocket Exploration of the Upper Atmosphere" (R. Boyd and M. J. Seaton, eds.), p. 143, Pergamon, London, 1954.
64. A. A. Blagonravov, *Vestnik Akad. Nauk SSSR* **6**, 25 (1957).
65. B. A. Mirtov and V. V. Mikhnevich, *Uspekhi Fiz. Nauk* (September, 1957).
66. F. S. Johnson, J. D. Purcell, and R. Tousey, *J. Geophys. Res.* **56**, 583 (1951).
67. F. S. Johnson, J. D. Purcell, R. Tousey, and K. Watanabe, *J. Geophys. Res.* **57**, 157 (1952).
68. F. S. Johnson, *Proc. Toronto Meteorol. Conf.* 17 (1953).
69. F. S. Johnson, J. D. Purcell, and R. Tousey, *in* "Rocket Exploration of the Upper Atmosphere" (R. Boyd and M. J. Seaton, eds.), p. 189, Pergamon, London, 1954.
70. J. W. Townsend, Jr., *Rev. Sci. Instr.* **23**, 538 (1952).
71. J. W. Townsend, Jr., Edith B. Meadows, and Eleanor C. Pressly, *in* "Rocket Exploration of the Upper Atmosphere" (R. Boyd and M. J. Seaton, eds.), p. 189, Pergamon, London, 1954.
72. C. Y. Johnson and Edith B. Meadows, *J. Geophys. Res.* **60**, 193 (1955).
73. C. Y. Johnson and J. P. Heppner, *J. Geophys. Res.* **60**, 533 (1955).
74. C. Y. Johnson and J. P. Heppner, *Trans. Amer. Geophys. Union* **37**, 350 (1956).
75. C. Y. Johnson and J. P. Heppner, *J. Geophys. Res.* **61**, 575 (1956).
76. E. B. Meadows and J. W. Townsend, Jr., *J. Geophys. Res.* **61**, 576 (1956).
77. C. Y. Johnson, J. C. Holmes, and Edith B. Meadows, *Trans. Amer. Geophys. Union* **38**, 397 (1957).
78. E. B. Meadows and J. W. Townsend, Jr., *Ann. Géophys.* **14**, 80 (1958).
79. J. W. Townsend, Jr., and Edith B. Meadows, *Ann. Géophys.* **14**, 117 (1958).
80. C. Y. Johnson, *J. Appl. Phys.* **29**, 740 (1958).
81. C. Y. Johnson, E. B. Meadows, and J. C. Holmes, *J. Geophys. Res.* **63**, 443 (1958).
82. C. Y. Johnson, J. P. Heppner, J. C. Holmes, and E. B. Meadows, *Ann. Géophys.* **14**, 475 (1958).
83. V. G. Istomin, "On Ion Composition of Upper Layers of Atmosphere," V CSAGI.
84. H. D. Edwards, J. F. Bedinger, and E. R. Manring, *in* "The Airglow and the Aurorae" (E. B. Armstrong and A. Dalgarno, eds.), Pergamon, London, 1956.
85. J. Pressman, L. M. Aschenbrand, F. F. Marmo, A. Jursa, and M. Zelikoff, *J. Chem. Phys.* **25**, 1 (1956).
86. O. E. Berg, M. Koomen, L. H. Meredith, and R. Scolnik, *J. Geophys. Res.* **61**, 302 (1956).
87. M. Koomen, R. Scolnik, and R. Tousey, *J. Geophys. Res.* **61**, 304 (1956).
88. J. P. Heppner and L. H. Meredith, *J. Geophys. Res.* **63**, 51 (1958).
89. L. H. Meredith, M. B. Gottlieb, and J. A. Van Allen, *Phys. Rev.* **97**, 201 (1955).
90. James A. Van Allen, *Proc. Natl. Acad. Sci.* **43**, 57 (1957).
91. L. H. Meredith, L. R. Davis, J. P. Heppner, and O. E. Berg, *IGY Rocket Rept. Ser.* **No. 1**, 169 (1958).

92. C. E. McIlwain, *IGY Rocket Rept. Ser.* **No. 1,** 164 (1958).

93. A. E. Chudakov, "Photon Study of III Satellite," V CSAGI.

94. J. A. Van Allen, C. E. McIlwain, and G. Ludwig, State University of Iowa, Physics Department Research Report No. SUI 58–8, Ames, Iowa.

95. S. N. Vernov and A. E. Chudakov, "Study of Cosmic Rays by Rockets and Sputniks in the U.S.S.R.", V CSAGI.

96. V. I. Krasovksy, "Measurements of Corpuscular Radiation from the Sun," V CSAGI.

97. O. E. Berg, *J. Geophys. Res.* **61,** 751 (1956).

98. H. E. LaGow, D. H. Schaefer, and J. C. Schaffert, "Micrometeorite Impact Measurements on a 20 inch Diameter Sphere at 700 to 2500 Kilometers Altitude," V CSAGI.

99. T. N. Nazarova, "Registration of Micrometeors," V CSAGI.

FIG. 1. Solar corona photographed at Khartoum during 1952 eclipse by David Hawkins, U. S. Naval Research Laboratory.

[*To face page* 133

Chapter 4

The Sun's Ionizing Radiations

Herbert Friedman

Introduction... 133
4.1 Solar Levels... 135
    4.1.1 The Photosphere... 136
    4.1.2 The Chromosphere.. 138
    4.1.3 The Corona.. 140
    4.1.4 Optical Indications of Solar Activity.............................. 149
4.2 Rocket Measurements of the Quiet Solar Spectrum......................... 151
    4.2.1 Spectrographic Instrumentation................................... 151
    4.2.2 Photoelectric Detectors... 154
    4.2.3 Energy Distribution in the Solar Spectrum........................ 165
4.3 Interaction of Solar Radiation with the Atmosphere...................... 178
    4.3.1 Optical Absorption in Gases...................................... 178
    4.3.2 Atmospheric Transmission.. 185
4.4 Formation of the Ionosphere... 186
    4.4.1 Theories of Ionization Processes.................................. 188
4.5 Solar Flares.. 193
    4.5.1 Optical Characteristics of Flares................................. 193
    4.5.2 Ionospheric Effects of Flares..................................... 195
    4.5.3 Rocket Measurements during Flares............................... 198
    4.5.4 Balloon Measurements during a Flare............................. 200
    4.5.5 Gamma-Radiation from outside the Atmosphere................... 201
4.6 X-Ray and Ultraviolet Radiation in the Night Sky....................... 202
    4.6.1 The Distribution of Lyman-α from Space......................... 202
    4.6.2 The Density of Neutral Hydrogen Atoms in Space................. 204
    4.6.3 The Electron Density of Interplanetary Space..................... 206
    4.6.4 Ultraviolet Nebulosities.. 207
    4.6.5 Sources of Radiation in the Night Sky............................ 207
4.7 Atmospheric Densities and Composition from Radiation Measurements...... 208
4.8 Auroral X-Rays... 214
    References... 215

Introduction

The electromagnetic spectrum of the sun spans the entire range of wavelengths from γ-rays to radio waves. We see visually only the narrow wavelength interval from 4000 to 7500 A. With the aid of ultraviolet- or infrared-sensitive detectors we can measure a wider spectrum at sea level in two broad bands, the optical window from 2900 to 30,000 A and the radio window from 1 cm to about 40 meters. Outside these windows the air above us is highly opaque. Since World War II, our knowledge of the atmosphere and of the solar spectrum beyond the cutoff at 2900 A has been greatly advanced by the use of high-altitude rockets in upper air research. To study the interaction of solar radiation with the ionosphere, spectrographs and photoelectric detectors have been carried aloft into the ionospheric regions.

By combining existing rocket data on atmospheric structure and composition with laboratory measurements and theoretical estimates of continuous absorption coefficients it is possible to construct curves of the penetration of the atmosphere by solar radiation over the entire short-wavelength spectrum. The curve of Fig. 2 defines the level at which the flux is e^{-1} of its

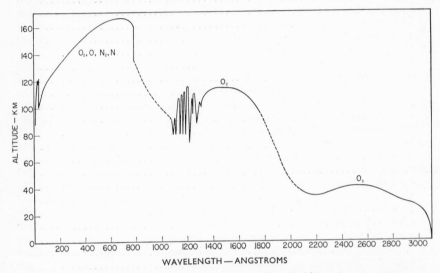

Fig. 2. Penetration of solar radiation into the atmosphere. The curve indicates the level at which the intensity is reduced to e^{-1}. Absorption above 2000 A is principally due to ozone, between 850 and 2000 A to molecular oxygen, and below 850 A to all constituents.

value outside the atmosphere with an overhead sun. This is the level at which solar radiation undergoes its maximum rate of absorption. Although there are uncertainties in the assumed composition of the high atmosphere and in the detailed variation of absorption coefficients in certain portions of the spectrum, Fig. 2 serves to indicate the general nature of the variation of atmospheric transparency with wavelength.

As the altitude increases above sea level, atmospheric pressure falls off approximately at the rate of a factor of 10 every 10 miles or 16 km. In the stratosphere, primary cosmic rays are strongly absorbed and converted to the myriad secondaries that shower down upon the earth. Next comes the ozone layer with its maximum concentration near 25 km. Between 3000 and

2100 A the absorption may be attributed entirely to ozone. If the atmosphere were compressed to sea level pressure its thickness would be 8 km. Ozone would constitute only 2 mm of this thickness, yet its absorption is so high that it attenuates the solar flux by a factor of 10^{40} at 2500 A. It is because of ozone that the solar cutoff at ground level is so sharply defined.

Throughout the wavelength interval 2000 to 1000 A of the so-called "vacuum ultraviolet" the primary atmospheric absorber is molecular oxygen, which dissociates in the absorption process. From 1400 to 1500 A, near the peak of the Schumann continuum, solar radiation penetrates to about 110 km. In the direction of shorter wavelengths, the absorption spectrum shows deep narrow windows. One window coincides almost perfectly with the wavelength of the hydrogen resonance line, Lyman-α (1215.7 A), permitting it to penetrate to the 75-km level in the D region. Lyman-α can produce the normal D region by ionizing nitric oxide, present as a trace constituent. On the short-wavelength side of 1000 A the atmosphere becomes progressively more opaque, and much of the solar flux is absorbed at heights as great as 170 km. This portion of the spectrum includes the resonance lines of neutral and singly ionized helium at 584 A and 304 A, which can effectively contribute to the formation of the F region by ionizing any of the major constituents of the high atmosphere. In the soft X-ray spectrum from 10 to 100 A, penetration again increases, and these rays are absorbed between 100 and 140 km, where they produce the largest portion of the E-region electron density. At times of solar activity X-ray wavelengths shorter than 10 A have been observed at altitudes below the E region.

In the pages that follow, an attempt will be made to fill in the details of the picture outlined above. The diurnal variation of the ionosphere clearly demonstrates that the sun is the primary source of upper atmosphere ionization. Any theory of the formation of the ionized layers should therefore start with the solar spectrum. The plan of this chapter is to discuss astrophysical concepts of the solar atmosphere and its radiation spectrum and to compare theoretical predictions with rocket observations. The interaction of solar radiation with the atmosphere will then be treated in terms of available data on absorption cross sections and atmospheric structure.

4.1 Solar Levels

The solar atmosphere may be described in terms of three layers: (1) the photosphere, a few hundred kilometers thick, which outlines the visible disk; (2) the chromosphere, which is observed during eclipses as a reddish ring about 10,000 km thick, above which rise the flamelike prominences; and (3) the corona, a thin hot outer atmosphere extending millions of km beyond the disk. Virtually all the known elements appear in the spectrum of the photosphere. With increasing height the percentage of lighter gases increases until they constitute almost all the chromosphere. The light of the chromosphere and prominences is made up almost entirely of bright emission lines of hydrogen, helium, and calcium. In the corona, hydrogen and helium are fully ionized and the heavier atoms highly ionized. Radiations from all the layers of the solar atmosphere contribute in various ways to the formation of the ionosphere.

4.1.1 *The Photosphere*

When we look into the sun the photosphere is the deepest layer to which our sight can penetrate. Radiation from deep within the sun diffuses outward by a process of repeated absorption and re-emission which produces a progressive degradation of the spectrum into longer-wavelength emission as the photosphere is approached. Near the surface, the amount of radiation escaping into space depends on the optical depth. The fraction that escapes decreases with increasing depth to zero. High in the photosphere the brightness falls off because the gas density decreases rapidly. Calculations indicate that the bulk of the emission is derived from a layer only a few hundred kilometers thick, subtending less than a second of arc on the limb of the sun when viewed from the earth. This accounts for the apparent sharpness of the edge of the disk.

The spectrum of the photosphere is a white-light continuum that can be approximated in its total power output by a black body radiating at about 6000°K. At that temperature hydrogen and helium are not ionized. The particle density is about 10^{16} cm^{-3}, about one-thousandth the density of our sea level atmosphere on earth. Metal atoms exist in the ratio of about 1 in 6000, and the electron density is about 10^{12} cm^{-3}. In the upper photosphere, the temperature falls to a minimum of about 4200°K. In this region thousands of dark Fraunhofer absorption lines are formed.

The fit with a 6000°K black body is good only in the visible spectrum. At shorter wavelengths the emission falls off more rapidly, so that even in the near ultraviolet observable from the ground a lower temperature is appropriate. Rocket measurements show that the difference is much more marked deeper in the ultraviolet. This is due to the denser accumulation of Fraunhofer lines, and molecular absorption in the solar atmosphere. In the extreme ultraviolet the emission temperature approaches 4200°K. The photospheric emission must be cut off at the Lyman series limit of hydrogen, 910 A, below which hydrogen at the base of the chromosphere absorbs radiation in the Lyman continuum.

It has been estimated[1] that the ionosphere requires an influx of 5×10^8 quanta cm^{-2} sec^{-1} of ionizing radiation in the E region, and 2×10^9 quanta cm^{-2} sec^{-1} in the $F1$ and $F2$ regions.* Planck's law of black-body radiation gives us the number of quanta radiated at frequencies greater than some limiting frequency as a function of temperature. Table I lists the computed intensities[2] above the ionization thresholds of O_2, 12 ev; O, 13.6 ev; and N, 14.55 ev. It is immediately apparent that the photosphere at $T = 4200°K$ cannot make any significant contribution to the ionizing radiations. If the temperature were as high as 6000°K, the flux would be adequate.

TABLE I

Logarithm of the Intensity ($h\nu$ cm^{-2} sec^{-1}) at the Top of the Atmosphere

Temperature	Limiting energy (ev)		
	12.2	13.6	14.55
5000°K	7.84	6.51	5.62
6000°K	9.97	8.88	8.15
7000°K	11.50	10.58	9.96

Photospheric light may ionize meteor atoms present at ionospheric heights. The photoelectric thresholds of atoms of Na, Al, Ca, Mg, Fe, and Si lie between the wavelengths 2413 and 1521 A. More important, however, from the standpoint of ionosphere formation is the dissociation of molecular oxygen in the broad photospheric continuum from 1350 to 1750 A known as the Schumann region. A knowledge of the solar flux in this range is essential to understand the height distribution of molecular and atomic oxygen. The percentage dissociation is particularly important in controlling the F-region recombination process.

* When a molecule of a gas is photoelectrically ionized, the ejected electron carries away as kinetic energy the difference between the quantum energy and the ionization potential. This difference is comparatively small when the absorbed wavelength is in the ultraviolet. The photoelectron then does not have sufficient kinetic energy for impact ionization, so that there exists nearly a one-to-one correlation between quanta absorbed and ions produced. One finds most often that discussions of the ultraviolet spectrum and its ionizing effects describe radiation fluxes in terms of numbers of quanta (quanta cm^{-2} sec^{-1}, or $h\nu$ cm^{-2} sec^{-1}). In the photoelectric absorption of X-rays, however, the ejected electrons may carry off enough kinetic energy to produce many more ions in subsequent collisions. It is, therefore, convenient to describe X-ray fluxes in units of ergs cm^{-2} sec^{-1} or ev cm^{-2} sec^{-1}. The conversion of X-ray energy to ionization takes place at the rate of about 30 ev per ion pair in most of the atmospheric gases. The relationships between units are as follows:

$$1 \text{ ev} = 1.6 \times 10^{-12} \text{ erg}$$
$$\lambda \text{ (Angstroms)} = 12,395/\text{ev}$$

4.1.2 *The Chromosphere*

At the time of an eclipse, a thin red annulus is seen surrounding the disk to a height of about 12,000 km. Its color is derived primarily from the red line, Hα, of hydrogen, at 6563 A. The flash spectrum obtained at an eclipse is an emission-line spectrum which for the most part corresponds to the Fraunhofer absorption lines of the photosphere.

Although theoretical models for the photosphere and corona appear to be quite adequate, the chromospheric transition layer between them is not well understood. Perhaps the greatest difficulty arises from the fact that the chromosphere is very inhomogeneous and cannot be approximated by a simple layer model. With regard to temperature, different theories propose temperatures as low as 5000°K and as high as 30,000°K in the lower chromosphere. Of the models that have been used to calculate the ultraviolet spectrum, most fall into two classes: (1) the temperature increases more or less uniformly from photosphere to corona; (2) the temperature remains low through the first several thousand kilometers and then rises very rapidly. The first model predicts an emission of ultraviolet radiation in excess of the ionosphere requirements. The second model, as developed by Woolley and Allen,[3] comes much closer to predicting the flux required to fit ionospheric observations. According to this model, the temperature of the lower chromosphere does not rise to more than 6000°K at a height of 6000 km. At that level the temperature gradient becomes very steep and reaches several hundred thousand degrees Kelvin, where the chromosphere merges into the corona. The most important change in the transition region is the conversion of hydrogen from the neutral to the ionized state.

Below the transition region the chromosphere is optically thick to wavelengths shorter than the Lyman limit, and the emission will be black-body. As the temperature increases, unit optical depth occurs near the level of half-ionization in the transition region. The corresponding radiation temperature is about 6200°K,[4, 5] and the predicted photon flux of ionizing radiation is 5×10^9 cm^{-2} sec^{-1} at the earth. This is more than is needed to account for the F-region electron production.

The upper chromosphere is optically thin. Its radiation is produced by radiative recombination of protons and electrons and by the excitation of line emissions in highly stripped atoms of the lighter elements. The expected contribution of the free-bound emission of hydrogen alone according to Woolley and Allen[3] is about 10^9 photons cm^{-2} sec^{-1}. They also computed the number of photons emitted by HeII, CII to CVI, NII to NVII, OII to OVII, NeII to NeIX, MgII to MgX, SiII to SiX, and FeII to FeXV. The predicted photon fluxes included important contributions of ionizing radiations from MgX (625 A), NeVII (430 A), OIV, OV (790 A, 630 A), and NIV (765 A). Table II summarizes the results of their computations after

Table II

Number of Quanta Cm^{-2} Sec^{-1} Available to the Ionosphere (Multiply by 10^8)

From R. v. d. R. Woolley and D. W. N. Stubbs, "The Outer Layers of a Star," Oxford Univ. Press, New York. 1953.

	Spectral range (ev)					
	12.2–13.6	13.6–14.6	14.6–15.6	15.6–50	50–100	100
Chromospheric line spectrum	0.3 NIII 4 H	0.6 NIV	0.6 OIII	14 many ions	5 × 10^{-5} FeVII 5 × 10^{-3} FeVIII 0.4 FeIX	2.2 × 10^{-5} CVI 1.8 × 10^{-5} SiV
Chromospheric continuum	M	3.0	2.3	0.1	—	—
Corona	—	—	—	—	2 MgX	—
Total	4	4	3	16	0.04	4 × 10^{-5}

some more recent corrections have been applied for the chromospheric electron density.[2] The total number of ionizing quanta including the Lyman continuum was estimated to be 2.7×10^9 cm^{-2} sec^{-1}.

Theoretical estimates of the intensity of the Lyman-α line depend very critically on the chromospheric model. Lyman-α propagates upward by diffusion and eventually escapes from the upper chromosphere where the electron temperature is many times as high as the apparent radiation temperature for the center of the line. De Jager,[6] for example, finds a radiation temperature of 6800°K, using the minimum flux observed with rockets. The corresponding electron temperature of the chromosphere was 66,000°K, which he estimated to occur at a height of 9500 km.

The inadequacy of any uniform shell model of the chromosphere becomes apparent when it attempts to explain the simultaneous appearance of metallic lines requiring temperatures of only 4000°K and the HeII line, λ 4686 A, which implies an excitation temperature of about 20,000°K. In order to reconcile such conflicting optical data, various two-stream models have been proposed, based on the observed spicule structure of the chromosphere. The spicules stand out from the limb like pointed jets, measuring several hundred miles in diameter and rising to a height of about 600 miles. Some investigators identify the hot regions with spicules, whereas others consider the spicules cooler. In a model proposed by Shklovsky and Kononovitch,[6a] the hot regions have a temperature of about 12,000°K and extend to about 8000 km, but cover only 10 % of the surface. The cool regions have a temperature comparable to the base of the photosphere, about 4000°K, and extend to heights of about 6000 km. To satisfy radio observations at 4 mm and 8 mm, Coates[6b] assigns the spicules a temperature of 6400°K and adopts a somewhat higher temperature than Shklovsky and Kononovitch for the interspicular gas. The source of excitation of higher-temperature emissions is attributed to radiation originating in the corona.

4.1.3 *The Corona*

For almost a century of eclipse observations preceding the development of the Lyot coronagraph, the corona was observed more for its aesthetic beauty than for the wealth of scientific information it could reveal. The true nature of the corona remained a complete mystery. It is now clear that most of its strange properties can be understood in terms of an extremely high kinetic temperature.

A temperature of the order of a million degrees is required to explain the following features: (1) the great extent of the corona; (2) the absence of Fraunhofer lines in the white-light corona; (3) coronal emission lines originating in highly ionized heavy atoms; (4) Doppler broadening of coronal lines in excess of 1 angstrom; (5) the absence of low-temperature spectrum lines such as are observed in the chromosphere and prominences; (6) the radio spectrum of the corona.

The temperature gradient from chromosphere to corona is very steep. The problem of the heating of the corona has remained one of the most baffling puzzles in astrophysics. Hoyle's accretion theory attributes the heating of the corona to the splash of interplanetary material scooped up by the sun in its passage through space. Heat is thereby conducted inward from the corona. Other theories assume that heat is conducted upward by gas bubbles breaking through the photosphere at supersonic speeds and dissipating their energies in shock waves at the base of the corona.

4.1.3.1 *The Extent of the Corona*

At the time of a solar eclipse the corona is visible as a thin white halo with a slightly greenish cast spreading millions of miles out into space. The outermost reaches may envelope the earth and extend far beyond it. In contrast, our terrestrial atmosphere is confined to a thickness of only a few thousand miles. Since the gravity of the sun is tremendously greater than that of the earth, the extended coronal gas must be correspondingly hotter than the terrestrial atmosphere. To support the coronal atmosphere in hydrostatic equilibrium against the gravitational field of the sun requires a temperature of the order of 10^6 deg K.

4.1.3.2 *The Visible Radiation of the Corona*

Close to the sun's disk, the brightness of the corona is comparable to that of the full moon, about a millionth of the brightness at the center of the solar disk. The coronal light falls off approximately as the inverse sixth power of the distance from the limb. Half of the light is concentrated within 3 minutes of the limb, and at a distance of 0.5 solar radius the intensity is down to 1 %. So tenuous is the coronal atmosphere that stars are easily visible through it and comets traverse it undamaged.

From the date of its discovery in 1851 to as late as 1930, the total time of eclipse observations of the corona did not exceed perhaps one hour. At no other time could the corona be observed, because of the overpowering glare of light from the solar disk. Attempts to photograph the corona and its spectrum without the benefit of an eclipse were unsuccessful until the French astronomer, Bernard Lyot, developed the modern coronograph. By taking great care to eliminate instrumental sources of scattered light and by choosing a high-altitude observing site, he was successful in imaging the corona while instrumentally eclipsing the disk. Coronagraphs are now used at many high-altitude observatories and make it possible to photograph routinely the spectrum of the inner bright portion of the corona out to 0.3 to 0.5 solar radius every clear day.

The visible light of the corona is derived from three components which are usually designated by the letters K, F, and L. The K corona is a white-

TABLE III

Coronal Emission Lines

Wavelength (A)	Relative intensity	Ion	Ionization potential (ev)
3328	1	CaXII	589
3388	16	FeXIII	325
3454	2		
3534			
3601	2	NiXVI	455
3643		NiXIII	350
3801			
3987	1	FeXI	261
3997			
4086	1	CaXIII	655
4231	3	NiXII	318
4311			
4351			
4359		AXIV	682
4412			
4567	1		
4586			
5116	3	NiXIII	350
5303 (green)	100	FeXIV	355
5445			
5536		AX	421
5694 (yellow)	1	CaXV	814
6375 (red)	13	FeX	233
6702	3	NiXV	422
7060	2	FeXV	390
7892	13	FeXI	261
8024	1	NiXV	422
10747	55	FeXIII	325
10798	35	FeXIII	325

light continuum, partially polarized, and shows no Fraunhofer lines. The F corona is also a white-light continuum, unpolarized, and contains the Fraunhofer lines. The L corona consists of some thirty-one emission lines between the wavelengths 3328 and 10,798 A, whose integrated brightness amounts to about 1 % of the coronal light.

The white color of the inner or K corona immediately suggests that it is scattered photospheric light. Thirty-seven per cent is polarized with the electric vector parallel to the limb. The scattering is accomplished by free electrons (Thomson scattering) without modification of the wavelength distribution of the incident light. To account for the missing Fraunhofer lines the electrons must be moving in random directions at such high speeds that the scattered light is Doppler-shifted over a broad-enough range to blur out the lines. Speeds of 7000 to 8000 km/sec are required, corresponding to electron temperatures of the order of 10^6 deg K.

Careful examination of the F corona, which is observable at larger radial distances than the K corona, reveals a slight reddening as would be expected if the light were scattered from discrete particles about 10 μ in diameter.

For almost forty years after Lockyer first photographed the six brightest coronal emission lines during the eclipse of 1898 in India, the origin of the L corona remained a baffling mystery. Since the lines did not correspond to the spectra of any known elements, they were attributed to some new element, "coronium." The solution of the problem came from the works of Grotrian[7] and Edlen,[8] who showed that the lines were attributable to common elements in highly ionized states, i.e., iron, nickel, and calcium atoms that had lost from 10 to 15 of their normal complements of electrons. Most intense is the green line, λ 5303 A, of FeXIV, which has lost 13 of its original 26 electrons. FeX is observed as a strong red line, λ 6374 A. Both FeXIV and FeX, which require comparatively low ionization energies, appear everywhere around the disk when observed with the coronagraph. The CaXV yellow line, λ 5694 A, which has the highest ionization potential of all, is indicative of the hottest regions of the corona and is observed only over the most active centers and in flare regions. Table III lists the wavelengths, identifications, ionization potentials, and relative intensities of twenty-nine coronal lines.

The coronal emission lines have widths of an angstrom unit or greater, indicating thermal velocities corresponding to temperatures greater than several hundred thousand degrees. The high kinetic energies required for collisional ionization of the coronal ions implies temperatures of about one million degrees Kelvin.

4.1.3.3 Temperature of the Undisturbed Corona from Thermal Radio Emission

Early attempts to observe radio emission from the sun were based on the idea that, if the sun were a 6000°K black body, its long-wavelength emission should be detectable out to the radio spectrum. Southworth in 1942 and 1943 actually succeeded in measuring solar emission at wavelengths of 1 to 10 cm but did not recognize that his results indicated a temperature as high as 18 000°K rather than 6000°K. By 1946 sufficient evidence had accumulated to show that there was a quiet sun background at meter wavelengths which indicated a source temperature of 10^6 deg K. In 1946 Martyn[9] worked out the relationship between wavelength and level of the solar atmosphere from which the radio emission could escape. Waves generated at the photosphere could not penetrate the corona unless the frequencies exceeded 30,000 Mc/sec (1 cm). Lower frequencies, for example, 30 Mc/sec (10 meters) could not get out unless produced at heights greater than 500,000 km. Martyn's theory has been substantially verified by experiments performed with radio interferometers, which reveal that centimeter waves originate at the 10,000°K level of the chromosphere, decimeter waves in the inner corona, and meter waves at heights of several hundred thousand kilometers where the corona reaches an apparent maximum temperature of 2 million degrees.

4.1.3.4 *The X-Ray Spectrum of the Corona*

A few decades ago astrophysicists still viewed the sun as a glowing sphere of hot gas, radiating into space like a black body at a temperature of 6000°K. This picture was inadequate to explain the X-ray emissions that are now known to play an important role in the formation of the ionosphere. Only with the realization that the temperature rises rapidly with elevation through the chromosphere to as high as a million degrees in the thin coronal atmosphere has it become possible to understand the extension of the solar spectrum to X-ray wavelengths.

It is possible to compute the emission spectrum of the corona if one knows the electron density, the intensities of the coronal lines, and the relative abundance of the elements. If we assume a state of ionization equilibrium in the corona, there must be a balance between the rate of ionization by electron impacts and radiative recombination. Several authors have developed formulas to describe the ionization equilibrium (Biermann,[10] Woolley and Allen,[3] Shklovsky,[11] Myamoto,[12] and Elwert[13]) and have estimated the X-ray intensity to be expected. If a uniform temperature distribution is assumed, the red- and green-line emissions should reach the same intensity at 7.10^5 deg K if they arise in the same region of the corona. At 10^6 deg K the green line reaches its maximum intensity.

Elwert[13] has carried through computations for these two temperatures and derived an emission spectrum. It is immediately apparent from the energies of the more abundant ionization states that the radiation will fall in the soft X-ray region corresponding to quantum energies of a few hundreds of electron volts. The emission spectrum is composed of a continuous background on which are superposed many discrete emission lines. Below the Lyman limit ($\lambda < 912$ A) part of the continuum is produced by bound-free transitions of hydrogen. A further contribution is derived from recombination in the HeII continuum below 204 A. At shorter wavelengths, continuous radiation is emitted by recombinations of electrons and heavy ions. Some of the line emissions follow recombinations into excited states, but most of the X-ray lines are produced by direct electron impact excitation.

Following Elwert's treatment, the recombination intensities are proportional to the product $N_e \cdot N_i$ or N_e^2, where N_e is the electron density and N_i is the ion density. Elwert treats the ions as hydrogen-like, assumes the corona to be isothermal, and uses the electron density derived according to

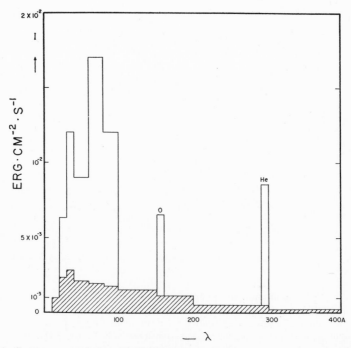

Fig. 3. Continuous emission (shaded) and line emission, summed up from Elwert's computations for wavelength intervals of 10, 20, 50, or 100 A according to the widths of the bars. From C. de Jager, *Ann. Géophys.* **11**, 30 (1955).

Baumbach,[14] who computed the density as a function of height from measurements of the intensity curve of the K corona. In the region of interest the electron densities range from 10^9 to 10^6 cm^{-3}.

After deriving the recombination spectrum, the next step is to compute the line emission. This is a considerably more complex problem involving: (1) an investigation of the energy-level schemes of highly ionized atoms to determine the possible emission wavelengths; (2) the probability of recombination into excited states followed by line emission; and (3) the probability of direct excitation by electron impact. Elwert finds that the process of electron impact excitation is the most important and that the maximum

10

intensity occurs near 80 A for 7.10^5 deg K and near 60 A for 10^6 deg K. De Jager[6] has represented Elwert's results in the form of the bar graph of Fig. 3. The continuum emission and the line intensities are summed up in intervals of 10 A or 20 A for wavelengths below 100 A and in larger intervals

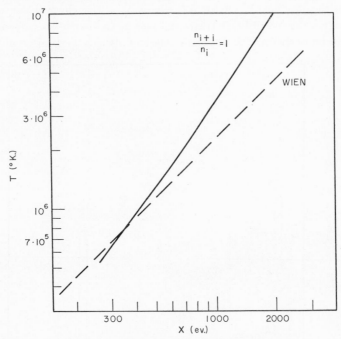

FIG. 4. Comparison of temperature dependence of the Wien's law maximum quantum energy and the ionization potential of the most abundant ion in an ionization equilibrium. In the coronal gas a particular kind of atom may appear in several different stages of ionization. For example, the emission lines of FeX, XI, XIII, XIV, and XV listed in Table III may all be observed simultaneously. But at any given temperature there is a frequency distribution of states of ionization centered about a most abundant ion. The maximum in the distribution curve is defined by the condition that $(N_i + 1)N_i = 1$; i.e., the ratio of the number densities of successive states of ionization is equal to 1. On either side of the maximum, the abundances of higher and lower states fall off rapidly. Since the intensity of the X-ray continuum is proportional to N_i^2, the maximum emission will come from the most abundant ion, and the wavelength will correspond to the ionization potential or series limit of that ion. From G. Elwert, Z. Naturforsch. 7a, 202 (1952).

above 100 A. It is quite clear that the emission lines make a much more important contribution than the continua. Elwert arrives at an integrated flux of about 0.1 erg cm⁻² sec⁻¹ at the earth with an uncertainty of $\pm 50\%$ caused by density fluctuations in the corona and by uncertainties in the choice of cross sections for the excitation processes.

The shape of the spectrum can be approximated by a Planckian distribution at the same temperature. The maximum of the intensity distribution occurs at nearly the same wavelengths as would be given by Wien's displacement law for black-body radiation:

$$\lambda_{max} T = 28.98 \tag{4.1}$$

where λ is in angstroms and T is in millions of degrees Kelvin. At a temperature of 10^6 deg K the maximum wavelength is about 29 A, corresponding to an ionization potential of 427 ev. Elwert computed, for different temperatures, the ionization potentials at which the quotient of the number densities of successive ionization states is equal to 1. These ionization energies are equal to the quantum energies at the intensity maxima of the recombination X-ray spectra for the various temperatures. Fig. 4 shows graphically the relationship between temperature, the Wien's law maximum of quantum energy, and the emission maximum based on the ionization equilibrium. At temperatures up to a million degrees, the black-body radiation law roughly approximates to the shape of Elwert's coronal X-ray spectrum. The total radiated energy is, of course, very much less than would be expected from a black body. We may describe the coronal emission of a quiet sun as approximating gray-body radiation with an emissivity of about 10^{-16}. At higher temperatures, the maximum emission from the ionization equilibrium occurs at lower energies than is indicated by Wien's law. For example, at 6.10^6 deg K, Wien's maximum is about 2500 ev, whereas Elwert's calculation requires only 1500 ev.

4.1.3.5 Coronal Condensations

According to Waldemeier,[15] coronal condensations are localized regions showing excessive brightening of the coronal yellow line of CaXV, (λ 5694 A; ionization potential 814 ev). They usually appear above large spot groups and may show prominence-type structures. Enhanced brightness of the coronal yellow line is also associated with flare-active regions. Waldemeier also discovered that the condensations show a brightening of the continuous spectrum of the scattered photospheric light attributable to an increase in electron density. He calculated a density of 0.5×10^{10} cm^{-3}. Billings,[16] in a similar treatment, required 2×10^{10} cm^{-3}. Undoubtedly there must be wide variations in density from one case to another, but the evidence points to the existence of condensations containing ten to twenty times the normal coronal density. From a study of line widths, Billings arrived at a temperature of 4.2×10^6 deg K in a condensation.

Further evidence for the existence of condensations comes from studies of solar radio emission in the decimeter wavelength region. A slowly varying component is observed which correlates with the area of sunspots.

Christiansen and Warburton,[17] using an interferometer consisting of 32 parabolic mirrors yielding a resolution of 2 minutes of arc, were able to isolate discrete bright emission regions. As was suggested earlier by the eclipse measurements of Christiansen *et al.*,[18] the areas appear to cover several thousandths of the solar disk and require temperatures of the order of 5.10^6 deg K and high electron density. Waldemeier and Muller[19] computed the radio spectrum of a condensation and arrived at the same temperature

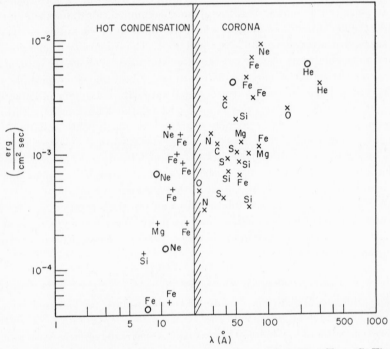

Fig. 5. X-ray spectrum of the corona and of a hot condensation. From G. Elwert, *Z. Naturforsch.* **7**a, 202 (1952).

requirement, Piddington and Minett[20] required a temperature of 10^7 deg K, taking account of a magnetic-field effect in their calculations.

Elwert has adopted Waldemeier's model of a condensation and computed the X-ray emission to be expected at a temperature of 6.10^6 deg K. His results are shown in Fig. 5, which compares the emission from a quiet corona at 10^6 deg K with that of a hot coronal condensation at 6.10^6 deg K. Whereas the normal coronal emission falls to a negligible flux below 20 A, the condensation contributes a substantial flux between 7 and 20 A. As Elwert points out, his computed flux of 10^{-3} erg cm^{-2} sec^{-1} from the condensation is consistent with the rocket data of Friedman *et al.*[21] in the same wavelength range. Furthermore, since the emission is sensitive to the square of the electron density, it should be highly variable, which is also in accord with rocket observations.

4.1.4 *Optical Indications of Solar Activity*

Certain optical features of the solar surface are statistically correlated with ionospheric effects. Among the features of greatest interest are the bright plages and faculae, dark flocculi and prominences, bright coronal green (5303 A) patches, coronal condensations, and flares. All these phenomena are closely tied to sunspot groups.

The sun in white light shows comparatively little surface detail except for sunspots. Other active phenomena that are visible in white light are the solar granules, and faculae. The small granules, which are often likened in appearance to rice grains, cover 50 to 60 % of the disk. They have angular diameters of the order of 1″ to 2″ and half-lives of the order of 2 minutes. From the contrast between granules and the darker interstices it is estimated that the granules are about 100° hotter. Faculae are disturbed areas brighter than the surrounding photosphere. Most often they are associated with sunspots, but sometimes they are seen at high latitudes where no sunspots occur. They have a characteristic lacey appearance and seem to be slightly elevated above the photosphere and about 100° hotter. The appearance of a new sunspot group is usually preceded by the development of a small bright facular region, which fades away much more slowly than the spot group.

Sunspots are the most readily recognized features of the disk in white light. They are generally confined to zones spaced from 5 to 40 degrees either side of the solar equator. They vary in size from about 50,000 km in diameter to the limit of optical resolution. The largest spot group on record appeared during the period January to May, 1946. It consisted of two large spots and numerous small spots joined by a complicated umbral pattern. The total length of the group was nearly 300,000 km, and it took 2 full days for the solar rotation to bring it completely into view. It remained visible for four transits and was last seen 99 days after its first appearance.

The subject of sunspots is worthy of a complete text by itself, and no attempt to discuss it in any detail will be made here. Their individual appearance on the sun is unpredictable, but their number waxes and wanes with a characteristic 11-year periodicity. As the sunspot cycle approaches a maximum, the ionosphere becomes more dense in direct correlation. This relationship is treated in detail in Chap. 9. Virtually all interesting manifestations of solar activity are related more or less directly to the appearance of sunspots.

The spectroheliograph permits observations of the sun in the light of Hα, the *H* and *K* lines of ionized calcium, and other strong lines. Sunspot groups are usually surrounded by extensive bright areas called "plages faculaires" when viewed in Hα or CaK. These plages are chromospheric phenomena overlying the photospheric faculae and also appear a few hours to a day in advance of sunspots. Spectroheliograms in Ca light reveal the entire chromosphere to be covered with bright areas about 10,000 km in diameter, giving a generally blotchy pattern. Plages in Hα have a finer structure. At other regions of the disk the spectroheliogram may reveal long dark filaments or dark flocculi which are prominences seen in projection. When seen on the limb these prominences appear as bright projections often extending out to heights of 50,000 km.

In the corona, the red, green, and yellow lines exhibit variations characteristic of varying degrees of excitation. "Red" regions of low excitation exist where λ 6374 A of FeX is strong, and "green" regions of high excitation where λ 5303 A of FeXIV is strong. The correlation between areas of high coronal excitation and spot groups is very strong, and there is also a strong correlation with chromospheric plages. The yellow line of CaXV, λ 5694 A,

TABLE IV

Time Lags of Optical Solar Features and Ionospheric Critical Frequencies behind Sunspot Number Variations

Solar		Ionospheric	
Hα plages	0.15 month	E region	0.43 month
CaK plages	0.31 month	F1 region	0.66 month
Faculae	0.56 month	F2 region	0.68 month
Coronal green line (5303 A)	0.87 month		

is observed only over active spot groups. Although it is normally about 5 % of the brightness of the green line, on one occasion it appeared three times as bright as λ 5303 A over an active spot group. Regions which are unusually strong in the green line were named C regions by Waldemeier. He related the transit of these regions across the solar meridian to the appearance of magnetic storms and aurorae.

Allen[1] has studied the time relationships between optical phenomena and ionospheric variations deduced from observations of critical frequencies. Table IV lists average time lags of optical features and ionospheric critical frequencies behind variations in sunspot numbers. According to the table, the earliest optical effect after the appearance of sunspots is the development of Hα plages at the photospheric level. The greatest lags correspond to those phenomena that appear highest in the solar atmosphere such as the coronal green patches. The E-region critical frequencies respond more rapidly to changes in sunspot number than do the F1 and F2 critical frequencies.

Allen points out that in behavior $F1$ and $F2$ are so similar that they appear to result from the same source. The E region, however, seems to derive from a different source.

4.2 Rocket Measurements of the Quiet Solar Spectrum

Rocket measurements over the past decade have provided a rough outline of the spectral energy distribution from the ground-level cutoff at 2900 A to X-rays as short as 2 A. Down to 977 A the spectrum is known in considerable detail. A rocket spectrogram showing the HeI (584 A) and HeII (304 A) resonance lines has been obtained, but details have not yet been published.[22] Below 100 A the X-ray spectrum has been measured in broad bands with photon counters. Altogether the available information on the radiations of a quiet sun amounts to no more than a few spectrograms and about a dozen sets of photoelectric measurements scattered over the solar cycle. These are admittedly few data, but as the first direct experimental measurements they are very valuable. In general, the major concepts of the interaction of solar radiation with the atmosphere have been verified, but there have also been some unexpected discoveries. Except for a few fine spectrograms, the first decade of rocket experimentation in solar radiation measurements may be considered primarily as a period of rough mapping out of areas of research and development of methods, rather than precision measurements. With the beginning of the International Geophysical Year, rocket techniques had advanced to the point where synoptic measurements and studies of transient events such as flares had become practical. Whereas the published work of the first decade was almost exclusively a United States program, the second decade will see a widespread participation by many countries. The accelerated effort generated by the IGY has already produced an order-of-magnitude advance in quantity and quality of rocket data.

4.2.1 *Spectrographic Instrumentation*

Before the advent of rocket spectroscopy attempts were made to photograph the solar spectrum from mountain tops and balloons. None was successful because the ozone layer reaches its maximum concentration at higher levels. Therefore, with the availability in 1946 of V-2 rockets for upper air research in the United States, one of the first programs established was solar spectroscopy in the ultraviolet. In addition to the problem of atmospheric absorption, the intensity of the solar spectrum falls so rapidly with decreasing wavelength that it becomes difficult to photograph the shorter wavelengths with the brief exposures available in a rocket flight. Serious difficulty is introduced by the roll and yaw of a ballistic rocket because it reduces the effective exposure time by a factor of from 10 to 100. To compensate for this inherent instability of the rocket as a platform for a spectrograph, the early instruments were designed with extremely wide useful fields of view.

The first rocket spectrum, obtained by Baum et al.[23] in 1946 with the spectrograph shown in Fig. 6, extended the short-wavelength limit to

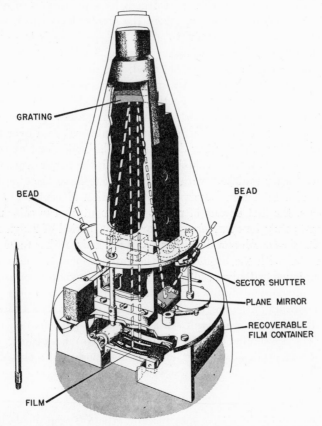

FIG. 6. Early rocket spectrograph using polished LiF spheres, 2 mm in diameter, to form image of the sun at equivalent slit position. From W. A. Baum, F. S. Johnson, J. J. Oberly, C. V. Strain, and R. Tousey, *Phys. Rev.* **70**, 781 (1946).

2100 A. The spectrograph used a concave grating of dispersion 40 A/mm in the first order without stabilization of either the rocket or the spectrograph. Conventional slits were replaced by 2-mm spheres of lithium fluoride. Tiny images of the sun were formed behind the beads, and these served as the source points for the spectrograph. The useful field of view was a wide cone, 140 degrees in diameter.

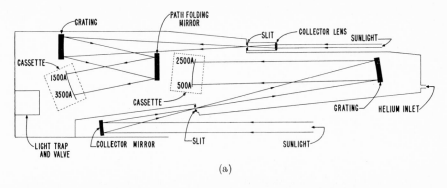

(a)

(b)

Fig. 7. Diagram and photograph of double spectrograph used with biaxial pointing control. From F. S. Johnson, H. H. Malitson, J. D. Purcell, and R. Tousey, *Astrophys. J.* **127,** 80 (1958).

[*To face page* 152

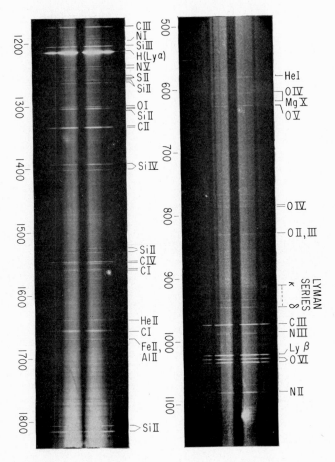

FIG. 8. Solar spectrum photographed from a height of 200 km on March 13, 1959. The shortest wavelength recorded was the He-I line at 584 A. (Courtesy of J. D. Purcell, D. M. Packer, W. R. Hunter, R. Tousey, U. S. Naval Research Laboratory.)

Below 2100 A, the intensity falls to such a low level that some form of pointing control is necessary to hold a focused image of the sun on the slit of the spectrograph and thereby increase the exposure by a large factor. At first, a single-axis sun-follower was tried, compensating only for rocket spin. In recent years, a sun-following biaxial pointing control described by Stacey et al.[24] has been used to compensate for yaw as well as roll with considerable success. By means of a servo-system directed by a photoelectric angular error-sensing device, the spectrograph is kept pointing at the sun for a time of the order of 5 to 10 seconds with an accuracy of 1 minute of arc. Over a period of 3 to 5 minutes, the error does not exceed 5 minutes of arc. With this pointing device, the Lyman-α line of hydrogen was first photographed in 1952 by Rense, using a grazing incidence spectrograph.[25] The image of the line was clearly present but was too faint for a reliable estimate of line width. With the same type of pointing control and a normal incidence spectrograph Johnson et al.[26] soon afterward obtained excellent resolution and many intense images of the Lyman-α line on short exposures.

Figure 7 shows two spectrographs built into a single housing, as used by Tousey and his co-workers since 1954. The lower instrument covers the 500- to 2500-A range with high speed at a resolution of 1 A and maximum freedom from stray light. The diffraction grating is concave, with 600 lines per millimeter and a 40-cm radius of curvature. The spectrograph's slit-and-mirror system is designed so that the spectrum is stigmatic with respect to the sun. As a result, when the solar image is centered on the slit each photographed spectrum line represents a slit image of the intensity distribution along a diameter of the sun in that wavelength. With accurate pointing control, this arrangement permits a determination of limb darkening or brightening.

At rocket take-off, the entire spectrograph housing is protected by the rocket's nose cone. At a height where air drag becomes small, the biaxial pointing control swings the spectrograph out so that the collector system may seek the sun. Correction for the rocket's roll is accomplished by rotating the entire nose section about the rocket axis. At the same time, correction for yaw and pitch is achieved by permitting the spectrograph to swing in trunions attached to the rotating nose section.

The most recent spectrogram (March 13, 1959) obtained by Purcell, Packer, Hunter and Tousey of NRL is shown in Fig. 8. Nearly a hundred emission lines were present on the recovered flight films, about sixty of which had not been previously observed. Among the new lines identified thus far are those produced by Mg-X, O-II, O-III, O-IV, Ne-I, N-II, N-III, S-I, Si-I, Si-II and C-I. At least eight lines of the Lyman series of hydrogen are present. The series ends at a fairly abrupt rise in background density, Fig. 9, suggesting the presence of the Lyman continuum which begins at 910 A and extends to shorter wavelengths. The Lyman-γ line of the series is

missing, probably because of absorption by residual N_2 between the
spectrograph and the sun even at the peak altitude of 200 km.

To photograph the spectrum below 1000 A, Rense has used a grazing
incidence spectrograph which provides much greater speed than the normal
incidence geometry. As of the spring of 1959, he had obtained four spectrograms on two flights that showed the He-II 304 A resonance line. His
estimated intensities are as follows:

June 4, 1958	212 km	Sun at Z of 80°	0.81 erg cm^{-2} sec^{-1}
June 4, 1958	140 km	Sun at Z of 80°	0.04 erg cm^{-2} sec^{-1}
March 30, 1959	195 km	Sun at Z of 60°	0.42 erg cm^{-2} sec^{-1}
March 30, 1959	175 km	Sun at Z of 60°	0.21 erg cm^{-2} sec^{-1}

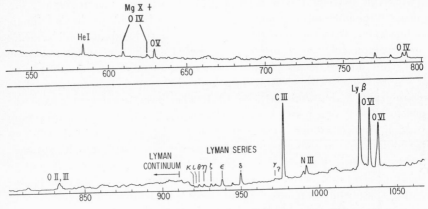

FIG. 9. Logarithmic densitometer trace of spectrogram of Figure 8.

Rense believes that there was still considerable air absorption at the peak
of each flight and that the flux above the atmosphere would have been much
higher than that reaching the rocket.

4.2.2 *Photoelectric Detectors*

Although high resolution spectra are of the utmost importance to the
astrophysicist, simple photoelectric intensity measurements in limited wavelength bands are adequate for understanding most features of the production
of the ionosphere. Experiments of this type were begun in 1949 with a variety
of narrow band detectors responsive to portions of the X-ray and ultraviolet
spectra.[21] In measuring X-rays, the spectral response is controlled by the
characteristic wavelength dependence of the X-ray transmission of thin
metal foils and plastic films. To measure ultraviolet radiations, use has been
made of the ultraviolet photoionization thresholds of gases and the transmission properties of various crystals.

4.2.2.1 *Photon Counters*

In the preparation of photon counters it is necessary to satisfy simultaneously the requirements of Geiger counting and spectral sensitivity. The subject of Geiger counters is treated exhaustively in the literature[28, 29] and only the factors related to spectral sensitivity will be discussed here. A variety of gas mixtures can be used successfully in Geiger counters, the most popular being combinations of a rare gas and a quenching agent. The latter may be a simple hydrocarbon vapor such as alcohol or ether, a halogenated hydrocarbon such as methylene bromide, the halogen gases, or nitric oxide.

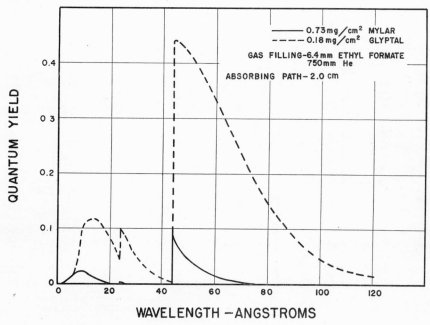

FIG. 10. X-ray quantum yields of photon counters with Mylar and Glyptal windows. From E. T. Byram, T. A. Chubb, and H. Friedman, *J. Geophys. Res.* **61,** 251 (1956).

The active chemical nature of chlorine, bromine, and nitric oxide imposes special restrictions on choices of material of which the tubes may be constructed.

Soft X-rays are counted by virtue of the photoelectrons which are ejected from the gas, since the photoelectric yield of the cathode is usually very much smaller. By choosing the rare gas from He, Ne, A, Kr, or Xe, the sensitivity to shorter wavelengths is increased in the order indicated. To minimize response to shorter wavelengths, for example, helium would be used at the lowest pressure capable of satisfying the Geiger counting requirements, and the absorption path length (tube diameter) would be kept small.

In the direction of longer wavelengths the photoelectric absorption of the gas approaches 100 %, but window materials become opaque unless extremely thin. For practical purposes, the windows must be thick enough to support the differential pressure between the gas filling within the tube and the exterior vacuum at high altitudes. Fortunately, X-ray absorption characteristics permit high transmission on the long-wavelength side of an absorption edge even in relatively thick metal foils or plastic films. Four types of

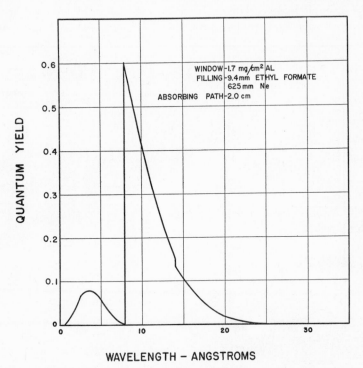

FIG. 11. X-ray quantum yield of photon counter with aluminum window. From E. T. Byram, T. A. Chubb, and H. Friedman, *J. Geophys. Res.* **61**, 251 (1956).

X-ray photon counter have been used to cover the range from 1 to 100 A, and their spectral sensitivities are shown in Figs. 10, 11, and 12. The effects of X-ray absorption edges at 43 A (carbon), 22 A (oxygen), and 8 A (aluminum) are clearly evident. The BeK edge is far from the region in which the tube of Fig. 12 is used. The transmission therefore follows the characteristic inverse λ^3 law, decreasing rapidly with increasing wavelength. Mylar polyester film is available commercially in rolled sheets, 0.00025 inch thick, and has very high tensile strength. Glyptal resin makes a tough film having the same chemical composition as Mylar, $C_{10}H_8O_4$. It can be cast in a very thin layer on a cleaved rock salt plate and removed by dissolution of the rock salt.

Between 100 and about 11 A it is difficult to prepare windows that can meet the requirements of vacuum tightness and mechanical strength. Nitrocellulose films, 1000 A thick, transmit about 44 % at 46 A and become monotonically more opaque with increasing wavelength, reaching 17 % at

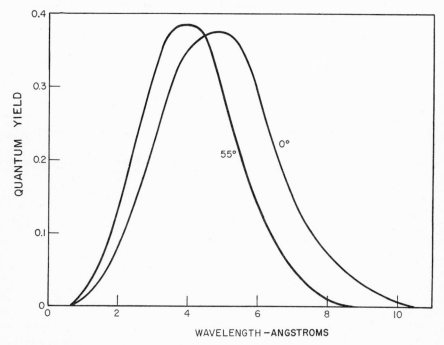

WAVELENGTH —ANGSTROMS

Fig. 12. X-ray quantum yield of a photon counter with a beryllium side window, 0.005 inch thick. The efficiency is dependent on the angle of incidence of the X-ray flux on the plane of the beryllium window. Increasing the angle between the normal to the window and the direction of the source increases the effective thickness of the window, and selectively filters the longer wavelengths. In a plane containing the long axis of the tube and the normal to the window oblique incidence also increases the gas path in the tube and thereby improves the short-wavelength efficiency as illustrated.

220 A. An aluminum film, 500 A thick, begins to transmit at 830 A, reaches 50 % transmission at 500 A, and remains fairly transparent down to the LIII edge at 170 A.

In the 100- to 1100-A region it is possible to use windowless photon counters of the " free-flow" type. The solar spectrum is sufficiently intense that a high counting rate can be obtained through a window as small as 0.010 inch in diameter. A small flask of gas may be used as a reservoir to maintain constant pressure within the photon counter as the gas flows out through the window orifice. By selecting the fill gas from the rare gases it is possible to control the long-wavelength threshold in a number of steps. The ionization potentials of He, Ne, A, Kr, and Xe are 507, 577, 791, 890, and 1027 respectively. Since there is evidence that the HeII line at 304 A is the strongest single emission line below the Lyman series, a helium flow counter at low pressure could be used to monitor this line almost exclusively.

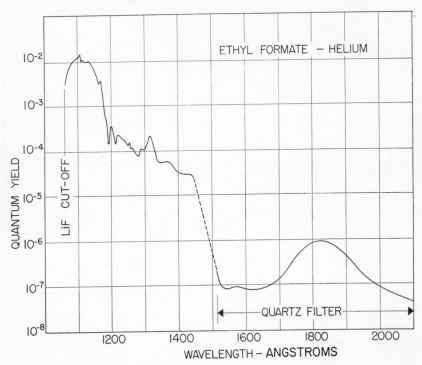

Fig. 13. Quantum yield of typical photon counter in 1100–2000 A region. From T. A. Chubb and H. Friedman, *Rev. Sci. Instr.* **26**, 493 (1955).

In the ultraviolet region above 1000 A, the spectral response is compounded of: (1) a long-wavelength surface photoelectric effect with a threshold above 2000 A for most metals; (2) an internal photoelectric effect confined to wavelengths below 1500 A; and (3) photoionization of the gas. The yield of the long-wavelength surface photoelectric effect is small, of the order of 10^{-5} to 10^{-7} electron per quantum, but the flux of solar radiation rises so rapidly at longer wavelengths that it must be considered carefully. For most metals a new threshold appears at a wavelength in the far ultraviolet, usually between 1000 A and 1400 A, at which the yield may multiply abruptly by as much as 1000 times. Finally, most gaseous molecules have thresholds for photoionization below 1500 A and reach such high cross sections for photoionization that yields of close to 100 % are possible.

Figure 13 illustrates the combined photoelectron contributions in a typical vapor-quenched Geiger counter equipped with a lithium fluoride window.[30] Between 3000 and 1500 A the sensitivity arises from the photoelectric effect on the cathode surface. Between 1800 and 1500 A the ethyl formate quenching vapor absorbs strongly, diminishing the intensity at the cathode. At about 1500 A the yield jumps abruptly by 10^2 to 10^3 as the inner photoelectric effect begins. A final fiftyfold increase in yield occurs below 1180 A, the photoionization threshold of ethyl formate. If the response of the tube can be limited to gas photoionization, it is possible to obtain a sharply defined threshold in the far ultraviolet. This end can be achieved by constructing the tube so that the photon beam does not strike the cathode surface. A simpler alternative is to add a trace of electronegative gas such as chlorine, bromine, or nitric oxide. These molecules scavenge almost all the slow electrons released at the cathode to form negative ions. The ions travel to the anode without detaching the electron and therefore fail to produce an avalanche discharge pulse or "count."

A wide variety of filter materials and gas absorbers are available for the construction of narrow-band photon counters. Tables V and VI list the transmission properties of various solids and gases. How to manipulate the various properties to produce a narrow-band photon counter may be illustrated by specifying the selection of window and gas filling for a tube sensitive to wavelengths near 1450 A. The window may be synthetic sapphire, which is transparent down to a short-wavelength limit of 1425 A. Xylene vapor is included because it has a photoionization threshold at 1500 A. Nitric oxide is nonphotosensitive above 1350 A but is added to the gas mixture because it effectively captures all electrons released by long-wavelength photoelectric effect on the cathode surface. The combination of a sapphire window and a gas mixture consisting of 40 mm NO, 0.5 mm xylene, and 650 mm He produces the spectral response curve of Fig. 14. If used to measure solar radiation, above the atmosphere, this tube responds strongly to the solar flux of about 3×10^{10} quanta cm^{-2} sec^{-1} between 1425 and 1500 A, while rejecting the photoelectric contribution of about 5×10^{12} quanta cm^{-2} sec^{-1} between 1500 and 2000 A. This spectral response characteristic is ideal for measuring the absorption of solar radiation by molecular oxygen in the dissociation continuum.

Two other ultraviolet photon counters are of special interest. A combination of a lithium fluoride window and a mixture of nitric oxide and a rare gas produces a response confined to the band 1150 to 1350 A, which includes the Lyman-α line of atomic hydrogen (λ 1216 A). Substituting CaF_2 for LiF cuts off the response at λ 1225 A so as to exclude Lyman-α. The former

TABLE V

Transmission Characteristics of Solid Material in the Vacuum Ultraviolet

Material	Approximate filter thickness (mm)	Wavelength regions in which transmission exceeds 10 % (A)	Wavelength regions of less than 1 % transmission (A)	Character of short-wave cutoff
LiF[a]	0.4	> 1050	< 1030	Sharp with moderate absorption up to 1300 A
X-rayed LiF	1	1200–2200, > 2800	2300–2700, < 1175	Depends on F center density
X-rayed and thermally bleached LiF[a]	1	1100–2000, > 2400	2100–2300, < 1075	Similar to uncolored LiF
CaF[a]	3	> 1220	< 1215	Sharp
Evaporated film CaF_2 on LiF base		> 1200	< 1150	Good transmission at λ > 1200 A compared to that for $\lambda\lambda$ 1150 to 1200 A
Sapphire (synthetic)[b]	0.5	> 1425	< 1415	Sharp
Fused quartz[c]	1	> 1560	< 1525	Gradual — general reduction of ultraviolet transmission by X-irradiation
Topaz (natural)	1	> 1550	< 1525	Sharper than fused quartz
Gypsum (natural)	1	> 1620	< 1600	Similar to topaz
NaCl[a]	1	> 1710	< 1700	Sharp
KCl[a]	1	> 1750	< 1740	Sharp
KBr[a]	1	> 2010	< 2000	Sharp
Teflon	0.006	> 1700	< 1660	Gradual—considerable loss of light due to scattering
SrF_2[d]	0.88	> 1300	< 1270	Sharp
NaF[a]	1.37	> 1310	< 1276	Sharp

[a] Harshaw Chemical Co.
[b] Linde Air Products.
[c] Central Scientific Co.
[d] Optovac Co.

TABLE VI

Transmission Characteristics of Gas Filters for the Vacuum Ultraviolet

Gas	Approximate filter thickness (cm) (reduced to NTP)	Regions of useful transmission (A)	Regions of high opacity (A)	References
O_2	6.0	1102–1110, and narrow transmission bands centered at 1124, 1158, 1166, 1189, 1216; > 1800	Other wavelengths shorter than 1750	a–c
CH_3Cl	0.1	1425–1460, > 1850	1475–1610, < 1420	
CH_3Br	0.05	1525–1575, > 1800	1610–1775, < 1520	
CCl_2F_2	0.0025	1200–1230, > 1375	1234–1325, < 1195	
CS_2	0.05	About 10 transmission bands between 1530 and 1780; > 2200	1800–2100, < 1520	
NH_3	0.1	About 10 transmission bands between 1450 and 1700; > 2150	1700–2050, < 1425	a
N_2O	0.025	1200–1220, > 1530	1220–1350, < 1190	a, d
SO_2	0.1	1625–1750, > 2250	1800–2150, < 1590	
H_2S	0.1	1600–1700, > 2300	1800–2200, < 1575	
CO_2	0.5	1175–1250, > 1650	1300–1550, < 1150	a, b, e
CCl_4	0.0025	1160–1200, > 1550	1220–1330, < 1150	
Cl_2	0.1	About 12 transmission bands between 1170 and 1310. One band transmits Lyman radiation; > 1450	1340–1420, < 1170	
CH_4	0.025	> 1400	< 1375	a
C_3H_3	0.1	> 1600	< 1575	
$(CH_3)_3CH$	0.1	> 1060	< 1640	
C_2H_4	0.025	> 1850	< 1750	

[a] K. Watanabe, M. Zelikoff, and C. Y. Inn, AFCRC Technical Report No. 52–23, Geophysical Research Papers No. 21 (1953).
[b] K. Watanabe, E. C. Y. Inn, and M. Zelikoff, J. Chem. Phys. 20, 1969 (1952).
[c] K. Watanabe, E. C. Y. Inn, and M. Zelikoff, J. Chem. Phys. 21, 1026 (1953).
[d] M. Zelikoff, K. Watanabe, and E. C. Y. Inn, J. Chem. Phys. 21, 1643 (1953).
[e] E. C. Y. Inn, K. Watanabe, and M. Zelikoff, J. Chem. Phys. 21, 1648 (1953).

tube can be prepared with a yield of more than 10 % for Lyman-α. Since cosmic-ray background constitutes all the noise, it is possible to obtain a signal-to-noise ratio of unity at a flux of a few Lyman-α quanta cm^{-2} sec^{-1} or about 10^{-10} erg cm^{-2} sec^{-1}.

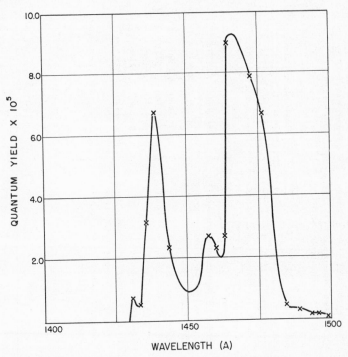

Fig. 14. Quantum yield of narrow band-width photon counter for 1450-A region. From T. A. Chubb and H. Friedman, *Rev. Sci. Instr.* **26**, 493 (1955).

4.2.2.2 *Ion Chambers*

If the voltage on the photon counter is reduced below that required for gas amplification by the Townsend avalanche process, the tube responds as an ionization chamber. Its photosensitive properties remain the same. In fact, rejection of long-wavelength photosurface response is comparatively easy. The simple step of operating with negative voltage on the collecting wire and positive on the cylinder effectively returns all surface photoelectrons to the cylinder and makes it possible to measure the ion current alone. To measure solar Lyman-α all that is necessary is a thimble-sized tube with a lithium fluoride window, filled with about 15 mm of nitric oxide gas. A flux of 1 erg cm^{-2} sec^{-1} produces about 10^{-8} amp of ion current, which is easily measured.

4.2.2.3 Photocells and Photomultiplier Tubes

The simple vacuum photocell would be a solution to the window problem in the 100- to 1100-A range if it were possible to suppress the long-wavelength response. Chubb[30a] has prepared tubes with evaporated lithium fluoride surfaces that exhibit yields of 40 % at 584 A and less than 1 % at Lyman-α. Hinteregger and Watanabe[30b] have applied the method of retarding potentials to scan the photoelectron energy distributions between Lyman-α (λ 1216 A) and HeII (λ 304 A).

The secondary emission multiplier (SEM) tube provides an internal gain of the order of a million or greater to amplify the primary photocurrent. In this respect it is competitive with the gas amplification process in photon counters. The dynodes (secondary emission electrodes) used in visible-light photomultipliers are alkali-treated metals which are also sensitive to visible light. It is possible, however, to use surfaces such as Ag–Mg which are insensitive to light above 3000 A and still provide secondary emission multiplication factors in excess of 2. Still more recent developments have produced secondary emission surfaces with photoelectric thresholds shorter than 1500 A. These multipliers can be used with photocathodes exhibiting the efficient internal photoelectric effect to provide narrow-band detection in the extreme ultraviolet.

An interesting version of the SEM technique was described in connection with the Russian experiment in Sputnik II. SEM tubes insensitive to long wavelengths were used in combination with rotating filter disks. The plan was to obtain the X-ray spectrum by comparing the responses through filters of beryllium, aluminum, and polyethylene, and the Lyman-α intensity by comparing transmissions through filters of lithium fluoride and calcium fluoride.

4.2.2.4 Telemetered Data

In a typical experiment, the photoionization chamber is mounted on the skin of the rocket looking outward. Its view of space therefore depends entirely on the spin and yaw motions of the rocket. The rocket is fired, and the ion chamber current is telemetered continuously as the rocket climbs. Figure 15 illustrates the kind of record usually obtained. When the rocket is deep in the earth's atmosphere there is no response because the overhead air absorbs the solar ultraviolet radiation completely. As the rocket approaches the upper reaches of the atmosphere the detector begins to see radiation, and at unit optical depth the rate of change of transmission reaches a maximum. From there on, the intensity changes less rapidly as the rocket climbs above the absorbing atmosphere. The undulating responses are due to the roll of the rocket, since the detector produces signals only when it sees the sun. Amplitude variations, after the rocket is "above the atmosphere," are produced by precession of the rocket which changes the angle of incidence of solar radiation on the window of the ion chamber.

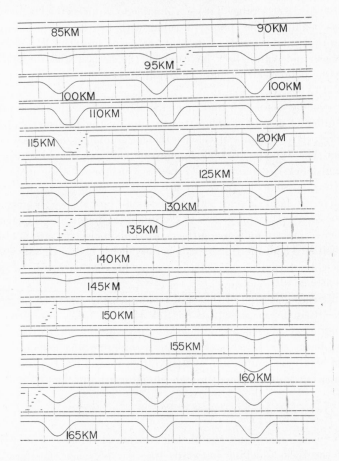

FIG. 15. Photograph of a section of telemetering record obtained in Aerobee NRL 35. The telemetering record shows the ionization current passed by a 1060- to 1350-A ionization chamber as a function of time. Increasing current produces a negative deflection of the trace. Vertical lines are half-second timing markers. Peaks in the ionization current occur when the spinning rocket brings the ionization chamber around toward the sun. Below 90 km, the air is opaque. As the rocket rises above 90 km, the signals increase in amplitude. The minimum at 150 km is the result of rocket precession which at that time caused the ion chamber to look "above" the sun at a large angle.

To determine the altitude variation of radiation absorption we must correct the individual responses to some constant aspect angle (angle between normal to detector window and direct line to sun). The aspect correction is obtained throughout flight from the signals of visible-light photocells having known angular responses to sunlight. Figure 16 illustrates the final result of analysis of the telemetering record of Fig. 15. The end product is a plot of intensity versus altitude or overhead air mass. Figure 16 represents an unusually simple situation, an almost monochromatic source, Lyman-α, and a single absorber, O_2.

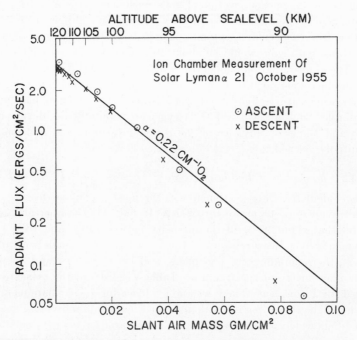

FIG. 16. Intensity of Lyman-α as a function of altitude and slant air mass for the sunset flight of Aerobee 35, October 21, 1955. Rocket Panel densities are used to obtain the slant air mass. If the absorption is attributed entirely to O_2, the slope of the line gives a coefficient of 0.22 cm^{-1} which is close to the accepted value. The fact that the data points fall close to a straight line is evidence that the ion chamber is responding almost exclusively to Lyman-α.

4.2.3 *Energy Distribution in the Solar Spectrum*

4.2.3.1 *Photospheric Radiation*

The most important contributions of photospheric radiation to the formation of the ionosphere are the dissociation of O_2 in the broad Schumann continuum from 1350 to 1750 A in the far ultraviolet and the photodetachment of electrons from negative ions by the entire spectrum below the visible yellow. Rocket spectrograms[31] and photoelectric measurements[32] verified the expected ultraviolet deficiency. Spectrographic observations of the region from 3000 to 2000 A showed that the solar intensity curve falls below that of a 6000°K black body by a factor of 3 at 3000 A and by a factor of roughly 10 to 20 at 2000 A. Ion chamber measurements at 1300 A indicate an effective temperature of 4200°K.

The weakness of the solar spectrum below 1750 A has an important bearing on the oxygen composition of the atmosphere in the E and F regions. A photochemical equilibrium based on a 6000°K sun implies a very rapid transition from molecular to atomic oxygen below the E region. The predicted transition region would be about 10 km thick and centered at about 95 km. The lower-radiation temperatures of 5000° to 4200°K in the Schumann region produce a slower rate of dissociation and raise the transition region to altitudes where atmospheric mixing and diffusive separation play an important role. Such a theory of the oxygen distribution was developed by Nicolet and Mange in advance of the rocket measurements, and has been substantially verified.[33]

4.2.3.2 *Chromospheric Radiation*

As is evident from Fig. 8, Lyman-α is the most prominent feature of the solar ultraviolet spectrum down to 977 A. In fact, ion chamber photometry indicates that about 94 % of the intensity between 1050 and 1350 A is in the Lyman-α line. Measurements of Lyman-α have been made with photon counters, thermoluminescent phosphors, and ion chambers, and by photographic photometry of spectrograms. Table VII lists all the measurements reported for a quiet sun. There was no evidence for a solar flare coincident with any of the rocket flights. Although the accuracy of individual measurements differs widely, there seems to be a large variation over the solar cycle.

The ion chamber technique used in the more recent measurements is simple and reliable. Only the window transmission and the ionization cross section of NO enter into the computation of efficiency. The window transmission is readily measurable, and the ionization efficiency is given by Watanabe[34] as 80 %. Any deterioration of the ion chamber between calibration and end of flight could only reduce the quantum yield and cause the computed intensity to be too low. Although the ion chamber measurements of Table VII give the highest values of Lyman-α intensity, there appears to be no possibility of these values being in error on the low side. Since the ion chamber measurements give a consistently high value of about 6 ergs cm^{-2} sec^{-1}, some doubt is cast on the earlier measurements, and attempts to explain a large solar cycle variation had perhaps better wait until data on the next solar minimum are available.

In the fine spectrogram of Fig. 8, Lyman-α stands out so strongly that the difficulty of obtaining a photographic exposure that shows the weaker adjacent lines without over-exposing Lyman-α is obvious. From the spectrogram

TABLE VII

Table of Lyman-α Measurements

References	Launch time	Intensity above atmosphere (ergs cm^{-2} sec^{-1})	Instrumentation	Band width (A)
a	1000 MST, 9/29/49	1–10	Photon counter	1100–1350
b	1101 MST, 2/17/50	0.4	Thermoluminescent phosphor	1050–1240
c	0659 MST, 4/30/52	0.15	Photon counter	1180–1300
c	0644 MST, 5/5/52	0.10	Photon counter	1180–1300
d	1238 MST, 12/12/52	0.5	Spectrograph	
e	0830 MST, 2/2/54	1.6	Spectrograph	
e	0830 MST, 2/21/55	0.6	Spectrograph	
f	1550 MST, 10/18/55	5.7 ($-1, +3$)	Ion chamber	1065–1350
f	1715 MST, 10/21/55	4.0 (± 0.8)	Ion chamber	1065–1350
f	0830 MST, 11/4/55	9.0 (± 3)	Ion chamber	1065–1350
g	1915 UT, 7/20/56	6.1 $\pm$ 0.5	Ion chamber	1065–1350
g	2113 UT, 7/25/56	6.7 $\pm$ 0.3	Ion chamber	1065–1350
h	1600 CST, 7/29/57	6.1 $\pm$ 0.3	Ion chamber	1065–1350
h	1208 CST, 3/23/58	6.3 $\pm$ 0.3	Ion chamber	1065–1350

[a] H. Friedman, S. W. Lichtman, and E. T. Byram, *Phys. Rev.* **83**, 1025 (1952).

[b] R. Tousey, K. Watanabe, and J. D. Purcell, *Phys. Rev.* **83**, 165 (1951).

[c] E. T. Byram, T. A. Chubb, H. Friedman, and N. Gailar, *Phys. Rev.* **91**, 1278 (1953).

[d] W. A. Rense, *Phys. Rev.* **91**, 299 (1953).

[e] F. S. Johnson, H. H. Malitson, J. D. Purcell, and R. Tousey, *Astrophys. J.* **127**, 80 (1958).

[f] E. T. Byram, T. A. Chubb, H. Friedman, and J. E. Kupperian, Jr., *Astrophys. J.* **124**, 480 (1956).

[g] T. A. Chubb, H. Friedman, R. W. Kreplin, and J. E. Kupperian, Jr., *J. Geophys. Res.* **62**, 389 (1957).

[h] E. T. Byram, T. A. Chubb, H. Friedman, and J. E. Kupperian, Jr., private communication; corrected for lines other than Lyman-α, included in band width.

it is possible to obtain good relative intensity values for the weaker lines, but absolute intensities are difficult to determine by photographic photometry. By comparing the responses of two ion chambers sensitive to 1100 to 1350 A and 1225 to 1350 A it is possible to evaluate both Lyman-α and the weaker lines on an absolute scale. The results of such an analysis[35] are listed in Table VIII.

TABLE VIII

Intensities of Solar Emission Lines Near Lyman-α

Spectrum line[a]	Wavelength (A)	Intensity (erg cm^{-2} sec^{-1})
NV	1238.8	0.010
SII	1259.5	0.008
SiII	1260.7	0.012
SiII	1265.0	0.020
OI	1302.2	0.039
OI	1304.9	0.052
OI	1306.0	0.064
SiII	1309.3	0.013
CII	1334.5	0.12
CII	1336.7	0.15
SiIII	1206.5	0.16

[a] The lines are those registered in the spectrogram of Fig. 8 and identified by F. S. Johnson, H. H. Malitson, J. D. Purcell, and R. Tousey, *Astrophys. J.* **127**, 80 (1958).

The registration of Lyman-β (1025.7 A) on the spectrogram of Fig. 8 is the only measurement published. Tousey *et al.*[27] estimated the intensity of Lyman-β to be 1/60 Lyman-α. The intensity of the Lyman continuum is comparable with that of Lyman-β.

4.2.3.3 *Solar X-Rays*

After earlier attempts to detect solar X-rays by exposing photographic emulsions[36] and thermoluminescent phosphors on rockets,[37] the first quantitative results were obtained with photon counters in 1949. Counters with beryllium windows were flown in a V-2 rocket to 150 km. X-rays were detected at 87 km and increased rapidly to an intensity of 10^{-4} erg cm^{-2} sec^{-1} before the rocket reached its highest altitude.[21] It was concluded that the short-wavelength limit of the spectrum was about 7 A and that the response was confined to a band only a couple of angstroms wide, since the beryllium became opaque above 10 A. On the assumption that the solar emission could be approximated by a million-degree Planckian distribution, it was estimated that the total X-ray flux could very well be at least 1000 times as great as the portion measured.

From 1949 to 1955, as the sunspot cycle declined, a number of useful measurements of intensities near the short-wavelength limit of the X-ray spectrum were obtained. In the range from 5 to 20 A great variability was observed. Although the individual measurements should be considered as only rough values, the large differences detected were much greater than the experimental inaccuracies. At sunspot minimum no intensity was detectable through 13 mg/cm² of beryllium (8 A cutoff) and very little through 1.6 mg/cm² of aluminum (20 A cutoff).

In Table IX are listed measurements from eight rocket flights.[38] In only one case was any flare activity recorded within several hours of the flight time. Rocket V-2 No. 49 was flown 160 minutes after a class 1 flare. The measurements sample only a small portion of the spectral energy curve. Since the spectral sensitivities of the detectors are not independent of wavelength, it is necessary to know the shape of the solar emission curve to compute an intensity in ergs cm⁻² sec⁻¹ incident on top of the atmosphere. In deriving the numbers for the last two columns of Table IX it was assumed that the emission below 20 A is approximated by a 2×10^6 deg K Planckian distribution. The reason for this choice of temperature will become apparent as we proceed with the discussion of later measurements.

The last four flights listed occurred during the minimum phase of the solar cycle. Extremely little or no intensity was detected in these flights below 8 A, and only weak intensities were detected between 8 A and 20 A. The detailed picture of coronal activity on the day of each flight showed a strong correlation with the ratio of intensity of coronal green line (FeXIV) to red line (FeX). To estimate the average condition of the variable corona over the disk on the day of each flight, the intensities observed on the east limb of the sun over the 7 days preceding firing were averaged with the intensities for the 7 days after the experiment. When the average green-line intensity was compared with the red-line intensity the ratio was as high as 2.5 for A-9, A-10, and Viking 9, but it dropped to about 0.5 during the A-14, A-15, A-16, and A-34 flights. Throughout the 11-year cycle the red-line intensity is known to be fairly constant. The coronal variation lies almost entirely in the green-line emission, which therefore appears to be a good index of X-ray emission below 20 A.

In 1953 the first measurements were made of longer-wavelength portions of the X-ray spectrum.[39] Table X summarizes the results obtained in two Aerobee flights. Rows 1, 2, and 3 describe the characteristics of the detectors. Again, to estimate the total intensity of solar X-ray emission from the counting rate data it is necessary to know the shape of the solar X-ray

TABLE IX

Solar X-Ray Emission as Measured by Photon Counters with Aluminum and Beryllium Windows

Rocket	Launching date	Window material and surface density (mg cm^{-2})	Above-atmosphere responses of photon counters with:		Intensity[a] below 8 A (erg cm^{-2} sec^{-1})	Intensity[a] 8 to 20 A (erg cm^{-2} sec^{-1})
			Be window (counts cm^{-2} sec^{-1})	Al window (counts cm^{-2} sec^{-1})		
V-2 No. 49	9/29/49	Be, 13	1.0×10^4		0.0015	
A-9	5/1/52	Be, 47	495		0.0017	
A-10	5/5/52	Be, 47	< 125		< 0.0005	
Viking 9	12/15/52	Be, 13	$< 1.5 \times 10^{3b}$		< 0.0006	
		Al, 1.59		2.9×10^{6b}		0.2
A-14	11/15/53	Be, 13	< 40		$< 6.7 \times 10^{-6}$	
		Al, 1.59		$< 3 \times 10^{4b}$		< 0.0015
A-15	11/25/53	Be, 13	332		2.9×10^{-6}	
		Al, 1.59		$< 2.6 \times 10^{4b}$		< 0.0013
A-16	12/1/53	Al, 1.59		4.5×10^4		0.0004
A-34	10/18/55	Al, 1.59		1.4×10^5		0.0012

[a] A 2×10^6 deg K gray-body emission curve is assumed for the sun. The spectrum is normalized to give the experimentally observed counting rates. The last two columns show the intensity of the normalized emission curve that falls within the indicated spectral limits.
[b] These counters were filled with helium plus quench agent. Other counters were filled with Ne + quench agent. The Be window counters using He have about one-twentieth the sensitivity of the Ne counters. The Al window counters using He have about one-fifth the sensitivity of the Ne counters.

TABLE X

Conversion of Counting Rates to X-Ray Intensities

Aerobee Rocket:	NRL 18	NRL 16	NRL 16	NRL 14
(1) Tube window	Aluminum	Mylar	Glyptal	Glyptal
(2) Limits of spectral response (A)	8–20	44–60	44–100	44–100
(3) Peak quantum yield of counter	60 %	9 %	44 %	44 %
(4) Counts^a cm^{-2} sec^{-1}	4.5×10^4	2.8×10^6	4.9×10^7	5.9×10^7
(5) Erg cm^{-2} sec^{-1} within limits of spectral response:				
7×10^5 deg K	0.00074	0.023	0.053	0.064
1×10^6	0.00069	0.021	0.042	0.051
2×10^6	0.00039	0.014	0.029	0.035
(6) Erg cm^{-2} sec^{-1} in total X-ray spectrum:				
7×10^5 deg K	0.094	0.099	0.10	0.12
1×10^6	0.011	0.11	0.12	0.14
2×10^6	0.00085	0.24	0.29	0.35

^{a} Extrapolated to top of atmosphere.

spectrum. In row 5, three temperatures were chosen as a basis for calculating intensities within the wavelength sensitivity bands of the detectors. To each temperature there corresponds a black-body emission curve, and the total intensity was adjusted to give the observed counting rate for each detector. The effect of varying the temperature from 7×10^5 to 10^6 deg K is fairly small in all three wavelength bands. If, however, as in row 6, the intensity for the entire spectrum is computed from the individual responses, the result is strongly temperature-dependent for the spectrum below 20 A, and only moderately affected at longer wavelengths. This, of course, is to be expected if one is dealing with a black-body curve. On the short-wavelength side of the maximum, the emission falls off steeply, whereas the decline is much more gradual toward longer wavelengths. Row 6 shows that a single temperature of 7×10^5 deg K gives a distribution that best fits all three detectors with a total intensity of about 0.1 erg cm^{-2} sec^{-1}. The solar spectrum can be approximated by a gray body with an emissivity of 4×10^{-16} at that temperature. It is interesting to note that, in the 2-week interval between the launchings of Aerobees 14 and 16, the intensity below 20 A varied by more than 400 %, yet the estimated total intensity remained constant within about 20 %.

The photon counters used in rocket experiments thus far have been called narrow-band detectors, but it is important to achieve still finer wavelength discrimination. It is, in fact, possible to extract more spectral detail from the rocket measurements within the band spreads of the detectors, if we study the variation of X-ray attenuation with altitude. The transmission of a parallel beam of monochromatic X-rays varies logarithmically with the total air mass per column of unit cross section (see § 4.3.1). As the rocket rises, the air mass between the detectors and the sun decreases, and the X-ray intensity increases until the rocket is above the absorbing atmosphere. Because the absorption coefficient of air in the wavelength range from 8 to 100 A varies sharply, as shown in Fig. 17, the X-ray attenuation measured in the upper air can be used to analyze the wavelengths of the incident X-rays, provided the atmospheric density is known. Alternatively, if we know the wavelength we can derive the air mass between any two levels and thereby the density. The problem is complicated by the fact that the photon counters have spectral responses varying over wavelength spans of 8 to 20 A, 44 to 60 A, and 44 to 100 A within which the absorption coefficients also change markedly. The response of any X-ray detector is determined by the product of its yield curve, which is known (Figs. 10 and 11), and the spectral emission curve of the solar corona, which is temperature-dependent. The purpose of the following analysis is to show how semiquantitative information about this temperature dependence can be derived from the X-ray transmission data.

If the solar spectrum were characterized by a gray body at a temperature of 5×10^5 deg K, the wavelength of maximum emission, λ_{max}, would be 58 A. By assigning the intensity per unit wavelength interval, $I_\lambda d\lambda$, the value unity at 58 A, the intensities at 44, 20, and 8 A are 0.82, 0.017, and

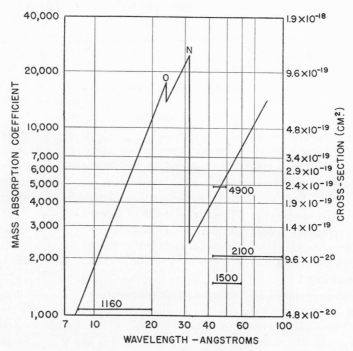

FIG. 17. X-ray mass absorption coefficients and cross sections of air. The detectors used in the rocket experiments (Figs. 10 and 11) covered band widths indicated by the lengths of the horizontal bars. Above each bar is indicated an apparent mass absorption coefficient computed from the measured X-ray transmission and adopting densities based on the Rocket Panel atmosphere. The coefficients computed for each of the three detectors are smaller by a factor of 2 or 3 than the correct values. A laboratory measurement of air absorption at 44 A, indicated by the short bar, was made with the same photon counter used in the rocket flight and yielded the correct absorption coefficient. From these results it was concluded that Rocket Panel densities were two to three times as great as true densities in the 100 to 130-km region. At higher altitudes (see Fig. 32) the discrepancies disappeared. From E. T. Byram, T. A. Chubb, and H. Friedman, *J. Geophys. Res.* **61**, 251 (1956).

less than 3×10^{-7}, respectively. Consider now the response of a photon counter with aluminum window (8 to 20 A) to such a spectrum. Virtually all the response would be concentrated near the 20-A boundary of the spectral yield band (Fig. 11). If the source temperature were 10^6 deg K, λ_{max} would be 29 A, and the intensities would be in the ratio 0.7 : 1.0 : 0.69 : 0.0014 at

44, 29, 20, and 8 A. At 2×10^6 deg K, the ratio would be 0.13 : 1.0 : 0.8 : 0.35 at 44, 14.5, 20, and 8 A. The effect of increasing temperature is to shift the short-wavelength limit of emission in the 8- to 20-A band from 20 A toward 8 A. This increase of short-wavelength emission, combined with the almost sawtooth yield curve (Fig. 11), shifts the bulk of the detector response toward the 8-A limit at the higher temperatures.

Reference to Fig. 17 shows that the absorption coefficient for air decreases by about a factor of 10 from 20 to 8 A. If the observed X-ray attenuation were attributed entirely to 20-A X-rays, the apparent air density would be ten times as great as if the attenuation were entirely due to 8-A X-rays. In Fig. 18 is plotted the apparent air density derived from X-ray attenuation measurements within the 8- to 20-A band (NRL Aerobee 16) for assumed source temperatures of 7×10^5, 10^6, and 2×10^6 deg K. The temperature of 2×10^6 deg K yields a density curve in best agreement with the results of measurements in the 44- to 60-A and 44- to 100-A bands. At these longer wavelengths the slope of a black-body curve is relatively insensitive to temperature, and the density determination is only mildly affected by varying the temperature. The curves deduced from the Mylar and Glyptal photon counters should therefore be representative of the true densities. The curve marked Rocket Panel is included in Fig. 18 for comparison with X-ray density data and is higher by a factor of 2 to 3. This discrepancy is discussed in § 4.7.

We had concluded above that a single temperature of 7×10^5 deg K and a total emission of 0.1 erg cm^{-2} sec^{-1} came closest to matching the responses of all three photon counters. The atmospheric attenuation data require, however, that the 8- to 20-A band be produced by a source at a temperature of $(1.5$ to $2) \times 10^6$ deg K. The X-ray flux at 2×10^6 deg K needed to supply the observed counting rate of the aluminum-window photon counter would enhance the intensity from 20 to 100 A by less than 1 %. The source would appear to be restricted to an area of less than 1 % of the disk in order for the contribution to the counting rates at the longer wavelengths to be less than 1 %. This is consistent with our ideas of the areas of coronal condensations. If at the same time the radiation supplying the counting rates at 44 to 60 A were coming from coronal regions at a temperature closer to 5×10^5 deg K, the short-wavelength contribution below 20 A would be negligible. This is the condition observed most often during the period of solar sunspot minimum when the frequency of coronal condensations is also minimum.

From the above analysis we may conclude that the rocket data support a picture of localized hot condensations of transient character spread over a base of cooler coronal gas covering the entire disk. Figure 19 attempts to summarize the rocket information on the spectrum of the sun. The stable coronal emission is represented by the unshaded areas under the curves for

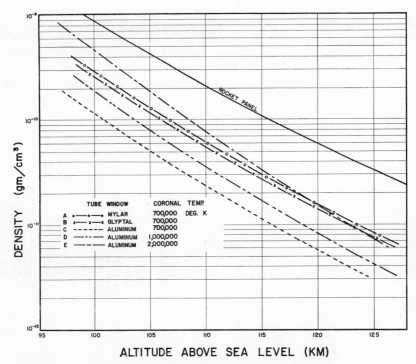

ALTITUDE ABOVE SEA LEVEL (KM)

FIG. 18. Air densities computed from X-ray transmission. Since the X-ray absorption coefficient varies by a factor of 10 from 8 to 20 A, the atmospheric attenuation measured by the Al window counter is very sensitive to the distribution of solar radiation within its band-width. At a coronal temperature of 700,000°K, the spectrum barely penetrates the long-wavelength boundary of spectral sensitivity at 20 A, and the photon counter responds primarily to wavelengths close to 20 A. At a temperature of 2×10^6 deg K the short-wavelength limit of the spectrum extends beyond the 8-A short-wavelength limit of the photon counter response. The sawtooth yield curve (Fig. 11) then emphasizes the response to radiation near 8 A. As a result, the effective X-ray absorption coefficient is much smaller for the higher-temperature spectrum, and the absorbing atmosphere appears more dense. In the 44- to 60-A and 44- to 100-A bands the shape of a black-body emission curve is comparatively insensitive to temperature in the range above 500,000°K, so that densities derived from attenuation of solar X-rays at these wavelengths should be almost independent of coronal temperature. To match the long-wavelength density results it appears necessary to ascribe a (1.5 to 2) $\times 10^6$ deg K temperature to the 8- to 20-A region. The curve marked Rocket Panel is two to three times as high as the soft X-ray densities. Recent rocket measurements with pressure gages support the X-ray density data.

the two extremes of measurements made thus far. A-43 was an Aerobee rocket launched in November, 1957, when the ratio of green- to red-line intensity was as high as any time in the past 10 years. A-16 was launched during a very quiet phase of coronal activity. The unshaded areas correspond to half-million-degree temperatures with total intensities as indicated, 1.0 and 0.13 erg cm^{-2} sec^{-1}. The shaded areas of the curves represent contributions of coronal condensations at temperatures closer to 2×10^6 deg K. In the case of A-16, the shaded portion amounted to 0.001 erg cm^{-2} sec^{-1}, or less than a hundredth of the total flux. The area labeled D-8 represents the X-ray flux from a small flare. This measurement will be discussed in § 4.5 on solar flares.

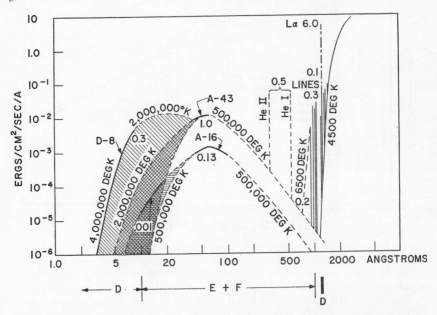

Fig. 19. Solar spectrum from rocket measurements. Solid-line portions of curves are derived from measurements. Dashed curves are extrapolations. X-ray spectrum is represented as 500,000°K gray body for two different total intensities corresponding to NRL Aerobees 16 and 43. Shaded areas represent short-wavelength X-rays originating in hot coronal condensations. D-8 is data obtained by Rockoon during a class 1 flare. Total flux under each curve is indicated: D-8, 0.3 erg cm^{-2} sec^{-1}; A-43, 1.0 erg cm^{-2} sec^{-1}; A-16, 0.13 erg cm^{-2} sec^{-1}. Measured intensity of Lyman-α line has varied from 0.1 to 6.0 ergs cm^{-2} sec^{-1} over the past 7 years. Lines in the neighbourhood of Lyman-α were obtained from spectrogram of Tousey et al. Helium resonance lines are estimated for purposes of ionosphere calculation. Effective ionosphere regions of absorption are indicated along abscissa.

4.2.3.4 *Solar Images in Ultraviolet and X-Rays*

Correlations between visible forms of solar activity and ionospheric behavior are discussed in § 4.1.4. From the appearance of calcium and hydrogen plages and patches of coronal green line emission, inferences may be drawn about the intensities of ultraviolet and X-ray emissions. It is most

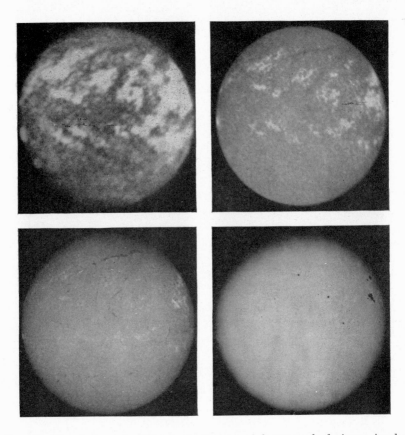

FIG. 19A. The photograph of the sun in the upper left was made duringan Aerobee flight on March 13, 1959, in the light of the ultraviolet Lyman-α line. The other three photographs were made at the same time from the ground. In the upper right is a calcium K line photograph made at the McMath-Hulbert Observatory. In the lower left, is a photograph made in the hydrogen-α line at the Naval Research Laboratory. The photograph in the lower right-hand corner was made in white light at the United States Naval Observatory. The optical system of the camera with which the rocket picture was made consisted of two concave replica gratings of 40 cm radius of curvature and 600 lines per mm. The surfaces of the gratings were coated with special thin films to give high reflection for the Lyman-α radiation. The first grating directed the first order Lyman-α image of the sun through a small aperture placed in the normal slit position. This grating was distorted into a toroidal shape to compensate for the total astigmatism of the system. The second grating was also used in the first order and was placed so as to enlarge the first grating image by a factor of 2. This resulted in a final stigmatic image of the solar disc of 3.6 mm diameter. The aperture of the solar camera was F/20 and the resolution was about ½ minute of arc. Transmittance of the system for Lyman-α radiation was 11%. Exposure time was 1/50 sec.

[To face page 177

important, however, to develop the means of comparing directly the distribution of ionizing sources of radiation on the sun with visible phenomena. What is needed are photographs of the sun in Lyman-α, the helium resonance lines, X-rays and other short wavelengths. However, the familiar techniques of photography in visible light are not at all applicable to photographing the sun in short wave lengths. On March 13, 1959, an unusually fine photograph of the sun was made in the light of Lyman-α. The camera with which this picture was produced was developed at the U. S. Naval Research Laboratory, by J. D. Purcell, D. Packer and R. Tousey. Since this ultraviolet light is strongly absorbed by all known optical materials, lenses could not be used and the entire camera had to be constructed with mirrors. These were not ordinary mirrors, however, but were diffraction gratings, parabolic mirror surfaces ruled with 15,000 lines to the inch. The rulings caused the intense visible light from the sun to be thrown out of the camera, leaving only the monochromatic Lyman-α radiation to form the solar image.

In Fig. 19A the rocket picture of the sun in Lyman-α is compared with simultaneous photos from the ground in CaK, Hα and white light. Within the limit of resolution of the Lyman-α picture, about ½ minute of arc, there is almost perfect correlation with every feature of the calcium plage picture. It is well known that the calcium plages tend to disappear at minimum of the eleven years solar cycle and cover a maximum area of the solar disc at the peak of the cycle. Densitometry of the Lyman-α picture showed that about 80 % of the intensity came from the plages and only 20 % from the background. If one assumes that the background is a stable feature of the emission, then the solar cycle variation of Lyman-α ought to be at least five to one.

The success achieved in photographing the sun in Lyman-α points the way to the attainment of photographs in other ultraviolet wave lengths, most important of which is the He-II resonance line at 304 A. From the point of view of routine observations of solar weather, a satellite vehicle and telemetered picture information are desirable. A television picture can be obtained by employing a telescopic mirror with a narrow band photodetector at its focus; by wobbling the mirror so as to produce a faster scan the photodetector can be made to transmit the solar image to ground.

Recording an X-ray image of the sun presents much greater difficulties. It is not practical to focus an X-ray image with a mirror. A pinhole camera should work, except for the length of exposure required, which has been beyond the scope of rocket experiments attempted thus far. However, a crude picture of the sun can be reconstructed from a sequence of measurements made during the course of a solar eclipse. Such an experiment was carried out by T. A. Chubb, R. W. Kreplin, J. C. Lindsay, and H. Friedman of the U.S. Naval Research Laboratory on the occasion of the eclipse of

12

October 12, 1958 in the South Pacific. As the moon crossed the face of the
sun, five rockets were launched in sequence; two passed through the eclipse
shadow during totality. A quantitative analysis of the data is still incomplete
at the time of this writing, but certain qualitative features are clear. At
totality the flux of Lyman-α was reduced to 0.05 % of the uneclipsed flux,
but the X-ray flux in the range 44 to 60 A did not fall below 15 %. Measurements on comparable areas of east and west limb crescents showed strong
limb brightening giving the X-ray sun the appearance of a doughnut; dark
in the center, bright at the rim, and somewhat larger than the visible disc.
The large residual flux of ionizing X-rays at totality is capable of providing
the residual E-region ionization always observed in ionospheric sounding
experiments conducted during eclipses over the past twenty years.

4.3 Interaction of Solar Radiation with the Atmosphere

In deriving a model of the production of the ionosphere, we are concerned
principally with the ionization of the major constituents of the atmosphere,
both molecular and atomic oxygen and nitrogen, and one trace constituent,
nitric oxide. The effective ionizing radiations are confined to the wavelength
range below 1300 A. The dissociation of molecular oxygen by the broad
spectrum of radiation below 2000 A plays a very important role, however,
in determining the altitude distribution of the absorbing constituents and
the nature of the recombination processes in the F region. It is therefore
essential to study both the distribution of solar radiation and the absorption
spectrum of the atmosphere for the entire spectral range from 2000 A to
X-rays as short as 1 A.

4.3.1 *Optical Absorption in Gases*

The attenuation of a parallel beam of radiation in a homogeneous gaseous
atmosphere is described by Lambert's law, which states that the intensity,
I, is diminished by the same fractional amount in equal successive increments
of path. This relationship is expressed by

$$- \Delta I = I \mu \, \Delta x \tag{4.2}$$

where ΔI is the change in intensity of the incident beam, I, after traversing
a path Δx, and μ is a constant of proportionality characteristic of the medium.
Integrating equation (4.2) gives the familiar exponential absorption law:

$$I = I_0 e^{-\mu x} \tag{4.3}$$

where I is the emergent beam intensity, and I_0 is the incident intensity.
If the path length, x, expressed in centimeters, is reduced to normal condi-

tions of temperature and pressure (0°C and 760 mm Hg, indicated by NTP) the absorption coefficient, μ, is in units of reciprocal centimeters. The ratio I/I_0 is called the transmission, T, and is given by

$$\log_e T = -\mu x. \tag{4.4}$$

Beer's law stated that the proportionality between μ and the concentration of absorber is independent of temperature and pressure. At NTP we have

$$\mu = \sigma N \tag{4.5}$$

where N is Loschmidt's number, 2.687×10^{19} molecules cm^{-3}. The proportionality constant, σ, has the dimensions of square centimeters and is called the absorption cross section. It represents the effective target area which one molecule presents to the beam of radiation.

Cross sections may be expressed as total absorption cross sections or related to specific processes. The absorption of solar radiation by atmospheric gases may follow a number of processes such as:

1. Continuous absorption due to direct ionization into a continuum.
2. Continuous absorption due to dissociation.
3. Dissociative ionization into an ion and an atom.
4. Resonance transitions giving sharp atomic absorption lines or molecular bands.
5. Preionization, or excitation to upper states of molecules which are close to an ionization continuum. (This process is characterized by a diffuseness of the structure in molecular bands.)
6. Predissociation, or excitation to molecular states adjacent to a dissociation continuum. (The absorption is characterized by a diffuse appearance with almost complete washing-out of the band structure.)

Photoionization efficiency is the ratio of the photoionization cross section to the total absorption cross section.

In treating the absorption or emission of radiation in a gaseous atmosphere it is convenient to use the concept of optical depth as a measurement of the attenuation between a reference level and a point outside the atmosphere. The optical depth, τ_h, is defined by

$$\tau_h = \int_h^\infty \mu \, dh \tag{4.6}$$

where τ_h refers to the depth at a point h within the atmosphere, and dh is directed inward from outside. Unit optical depth occurs where the number of molecules per square centimeter column equals the reciprocal of the molecular cross section.

4.3.1.1 *Absorption by Oxygen*

Molecular oxygen has a broad dissociation continuum associated with the Schumann-Runge bands. The discrete bands begin at 2026 A with a small absorption cross section, 10^{-23} cm². At 1759 A, the convergence limit of the bands, the cross section reaches 5×10^{-19} cm². Between the discrete bands oxygen is relatively transparent, and solar radiation penetrates well below the ionosphere. From 1759 A, the absorption is continuous and very strong, leading to dissociation according to

$$O_2(^3\textstyle\sum_g^-) + h\nu \rightarrow O(^3P) + O(^1D). \tag{4.7}$$

The cross section exhibits a broad maximum with a peak at 1450 A (Fig. 20) and reaches half-value at 1567 A and 1370 A on either side. Ditchburn and

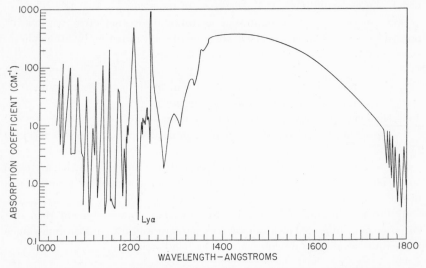

FIG. 20. Absorption coefficients of O_2 in the far ultraviolet. After K. Watanabe, M. Zelikoff, and C. Y. Inn, AFCRC Technical Report No. 52–53, Geophysical Research Papers No. 21 (1953).

Heddle[40] find the maximum value of σ to be 18.1×10^{-18} cm², whereas Watanabe and Marmo[41] find a somewhat lower maximum cross section, 14.4×10^{-18} cm². The high absorption cross section means that a layer of oxygen, 0.002 cm (NTP) in thickness, will attenuate solar radiation to e^{-1}.

The region between 1300 and 1040 A is of especial interest because it includes the hydrogen Lyman-α line (1215.7 A). Over this range, narrow transparent windows, in which σ falls to less than 4×10^{-19} cm², separate bands in which σ rises to more than 4×10^{-17} cm². The absorption region about the Lyman-α line has been studied in detail by Ditchburn *et al.*[42] and by Po Lee.[43] The latter's results are shown in Fig. 21. At the center of the

Lyman-α line, σ is 8.5×10^{-21} cm². The transmission window is so narrow that it would strongly filter the wings of a broad solar Lyman-α line as the depth of penetration increased. This effect has been used in conjunction with rocket measurements of Lyman-α intensity versus height to set a limit of less than 1 A on the width of the solar line.[42]

Watanabe et al.[44] investigated the absorption of Lyman-β (1025.7 A) by O_2 and found $\sigma = 1.54 \times 10^{-18}$ cm² with a photoionization efficiency of

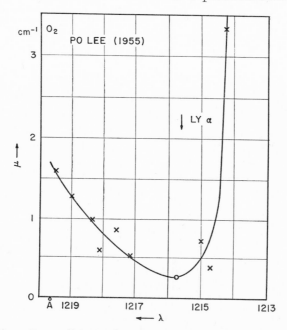

Fig. 21. Absorption coefficients of molecular oxygen in the vicinity of the Lyman-α line. The smooth curve is drawn through points representing experimental measurements by Po Lee, J. Opt. Soc. Amer. **45**, 703 (1955).

58 %. The first ionization potential of O_2 fell at 12.08 ± 0.01 ev, corresponding to a wavelength of 1027 A. It follows, therefore, that Lyman-β can efficiently ionize molecular oxygen.

The first ionization limit marks the beginning of the second absorption continuum of O_2 in which σ reaches a maximum of about 3.7×10^{-18} cm² near the beginning of the Lyman continuum according to Po Lee.[43] Toward shorter wavelengths he found a decreasing absorption to 850 A, where a new region of continuous absorption set in. The general shape of the continuous absorption spectrum is shown in Fig. 22, after Po Lee. Superimposed on the continuum between 1027 and 850 A are many diffuse bands in which the absorption cross section reaches values an order of magnitude greater

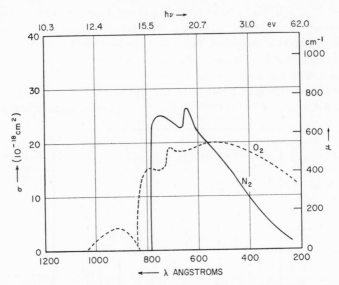

FIG. 22. Absorption continua of O_2 and N_2 below 1000 A. From Po Lee, *J. Opt. Soc. Amer.* **45**, 703 (1955).

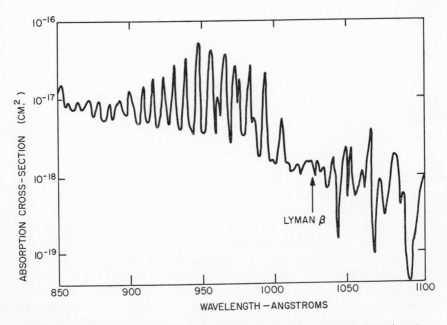

FIG. 23. Absorption continuum of O_2 and Hopfield bands in 850- to 1100-A region. From K. Watanabe, F. Marmo, and J. Pressman, *J. Geophys. Res.* **60**, 513 (1955).

than in the continuum, indicating strong preionization. Figure 23, after Watanabe *et al.*, shows this portion of the spectrum in detail. The unusual difficulties involved in accomplishing such absorption measurements are responsible for the minor discrepancies between results obtained by the various experimenters.

The region between 850 and 740 A is marked by strong resonance bands superimposed on the continuous absorption. The main absorption continuum

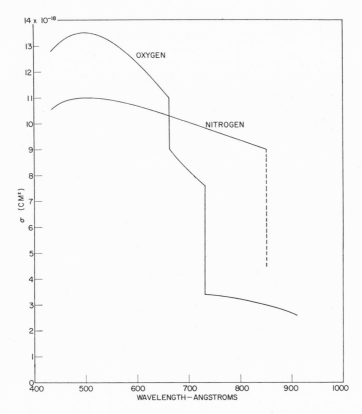

Fig. 24. Theoretical absorption cross sections of atomic oxygen and nitrogen above the first ionization potentials in the extreme ultraviolet. From D. R. Bates and M. J. Seaton, *Proc. Phys. Soc.* **63,** 129 (1950).

below 740 A reaches a maximum cross section of 2.2×10^{-17} cm^2 at 510 A. This may be almost a pure ionization continuum. Here, too, there are observed many resonance bands of diffuse appearance. In most of these bands the cross section does not exceed 4×10^{-17} cm^2, although there are a few that reach 6×10^{-17} cm^2.

The ionization threshold for atomic oxygen is 910 A (13.61 ev). Theoretical estimates[45] of the absorption coefficient must be used, since no experimental values are available. As shown in Fig. 24, the computed cross section varies from 2.6×10^{-18} cm^2 to 3.4×10^{-18} cm^2 between 910 and 732 A. At the second ionization limit, 732 A, the cross section jumps to 7.6×10^{-18} cm^2 and increases steadily to 9×10^{-18} cm^2 at 663 A. At the latter wavelength, σ jumps again to 1.1×10^{-17} cm^2 and reaches a maximum of 1.35×10^{-17} cm^2 near 500 A.

4.3.1.2 *Absorption by Nitrogen*

Above 1200 A, no detectable absorption has been found in nitrogen. It can be safely assumed that the absorption coefficient must be less than 10^{-3} cm^{-1}, or that σ is less than 10^{-22} cm^2. Beginning near 1200 A, Weissler *et al.*[46] found band absorption. From 1040 to 910 A the cross sections are less than 4×10^{-20} cm^2 between the bands. Worley[47] and Tanaka[48] showed that the resonance bands below 1040 A could be grouped into Rydberg series converging on two ionization limits at 796 A (14.46 ev) and 661 A (18.7 ev). This accounts for the ionization continuum below 800 A, where the photoionization efficiency rapidly approaches 100 %. The maximum cross section in the continuum is 2.4×10^{-17} cm^2 at 750 A. In the strongest resonance band σ reaches 10^{-16} cm^2 but does not exceed 3×10^{-17} cm^2 in most of the bands.

The first ionization threshold of atomic nitrogen falls at 852 A (14.55 ev), and the theoretical cross section[45] is 9×10^{-18} cm^2. A maximum σ of 1.1×10^{-17} cm^2 is reached at 500 A and then decreases continuously with wavelength. Between 910 and 852 A, nitrogen in either molecular or atomic form is transparent to the Lyman continuum.

4.3.1.3 *Nitric Oxide*

Among the molecules present as trace constituents above 70 km, nitric oxide can be ionized by Lyman-α. Its photoionization threshold[49] is 9.2 ev, or 1345 A. At shorter wavelengths more than 80 % of the absorption is due to photoionization,[34] with a cross section of about 2×10^{-18} cm^2.

4.3.1.4 *X-Ray Absorption in Air*

In the wavelength region below 200 A, absorption involves inner shell electrons and therefore is characteristically atomic. The absorption coefficient becomes a function of density alone and does not depend on molecular association. Figure 17 is a plot of the mass absorption coefficient of air (80 % nitrogen, 20 % oxygen) from 7 to 100 A. The data of Victoreen[50] were used on the short-wavelength side of the K edges. Jonsson's[51] universal absorption curve was fitted to pass through Allen's[52] experimental values at the longer wavelengths. The mass absorption coefficient multiplied by the density of air at NTP, 1.293×10^{-3} gm cm^{-3}, gives the linear absorption coefficient in units of cm^{-1}. At the K limit of nitrogen the cross section reaches 10^{-18} cm^2. The L_1 limits of oxygen and nitrogen fall at about 125 A and 175 A, respectively, and the computed X-ray cross section for air reaches its highest value, 9×10^{-18} cm^2, at 175 A.

At times of solar flares, solar X-rays have been observed in the 1- to 10-A range. Absorption coefficients for these shorter wavelengths are listed in Table XI.

TABLE XI

X-ray Absorption Coefficients and Cross Sections of Air (1 to 10 A)

Wavelength (A)	Mass absorption Coefficient (cm^2/gm)	Linear coefficient (cm^{-1})	Cross Section (cm^{-2})
1.0	2.9	3.7×10^{-3}	1.4×10^{-22}
1.2	4.8	6.3×10^{-3}	2.3×10^{-22}
1.5	9.1	1.2×10^{-2}	4.3×10^{-22}
2.0	21.0	2.7×10^{-2}	1.0×10^{-21}
2.5	40.0	5.2×10^{-2}	1.9×10^{-21}
3.0	67.8	8.8×10^{-2}	3.3×10^{-21}
4.0	136	0.18	6.7×10^{-21}
5.0	261	0.34	1.3×10^{-20}
6.0	443	0.57	2.1×10^{-20}
8.0	1009	1.3	4.8×10^{-20}
10.0	1893	2.4	8.9×10^{-20}

4.3.2 Atmospheric Transmission

Figure 25 is a plot of the penetration of solar radiation into the earth's atmosphere. Rocket Panel[53] density was used in constructing the curves. The combined effects of exponential absorption and an exponential atmosphere confine most of the absorption of monochromatic radiation to a range of approximately two scale heights. The X-ray spectrum from 10 to 100 A is largely absorbed in the altitude range of the E region. Except for a few resonance bands, the spectrum from 100 to 910 A is absorbed below 220 km, and the maximum rate of absorption is in the neighborhood of 180 km. The Lyman continuum can contribute to the E region by ionizing atomic and molecular oxygen between 910 and 850 A. At shorter wavelengths the absorption of Lyman continuum radiation rapidly moves to higher altitudes. The Lyman-β line should be absorbed near the base of the E region and may contribute substantially to the electron density by ionizing O_2. With

$\sigma = 1.54 \times 10^{-18}$ cm², unit optical depth occurs at a level where the total number of O_2 particles per square centimeter column is equal to the reciprocal of σ, or 6.5×10^{17} cm⁻². According to rocket measurements this level is somewhere between 100 and 105 km. In the lower ionosphere Lyman-α is effective in the D region but can be matched by X-rays of wavelength 2.5 A.

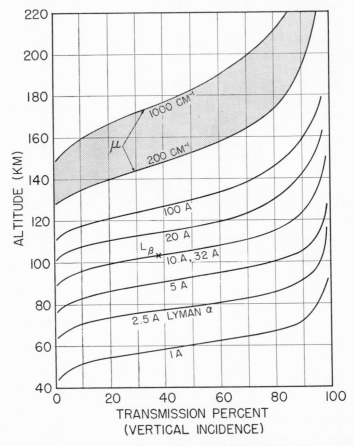

FIG. 25. Atmospheric transmission in X-ray and ultraviolet ionizing wavelengths when the sun is overhead. The limits of the shaded band are drawn for absorption coefficients of 200 and 1000 cm⁻¹. Almost the entire wavelength range of 200 to 850 A is included within these limits. The cross marked Lyman-β indicates unit optical depth in that wavelength.

4.4 Formation of the Ionosphere

Past literature is filled with speculative theories of the origin of the ionospheric layers. With only indirect experimentation on which to base their hypotheses it is not surprising that many theorists were grossly in error. Rocket data, although still incomplete and somewhat lacking in desired accuracy, provide a much more substantial basis for theory. Knowledge of the spectral distribution of the ionizing radiation derived from rockets has introduced some new considerations. For example, whereas most early theories of the E region were based exclusively on an ultraviolet radiation source, we must now deal with large amounts of X-ray energy as well as ultraviolet.

In his original theory, which still remains the basis for more refined calculations, Chapman[54] made a number of simplifying assumptions. By assuming a single absorption cross section, an isothermal atmosphere in gravitational equilibrium, and a recombination coefficient independent of height, he derived a characteristically shaped layer of ionization. From the foregoing discussions of the solar spectrum and atmospheric absorption it is clear that only in the D region is the condition of monochromatic radiation, and therefore a single absorption coefficient, fulfilled, and only for a quiet sun; the E region may receive contributions from a broad range of X-ray wavelengths, from the Lyman continuum, and from the Lyman-β line. At times of high sunspot activity and the accompanying coronal excitation, X-rays of shorter wavelength contribute ionization to the transition region between D and E. The F region may be ionized by the broad range of extreme ultraviolet between 200 and 850 A and receives an appreciable contribution from the X-ray spectrum.

Throughout the ionosphere, the recombination coefficient is a continuously variable function of altitude. Under equilibrium conditions the electron density, N_e, is related to the photoionization rate, q, and the recombination coefficient, α, by

$$q = \alpha N_e^2 \tag{4.8}$$

In the F region, the variation of loss process with height plays a major role in modifying the electron density distribution.[55] The recombination coefficient depends directly on the percentage dissociation of O_2, which is in turn controlled by the solar ultraviolet spectrum.

Whereas Chapman's original idea was to account for a number of discrete layers, each produced by a different monochromatic radiation, our present picture of the ionosphere is more nearly a continuum of ionization from the D region to the outermost limits of F. The various regions represent banks of ionization each merging into the next higher region without pronounced minima between them. This picture seems to be verified by direct measurements of electron density with rockets.[56]

Although much progress has been made toward determining the distribution of solar radiation, the atmospheric structure, and the nature of recombination processes, it is not yet possible to explain the production of the ionosphere in accurate detail. Each theory proposed thus far is based on assumptions which may introduce errors of considerable magnitude. A brief historical summary and two recent examples are given below to illustrate some of the problems involved.

4.4.1 *Theories of Ionization Processes*

There is general agreement that most of the observed electron density of the F region is attributable to ionization of atomic oxygen by the entire broad spectral range from 200 to 850 A. The processes in the lower ionosphere are much more complicated. In 1923, Vegard,[57] and later again in 1938, both Hulburt[58] and Vegard[59] independently suggested X-rays as the source of the E region. At about the same time, Wulf and Deming[60] proposed the ionization of molecular oxygen at the first ionization limit, 12.2 ev. Although most subsequent theories sought for an ultraviolet explanation, they ran into serious difficulties for the following reasons:

1. Penndorf's[61] theory of the dissociation of O_2 by a 6000°K sun was based on a photochemical equilibrium. The transition region centered near 90 km and was no more than 10 km in thickness. It followed that oxygen in the E region would be purely atomic.

2. The cross section of the ionization continuum was believed to be very small, less than 10^{-20} cm², which would place the ionization level in the D region.

Nicolet proposed a way out of the dilemma by : (1) showing theoretically that photochemical equilibrium did not exist and O_2 was only partially dissociated in E-region; (2) considering the possibility of preionization of O_2 in the Hopfield bands according to

$$O_2 + h\nu(< 12.0 \text{ ev}) \rightarrow O_2^* \rightarrow O_2^+ + e. \qquad (4.9)$$

He suggested that absorption cross sections in the Hopfield bands could be greater than 10^{-17} cm², which would place the ionization in the E region. No experimental evidence has been developed to support the preionization hypothesis.

In 1948, Hoyle and Bates[62] revived the X-ray hypothesis and suggested that a photon group centered at about 324 ev (38 A) would produce an E region with proper height distribution. Furthermore, such emission was consistent with solar theory. The following year positive evidence for an important solar X-ray flux was derived from a rocket experiment.[21] Various theories of the E region based on ionization by X-rays from 10 to 100 A quickly followed.

4.4.1.1 *Ionization by X-rays and Helium Resonance Lines*

Havens *et al.*[63] ascribed the formation of the E region in its entirety and an appreciable portion of the F region to X-rays. Their analysis is summarized here to illustrate the extent to which X-radiation may be effective. The X-ray spectrum was assigned 0.1 erg cm^{-2} sec^{-1} between 15 and 200 A, with the energy content divided equally on either side of 50 A. The energy distribution was adjusted to make the best fit both with rocket data and Elwert's[13] theoretical spectrum including the HeII continuum and the He resonance lines. The latter were assigned a combined intensity of 0.05 erg cm^{-2} sec^{-1}, and no other ultraviolet radiation was included. For the atmospheric structure they followed the Rocket Panel with some adjustments of density, O_2 dissociation, and temperature, to fit more recent rocket data.

At any altitude, the rate of ionization, q_λ, by radiation of wavelength λ is given by

$$q_\lambda = \sigma_\lambda n I_\lambda / x \qquad (4.10)$$

where σ_λ is the cross section of the absorbing constituent, n is its concentration, and I_λ is the radiation arriving at that level. The energy per ion pair, x, was taken to be 30 ev. At each level, I_λ was evaluated for all X-ray wavelengths and the helium resonance lines. Figure 26 shows the resulting ion production curve. A strong peak appears at 120 km due to X-rays, and a secondary peak at 160 km due to the helium lines. At higher altitudes the ionization is proportional to the particle density.

To obtain the electron density from the production curve requires that we know the recombination rate. Havens *et al.* considered three processes affecting the recombination rate:

1. Dissociative recombination:

$$e + O_2^+ \to O' + O'' \qquad \alpha = 3 \times 10^{-8} \, \text{cm}^3 \, \text{sec}^{-1}. \qquad (4.11)$$

2. Photorecombination:

$$e + O^+ \to O + h\nu \qquad \alpha = 1.5 \times 10^{-12} \, \text{cm}^3 \, \text{sec}^{-1}. \qquad (4.12)$$

3. Charge exchange:

$$O^+ + O_2 \to O_2^+ + O \qquad \sigma = 10^{-17} \, \text{cm}^2. \qquad (4.13)$$

Molecular nitrogen was treated as equivalent to molecular oxygen. To obtain an effective recombination coefficient versus altitude, it was assumed that X-rays ionized all constituents with equal efficiency. In the E region, the radiation is absorbed principally by the molecular species which combine at the rapid rate of dissociative recombination. At higher altitudes the atomic oxygen concentration soon exceeds that of molecular oxygen. A major portion of the radiation is then absorbed by N_2, which recombines rapid-ly, leaving the atomic oxygen ions to disappear by radiative recombination or by charge exchange with O_2. Only when O_2 and N_2 are completely dissociated does the recombination coefficient reach the minimum value of radiative recombination. The variation of effective recombination coefficient according to Havens *et al.* is shown in Fig. 26 together with the resultant electron density distributions.

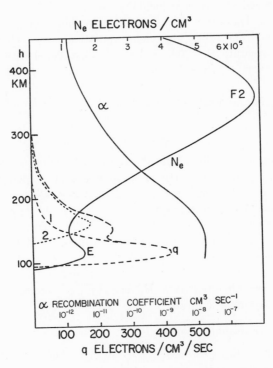

FIG. 26. The dashed curve, 1, is the ionization rate produced by the X-ray spectrum containing 0.1 erg cm^{-2} sec^{-1} between 10 and 100 A. Curve 2 is the ionization rate produced by the helium resonance lines containing 0.05 erg cm^{-2} sec^{-1}. Rocket Panel densities were used in the computations. The shape of the electron density curve in the F region is controlled primarily by the effective recombination coefficient, α.

In spite of the uncertainties in the parameters applied to the above theory the gross features are probably correct. Though the maximum rate of ion production occurs below 200 km, the decreasing rate of recombination shifts the electron density maximum to altitudes above 300 km. One of the weakest assumptions in the above treatment was the choice of 3×10^{-8} cm^3 sec^{-1} as the recombination coefficient for N_2. Laboratory measurements give

values in the range from 10^{-6} to 10^{-7} cm³ sec⁻¹. At these high rates of recombination, nitrogen molecules will absorb their fraction of the ionizing
radiation without contributing detectably to the equilibrium ionization,
which is then controlled almost entirely by the most slowly recombining
species of ion. In the E region, the higher recombination rate of N_2 would
have the effect of absorbing four-fifths of the X-ray flux without affecting
the electron density. At higher altitudes, where atomic oxygen becomes
the controlling ion, the calculation of Havens *et al.* would not be appreciably
affected by choice of a higher value of α for N_2; i.e., once the effective recombination coefficient falls below 10^{-9} cm³ sec⁻¹ it matters very little that
α for N_2 is 10^{-7} rather than 10^{-8} cm³ sec⁻¹.

Since only the helium resonance lines were introduced into the calculation,
other ultraviolet lines would be expected to affect the exact shape of the
ionization curve.* However, the limited range of cross sections for the
wavelengths from 200 to 850 A forces nearly all radiation in this interval
within the shaded band of atmospheric absorption shown in Fig. 25. The
total energy content is therefore more significant than the spectral distribution in its ionospheric effect. It is clear from the curves of Fig. 26 that the
recombination coefficient is the most important factor in shaping the F
region.

4.4.1.2 *Contributions of Lyman-β and the Lyman Continuum*

By 1955, it had become clear from the theoretical work of Nicolet and
Mange[33] and from rocket measurements[64] that the O_2 distribution departed
completely from photochemical equilibrium. Penndorf's[61] earlier theory of
the dissociation of molecular oxygen, based on a photochemical equilibrium,
had predicted complete dissociation below the E region. The rocket measurements showed instead that the percentage dissociation in the E region was
about 70 % and that O_2 persisted in important concentrations to much
higher altitudes. Watanabe *et al.*[44] renewed support for the ultraviolet
theory by their work on the absorption of O_2 and N_2 in the wavelength range
850 to 1100 A. They found the first ionization potential of O_2 to be 12.07 ev
rather than 12.2 ev and that Lyman-β ionized O_2 with an efficiency of the
order of 50 %. As Fig. 23 shows, the minimum cross section in the continuum
was found to vary from 10^{-18} cm² to 5×10^{-18} cm² between 1027 and 900 A,
about 100 times as great as had been thought previously. These new cross
sections moved the absorption of the O_2 continuum up to 95 to 105 km for
an overhead sun. All the strong bands in the same wavelength range were
pre-ionized with cross sections as great as 5×10^{-17} cm², thus putting the
maximum rate of absorption in these bands at 120 km.

* Rense's recent rocket spectrogram, referred to in § 4.2.1, shows the HeII line
at 304 A as the outstanding feature of the spectrum below Lyman-α.

Houston[65] attempted to incorporate the newer data in a theory of the lower ionosphere that included the contributions of X-rays, Lyman-α, Lyman-β, and the Lyman continuum. He used the values

$$I(10\text{--}200 \text{ A}) = 0.1 \text{ erg cm}^{-2} \text{ sec}^{-1}$$
$$I(1215.7 \text{ A}) = 0.2 \text{ erg cm}^{-2} \text{ sec}^{-1}$$
$$I(1024.7 \text{ A}) = 0.008 \text{ erg cm}^{-2} \text{ sec}^{-1}$$
$$I(850\text{--}912 \text{ A}) = 0.11 \text{ erg cm}^{-2} \text{ sec}^{-1}.$$

Houston also assigned a recombination coefficient of 10^{-6} cm^3 sec^{-1} to N_2 in the E region and thereby dissipated four-fifths of the X-ray flux in production of undetected ionization. The combined effect of all the various radiations is shown in Fig. 27. The D region is accounted for entirely by Lyman-α. The E region still receives its major contribution from X-rays, but the base of the E layer is sharpened and shows a "nose" due to Lyman-β. The Lyman continuum provides about one-fourth of the electron density at 120 km.

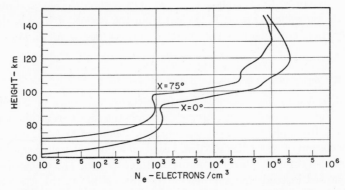

Fig. 27. Electron density in the lower ionosphere computed by Houston for two solar elevation angles, 0° and 75°. From R. E. Houston, Jr., Scientific Report No. 95, Pennsylvania State University, State College, 1957.

4.4.1.3 *The D Region*

The most acceptable process for ionization of the D region is the photo-ionization of nitric oxide:

$$NO + \text{Lyman-}\alpha \rightarrow NO^+ + e \qquad (4.14)$$

as was originally proposed by Nicolet.[66] Ultraviolet radiation of energy greater than 12 ev cannot penetrate to the D region. Since none of the major constituents can be ionized by less energetic quanta, various trace constituents must be considered. Although NO has not been detected experimentally in the D region, a concentration of less than a part per million would satisfy the ionization requirement. Such amounts of NO are theoretically justifiable.

4.4.1.4 *Summary*

Newer rocket data have become available since Havens *et al.* and Houston selected their radiation values. The Lyman-α intensity is about 6 ergs cm⁻² sec⁻¹ rather than 0.2 erg cm⁻² sec⁻¹, and X-ray intensities as high as 1.0 erg cm⁻² sec⁻¹ have been observed. Since the intensity adopted for Lyman-β was based on a comparison with Lyman-α in Tousey's spectrogram,[27] increasing the latter by a factor of 30 requires that Houston increase his estimate of Lyman-β by the same factor.

Kallmann[67] has shown that it is possible to adjust the radiation spectrum and the atmospheric parameters to produce detailed agreement with electron density distributions measured directly from rockets. In view of our uncertain knowledge of each of the parameters, it seems hardly justified at this time to seek for detailed agreement. In a qualitative way, however, we may conclude that the Bradbury hypothesis of the control of the F region by a loss process that decreases rapidly with altitude is strongly supported by rocket observations. X-rays must play a major role in ionizing the broad altitude range of the E region, and Lyman-β may be an important factor in shaping the base of the E layer.

4.5 Solar Flares

4.5.1 *Optical Characteristics of Flares*

A flare is a sudden, short-lived brightening of the solar surface in the neighborhood of a sunspot. Only on a few rare occasions have flares been seen in white light. Ordinarily the flare is undetectable unless viewed in monochromatic light with the aid of a Lyot filter or a spectrohelioscope. In the light of Hα (6563 A) the flare region may appear to increase almost tenfold in brightness. Within a matter of minutes from its inception, a large flare expands over a hundred million to a billion square miles of the disk and flashes to peak brightness. It then decays more slowly in half an hour to several hours, depending on its size.

All flares are observed in the plage regions around sunspots, and rarely does a flare occur more than 100,000 km from a sunspot. The greatest frequency of occurrence is associated with magnetically complex spot groups of the β and γ types. Small flares appear as simple bright circular patches with no filamentary structure, but intense flares appear to be irregular patterns of bright filaments of the order of 10^4 to 10^5 km in size. In addition to the bright Balmer lines of hydrogen and the lines of ionized calcium, the flare produces emission lines of HeI, FeII, and other metallic elements.

Flares are classified according to area covered as class 1, 2, or 3 in order of increasing size with the additional notation of $+$ or $-$ to indicate larger or

13

smaller than average in any class. Another index of flare size is the line width or central intensity of Hα. In an intense flare, the line width may grow from 2 to 20 A at the peak of the flash, and, at the same time, the central intensity of the line may increase to about twice the brightness of the adjoining continuum. Table XII lists the visual characteristics of the various classes of flares.[68] Classification 1 — refers to microflares, and the 3 + classification to flares producing remarkable terrestrial effects. The relative frequencies of occurrence are in the ratio of 0.72 : 0.25 : 0.03, for flares of importance 1, 2, and 3.

TABLE XII

Flare Characteristics

Class	Duration (min)		Area limits (10⁻⁶ visible disk)	Hα line width at max.
	Average	Range		
1 −	—	—	100	1.5 A
1	20	4–43	100–250	3.0 A
2	30	10–90	250–600	4.5 A
3	60	20–155	600–1200	8 A
3 +	180	50–430	1200	15 A

Visual studies of the flare structure[69, 70] reveal the following geometrical characteristics: (1) flares are flat structures extended parallel to the solar surface; (2) the thickness of the flare is three or four times the thickness of the chromosphere with the uppermost portions penetrating into the corona; and (3) flares are essentially stationary. These characteristics clearly differentiate flares from surges or eruptive prominences which rise high in the corona with velocities of hundreds of kilometers per second. The vertical motion in the growth of a flare rarely exceeds 10 km/sec.

4.5.1.2 Frequency of Flares

Strong statistical correlations exist between sunspots and flares. Waldemeier[71] gave the relationship between sunspot number, R, class of flare, and number of flares, F as follows:

$$F = 0.044R \text{ for class } 1$$
$$F = 0.015R \text{ for class } 2$$
$$F = 0.002R \text{ for class } 3$$

For $R = 100$, there were, on the average, six flares per day, one or two of which were class 2. An active spot group could produce as many as thirty to fifty flares during a single disk passage.

4.5.2 *Ionospheric Effects of Flares*

Simultaneously with the appearance of the visible flare, there occurs an increased ionization of the 60- to 100-km region of the ionosphere over the sunlit hemisphere. The variety of prompt ionospheric effects that stem from the enhanced ionization are referred to as sudden ionospheric disturbances, or SID. These effects may be listed as follows:

1. SWF, sudden short-wave fade-out. Radio transmission on 5 to 20 Mc/sec fades out as a result of enhanced D-region absorption.

2. SCNA, sudden cosmic noise absorption. Cosmic radio noise at 18 Mc/sec is strongly absorbed in passing through the D region.

3. SPA, sudden phase anomalies. Very long radio waves are reflected from a lowered ionospheric ceiling at the base of the D region.

4. SEA, sudden enhancement of atmospherics at 27 kc/sec. Increased signal strength results from enhanced reflectivity of the D region at oblique incidence.

5. Magnetic crochets. A prompt augmentation of the magnetic field is superimposed on the normal daily variation of the magnetic field resulting from the ionospheric current sheet.

When the sun is quiet, rocket measurements rarely show any X-ray penetration below 100 km. It is quite well established that the only ionizing radiation penetrating to the D region at all times is Lyman-α. Although it cannot ionize the major constituents of the atmosphere, it ionizes nitric oxide very efficiently. The flux of Lyman-α is so great that less than one part per million of NO is sufficient to produce the D-region ionization. With this background one is naturally inclined to seek an enhanced Lyman-α emission during flares as the source of the increased D-region ionization. Difficulties arise, however, in attempting to explain the SID phenomena associated with the lowest levels of the D-region on the basis of a Lyman-α flash. On the other hand, X-ray emission from the flare region has been experimentally observed, and the intensity and penetration are adequate to explain the ionospheric effects. It is, of course, possible that both Lyman-α and X-ray emission are enhanced during a flare and that the former is effective in the upper portion of the D region, whereas the latter supplies the lower level ionization.

4.5.2.1 *Enhancement of D-Region Ionization*

Consider the requirements imposed by the ionospheric effects. Mitra and Jones[72] attempted to explain the fade-out phenomenon as resulting from an over-all enhancement of D-region ionization by flare Lyman-α. The required increase in ionization was estimated from the time delays between maxima in the ionospheric disturbances (SWF, SEA, SPA) and the visible flare. According to Appleton[73] the relaxation time, τ, in an ionospheric region is given by

$$\tau = 1/2\alpha N \qquad (4.15)$$

where α is the recombination coefficient and N is the electron density. This relaxation effect introduces a sluggishness in the response of the ionosphere to the source of ionization. Mitra and Jones, assuming that α remains unaffected by the flare, deduced that

$$N_f/N_n = \tau_n/\tau_f \qquad (4.16)$$

at a given height, where subscripts n and f refer to normal and flare conditions. If, for example, τ_n is 21 minutes at 60 km and τ_f is 7 minutes for a class 2 flare, equation (4.16) gives $N_f/N_n = 3.0$. Following this analysis, Mitra computed electron enhancements of 2.5, 4.5, 7.0, and 9.4 for flares of 1, 2, 3, and 3 + importance. These values are consistent with the apparent increase in electron density derived from absorption measurements during a SWF by Appleton and Piggot.[74] The Lyman-α flux would need to increase by factors of 6, 20, 50, and 90, respectively. If the normal quiet sun intensity of Lyman-α is about 6 ergs cm^{-2} sec^{-1}, about 120 ergs cm^{-2} sec^{-1} would be required in a class 2 flare. Such an intensity seems high but perhaps is not impossible.

4.5.2.2 *Sudden Phase Anomalies* (See also § 9.11.2)

Sudden phase anomalies are much more difficult to explain on the basis of a Lyman-α source of ionization. The SPA measurements are made with very low-frequency radio waves (16 kc/sec) reflected from the base of the ionosphere, where the electron density is about 300 per cubic centimeter.[75] The phase difference between ground wave and ionosphere-reflected wave provides a measure of the height of the reflecting ceiling. With the onset of a flare, the phase changes rapidly, indicating a drop in reflecting height. The average change in reflecting height is about 4 km for most flares but may be as much as 16 km for the largest flares.

To produce the required electron density of 300 per cubic centimeter at the lower heights the flux of Lyman-α during the flare must increase to where the fraction penetrating to the lowered ceiling equals the intensity previously existing at the original ceiling. This requirement assumes that the nitric oxide particle density has the same scale height as the main atmosphere and that the recombination coefficient is directly proportional to the atmospheric pressure. According to Friedman and Chubb,[76] the changes in required Lyman-α flux for a range of phase heights are listed in Table XIII. If Lyman-α were the sole source of D-region ionization, the flux would need to increase by as much as 10^5 times the normal emission from the entire disk in order to explain changes in phase height as large as 15 km. Since the flare region is about one-thousandth the area of the disk, the flux from the flare region must increase by a factor of 10^8. It does not seem possible to justify such an increase by any known astrophysical mechanism.

TABLE XIII

Required Variation in Lyman-α during Flares

Height of D-layer base (km)	74.6	71.8	67.2	64.4	62.2	60.5
Lyman-α, % transmission[a]	25	10	1.0	0.1	0.01	0.001
Required increase in Lyman-α	1	2.5	25	2.5×10^2	2.5×10^3	2.5×10^4

[a] Absorption coefficient of Lyman-α in air was taken as 0.063 cm^{-1}.

X-rays of wavelength 2.5 A have the same absorption coefficient in air as Lyman-α; however, X-rays are several thousand times as efficient in ionizing the D region as Lyman-α. This is because X-rays ionize all constituents of the air, whereas Lyman-α can ionize only a trace constituent, nitric oxide. Virtually all the energy delivered by 6 ergs cm^{-2} sec^{-1} of Lyman-α is dissipated in dissociation of O_2. Approximately 10^{-3} erg cm^{-2} sec^{-1} of 2.5 A X-rays would be sufficient to produce the normal D region. Although X-rays of wavelength shorter than 6 A are rarely observed when the sun is quiet, recent rocket measurements detected wavelengths as short as 2 A and intensities as high as 10^{-2} erg cm^{-2} sec^{-1} in solar flares. Radiation of 2 A wavelength at 65 km would produce 300 electrons cm^{-3} if the intensity were only 10^{-5} erg cm^{-2} sec^{-1} ($\alpha = 5 \times 10^{-6}$ cm^3 sec^{-1}).

4.5.2.3 *Magnetic Crochets*

Magnetic crochets are observed only in conjunction with the largest flares (classes 3, 3 +) and only rarely during a class 2 flare. Yet, if we attribute the crochet to an augmentation of the normal daily current variation (S_q) the required increase in ionospheric conductivity is only a factor of 2. When a crochet occurs, its duration never exceeds that of the visible $H\alpha$ flare and is sometimes shorter. Whereas most SID phenomena exhibit time lags of 5 minutes or more, crochets lag only 2.5 minutes behind the $H\alpha$ maximum.[77] All these observations indicate that the ionization source of the crochet phenomenon may not occur in the same region of the ionosphere as the SWF, SCNA, and SPA.

If the crochet current flows in the E region at the same level as the normal S_q current system, it would be necessary for the flare radiation to increase the E-region ionization for a shorter duration than the D-region ionization. It is probably true that the enhancement of solar X-ray emission in a flare extends to the longer wavelengths from 10 to 100 A which are absorbed in the E region. Thermal excitation of the corona would be expected to persist longer at the longer wavelengths, however, so that it is difficult to understand the short duration of the crochet. Ellison[78] has suggested that the crochets may represent the establishment of an independent current system at a level below 70 km. This could be a region ionized only by the peak of the X-ray flash of a large flare.

4.5.3 Rocket Measurements during Flares

The unpredictability and short life of a flare make it difficult to obtain rocket measurements of the X-ray and Lyman-α radiations while it is in progress. A "push-button" type of rocketry and operation in areas where unscheduled firings are permissible are major requirements. In 1956, a number of attempts were made with the Rockoon system. Early each morning a small solid propellant rocket was lifted from the deck of a ship to a height of 80,000 feet by a large plastic helium-filled balloon. It would float at that altitude throughout the day until a flare was observed, at which time the experimenters could fire the rocket by means of a radio relay.

One rocket was successfully fired during a flare and gave positive evidence of X-ray emission.[39] Solar observatories classified the flare as something between class 1 and a subflare. Data were recorded between 10 and 12 minutes from the beginning of the flare, at which time the flare was rapidly fading but still visible in Hα emission. No radio fade-out was observed, and only a marginal indication of cosmic noise absorption.

The detectors in the rocket included an X-ray photon counter with beryllium window sensitive to a 1- to 8-A band, and an ion chamber sensitive to Lyman-α (1100 to 1350 A). The observed Lyman-α intensity was not significantly different from the normal quiet sun emission measured before and after the flare. The X-ray flux, however, extended to a short-wavelength limit of about 3 A and included 5×10^{-3} erg cm^{-2} sec^{-1} between 3 and 8 A. From the variation of X-ray intensity with altitude it was possible to deduce the shape of the X-ray spectrum. It could best be fitted to a thermal distribution characterized by a 1.3×10^6 deg K source for the wavelengths near 8 A and 3.2×10^6 deg K near 3 A. The X-ray emission is indicative of a strong intensification of the coronal excitation over the flare region. Since the X-ray emission was still strong, though Hα had almost returned to normal, it appears that the X-ray excitation may linger after the primary flare event has dissipated.

In 1957, as part of the IGY program, the U.S. Naval Research Laboratory continued its studies of flares with a ground-launched two-stage solid propellant rocket. Data were obtained on class 1 +, 2, and 3 flares. In each case strong X-ray emission was observed, but no evidence for large increases in Lyman-α. It is possible that Lyman-α could have flashed earlier in the flare process than the times of firings of the rockets. In each launching an attempt was made to time the rocket firing to coincide with the maximum phase of the flare, so that the first few minutes of flare development were always bypassed. The X-ray emission below 8 A exceeded 0.02 erg cm^{-2} sec^{-1} in the class 2 flare. In the class 3 flare, the maximum depth of penetration was 63.5 km. Table XIV summarizes the results obtained from four rockets.

TABLE XIV

X-ray Emission associated with Solar Flares

Rocket	Launching time Z	Class flare	X-ray penetration (km)	X-ray wavelength (A)	X-ray flux (erg cm^{-2} sec^{-1})
Rockoon NN5.31	7/20/56, 1217	1 ; no SWF	77	3–8	$5 \times 10^{--3}$
Nike-Deacon NN7.42F	8/20/57, 0949	1 + ; weak SWF	70	2.5–?	3×10^{-3}
Nike-Deacon NN7.45F	8/29/57, 1412	2 ; $\frac{1}{2}$ hr SWF	77	3–8	2×10^{-2}
Nike-Asp NN7.49F	9/18/57, 1054	3 ; 2 hr SWF	63.5	1.5–?	4×10^{-5} at 63.5 km 1.2×10^{-4} at 70 km

These rocket measurements can be understood in terms of intense heating of the coronal atmosphere above the flare. With reference to Fig. 28, reproduced from Elwert,[13] the effect of increasing the temperature of the coronal gas is to increase the degree of ionization of the various elements. At a million degrees, the M shells of all the lighter atoms are stripped of electrons, and the corresponding ionization potentials fall in the range of a few hundred electron volts. The X-ray emission associated with such an electron-ion plasma lies in the wavelength range from about 20 to 200 A. At 5 million degrees the L shell of iron is stripped, and even the K shells of the lighter elements up to oxygen are emptied, corresponding to ionization potentials as high as 1500 ev or a wavelength of 8 A. At temperatures above 10 million degrees even the comparatively heavy iron atoms lose all their electrons. The resulting recombination radiation would have a series limit of 1.4 A. Since the abundance of elements heavier than iron in the corona is negligibly small, thermal excitation of the corona should produce a short-wavelength emission limit near 1.4 A.

The observations of SPA tend to support the above picture of thermal excitation of X-ray emission. In connection with the largest flares the base of reflection may drop as much as 16 km. This distance is approximately the difference in penetration of the atmosphere by Lyman-α and by 1-A X-rays.

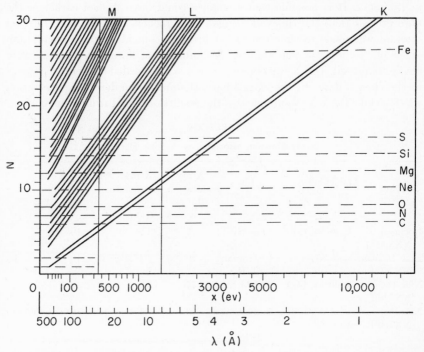

FIG. 28. Ionization potentials and corresponding wavelengths of series limit continua as a function of atomic number (Z) and degree of ionization. After G. Elwert, Z. Naturforsch. 7a, 202 (1952).

4.5.4 Balloon Measurements during a Flare

Peterson and Winckler[79] have reported the observation of a short burst of penetrating radiation during a balloon flight (10 gm/cm² depth) at Cuba (30° geomagnetic latitude). The burst began approximately half a minute before the reported visual observation of a class 2 flare and the beginning of a sudden ionospheric disturbance at 1305 UT on March 20, 1958. The balloon carried both a Geiger counter and a high-pressure ionization chamber. The duration of the burst could not have exceeded 18 seconds, which was the resolution time of the data output from the counter-scaler apparatus. On the basis of the relative responses of the Geiger counter and the ion chamber it is possible to discriminate between particles and X-rays or γ-rays. Peterson and Winckler identified the burst as a flash of 0.5-Mev γ-radiation.

Furthermore, they concluded that the radiation did not appear to be bremsstrahlung and suggested a possible origin in nuclear processes associated with production of the flare. With 0.5-Mev γ-rays assumed, the observed flux corresponded to 7.6×10^{-5} erg cm^{-2} sec^{-1}.

Severny[80] has developed a theory of flare production based on a magnetic pinch effect. His theory predicts a bremsstrahlung capable of producing maximum energies of 10 to 100 electron rest masses. Such a process could easily produce the γ-ray energy observed by Peterson and Winckler. Severny also points out the strengthening of the Balmer-α line of deuterium in flare spectra, indicating the possibility of neutron production.

4.5.5 Gamma-Radiation from outside the Atmosphere

In connection with some of the solar flare rocket experiments conducted by the U.S. Naval Research Laboratory, instrumentation was included to

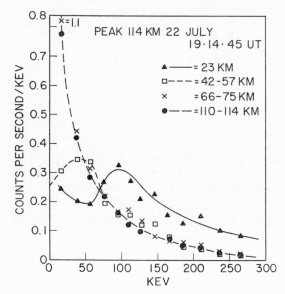

FIG. 29. Flux of γ-rays, 20 to 300 kev, measured by means of scintillation counter in the Rockoon. Although the detector was shielded to provide directional response, the intensity was so low that statistical accuracy was not adequate for directional definition. At 23 km, the response is due to cosmic-ray secondaries in atmosphere. Cosmic-ray albedo still predominates response at 42 to 57 km. Above 66 km the flux consists principally of soft component and shows no further change with altitude.

measure radiation in the energy range from 20 to 300 kev.[81] The detector was a scintillation counter consisting of a NaI–Th crystal, $\frac{3}{8}$ inch thick, cemented to an RCA 6199 photomultiplier tube. From telemetered amplitudes of individual pulses, the curves of Fig. 29 were obtained when the sun was quiet. Several attempts during solar flares were unsuccessful owing to instrumentation failures.

At 23 km the detector responded largely to cosmic-ray secondary radiation. With increasing altitude there was a progressive softening of the spectrum, indicating an incoming flux of quanta containing energies up to 50 kev. The total flux was so small that it was not possible to obtain directional information to indicate whether or not the sun was the source. A repeat of the experiment at night would identify the radiation with the sun if the flux should vanish. If it persists at night, it may be attributable to atmospheric bremsstrahlung from the Van Allen radiation belt or to a cosmic source.

Sputnik III was instrumented with a scintillation counter to search for a weak γ-radiation from the sun.[82] Although flares occurred on June 6, 1958, while the instrumentation was operational, no detectable intensity was observed. Neither was it possible to detect any day-night effect. Table XV indicates the upper limits set by these negative results.

TABLE XV
Upper Limits of Extraterrestrial γ-Ray Fluxes

Photon energy (kev)	Energy flux (erg cm^{-2} sec^{-1}) is less than:
10	1
30	10^{-4}
50	10^{-6}

Referring again to Fig 29, we find that the soft radiation at high altitudes amounted to between 10^{-6} and 10^{-7} erg cm^{-2} sec^{-1}, which is less than the lower limit detectable in the Sputnik III experiment.

4.6 X-ray and Ultraviolet Radiation in the Night Sky

Attempts to detect X-ray radiation in the 50 A region from the night sky have been unsuccessful. It is possible to set an experimental upper limit of 10^{-8} erg cm^{-2} sec^{-1} per Angstrom on any influx from celestial sources in this soft X-ray range. At Lyman-α and neighboring ultraviolet wavelengths, however, the nighttime flux is quite large.[83] The entire night sky is aglow with a diffuse Lyman α emission amounting to about 3×10^{-3} erg cm^{-2} sec^{-1} per steradian.

4.6.1 *The Distribution of Lyman-α from Space*

The measurement of Lyman-α at night was accomplished by means of ion chambers flown in an Aerobee rocket to a height of 146 km. The detectors were collimated to restrict the angular field of view and were mounted on the skin of the rocket looking outward in directions normal to the rocket's long axis. A spatial scan of the sky was produced by the combined spin and yaw motions of the rocket. The rocket flight approximated an arrow trajectory turning horizontal near the peak of the flight and rolling slowly with a period of 16 sec. In this way a broad scan of the sky was obtained.

At the peak of the flight the signals from the rolling rocket showed a maximum intensity when the windows looked out into space and a minimum, but not zero, when looking back toward the earth. The flux from above is

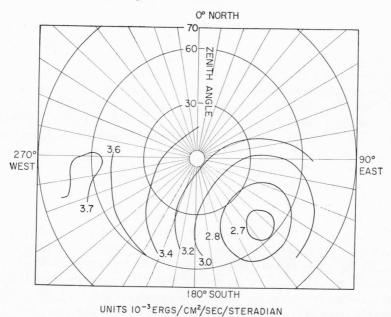

FIG. 30. Lyman-α directional intensity contours in the night sky. The data were obtained above 130 km from NRL Aerobee 31 on March 28, 1957, at 2200 local time. The smallest-intensity contour loop contains the antisolar direction. No correction to the data was made for the contribution of discrete sources between 1225 and 1350 A which appear in the west.

believed to come from hydrogen atoms in space and the radiation from below to originate in hydrogen atoms in the terrestrial atmosphere. It appears that the Lyman-α flux from space excites Lyman-α resonance radiation of the terrestrial hydrogen. The albedo* of the earth's atmosphere in Lyman-α was 42 %.

Fig. 30 is a plot of the measured distribution of Lyman-α radiation over the night sky. Whenever the detectors looked at the sky directly opposite the sun the intensity reached a shallow minimum. The zenith is at the center of

* As used here "albedo" is the ratio of outgoing flux from the atmosphere to the flux incident upon the atmosphere from the night sky.

the chart and the minimum isophote contour includes the anti-solar point. It is quite striking that the isophotes are almost circular about the anti-solar direction. This feature strongly suggests that the primary source of the night sky Lyman-α is the sun and that solar Lyman-α radiation traveling out into space is resonantly scattered back to the dark side of the earth by neutral hydrogen atoms in interplanetary space.

4.6.2 *The Density of Neutral Hydrogen Atoms in Space*

Let us assume first that the hydrogen atoms are distributed in interplanetary space. If we knew the contour of the solar Lyman-α line, we could estimate the density of neutral hydrogen, n_H, in interplanetary space, from the observed night sky flux. Each atom of hydrogen in space has an effective scattering cross-section dependent on its temperature and the breadth of the solar line (see § 2.7). Struve[84] assumes a line width of one Angstrom and a cross-section, σ, of 10^{-14} cm². Within a range of one-half Angstrom on either side of the line center a neutral hydrogen atom would absorb Lyman-α as though opaque within an area of 10^{-14} cm². If the solar Lyman-α flux is 5 ergs cm⁻² sec⁻¹ at one astronomical unit (1 A.U. $= 1.5 \times 10^{13}$ cm), each atom absorbs on the average 5×10^{-14} erg sec⁻¹ from the primary flux. If n_H were 0.1 per cm³, each cubic centimeter of space would absorb 5×10^{-15} erg sec⁻¹. The excited atoms would then re-radiate Lyman-α quanta in all directions. Per unit solid angle the scattered radiation would be $\frac{1}{4}\pi$ (5×10^{-15}) erg sec⁻¹ from each cm³ of space or approximately 4×10^{-16} erg sec⁻¹. Struve made the simplifying assumptions that both the hydrogen gas and the radiation density were uniform in space and that the scattered flux originated in a layer one astronomical unit thick. Such a layer would scatter (4×10^{-16}) (1.5×10^{13}) or 6×10^{-3} erg cm⁻² sec⁻¹ per steradian. This compares well with the observed flux.

Shklovsky in a similar treatment[85] used a solar flux of only 0.5 erg cm⁻² sec⁻¹ and a line width of 0.2 A and arrived at a density of 0.5 neutral atom per cm³. It is apparent that accurate knowledge of the contour of the solar line is essential to the solution of the problem. Kupperian[86] concluded that the presence of a deep core in the center of the line can be inferred from the weak albedo (< 2 %) of the earth's atmosphere when directly irradiated by solar Lyman-α during the day. Such a deficiency in the center of the solar line seriously affects the value of σ and consequently the computation of n_H.

Chamberlain and Brandt have considered the distribution of interplanetary hydrogen that would lead to the isophotes of Fig. 30. Assuming that the interplanetary hydrogen is optically thin in Lyman-α and confined to a fairly thin shell, spherically symmetric about the sun, they find that the shell must be located between 1.3 and 1.5 A.U. from the earth.

Shklovsky has suggested that, if the identification of the nighttime Lyman-α radiation scattered by neutral hydrogen atoms is correct, we should also expect to find excitation by Lyman-β. This should lead to the emission of the Balmer line Hα (6563 A) in the visible since absorption of Lyman-β raises a hydrogen atom to the quantum 3 state from which it may radiate Hα and Lyman-α in succession. Taking the intensity of Lyman-β to be 1/40 Lyman-α, Shklovsky derives a ratio of the number of Hα quanta to Lyman-α quanta in interplanetary space. The expected intensity is 2×10^7 photons cm^{-2} sec^{-1} of Hα if the solar Lyman-α flux is 5 ergs cm^{-2} sec^{-1} and n_H is 0.5 cm^{-3}. Spectra of the night sky at Zvenigorod show a narrow Hα line varying in intensity from night to night between limits of 0.5×10^7 and 2×10^7 photons cm^{-2} sec^{-1}. It may be concluded that the observations of Hα in the night sky are in reasonable agreement with the intensities to be expected from an interplanetary distribution of a few tenths of a neutral hydrogen atom per cubic centimeter.

An alternative possibility is that the hydrogen responsible for the night sky glow is part of the terrestrial atmosphere. Whichever interpretation is placed on the source of the flux, the total number of hydrogen atoms per column of unit cross section above the earth must be about 3×10^{12}. F. S. Johnson has developed a model of the atmosphere in which virtually all of this hydrogen is confined to 10 earth radii. At that distance the concentration is 10 per cubic centimeter and increases to 4×10^4 at the base of the exosphere.

In attempting to choose between an interplanetary or geo-coronal distribution, the observed 42 % albedo is a most important factor. To support his model, Johnson pointed out that the motion of the earth through an interplanetary gas would produce a Doppler shift large enough to minimize the albedo scattering by atmospheric hydrogen. The orbital velocity of the earth is about 30 km sec^{-1} compared to an average velocity of about 2 km sec^{-1} for a hydrogen atom at a temperature of about 300°K. Only that portion of the Lyman-α flux incident from the anti-solar direction could be scattered with an albedo as high as 42 %. Averaged over all directions, the albedo should be much smaller. Johnson therefore concluded that the hydrogen must be in the form of a geo-corona traveling with the earth, thereby eliminating any Doppler effect. It is possible, however, that only part of the so-called albedo is resonantly scattered. A major portion may be an airglow phenomenon arising from bombardment of the atmosphere by energetic particles.

Perhaps the simplest experiment capable of resolving the question of the hydrogen distribution would be a measurement of the variation of overhead brightness in Lyman-α with altitude up to a few thousand miles. It is also desirable to compare the atmospheric absorption of Lyman-α incident from the anti-solar direction with that incident from the direction in which the earth is moving. Accurate measurements of the daytime albedo and a spectrogram of the Lyman-α profile with sufficient resolution to reveal the presence of any self-reversal in the center of the line would provide the information necessary to solve the questions of the ratio of H to O_2 in the mesosphere and the temperature of the hydrogen gas responsible for the primary scattering of the solar Lyman-α line. All these suggested measurements are well within the capabilities of present rocket experimentation.

A similar night sky glow ought to be observable in the resonance line of HeII (304 A). The solar flux of the 304 A line may be comparable to Lyman-α and most of the helium in interplanetary space ought to be singly ionized, so that the scattered intensity may be quite high in spite of the helium abundance being an order of magnitude less than hydrogen.

4.6.3 *The Electron Density of Interplanetary Space*

If the neutral hydrogen content and the solar flux below the Lyman limit are known, we can compute the number of protons and electrons per cubic centimeter in an ionization equilibrium. The ionizing radiations are comprised primarily of the Lyman continuum, the HeII resonance line at 304 A, and the X-ray spectrum below 100 A. At the Lyman limit the absorption cross section is of the order of 10^{-17} cm^2. As the wavelength decreases, the cross section falls as λ^3. At the HeII line (304 A) the cross section is approximately 10^{-18} cm^2.

Although Rense's spectrogram[22] shows the importance of the HeII line, it is difficult to assign absolute intensities to it or to the Lyman continuum. If the ionosphere is taken as a gage of the ionizing flux, it appears that about 0.1 erg cm^{-2} sec^{-1} is sufficient to account for an equilibrium density of 10^6 electrons cm^{-3} at the maximum of the $F2$ region. The recombination of electrons and protons in space is controlled by the radiative recombination coefficient ($\alpha \simeq 1.5 \times 10^{-12}$ cm^3 sec^{-1}). Accordingly if we adopt $n_H = 0.2$ cm^{-3} and a flux of 0.1 erg cm^{-2} sec^{-1}, the corresponding electron or proton densities lie between 15 and 45 cm^{-3}, depending on where the appropriate cross section lies between the values of 10^{-18} and 10^{-17} cm^2. If the true value of the solar flux is higher than 0.1 erg cm^{-2} sec^{-1}, the computed electron density will be greater in proportion to the square root of the flux.

Although the above discussion offers substantial arguments for treating the night sky Lyman-α as resonantly scattered from neutral hydrogen, it is of interest to estimate the electron-proton density required if the emission were produced by radiative recombination. A photon may recombine with an electron in several ways. Recombination into the ground state produces the Lyman continuum. Recombination into the second quantum state is followed by emission of Lyman-α. If the electron is captured into higher excited states it may reach the ground state directly with the emission of one of the Lyman series lines, β, γ, etc., or it may cascade to the ground state with emission of the Lyman-α line and one or more lines of the Balmer, Paschen, and Bracket series. If we assume that all recombinations lead to emission of Lyman-α and take the recombination coefficient to be 1.5×10^{-12} cm^3 sec^{-1}, then an emission of 5×10^{-15} erg sec^{-1} cm^{-3} requires an electron-proton density of 4,000 cm^{-3}. Since some of the recombinations produce the Lyman continuum and other Lyman series lines, the required electron-proton density should be closer to 20,000 cm^{-3}. This is much too high a concentration for interplanetary space.

4.6.4 *Ultraviolet Nebulosities*

At a slightly longer wavelength than Lyman-α, direct measurements of far ultraviolet radiation from celestial sources have been made[87] in a wavelength band from 1225 to 1350 A. This radiation has been identified with extended regions of nebulosity distributed throughout the galaxy.[88] The brightest individual source observed thus far is the Orion complex, which delivers about 2×10^{-5} erg cm^{-2} sec^{-1} at the top of the atmosphere. The total flux averaged over all observed sources is 10^{-4} erg cm^{-2} sec^{-1} between 1225 and 1350 A. The mechanism of this emission has not been identified, and it remains to be seen if there is a comparably high flux at wavelengths shorter than Lyman-α.

4.6.5 *Sources of Radiant Energy in the Night Sky*

Table XVI lists the solar constant and the intensities of various sources of radiant energy in the night sky. It is interesting to note that the Lyman-α

TABLE XVI

Radiation Sources in the Day and Night Skies

Source	Flux (ergs cm^{-2} sec^{-1})
Sun	1.4×10^6
Full moon	3000×10^{-3}
Total starlight	1.8×10^{-3}
Airglow (visible)	16×10^{-3}
OH (infrared)	19×10^{-3}
Lyman-α	10×10^{-3}
Celestial sources (1230—1350 A)	0.1×10^{-3}
Cosmic rays	3.8×10^{-3}

contribution exceeds the sum total of visible starlight and is comparable to
all the visible airglow. The contribution from ultraviolet nebulosities between
1225 and 1350 A is approximately one-hundredth of the Lyman-α flux.

The nighttime flux of Lyman-α is capable of producing between one-tenth
and one-hundredth of the electron density of the D region produced by the
daytime flux, if the same ionization and recombination processes are operative
both day and night. At altitudes near 100 km, Lyman-α may ionize the Ca
atoms accumulated at that level from the influx of meteorites. If Nicolet's
value[89] is accepted for the Ca atom density at 100 km, it can be shown that
the rate of ionization by nighttime Lyman-α may approach the ionization
contribution from the ablation of meteorites.

4.7 Atmospheric Densities and Composition from Radiation Measurements

In the laboratory, the density of a gas can be determined by interposing
a column of the gas between a monochromatic light source and a detector.
If the absorption coefficient is known, the mass of absorber is derived from
a measurement of the attenuation. This method is applicable to density
determination in the upper atmosphere if the sun is used as a light source
and the detector is carried on a rocket. The change in overhead mass of
atmospheric gas can then be determined by measuring the variation in
solar intensity received by the rocket as it climbs through the atmosphere.
By differentiating the curve of air mass with respect to altitude, one obtains
the air density as a function of altitude.

The optical depth of an atmospheric constituent is the product of its
absorption cross section and the number of molecules per square centimeter
column above that altitude. If a solar wavelength is selected which is absorbed
by only one constituent, its concentration can be accurately determined for
a range of about plus or minus one scale height above and below the altitude
of unit optical depth. Because the ultraviolet spectrum from 1000 to 2000 A
is absorbed almost exclusively by molecular oxygen, this region is especially
useful in determining the O_2 concentration.[90] At X-ray wavelengths near
50 A the absorption depends only on the total number of atoms independently
of chemical combination. This spectral range has been particularly useful in
determining the total air density without requiring a knowledge of composition.

In principle it is possible to fly a grating monochromator and a photocell
to measure the transmission of monochromatic radiation, but much simpler
techniques have proved practical. It is sufficient for the determination of
molecular oxygen to use the narrow-band photon counters and ion chambers
described in §§ 4.2.2.1 and 4.2.2.2. The 1425- to 1500-A photon counter of

Fig. 14 matches the wavelength region of the nearly flat maximum of the Schumann dissociation continuum where the absorption cross section is about 1.4×10^{-17} cm² and unit optical depth is reached at about 110 km. A 1225- to 1350-A ion chamber covers an absorption region where the average cross section is about 10^{-18} cm². When the band width is expanded to cover 1060 to 1350 A, the ion chamber responds principally to Lyman-α at 1216 A, where the absorption coefficient of O_2 is only 0.8×10^{-20} cm².

With more than three decades of range in absorption cross sections, the three detectors mentioned above can be used to determine the molecular oxygen content between 70 and 130 km when the sun is overhead. If the measurement is made close to sunrise or sunset, the slant air mass may be as much as thirty-eight times the vertical mass, and the absorption region may be moved upward as much as three scale heights. Table XVII lists the results of O_2 measurements in three different rocket flights made in the

TABLE XVII

Concentration of Molecular Oxygen

(Number per cubic centimeter)

Altitude (km)	Flight time		
	Aerobee 16 0829 12/1/53	Aerobee 34 1550 10/18/55	Aerobee 35 1715 10/21/55
110	16×10^{10}		
114	7.5×10^{10}	12×10^{10}	
116	5.4×10^{10}	9×10^{10}	
118	4×10^{10}	2.3×10^{10}	
120	3×10^{10}	1.8×10^{10}	
130	1×10^{10}		
150			4×10^{9}
160			1.4×10^{9}
170			8×10^{8}
180			4×10^{8}

morning, afternoon, and at sunset[90] with the 1425- to 1500-A photon counter. The results obtained with Aerobees 16 and 34 in the same altitude range are slightly different but not very far apart. The differences may be in fact largely real and only partly experimental errors. Since the concentration is controlled by atmospheric mixing as well as by diffusion, it will depend on the turbulence of the atmosphere at the time of flight, and perhaps we should not expect identical results on different days.

Using the 1225- to 1350-A and 1060- to 1350-A detectors, it is possible to determine O_2 over a range of lower altitudes, including the region of the

14

mesosphere. Figure 31 shows the results of recent measurements made in two different seasons of the year at Fort Churchill, Canada.[91] Because the ionization chamber techniques are more accurate than the photon counter

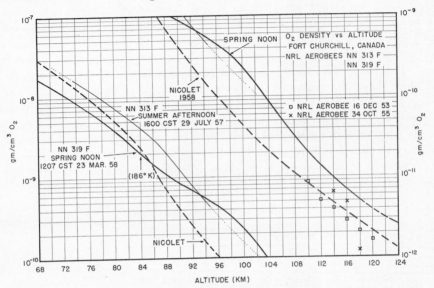

FIG. 31. O_2 density versus altitude at Fort Churchill, Canada. The data from Aerobee NN319F were obtained from measurements with a pair of 1060- to 1350-A and 1225- to 1350-A ion chambers. Flight NN313F used only the 1060- to 1350-A detector and therefore did not cover as wide a range of altitudes. Nicolet's theoretical curve (Scientific Report No. 102, Ionospheric Research Laboratory, Pennsylvania State University, State College, 1958) and some points from the Aerobee 16 and 34 flights are included for comparison.

measurements of earlier experiments, the variation of concentration with height can be much more accurately determined. The accuracy of the data in Fig. 31 is sufficiently good that the following conclusions could be drawn:

1. The O_2 densities differed in the 70- to 86-km region by a factor of 1.8, being higher in the summer. Since dissociation is negligible at these altitudes, the same factor applies to the density of the total atmosphere.

2. The "dissociation level" appeared as a rapid change in scale height beginning at about 86 km in the midsummer flight and 96 km in the early spring flight. A difference of 10 km in the "dissociation level" may be attributed to the seasonal change in average solar elevation. This effect should be greater at Fort Churchill's latitude than at White Sands, New Mexico.

3. The temperature minimum for flight 3.19 in March was 186°K (+4°, −8°) at an altitude of 83 to 85 km. It is unlikely that dissociation has an

appreciable effect on the scale height from which this temperature is derived. (At all altitudes the scale height determined from the O_2 data must be lower than the atmospheric density scale height if any dissociation occurs.)

4. There appeared to be an increase in scale height and therefore temperature in flight (3.19) above the temperature minimum, before dissociation introduced a rapid decrease. This indication of temperature rise would follow the atmospheric gradient into the E region if not for dissociation.

5. The lower density at 70 km for the early spring flight implies a colder winter than summer atmosphere below this level.

6. Below 80 km, the Rocket Panel[53] White Sands density is within the spread of the two Fort Churchill measurements.

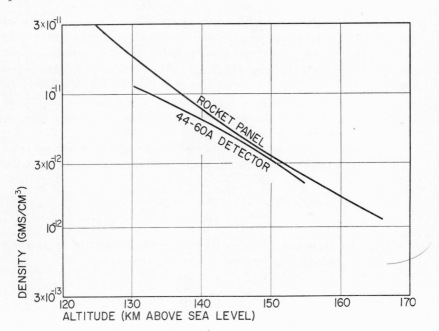

FIG. 32. Atmospheric density from X-ray transmission data and from the Rocket Panel.

In § 4.2.3.3, the discussion of X-ray flux measurements included a description of density determination from transmission data. When X-ray density measurements were first carried out, the results were smaller than those given by the Rocket Panel by a factor of about 3. In Fig. 17, each bar representing the band width of an X-ray photon counter is labeled with a mass absorption coefficient. These coefficients were derived by measuring the slopes of the curves of the logarithm of X-ray intensity plotted against air mass based on the Rocket Panel atmosphere. It was immediately apparent that the derived coefficients were too small by a factor of between 2 and 3, implying that Rocket Panel densities were correspondingly too high. Figure 32 shows the results of X-ray densities obtained from the sunset flight of Aerobee 35. As the altitude increases, the discrepancy between Rocket Panel and X-ray densities decreases until the two curves almost match at 160 km.

An extension of density determination by the radiation method to higher altitudes can be accomplished by using the portions of the 500- to 800-A region of the spectrum where absorption coefficients are fifty to a hundred times the values in the 44- to 60-A band. The highest absorption cross sections reach values between 10^{-17} and 10^{-16} cm.^{2} In resonance absorption, however, the cross section may be greater than 10^{-13} cm^2 in the center of the absorption line. Cross sections of this magnitude were used in the analysis of the scattering of Lyman-α by neutral hydrogen in § 4.6.1. It appeared there that interplanetary hydrogen absorbed the central portion of the solar Lyman-α line to the extent that a column 1 A.U. long corresponded to unit optical thickness. In principle, it should be possible to determine the concentrations of hydrogen and various other atmospheric constituents to heights of several thousands of kilometers by measuring the amount of self-reversal in the core of the appropriate solar emission line as a function of altitude of a vertical rocket probe.

In an absorption line formed by Doppler broadening, the absorption cross section, σ_λ, at a wavelength λ, displaced $\Delta\lambda$ from the wavelength λ_0 at the center of the line, is given by

$$\sigma_\lambda = \frac{\pi^{\frac{1}{2}} e^2 \lambda_0^2 f}{mc^2 \Delta\lambda_D} e^{-(\Delta\lambda/\Delta\lambda_D)^2} \qquad (4.17)$$

where e is the electronic charge, m its mass, c the velocity of light, and f the oscillator strength. The Doppler width, $\Delta\lambda_D$, is given by

$$\Delta\lambda_D = \frac{\lambda}{c} \sqrt{\frac{2kT}{M}} \qquad (4.18)$$

where k is the Boltzman constant, T the absolute temperature, and M the molecular mass. For Lyman-α, the f value is 0.42. At the line center the exponential factor is unity, and σ_0 can be calculated for any T. If the attenuation in the core of the line is measured versus altitude, it is possible to compute the hydrogen density versus height.

For the purpose of illustration let us use the model hydrogen distribution proposed by Chapman,[92] as shown in Table XVIII. At 2000 km he derives a temperature of 7920°K and a number density of hydrogen atoms, n_H, equal to 2.75×10^4. Multiplying n_H by the scale height, H, which is 7330 km at that height, gives 2×10^{13} cm^{-2} for N_H, the number of hydrogen atoms per square centimeter column above that altitude. Substituting 2000°K for T

and 1.67 $\times$ 10^{-24} gm for M in equations (4.17) and (4.18), we get $\Delta\lambda_D =$ 0.046 A and $\sigma_0 = 6.7 \times 10^{-14}$ cm^2. The optical thickness in the center of the Lyman-α line is $\sigma_0 N_H$, which should accordingly be about 1.3 at the height of 2000 km. The solar Lyman-α line may, therefore, be expected to exhibit almost complete self-reversal over a width of about 0.05 A about the central wavelength. At the lower heights of 520 and 160 km listed in Table XVIII, the corresponding optical depths are 4 and 10.4 It would appear that, up to and possibly well beyond 2000 km, the variation in depth and width of the core of the Lyman-α line should be a sensitive index of the variation of hydrogen concentration with height. The optical thickness of terrestrial hydrogen deduced here by using Chapman's hydrogen distribution is so great, however, as to form an opaque barrier to resonantly scattered radiation from interplanetary space. If, as was proposed in § 4.6.1, the night-sky Lyman-α originates in interplanetary space, then the hydrogen concentration of Table XVIII must be more than an order of magnitude too high.

TABLE XVIII

Theoretical Distribution of Hydrogen in Terrestrial Atmosphere

	Height (km)		
	160	520	2000
T (°K)	560	2000	7920
n_H (cm^{-3})	8×10^5	1.6×10^5	2.75×10^4
H (km)	490	1850	7330
N_H (cm^2 column)$^{-1}$	4×10^{13}	3×10^{13}	2×10^{13}

To map the line contour in sufficient detail for a determination of the hydrogen distribution will require a resolution of the order of a hundredth of an angstrom. In preparation for such an experiment, Purcell and Tousey, at the U. S. Naval Research Laboratory, are experimenting with reflections in high orders from concave gratings. Working in the thirteenth order with a compact spectrograph designed for an Aerobee-Hi rocket they can obtain a resolution of 0.03 A with sufficient intensity for photographic registration of the solar line. If such an experiment is successful, the next step will involve instrumentation of photoelectronic scanning of the line contour with continuous telemetering in a rocket capable of carrying the apparatus to several thousand miles.

The method just described is applicable to resonance absorption by other constituents such as atomic oxygen and nitrogen. In the spectrum of Fig. 8, the OI triplet at 1302.2, 1304.9, and 1306.0 A arises from the optical transition $2p^4\ ^3P-2p^33s\ ^3S^0$. The theoretically expected intensities are in the ratio

5 : 3 : 1, but, in the spectrogram photographed at 115 km, the intensities are reversed. Johnson et al.[27] attributed the inversion to atmospheric absorption and pointed out that intensity measurements as a function of altitude could reveal the height distribution of atomic oxygen, provided that the contours of the solar lines and the absorption coefficient were known.

According to the model atmosphere of Hulburt,[93] the atmospheric temperature in the height range 200 to 500 km is about 1100°K. The Doppler half-width for atomic oxygen ($M = 2.7 \times 10^{-23}$ gm) at 1100°K according to formula (4.18) is 0.0043 A. If the f value is taken to be 0.1, the cross section σ_0, at the center of the 1302-A line is 2×10^{-13} cm^2. In Hulburt's model atmosphere the scale height is about 45 km at 200 km where the number density, $n(O)$, is 2.4×10^9. This makes the optical depth equal to 2×10^3 for atomic oxygen at 200 km. At 350 km and at 500 km the optical depths are 300 and 28, respectively. Measurements of the depth and width of the core of the solar 1302-A line as it is attenuated in the terrestrial atmosphere should therefore provide a specific measurement of the density of atomic oxygen well above 500 km.

NRL Aerobee 35 was flown at sunset[90] and was equipped with a photon counter sensitive to the 1225- to 1300-A band of wavelengths. As the rocket rose, its spinning and precessing motions permitted the detector to look alternately down and up at right angles to the beam of sunlight illuminating the atmosphere. Near the peak of the flight the measured ratio of intensity looking up to looking down began to diminish. At 180 km, a flux of 3×10^{-3} erg cm^{-2} sec^{-1} ster^{-1} was still observed from above. This airglow may have been a fluorescence of the atmosphere under excitation by solar radiation below the Lyman limit or a resonance scattering of the solar 1302-A line of atomic oxygen. The intensity was high enough at 180 km so that it could undoubtedly be measured to much greater heights and thereby provide a measure of the atmospheric density or the oxygen concentration.

The above discussion indicates the possibilities of composition measurements to great altitudes by both broad-band absorption and fluorescence measurements and by high-resolution spectroscopic absorption measurements. Such approaches should be fully exploited to provide a model of the terrestrial atmosphere to several thousand kilometers.

4.8 Auroral X-rays

The production of auroras is generally attributed to neutral streams of charged particles, protons, and electrons, emitted from active regions of the solar surface. These gas clouds reach the earth in approximately one day and under the influence of the geomagnetic field are deflected toward the auroral zones. The particles spiral down the lines of magnetic force and penetrate to depths depending on their energies. Protons of 0.5-Mev energy may penetrate to the 100-km level, which is the average base of auroral arcs. Electrons of 10 to 100 kev energy would penetrate to the 90- to 110-km region. In 1953, Meredith et al.[94] discovered X-ray emission in the auroral zones which may be identified with such electrons. The first experiments were carried out by means of Rockoons in a series of measurements across the auroral zone from the North Atlantic through the Davis Straits off Greenland. The electron flux has since been directly detected at Fort Churchill in a series of IGY rocket launchings.

The X-ray intensities observed at altitudes of 40 to 70 km were of the order of 10^3 to 10^5 photons cm^{-2} sec^{-1} in the energy range 10 to 100 kev. Van Allen attributes the X-rays to bremsstrahlung of the electrons as they are stopped in the atmosphere above 90 km. If the bremsstrahlung were attributed to protons, the required flux of protons would exceed the solar constant.

Chapman and Little[95] have considered the effects of the auroral X-rays on the ionization of the lower ionosphere, leading to absorption of radio waves. Although there is a minimum of auroral activity in the middle of the day, they propose that the absorption effect should be present both night and day. Even though the X-ray flux may be much weaker during the day, the resulting ionization should persist longer because the loss of electrons by attachment to oxygen atoms is overcome by photodetachment by visible sunlight. At night the attachment process is effective, and a much greater X-ray flux is required to maintain the ionospheric absorption. Another possibility is that sporadic E associated with auroras may be produced by X-rays.

Acknowledgments

The author wishes to express his appreciation to his colleagues, T. A. Chubb, P. Mange, E. T. Byram, R. W. Kreplin, and R. Tousey for many discussions of the material covered in this chapter.

References

1. C. W. Allen, *Terr. Mag.* **53**, 433 (1948).
2. R. v. d. R. Woolley and D. W. N. Stibbs, in "The Outer Layers of a Star," pp. 263, 265, Oxford Univ. Press, New York, 1953.
3. R. v. d. R. Woolley and C. W. Allen, *Monthly Not. Roy. Astron. Soc.* **108**, 292 (1948).
4. R. v. d. R. Woolley and C. W. Allen, *Monthly Not. Roy. Astron. Soc.* **110**, 358 (1950)
5. L. Goldberg, *Astrophys. J.* **120**, 185 (1954).
6. C. de Jager, *Ann. Géophys.* **11**, 330 (1955).
6a. I. S. Shklovsky and W. E. Kononovitch, *Russ. Astron. J.* **35**, 37 (1958).
6b. R. J. Coates, *Astrophys. J.* **128**, 83 (1958).
7. W. Grotrian, *Naturwissenschaften* **27**, 214 (1939).

8. B. Edlen, *Z. Astrophys.* **22**, 30 (1942).
9. D. F. Martyn, *Nature*, **158**, 632 (1946).
10. L. Biermann, *Naturwissenschaften* **34**, 87 (1947).
11. I. S. Shklovsky, *Isw. Krynsk. Ap. Obs.* **6**, 104 (1950).
12. S. Myamoto, *Publ. Astron. Soc. Pacific I* (1950).
13. G. Elwert, *Z. Naturforsch*, **7a**, 202 (1952).
14. S. Baumbach, *A.N.* **267**, 273 (1939).
15. M. Waldemeier, *Z. Astrophys.* **39**, 219 (1956).
16. D. E. Billings, *Astrophys. J.* **125**, 817 (1956).
17. W. N. Christiansen and J. A. Warburton, *Austral. J. Phys.* **6**, 262 (1953).
18. W. N. Christiansen, D. E. Yabsley, and B. Y. Mills, *Austral. J. Sci. Res.* A2, 506 (1949).
19. M. Waldemeier and H. Muller, *Z. Astrophys.* **27**, 58 (1950).
20. J. H. Piddington and H. C. Minnett, *Austral. J. Sci. Res.* A4, 131 (1951).
21. H. Friedman, S. W. Lichtman, and E. T. Byram, *Phys. Rev.* **83**, 1025 (1952).
22. W. A. Rense, private communication.
23. W. A. Baum, F. S. Johnson, J. J. Oberly, C. V. Strain, and R. Tousey, *Phys. Rev.* **70**, 781 (1946).
24. D. S. Stacey, G. A. Stith, R. A. Nidey, and W. A. Pietenpol. *Electronics* **27**, 149 (1954).
25. W. A. Rense, *Phys. Rev.* **91**, 299 (1953).
26. F. S. Johnson, J. D. Purcell, and R. Tousey, *Phys. Rev.* **95**, 621 (1954).
27. F. S. Johnson, H. H. Malitson, J. D. Purcell, and R. Tousey, *Astrophys. J.* **127**, 80 (1958).
28. S. A. Korff, "Electron and Nuclear Counters," Van Nostrand, New York, 1946.
29. H. Friedman, *Proc. IRE* **37**, 791 (1949).
30. T. A. Chubb and H. Friedman, *R.S.I.* **26**, 493 (1955).
30a. T. A. Chubb, private communication.
30b. H. E. Hinteregger and K. Watanabe, *J. Opt. Soc. Amer.* **43**, 604 (1953).
31. F. S. Johnson, J. D. Purcell, and R. Tousey, *J. Geophys Res.* **56**, 583 (1951).
32. H. Friedman, *Ann. Géophys.* **11**, 174 (1955).
33. M. Nicolet and P. Mange, *J. Geophys. Res.* **59**, 15 (1954).
34. K. Watanabe, *J. Chem. Phys.* **22**, 564 (1954).
35. J. E. Kupperian, Jr., private communication.
36. T. R. Burnight, *Phys. Rev.* **76**, 165 (1949).
37. R. Tousey, J. D. Purcell, and K. Watanabe, *Phys. Rev.* **83**, 792 (1951).
38. T. A. Chubb, H. Friedman, R. W. Kreplin, and J. E. Kupperian, *J. Geophys. Res.* **62**, 389 (1957).
39. E. T. Byram, T. A. Chubb, and H. Friedman, *J. Geophys. Res.* **61**, 251 (1956).
40. R. W. Ditchburn and D. W. O. Heddle, *Proc. Roy. Soc.* A220, 61 (1953).
41. K. Watanabe and F. F. Marmo, *J. Chem. Phys.* **25**, 965 (1956).
42. R. W. Ditchburn, J. E. S. Bradley, C. G. Cannon, and G. Munday, in "Rocket Exploration of the Upper Atmosphere," p. 327, Interscience, New York, 1954.
43. Po Lee, *J. Opt. Soc. Amer.* **45**, 703 (1955).
44. K. Watanabe, F. Marmo, and J. Pressman, *J. Geophys. Res.* **60**, 513 (1955).
45. D. R. Bates and M. J. Seaton, *Proc. Phys. Soc.* **63**, 129 (1950).
46. G. L. Weissler, Po Lee, and E. I. Mohr, *J. Opt. Soc. Amer.* **42**, 84 (1952).
47. R. E. Worley, *Phys. Rev.* **64**, 207 (1943); **89**, 863 (1953).
48. Y. Tanaka, *J. Opt. Soc. Amer.* **45**, 663 (1955).
49. K. Watanabe, F. Marmo, and E. C. Y. Inn, *Phys. Rev.* **90**, 155 (1953).

50. J. A. Victoreen, *J. Appl. Phys.* **20**, 1141 (1949).
51. E. Jonsson, Thesis, Upsala, 1928; M. Siegbakn, "Spectroskopie der Rontgenstrahlen," p. 470, Springer, Berlin, 1931.
52. S. J. M. Allen, *in* "X-rays in Theory and Experiment" (A. H. Compton and S. K. Allison, eds.), p. 799, 1943.
53. The Rocket Panel, *Phys. Rev.* **88**, 1027 (1952).
54. S. Chapman, *Proc. Phys. Soc.* **43**, 26 (1931).
55. N. E. Bradbury, *Terr. Mag.* **43**, 55 (1938).
56. J. C. Seddon, A. D. Pickar, and J. E. Jackson, *J, Geophys. Res.* **56**, 487 (1951).
57. L. Vegard, *Phil. Mag.* **46**, 193 (1923).
58. E. O. Hulburt, *Phys. Rev.* **53**, 344 (1938).
59. L. Vegard, *Geofys. Publ.* (*Oslo*) **12**, No. 4 (1938).
60. O. R. Wulf and L. S. Deming, *Terr. Mag.* **43**, 283 (1938).
61. R. Penndorf, *J. Geophys. Res.* **54**, 7 (1949).
62. F. Hoyle and D. R. Bates, *Terr. Mag.* **53**, 41 (1948).
63. R. J. Havens, H. Friedman, and E. O. Hulburt, "Physics of the Ionosphere," p. 237. Physical Society, London (1954).
64. E. T. Byram, T. A. Chubb, and H. Friedman, *in* "The Threshold of Space" (M. Zelikoff, ed.), p. 211, Pergamon, London, 1957.
65. R. E. Houston, Jr., Scientific Report No. 95, Pennsylvania State University, State College, 1957.
66. M. Nicolet, *Mem. Inst. Roy. Met. Belg.* **19** (1945).
67. H. K. Kallmann, Scientific Report No. 4, Institute of Geophysics, University of California at Los Angeles, 1956.
68. M. A. Ellison, *Trans. IAU* **9**, 146 (1957).
69. J. Warwick, *Astrophys. J.* **121**, 376 (1955).
70. C. S. Warwick, *Astrophys. J.* **121**, 285 (1955).
71. M. Waldemeier. *Z. Astrophys.* **16**, 276 (1938).
72. A. P. Mitra and R. E. Jones, *J. Atmos. Terr. Phys.* **4**, 104 (1954).
73. E. V. Appleton, *J. Atmos. Terr. Phys.* **3**, 283 (1953).
74. E. V. Appleton and W. R. Piggot, *J. Atmos. Terr. Phys.* **5**, 141 (1954).
75. R. N. Bracewell and T. W. Straker, *Monthly Not. Roy. Astron. Soc.* **109**, 28 (1949).
76. H. Friedman and T. A. Chubb, "Physics of the Ionosphere," p. 58, Physical Society, London (1954).
77. M. A. Ellison, *Publ. Roy. Observ. Edinburgh* **1**, 53 (1950).
78. M. A. Ellison, *J. Atmos. Terr. Phys.* **4**, 226 (1953).
79. L. Peterson and J. R. Winckler, private communication.
80. A. B. Severny, Tenth General Assembly of the IAU, Moscow, 1958.
81. J. E. Kupperian, Jr., and H. Friedman, paper presented at Fifth CSAGI Assembly, Moscow, 1958.
82. S. N. Vernov, A. E. Chudakov, E. V. Gorchakov, J. I. Lozachev, and P. V. Vakulov, paper presented at Fifth CSAGI Assembly, Moscow, 1958.
83. J. E. Kupperian, Jr., E. T. Byram, T. A. Chubb, and H. Friedman, *Ann. Géophys.* in press.
84. O. Struve, *Sky and Telescope* **17**, No. 9, 445 (1958).
85. I. S. Shklovsky, paper presented at Fifth CSAGI Assembly, Moscow, 1958.
86. J. E. Kupperian, Jr., private communication.
87. T. A. Chubb, E. T. Byram, H. Friedman, and J. E. Kupperian, Jr., *in* "The Threshold of Space" (M. Zelikoff, ed.), p. 203, Pergamon, London, 1957.
88. J. E. Kupperian, Jr., A. Boggess, III and J. E. Milligan, *Astrophys. J.* in press.

89. M. Nicolet, in "Meteors" (T. Kaiser, ed.) p. 99, Pergamon, London, 1955.
90. E. T. Byram, T. A. Chubb, and H. Friedman, *in* "The Threshold of Space" (M. Zelikoff, ed.), p. 211, Pergamon, London, 1957.
91. J. E. Kupperian, Jr., E. T. Byram, H. Friedman, and A. Unzicker, paper presented at Fifth CSAGI Assembly, Moscow, 1958.
92. S. Chapman, *in* "The Threshold of Space" (M. Zelikoff, ed.), p. 65, Pergamon, London, 1957.
93. E. O. Hulburt, "Advances in the Physics of the Upper Air since 1950," *NRL Rept.* No. **4600,** 5 (1955).
94. L. H. Meredith, M. B. Gottlieb, and J. A. Van Allen, *Phys. Rev.* **97,** 201 (1955).
95. S. Chapman and C. G. Little, *J. Atmos. Terr. Phys.*

Chapter 5

The Airglow*

D. R. Bates

5.1 Nightglow 219
    5.1.1 Spectrum 219
    5.1.2 Polarization 226
    5.1.3 Temperature 226
    5.1.4 Temporal Variation.. 228
    5.1.5 Morphology.. 237
    5.1.6 Absolute Intensities.. 239
    5.1.7 Altitude 240
    5.1.8 Excitation Processes.. 242
5.2 Twilightglow 251
    5.2.1 λ 5893 of NaI... 251
    5.2.2 λ 6300-6364 and λ 5577 of OI..................... 256
    5.2.3 λ 5199 of NI... 258
    5.2.4 Band Systems.. 259
5.3 Dayglow 260
    References 261

Following a suggestion by Otto Struve,[1] the word *airglow* has been adopted as a convenient designation for the radiation emitted by the earth's upper atmosphere, other than that due to aurora. If it is desired to specify the nocturnal emission alone, *nightglow* is used. *Dayglow* and *twilightglow* are defined analogously. Of the three radiations, the nightglow has been the longest and the most extensively studied. In the older literature it is often referred to as the *nonpolar aurora* or as the *light of the night sky*. When the last phrase is now employed, starlight, galactic light, and zodiacal light are always included (as they were sometimes in the past).

5.1 Nightglow

5.1.1 *Spectrum*

The nightglow is extremely feeble, the illumination it gives to the ground being of the same order as that from a candle at a height of 100 meters.

---

* Because of language difficulties full justice has not been done in this, and in the two succeeding chapters, to research carried out in the Soviet Union. Attention is called to the article by B. A. Bagaryatskii entitled "The work of Soviet scientists on the night airglow and the polar aurorae". [*Izv. Akad. Nauk. SSSR, ser. geofys.*, No. 11, 1410 (1957); or in the English translation, *Bull. Acad. Sci. U.S.S.R. Geophys. Ser.* (Pergamon Press), No. 11, 108 (1957).]

Spectroscopic studies are therefore extremely difficult, and the success that has been attained in them has been possible only because of the great technical advances in recent years. Even with lengthy exposures (perhaps over the dark hours of many nights), it is generally necessary to resort to fast instruments of low dispersion and resolving power. The consequent lack of precision in the wavelength measurements hinders an assured identification of individual lines and bands. To identify a line conclusively an interferometer must be used. In the case of bands the problem is in certain respects less acute in that the intensity distribution through the system and the appearance of the various members may provide supplementary evidence. There are, however, complications which must be taken into account: thus the intensity distribution may be affected by atmospheric absorption and by a background of starlight and zodiacal light with embedded Fraunhofer lines; and again, the appearance of the various members may be indistinct and may in any event be unfamiliar, owing to the low temperature of the source.

In spite of the difficulties that have had to be overcome, the main features of the nightglow spectrum have been identified. This is a considerable achievement on the part of the observers, especially since some of the features were utterly unexpected and since at the time of their identification many were unknown in laboratory emission sources.

Stress must be laid on the limited nature of the information provided by a catalog of identifications. The loose statement that a given spectral feature is absent, or is present, merely means that its intensity is below, or is above, some rather ill-defined and usually unknown value. Clearly, the threshold intensity for detection depends on the other features occurring and on the wavelength region concerned. Consequently, a feature which is given as absent may in fact be stronger than some features which are listed as present. An investigation on threshold intensities (absolute or relative) for some lines and band systems of interest would be useful.

Descriptions of the different spectral regions have been given by a number of observers: 3100 to 3800 A, Chamberlain;[2] 3400 to 4000 A, Dufay and Dufay;[3] 3500 to 6600 A, Babcock;[4] 3700 to 4900 A, Chamberlain;[4a] 3800 to 5200 A, Cabannes and Dufay;[5] 4300 to 6400 A, Bappu;[6] 5800 to 6900 A, Cabannes et al.;[7] 6800 to 9000 A, Dufay and Dufay;[8] 7000 to 8900 A, Meinel;[9] 7000 to 9000 A, Chamberlain and Roesler;[10] 8800 to 11,000 A, Krassovsky;[11] and 10,000 to 20,000 A, Gush and Jones.[12]

Barbier[13] has compiled a useful list of papers in which a representative selection of reproductions or microphotometer tracings of spectra is to be found.

5.1.1.1 Lines

The green line which had for many years been a familiar component of the auroral spectrum was in 1895 detected visually in the nightglow spectrum by Campbell.[14] Its occurrence was also noted by Wiechert[15] in 1902. Both found it to be always present. This early work was largely forgotten, and in 1919 Slipher[16] reported the rediscovery of the line by photographic means and gave its wavelength as approximately 5578 A. His investigations and those of Rayleigh[17] again established that the line is a permanent feature of the nightglow. Its identification was long delayed. In 1923 a vital contribution toward the solution of the problem was made by Babcock,[18] who carried out a very accurate wavelength measurement using a Fabry-Perot interferometer. He found the value to be 5577.350 $\pm$ 0.005 A.* At the time spectroscopists were unaware of any line having precisely this wavelength. After much effort, however, McLennan and his associates[20] succeeded in showing that atomic oxygen emits a line at 5577.341 $\pm$ 0.004 A. This line is due to the forbidden transition between the ^1S and ^1D terms of the ground configuration. An electrical discharge through a mixture of oxygen and an inert gas provides a satisfactory source. In view of the agreement of the wavelengths there can be no doubt that the lines are identical. Unless collisional deactivation occurs, the red triplet O1, $^1D \to {}^3P$ must also be emitted, the initial term concerned being the same as the final term of the transition responsible for the green line. In 1928 Slipher[21] observed this triplet as a feature near λ 6315 in the nightglow spectrum, and shortly afterward Paschen[22] excited it in the laboratory. Only two of the lines of the triplet, those corresponding to the transitions $^1D_2 \to {}^3P_2$ and $^1D_2 \to {}^3P_1$, are of appreciable intensity. Cabannes and Dufay[19] find the wavelengths of these to be 6300.308 $\pm$ 0.004 A and 6363.790 $\pm$ 0.004$_5$ A, respectively.

At the same time as he discovered the red lines Slipher noticed a yellow feature at 5892 A. He remarked on the closeness to the D doublet of sodium, the components of which, D_1 and D_2, are at 5895.92 A and 5889.95 A. Naturally enough this was at first regarded merely as a coincidence, for it did not seem likely that such an element as sodium could contribute to the nightglow. Some authors sought to invoke either a certain band of nitrogen or a certain band of water vapor. In 1938, however, Bernard[23] and Cabannes et al.,[24] by a comparison of interference fringes, proved that the yellow feature is in fact to be attributed to the D doublet.

Courtès[25] and Dufay[26] have reported that NI, $^2D \to {}^4S$ λ 5198.5-5200.7 may be present. The discussion on this is deferred to the section on the twilightglow.

The suggestion has been made[1] that a broad feature centered at 6563 A is due to the first Balmer line of atomic hydrogen, Hα λ 6562.82, Doppler-displaced as in auroras. Meinel[27] has argued, however, that the (6, 2) hydroxyl

---

* As Cabannes and Dufay[19] have pointed out, Babcock's value must be reduced to 5577.348 A because of a change in the accepted wavelength of the comparison mercury line used.

band (§ 5.1.1.2) is responsible for the feature. In a nightglow spectrum obtained in the absence of appreciable magnetic disturbance, Prokudina[27a] has discovered what is perhaps another feature which can in fact be identified with the Hα line, *narrow* and *undisplaced*. Shklovsky[27b] attributes its presence to the fluorescent scattering of solar Lyβ radiation by interplanetary hydrogen.

Byram *et al.*[28] have carried out surveys of the night sky in the ultraviolet, using Aerobee rockets. They discovered the presence of an intense radiation which they identified by its atmospheric absorption as the Lyα line of hydrogen. The radiation was observed not only when the viewing direction was upward but also when it was downward. In the latter case the signal first appeared at the 85-km level and ceased to increase in intensity after the 120-km level was passed. Byram *et al.* attribute the effect to resonance scattering of the incident Lyα by hydrogen in the region between the 85- and 120-km levels.

5.1.1.2 *Bands*

It is scarcely worth attempting to give a connected account of the identification of the various band systems. Progress has been far from steady, some identifications being proposed, accepted, and then later rejected. The rather confusing development is perhaps best appreciated by examining the striking difference between the lists of band systems given in surveys published within a few years of each other (cf. Déjardin,[29] Frongia,[30] Pearse,[31] Kastler,[32] Swings,[33] Meinel,[34] Chamberlain and Meinel,[35] and Barbier[13]). Among the band systems whose presence was at one time advocated but whose absence is now generally accepted are the following: O_2, Schumann-Runge system; N_2, Second Positive, Lyman-Birge-Hopfield and Goldstein-Kaplan systems; NO, β and γ systems; CO, Cameron system. We shall not discuss the numerous changes in the identifications and shall confine ourselves to presenting the current views regarding which band systems are emitted. For convenience we shall discuss the contribution from each species of molecule in a separate subsection.

Oxygen. In 1941 Dufay[36] suggested that the O_2, $A\ ^3\sum_u^+ \rightarrow X\ ^3\sum_g$ system occurs in the nightglow. Many years earlier this system had been discovered in absorption by Herzberg[37] (after whom it is named), and it has since been studied extensively by him[38] (again in absorption); but it was not until 1954 that a laboratory emission source was found by Broida and Gaydon,[39] and the vibrational quantum numbers were finally determined.

Swings[40] examined Dufay's suggestion critically shortly after it was put forward and confirmed that the Herzberg system can indeed account for many of the ultraviolet features. The possibility of this being purely fortuitous had to be considered, however, the spectra compared being rich and the accuracy of the wavelength determinations being rather poor. A quantitative assessment of the position was therefore attempted by Dufay and Déjardin.[41] They concluded that the number of coincidences between members of certain progressions of the Herzberg system and nightglow features in the interval from 3068 to 3954 A is such that it cannot reasonably be attributed to chance alone. Support for the presence of the Herzberg system is provided by later studies by Barbier[42] and by Dufay[43] extending further into the visible, and by a comparison made by Broida and Gaydon[39] of the intensity distribution observed in their laboratory source with that observed in the nightglow.

Though the evidence that has been indicated is telling, it is far from conclusive. The identification was not fully established until 1955, when Chamberlain[2] obtained a high-resolution spectrum in the ultraviolet showing the rotational structure. His work leaves no doubt but that the Herzberg system is prominent and highly developed ($v' \leqslant 7$) in the nightglow.

The presence of the (0, 1) band of the Atmospheric system O_2, $b\,^1\Sigma_g^+ \rightarrow X\,^3\Sigma_g^-$ was announced by Meinel[44] in 1948, the P and R branches at 8629 A and 8659 A being clearly resolved, and the identification unambiguous. This band (and others originating from the same upper level) had earlier been discovered by Kaplan[45] in the luminescence from the oxygen afterglow. It is sometimes referred to as the Kaplan-Meinel band.

In the case of the nightglow the (0, 0) band at about 7619 A cannot be detected from a station on the earth's surface, since it is completely absorbed in passing through the air. It has been suggested that a feature at about 9976 A noticed by Krassovsky[11] may be attributed to the (0, 2) band at 9965 A, but, as Meinel[34] has pointed out, the suggestion must be rejected, since the feature is stated to be stronger than the (0, 1) band, whereas the (0, 2) band is known (cf. Nicholls[46]) to be very much weaker.

The lack of development of the Atmospheric system in the nightglow is remarkable. Only the single band mentioned is observed. From his failure to detect it Meinel[47] estimates that the (1, 1) band at 7708 A (which is the most prominent member of the $v' = 1$ progression) is not more than one-fifteenth as intense as the (0, 1) band.

Some evidence for the presence of the O_2, $^3\Delta_u \rightarrow a\,^1\Delta_g$ system has been announced by Chamberlain.[4a]

Nitrogen. Numerous coincidences between nightglow features in the spectral region from 3500 to 5000 A and bands of the Vegard-Kaplan system N_2, $A\,^3\Sigma_u^+ \rightarrow X\,^1\Sigma_g^+$ were reported in 1935 by Kaplan[48] and by Cabannes and Dufay.[49] The occurrence of these coincidences was confirmed in subsequent investigations,[41, 42] and up to about 1950 the proposed identification was widely accepted. Several workers then became suspicious, being disturbed in particular by the peculiar intensity distribution observed in the nightglow.

Meinel,[34] for example, made a comparison with the intensity distribution observed in auroras (where the identification is beyond dispute). He found that bands arising from a common level have different relative intensities in the two sources. Chamberlain and Oliver[50] have also emphasized this discrepancy, though they[51] suggested that the issue may be confused by the background continuum. Another difficulty has been raised by Barbier,[52] who reports that the contours of the two principle features attributed to the system, $\lambda\,4166$ and $\lambda\,4416$, are utterly different from the contours of the bands of the Vegard-Kaplan system recorded in auroras by himself and Williams.[53] The spectroscopic studies of Dufay[54] have led him also to conclude that the old identification must be abandoned.

The only nightglow feature now assigned by most observers to a system of nitrogen is a feeble one near 3911 A, which Chamberlain and Oliver[51] and Meinel[55] in 1953 suggested may arise from the emission of the (0, 0) band of the First Negative system N_2^+, $B\,{}^2\sum_u^+ \to X\,{}^2\sum_g^+$ at 3914 A. Work by Barbier[52] and Dufay[54] lends support to the identification. Some indication of the possible presence of the (0, 1) band at 4278 A (Chamberlain and Oliver,[51] Dufay[54]) and the (1, 0) band at 3582 A (Dufay[54]) has been reported, but the evidence is acknowledged to be inconclusive. Chamberlain[4a] comments that direct or scattered auroral contamination is a hazard at Williams Bay so that the observations carried out there do not determine whether or not the First Negative system should be regarded as part of the true nightglow.

Hydroxyl. Perhaps the greatest single advance in knowledge concerning the nightglow was that made by Meinel[56] when in 1950 he succeeded in obtaining a spectrum of the infrared region showing the detailed structure of the main features and was hence able to determine the rotational constants of the vibrational levels. The derived values of these constants proved that the emitter must be a hydride and together with the observed doublet structure limited consideration to the hydroxyl radical. Herzberg, to whom the results were communicated, immediately noted excellent coincidences with extrapolated positions of the rotational-vibrational bands in the ground $X\,{}^2\prod$ term (the constants required for the extrapolation being, of course, known from earlier work on the electronic bands[57]). A detailed analysis by Meinel[56] placed the identification beyond all possible doubt. Since then the Meinel system (as it is now called) has been discovered in the spectra of oxyacetylene and oxyhydrogen flames (Benedict *et al.*[58]) and has been extensively studied (Déjardin *et al.*,[59] Herman and Hornbeck[60]). As a result, the wavelengths of all the bands are known accurately. Those originating from levels with vibrational quantum number 10 or greater do not appear in the nightglow. The others account for many of the features in the spectral region between 5500 and 20,000 A (cf. Krassovsky,[11] Cabannes *et al.*,[7] Kron,[61] Dufay,[62] Chamberlain and Oliver,[63] Chamberlain and Roesler,[10] Gush and

Jones,[12] Fedorova[64]). Some of these features had previously been attributed to the First Positive system of nitrogen (Elvey *et al.*,[65] Stebbins *et al.*[66]). A useful survey of the work done up to the end of 1955 has been compiled by Andrillat.[67]

Information on the relative intensities of the bands has been collected together by Chamberlain and Smith.[67a] Further information has since been obtained by Dufay.[67b]

The presence of the Meinel system has occasionally in the past led to erroneous conclusions being drawn on the correlations that exist between the intensities of the various spectral features and on other matters, because of failure to realize that, if the dispersion used is low, then λ 6300-6364 may be contaminated with the (9, 3) band and λ 5893 with the (8, 2) band.

Götz and Nicolet[68] have suggested tentatively that the hydroxyl resonance system $A\ ^2\sum^+ \to X\ ^2\prod$ may appear in the ultraviolet region.

Polyatomic constituents. Ozone, carbon dioxide, water vapor, and other polyatomic constituents contribute radiation of thermal origin to the infrared part of the spectrum.[69] This radiation is emitted from the lower rather than the upper atmosphere and is therefore outside the scope of the present volume.

5.1.1.3 *Continuum*

As has been recognized for many years, the spectrum of the night sky contains a strong continuum. This continuum first becomes apparent just below 4000 A and extends indefinitely to the red. In comparison with the resolved discrete features, it is most intense in the blue-violet, where indeed it is actually dominant. The distribution with wavelength has been studied by Shefov.[69a]

Stellar absorption lines such as the H and K lines of CaII are present (Rayleigh,[70] Dufay[71]), indicating that some of the light is extraterrestrial in origin. The importance of the extraterrestrial part has been stressed in particular by Chamberlain and Oliver[51] * and by Meinel.[55]

Evidence for a contribution from upper atmospheric emission is provided by the dependence of the measured intensity on the angle which the viewing direction makes with the vertical and by the seasonal variation (Barbier,[13] Dufay and Dufay[3]). Little reliable information on this contribution is available. Barbier *et al.*[72] have inferred from their observations that a true nightglow continuum exists in the visible. According to Roach and Meinel,[73] about 20 % of the continuum near 5300 A is emitted from the upper atmosphere. Rocket experiments have led Heppner and Meredith[74] to conclude that rather more, at least about 50 %, is so emitted. The numerous bands

---

* Chamberlain[4a] now considers that he overemphasized the extraterrestrial contribution to the continuum in his early work.

in the blue-violet obscure the position there. Barbier[75] has suggested that there is no need to invoke any nightglow continuum other than that resulting from the superposition of these bands. Robley[76] has found little correlation, however, between the variation in the intensity of the bands and the variation in the intensity of the background.

5.1.2 *Polarization*

It would be very surprising if the nightglow emissions exhibited any polarization effect. Nevertheless, Khvostikov[77] carried out measurements on the lines and announced that a polarization of some 14 % appears to exist. Bricard and Kastler[78] have reinvestigated the supposed phenomenon, using a Savart-Lyot polariscope. They showed that $\lambda\,5577$ and $\lambda\,6300$, if polarized at all, are polarized to *less than* 1.5 %, so that Khvostikov's results must be in error.

5.1.3 *Temperature*

Information on the temperatures of the luminous layers may be obtained from the detailed structure of the spectral features, provided the departure from thermal equilibrium which may be caused by the excitation mechanism is dissipated before appreciable emission occurs. This requires that

$$A \ll \kappa n(\mathrm{M}) \tag{5.1}$$

where A is the spontaneous transition probability, κ is a rate coefficient describing how collisions redistribute the energy in the mode concerned, and $n(\mathrm{M})$ is the concentration of the atoms or molecules effecting the redistribution. For translational and rotational energy κ is quite large, perhaps of the order of $3 \times 10^{-10}\,\mathrm{cm^3/sec}$, so that condition (5.1) is satisfied for many forbidden transitions up to and even above the altitude where $n(\mathrm{M})$ is $10^{11}\,\mathrm{cm^{-3}}$. In contrast, for vibrational energy it is usually assumed that κ is so small that condition (5.1) is not satisfied in the altitude range of interest. It should be noted, however, that though the *direct* redistribution of vibration energy may proceed slowly the *indirect* redistribution may proceed rapidly through atom-atom interchange[79] or through the transference of electronic energy.[80]

The first serious attempt at an interferometric study of a nightglow line was made by Babcock,[18] who succeeded in obtaining sharp fringes from $\lambda\,5577$ at an order of 85,000. It was at one time thought that a useful upper limit to the Doppler width, and so to the temperature, could be derived from his results, but Spitzer[81] and Armstrong[82] have shown that this is not possible. Taking advantage of modern optical techniques, Wark and Stone[83] and Armstrong[84] independently made fresh attacks on the observational problem a few years ago. The conclusions they reached are in satisfactory harmony. Wark and Stone found that the temperature lies between 155° and 230°K; Armstrong found that it lies between 180° and 220°K and is probably near 190°K.

From a preliminary interferometric study they have made of $\lambda\,6300$, Cabannes and Dufay[85] have deduced that the temperature corresponding to the Doppler width of the nightglow line is less than 700°K.

Several temperature determinations based on the rotational distributions in the various band systems have been made.

For the hydroxyl system he discovered, Meinel[86] got a rotational temperature of $260° \pm 5°$K. Dufay and Dufay[87, 67b] obtained almost exactly the same value, but Gush and Jones[12] obtained only $200° \pm 20°$K. All three determinations were carried out in middle latitudes. Working at high latitudes (northern Greenland), on the same system Chamberlain and Oliver[88] found the temperature to be between 300° and 350°K. A pronounced latitude effect is tentatively suggested. Supporting evidence has been put forward by Mironov *et al.*[88a]. Diurnal and seasonal and possible secular variations must be investigated, however, before the pattern of the results can be properly discerned. The pattern may be quite complex: thus the temperature must be sensitive to the altitude of the luminous layer, and this altitude is probably not constant.

Accurate measurements have also been made on the Kaplan-Meinel band of oxygen. Meinel[47] found the rotational temperature to be normally $150° \pm 20°$K, but on an occasion when the intensity was unusually high he found it to be $200° \pm 10°$K. A value of about 130°K has been obtained by Dufay and Dufay,[87] and a value of about 150°K by Mironov *et al.*[88a] Clearly the observed radiation must originate from near the temperature minimum at the 82-km level. Inspection of figures published by Chamberlain[89] shows that the amount of oxygen above this level is insufficient to cause significant degradation[80] of the (0, 0) band $\lambda\,7620$ to the (0, 1) band $\lambda\,8645$ through

$$\lambda\,7620 + O_2(X\,^3\textstyle\sum_g^-\ v = 0) \rightarrow O_2(b\,^1\textstyle\sum_g^+\ v = 0) \tag{5.2}$$

followed by

$$O_2(b\,^1\textstyle\sum_g^+\ v = 0) \rightarrow O_2(X\,^3\textstyle\sum_g^-\ v = 1) + \lambda\,8645 \tag{5.3}$$

From the low values found for the rotational temperature it may be inferred that collisional deactivation is too rapid to allow the degradation sequence to operate deep in the atmosphere. This is of considerable importance, since the photon intensity in the unobserved $\lambda\,7620$ band is about twenty times that in the observed $\lambda\,8645$ band.*

* The Franck-Condon factors for $\lambda\,7620$ and $\lambda\,8645$ are 0.93_3 and 0.06_5, respectively (Nicholls[46]).

From studies of the profiles of the bands of the Herzberg system, Swings[90] deduced that the rotational temperature of the emitting oxygen molecules is about 150°K, and Barbier[91] that it is between 170° and 220°K. The accuracy of these estimates is poor. In 1955 Chamberlain[2] re-examined the problem, and, in spite of the much better spectra he had available, he considered that all that could be concluded is that the rotational temperature does not exceed 200°K.

5.1.4 *Temporal Variation* *

5.1.4.1 *Diurnal Variation*

Careful studies of the diurnal variations in the intensities $I(\lambda)$ of the atomic emissions have been carried out by Dufay and Tcheng[92] at Haute Provence (44° N) and by Pettit *et al.*[93, 94] at Cactus Peak, California (36° N). Figure 1 shows the closely similar mean variations at the two stations. The variations during individual nights may be very different from the means (cf. Fig. 2).

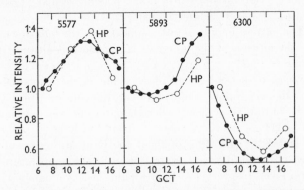

Fig. 1. Mean diurnal variation of intensity of atomic lines in the nightglow. Solid lines, Cactus Peak; dashed lines, Haute Provence. After H. B. Pettit, F. E. Roach, P. St. Amand, and D. R. Williams, *Ann. Géophys.* **10**, 326 (1954).

The tendency for $I(5577)$ to pass through a maximum shortly after midnight is also observed[95] at Mount Elbrus, Georgia (43° N), and at other stations in mid-latitudes. Karandikar[96] has stated, however, that there is a minimum near midnight at Poona, India (18° N). The possibility that the form of the variation may depend on latitude is thus raised. Pettit and Manring[97] have suggested that Sacramento Peak, New Mexico (33° N), may lie in a region of transition from one form to another, for in a series of observations there they found a maximum on 54 % of the nights, a minimum on 36 %, and little variation on the remaining 10 %.

* Twilight effects are discussed in § 5.2.

It is seen from Fig. 1 that I (6300) is greatest in the evening immediately after sunset, falls to a minimum, and then rises slightly toward dawn. The fall and the rise are sometimes referred to as the post- and pretwilight effects. They were discovered by Elvey and Farnsworth.[98] Barbier[99] has found that the posttwilight effect is pronounced throughout the year, whereas the pretwilight effect disappears during the summer and is marked only in

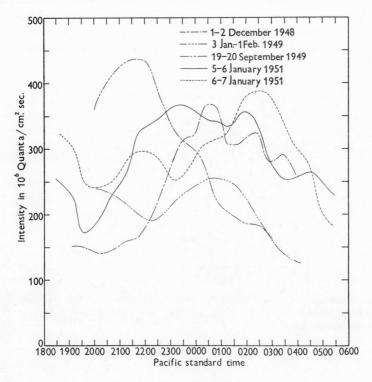

FIG. 2. Examples of diurnal variation of intensity of green line at Cactus Peak. After F. E. Roach and H. B. Pettit, *J. Geophys. Res.* **56**, 325 (1951).

November, December, and January. This is in accord with later results of Manring and Pettit[100] (Fig. 3). Barbier[101] reports that the behavior at Tamanrasset, Algeria (23° N), is very peculiar in that in about one night in three I(6300) rises for several hours to perhaps ten times its normal value.

After an uncertain start in the early hours of the night I(5893) increases to about 1.3 times its initial value (Fig. 1).

The Herzberg system of oxygen has been studied by Barbier,[102] who reports that the behavior is rather erratic but that there is a tendency for the intensity to rise to a maximum.

Berthier[103] has investigated the (0, 1) band of the Atmospheric system of oxygen. It appears from his work that the intensity is in general weakest at the beginning of the night and increases by a factor of 1.4 to 2.4 (or occasionally by much more) before dawn.

Photometric measurements in the infrared region were made in 1942 by Elvey.[104] As is now realized, they refer to the Meinel hydroxyl system. They indicate that the emission sometimes decays slowly during the entire night and sometimes decays only for an initial period and then recovers. Armstrong[105] has observed these and also other types of variation. It may be that all that can be said is that the variation is irregular.* Certain nights are characterized by a fluctuating emission of abnormally high intensity.[104] †

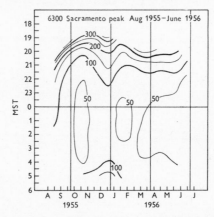

FIG. 3. Contours of equal intensity of λ 6300 (averaged over each observing month). After E. R. Manring and H. B. Pettit, *in* "The Threshold of Space" (M. Zelikoff, ed.), p. 58, Pergamon, London, 1957.

Perhaps even more significant than the diurnal variations themselves is the fact that the intensities are maintained to a remarkable extent throughout the dark hours. As Chapman[106] has pointed out, this is of great importance in connection with the problem of determining what is the source of the energy of the nightglow.

5.1.4.2 *Annual Variation*

Using visual photometers fitted with color filters, Rayleigh and Jones[107] investigated the variation through several years in the blue, green, and red regions at Terling, England (52° N), Cape Town (34° S), and Canberra (35° S).

* See, however, Berthier.[103]

† The possibility that this abnormal emission is due to the Atmospheric system of oxygen is not excluded by Elvey's measurements.

The green filter transmitted light between about 5470 and 5670 A, so that readings taken with it may be assumed to refer to λ 5577 alone. Both the

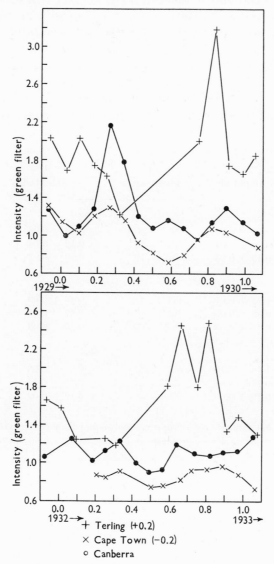

FIG. 4. Variation of intensity of green line in 1929 and 1932 at Terling, Cape Town, and Canberra. From Lord Rayleigh and H. S. Jones, *Proc. Roy. Soc.* A**151**, 22 (1935).

other filters were opaque to this line, the blue transmitting only at shorter wavelengths and the red only at longer wavelengths. There is a regrettable lack of spectral purity, for the Herzberg system and the continuum contribute to the blue, and λ 5893, λ 6300-6364, the Meinel system, and, once again, the continuum contribute to the red.

Figure 4 shows the variation of the green intensity in 1929 and 1932 (during which the mean sunspot areas were 1.24 and 0.16, respectively). The changes occurring are obviously complicated. To elucidate the position,

TABLE I

Harmonic Analysis of Intensities

From Lord Rayleigh and H. S. Jones, *Proc. Roy. Soc.* A**151**, 22 (1935).

Station	12-month term		6-month term	
	Amplitude	Phase angle	Amplitude	Phase angle
Blue filter				
Terling[a]	0.69 ± 0.06	$180° \pm 10°$	0.09 ± 0.08	$(325° \pm 55°)$
Canberra[a]	0.20 ± 0.04	$337° \pm 12°$	0.12 ± 0.04	$67° \pm 20°$
Cape Town[a]	0.13 ± 0.03	$52° \pm 12°$	0.10 ± 0.02	$117° \pm 15°$
Green filter				
Terling	1.22 ± 0.07	$171° \pm 4°$	0.48 ± 0.09	$295° \pm 10°$
Canberra	0.53 ± 0.05	$351° \pm 6°$	0.52 ± 0.05	$208° \pm 6°$
Cape Town	0.28 ± 0.03	$87° \pm 6°$	0.33 ± 0.03	$216° \pm 5°$
Red filter				
Terling	1.15 ± 0.10	$127° \pm 5°$	0.31 ± 0.08	$212° \pm 15°$
Canberra	0.74 ± 0.04	$297° \pm 3°$	0.25 ± 0.04	$184° \pm 9°$
Cape Town	0.19 ± 0.03	$260° \pm 8°$	0.19 ± 0.02	$160° \pm 7°$

[a] Cape Town and Canberra are at approximately equal distances from the geographical equator, and Terling and Canberra are at approximately equal distances from the magnetic equator.

Rayleigh and Jones subtracted out from their data (expressed on a logarithmic scale) a constant term and a secular term and represented the remainder in the form

$$R = a \sin (\theta + \alpha) + b \sin (2\theta + \beta) \qquad (5.4)$$

where θ is the time measured from the beginning of the year in units such that 2π radians represents one year, so that the first term corresponds to a variation of period 12 months and the second to a variation of period 6 months. The derived values of the amplitudes a and b and the phase angles α and β for each of the three spectral regions studied are given in Table I.

Rayleigh and Jones offer the following comments:

1. The amplitudes a are greatest at Terling and smallest at Cape Town.

2. The angles α at Terling and Canberra differ by approximately 180°, which by itself would suggest that the 12-month term is opposite in phase in one hemisphere (geographical or geomagnetic) from what it is in the other. The Cape Town results show, however, that the dependence on latitude is not simple.

3. The corresponding amplitudes b and angles β (excluding the first entry in the table, which is unreliable) are about the same at all stations.

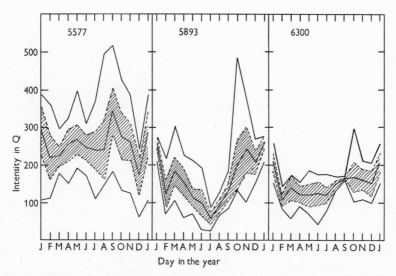

FIG. 5. Seasonal variation of intensity of atomic lines in the nightglow at Cactus Peak. The upper and lower curves represent the maximum and minimum intensity observed during each month; and the central curve represents the average. The shaded portion indicates the probable error based on the scatter of the included data. After H. B. Pettit, F. E. Roach, P. St. Amand, and D. R. Williams, *Ann. Géophys.* **10,** 326 (1954).

Although these comments are suggestive, it is apparent that the global pattern of the variations remains very uncertain. Unfortunately the more recent observations [prior to the International Geophysical Year (IGY)] have been carried out almost entirely at middle northern latitudes and thus contribute little to this particular topic.

The groups at Haute Provence and Cactus Peak have added much to our knowledge of the behavior of the atomic lines. Both remark on the considerable night-to-night fluctuations in intensity which tend to obscure the annual variations (cf. Fig. 5). By an analysis rather similar to that of Rayleigh and

Jones, Dufay and Tcheng[108] find that their smoothed observed intensities, $I(\lambda)$, may be expressed by the formulas

$$I(5577) = 30.36(\pm\ 0.77) + 4.92(\pm\ 0.74) \sin [\theta + 163.8°(\pm\ 15.6°)]$$
$$+ 2.03(\pm\ 1.21) \sin [2\theta + 263.2°(\pm\ 26.8°)] \qquad (5.5)$$

$$I(6300) = 27.51(\pm 0.35) + 12.00(\pm 0.40) \sin [\theta + 100.2°(\pm 2.7°)]$$
$$+ 1.34(\pm 0.56) \sin [2\theta + 81.3°(\pm 18.9°)] \qquad (5.6)$$

$$I(5893) = 13.80(\pm 0.34) + 9.08(\pm 0.34) \sin [\theta + 105.7°(\pm 3.6)]$$
$$+ 0.71(\pm 0.33) \sin [2\theta + 163.4°(\pm 48.2°)] \qquad (5.7)$$

arbitrary units being used. The phase angles appearing in formula (5.5) are in satisfactory accord with the corresponding (green-filter) phase angles of Rayleigh and Jones.[107] For λ 5577 the 12-month term and the 6-month term are of comparable magnitude, whereas for the other emissions the former term is much larger than is the latter. The close coincidence between the phase angles of the dominant terms associated with λ 6300 and λ 5893 is striking. According to Pettit et al.,[94] Dufay and Tcheng may have slightly overestimated the variations. In general, however, the agreement between the observational results of the two groups is excellent.

Attention is drawn to the extent by which λ 5893 weakens in going from winter to summer: Manring and Pettit,[100] observing at Sacramento Peak, report that the intensity at the maximum in November is more than twenty-five times the intensity at the minimum in June.

The Herzberg system has an annual variation rather similar to that of λ 5577 (Barbier[102]), and so also has the band of the Atmospheric system (Berthier[103]). It is to be noted that this latter is erratic, becoming sometimes extremely strong (Meinel[47]).

Though there is some evidence for an October-November peak and perhaps a May peak, the intensity of the Meinel hydroxyl system in general changes remarkably little through the year (Berthier,[103] Barbier,[99] Dufay[67b]).

5.1.4.3 *Secular Variation*

Table II gives the mean yearly intensities obtained by Rayleigh and Jones,[107] using their blue, green, and red filters together with the corresponding mean yearly sunspot areas. As can be seen, the mean intensities change only slightly—much less, for example, than does the electron concentration in the nocturnal F layer.

Though the changes are but minor, Rayleigh and Jones inferred from them that there is probably a real tendency for the intensities to increase with increasing sunspot area. The derived correlation coefficients between the mean yearly intensities and the sunspot areas are shown in Table III. All are positive, but only in the case of the green filter is the correlation well

TABLE II

Mean Yearly Intensity

From Lord Rayleigh and H. S. Jones, *Proc. Roy. Soc.* **A151,** 22 (1935)

(Arbitrary units—same for each station but dependent on filter)

Station	1924	1925	1926	1927	1928	1929	1930	1931	1932	1933
					Blue filter					
Terling	—	—	—	3.96	4.71	4.16	4.34	4.16	4.13	4.05
Canberra	—	—	4.97	4.44	4.84	4.69	4.94	4.67	4.71	4.60
Cape Town	—	—	5.27	5.14	5.20	4.94	4.70	4.75	4.69	—
					Green filter					
Terling	1.11	1.29	1.37	1.35	1.53	1.59	1.44	1.43	1.33	1.24
Canberra	—	—	1.30	1.08	1.26	1.23	1.13	1.10	1.09	1.11
Cape Town	—	—	1.23	1.17	1.26	1.22	1.10	1.07	1.05	—
					Red filter					
Terling	—	—	—	5.85	6.81	6.10	6.25	6.49	6.27	6.10
Canberra	—	—	5.62	5.10	5.14	4.84	5.06	5.21	5.03	5.13
Cape Town	—	—	5.86	5.92	6.22	6.17	5.77	5.56	5.60	—
				Mean yearly sunspot area						
	0.28	0.83	1.26	1.06	1.39	1.24	0.52	0.28	0.16	0.09

marked at the three stations. The evidence provided by the observations carried out at Haute Provence and Cactus Peak before 1955 is inconclusive (Roach *et al.*[94]). In 1959, however, Barbier[108a] reported later evidence which suggests that λ 5577 and the Herzberg system have the tendency suspected by Rayleigh and James. He found that secular changes in the intensities of λ 5893 and of the Meinel system are slight or non-existent.

TABLE III

Correlation Coefficients between Intensities and Sunspot Areas

From Lord Rayleigh and H. S. Jones, *Proc. Roy. Soc.* **A151,** 22 (1935)

Station	Blue filter	Green filter	Red filter
Terling	+0.45	+0.60	+0.12
Canberra	+0.23	+0.79	+0.15
Cape Town	+0.89	+0.99	+0.91

Cabannes *et al.*[109] have found some indication that there is a 27-day periodicity in the intensity of λ 5577 (though not in that of λ 6300 or that of λ 5893).

5.1.4.4 *Correlations*

Considerable effort has been devoted to seeking correlations involving the nightglow features. Some correlations have been confidently claimed and later abandoned; others are merly due to chance similarities in the diurnal or annual variations of the quantities concerned and have no real physical significance. Caution must therefore be exercised.

St. Amand[110] and Barbier[111] have adduced evidence that $I(6300)$ is approximately proportional to the total electron content of the overhead F layer. The proposed relation is plausible (cf. § 5.1.8.3). Correlations between $I(5577)$ and various properties of the F layer have been suggested[112,113,110] but are difficult to accept in view of the altitude of the level from which the green line is emitted (cf. § 5.1.7). No correlation with the E layer has been established.

In the absence of auroras the night-to-night fluctuations in the intensities do not appear to be connected with solar activity or magnetic disturbance.

Throughout a given night there seem to be correlations between certain of the emissions. The two most definite cases of correlation are the Meinel system—$\lambda\,5893$ (Berthier,[103] Barbier[99,102]) and the Herzberg system—$\lambda\,5577$ (Barbier[99,102]).

5.1.4.5 *Bright Nights*

On occasional nights the sky becomes exceptionally bright—so much so that the Milky Way vanishes in the background luminosity. Rayleigh[114] found, for example, that the brightness on the night of November 8, 1929, was about four times the normal. The most obvious supposition to make is that such so-called *bright nights* are simply a manifestation of the occurrence of auroras, but, as Rayleigh has emphasized, the two phenomena are quite different. Perhaps the most striking difference is that the First Negative system of nitrogen, which is so characteristic of auroras, is not detectable during bright nights. Observers (Störmer,[115] Tcheng and Dufay,[116] Götz[117]) are agreed that, compared with normal nights, the continuum and the red lines are greatly enhanced, and that the green line is also enhanced, but to a less extent. The behavior of the D doublet does not appear to be always the same: thus, in the bright night they studied, Tcheng and Dufay found no enhancement of it, whereas Götz has reported that very marked enhancement occurs.

Bright nights have a tendency to recur at intervals of 27 days and may form quite a lengthy series. According to Götz they are most common in years between maximum and minimum of solar activity. They are accompanied by magnetic disturbances.

Several workers (Rayleigh,[114] Störmer[115]) have commented on the steadiness of the emission and on the uniformity with which the entire sky is illuminated. Götz,[117] however, reports structures which he describes as some-times resembling faint homogeneous auroral arcs with dark segments.

5.1.5 *Morphology*

5.1.5.1 *Latitude Dependence*

The pattern of the variation with latitude of the intensity of the nightglow is of considerable interest to theorists. Unfortunately, it is difficult to de-termine properly. The main spectral features must be treated separately, and account must be taken of the possibility that the variation of each may depend on the time of the day, of the year, and of the sunspot cycle. Care must be exercised to ensure that the observed intensities are not influenced by feeble auroras (which are quite common even at middle latitudes; cf. Abadie *et al.*,[118] Barbier[119]).

By making observations toward the north and toward the south, a significant range of latitudes * can ideally be covered from a single station; and the local gradient of any intensity-latitude curve can be found. Though this is useful, it is clear that a chain of cooperating stations is essential so that progress can only be made by an effort such as that of the IGY. The relevant information so far available is fragmentary and need only be presented very briefly.

The pioneer work of Rayleigh and Jones[107] showed that the mean intensities of the green line at Terling (52° N) and Canberra (35° S) are about 30 % and 22 % greater than at Cape Town (34° S). As far as the sense is concerned, this is in harmony with the investigation of Barbier,[119] which indicates that the intensity is always greater at Haute Provence (44° N) than at Tamanrasset (23° N). The trend does not necessarily continue, to judge from a few measurements at College, Alaska (65° N), reported by Barbier and Pettit.[120] According to Roach *et al.*,[120a] however, the intensity at Thule (76° N) is about twice that at Fritz Peak (40° N). It would seem that the pattern must be quite complicated since the ratio of the intensity from the north of Fritz Peak to that from the south exhibits a semi-annual effect passing through maxima at the solstices and through minima at the equinoxes (Roach[120b]). Gold[120c] has put forward this particular facet of the behaviour of the green line as evidence favouring his hypothesis that the nightglow is closely associated with motions of the earth's outer atmosphere. The support it provides is tenuous.

Barbier[119] finds that in summer the red lines are more intense at Haute Provence than at Tamanrasset, whereas in winter the reverse is true; and that in summer the *D* doublet is about the same intensity at the two stations

* In the case of a luminous layer at an altitude of 100 km almost 20° of latitude may be explored by viewing north and south at zenith angles up to 85°.

whereas in winter it is more intense at Haute Provence than at Tamanrasset. Roach and his associates[94] report that for both spectral features the region of maximum luminosity appears to be to the south of Cactus Peak (36° N) in summer and to the north in winter.

5.1.5.2 Sky Surveys

Using a very fast photometer of high spectral purity, Manring and Pettit[100] have obtained a series of $\lambda\,5577$, $\lambda\,6300$, and $\lambda\,5893$ isophote maps of the night sky. They find that $O(z, \alpha, t)$, the observed brightness at zenith angle z, azimuth α, and time t, may be expressed in the form

$$O(z, \alpha, t) = A(t)B(z, \alpha) + R(z, \alpha, t) \tag{5.8}$$

where A is a function of t only, where over a period of several nights B may be taken as a function of z and α only, and where R is a small irregular residual.

Relation (5.8) signifies that if the residual is ignored the nightglow may be regarded as having a positional pattern which suffers an over-all diurnal variation in intensity. The diurnal variation, $A(t)$, has already been discussed. As will be recalled, it is somewhat erratic. According to Manring and Pettit, the positional pattern $B\,(z, \alpha)$ can be closely represented by the first two terms of a Fourier series:

$$B(z, \alpha) = C_1(z) + C_2(z) \cos(\alpha - \delta) \tag{5.9}$$

where the functions $C_1(z)$ and $C_2(z)$ and the angle δ change only slowly through the year. This formula is remarkably simple mathematically; but it is not so simple physically, as δ does not in general correspond to the north-south azimuth.

The patchiness of the nightglow has been noted by many observers. Manring and Pettit find that it is less pronounced than has usually been supposed; thus their residual R is not often more than 20 % of the background, and during about half the time it is very much less. The patches are usually in the form of small areas of perhaps 20° in diameter and may persist in recognizable form for several hours. On a few nights Manring and Pettit recorded long narrow arclike structures in the $\lambda\,5577$ emission, uncorrelated with magnetic, ionospheric, or auroral activity, and with no corresponding effect in the other emissions.

Roach et al.[120d] report that their observations on $\lambda\,5577$ indicate the existence of nightglow cells which have linear dimensions of about 2500 km (and are therefore larger than the field of view) and which have translatory motions with speeds of about 100 m/sec and rotatory motions with periods of about 5 hours. In their analysis of the data they introduce a correlation coefficient to express the degree of concordance of the variations in the

intensities from different directions. They find that the value of this coefficient in general decreases with increase in the distance between the two areas
of the nightglow layer being compared which suggests that formula (5.8)
oversimplifies the situation. Further, though they agree that the variation
of the intensity with azimuth (for a given zenith angle) is often approximately
sinusoidal they find that the phase angle δ appearing in formula (5.9) changes
through the night at Fritz Peak. Barbier and Glaume[120e] report that the
variation of the intensity with azimuth at Haute Provence is also rather
more complicated than at Sacramento Peak (the observing station of
Manring and Pettit). Much remains to be done before the irregularities can
be disentangled and the pattern be perceived.

5.1.6 *Absolute Intensities*

The angular surface brightness, B, is what is measured in nightglow
photometry. If the value at the zenith is expressed in units of photons/cm²
sec sterad, then $4\pi B$ is the photon intensity that is the apparent* number of

TABLE IV

Photon Intensities of the Nightglow Lines

From H. B. Pettit, F. E. Roach, P. St. Amand, and D. R. Williams, *Ann. Géophys.*
10, 326 (1954)

Line	Zenith photon intensity (rayleighs)		
	Maximum	Minimum	Mean
λ 5577	518	62	259
λ 6300[a]	259	42	146
λ 5893	488	25	149

[a] The photon intensity of λ 6364 is one-third that of λ 6300.

photons emitted per second from a vertical column of the atmosphere having
a cross section of 1 square centimeter. Some authors[121] favor the introduction
of the *rayleigh* (symbol R) as the unit of photon intensity, defining it to be
10^6 photons/cm² sec.

The first absolute measurement was carried out in 1930 by Rayleigh.[122]
It gave the photon intensity of λ 5577 to be 1.8×10^8 cm⁻² sec⁻¹ (180
rayleighs). Many absolute measurements on this and other emissions have
since been made. The results show the scatter to be expected from the

* The apparent number equals the actual number, provided the emission is isotropic
and provided also absorption is negligible.

variability of the nightglow.* We shall make no attempt to quote them in full. Instead we shall content ourselves with giving only sufficient to provide a crude quantitative model of the spectrum suitable for theorists.

In a summary of the work done at Cactus Peak, Pettit et al.[94] present Table IV, which, besides giving the mean photon intensities of $\lambda 5577$, $\lambda 6300$, and $\lambda 5893$, gives also maxima and the minima values. The following are the approximate zenith photon intensities of other features: Herzberg system, 1.5×10^2 rayleighs;[102] Kaplan-Meinel band of Atmospheric system, 2×10^3 rayleighs;[123] (4, 2) band of Meinel system, 1.75×10^5 rayleighs,[124] total for this system, 6.7×10^6 rayleighs;[124a] $\lambda 5300$ continuum, 0.8 rayleigh/A.[99]

5.1.7 *Altitude*

In principle it is possible to determine the altitude of a uniform thin luminous layer by studying how the intensity of the light received depends on the angle which the observing direction makes with the vertical. The method, which is named after van Rhijn, has been extensively used during the past decade. Unfortunately it is difficult to apply in practice, and it has added little to our knowledge of the altitudes of the layers responsible for the nightglow.

Though the results obtained by the van Rhijn method are sadly lacking in harmony, there is general agreement that the $O(^1D)$ altitude exceeds the $O(^1S)$ altitude (Dufay and Tcheng,[125] Barbier,[126] Roach and Meinel[73]); and that the $O_2(b^1\sum_g^+ v = 0)$ altitude is not greatly different from the $OH(X\,^2\prod, v \doteqdot 0)$ altitude (Meinel,[47] Berthier[103]). Roach et al.[127] inferred from their observations that the last-mentioned altitude is approximately 70 km, which is in reasonable accord with theoretical prediction and with rocket experiments (see below). This apparent success is, however, marred by the fact that Huruhata[128] found that the van Rhijn method gave a value of about 300 km for the same altitude, and Berthier[103] that it gave a value of about 170 km.

The van Rhijn method does not justify further discussion here. An appreciation of the causes of its many failures may be obtained from the more recent papers (cf. Barbier,[129] Barbier and Glaume,[130] Roach and Meinel,[73] Roach et al. [131]).

Several workers have sought to exploit the lack of uniformity of the nightglow in making altitude determinations—for example, by triangulation on a bright patch or other irregularity. Judging from the published results, such determinations are as yet not sufficiently objective to be of value.

---

* Interesting histograms of the intensity of $\lambda 5577$ have been given by Roach et al.[120a,122a] and by Barbier.[122b]

Use has also been made of the normal diurnal variation. Barbier[132] has carried out an interesting study of λ 6300-6364 during the period of the posttwilight fall in intensity. Observing at an angle of 15° above the horizon, he found that the intensity from the west corresponded to the intensity from the east, 80 minutes earlier. Assuming that the photon emission rate from any region is a function only of the time, he deduced that the luminosity lies at an altitude of about 300 km.

TABLE V

Temperatures and Altitudes of Luminous Layers

Nightglow line or band system	Measured temperature (°K)	Deduced altitude (km)
λ 5577 of OI	190	95
(λ 6300 of OI	⩽ 700	< 200)
Meinel, OH	260	65 (or ∼ 110)
	200	75 or 95
Atmospheric, O_2	150	82
	200	75 or 95
Herzberg, O_2	⩽ 200	> 75 and < 95

If the temperature-altitude curve is known, a temperature determination is, in effect, an altitude determination. Table V gives the temperatures quoted in § 5.1.3 with the corresponding altitudes as read from the rocket temperature-altitude curve of Michnevich.[132a]

Several theoretical papers concerning the probable altitudes have been published. Bates and Nicolet[133] have discussed the emission of λ 5893; Bates and Dalgarno[134] have in addition discussed the emission of the other main spectral features. They concluded that for most of the features * it is extremely difficult to accept altitudes well above 100 km such as were advocated until recently by the observers. No collision process could be found which could proceed rapidly enough at the low gas densities prevailing at these great altitudes to yield the measured photon intensities. In the special case of λ 5577, a cogent additional argument was advanced. From the intensity of the line relative to that of λ 6300-6364 it may be inferred that the emission must take place in a region where $O(^1D)$ suffers marked collisional deactivation; and an examination of the various possibilities revealed that deactivation could scarcely be effective enough much above the 100-km level.

By far the most reliable information on the altitudes is that gathered by the group at the U.S. Naval Research Laboratory using rocket-borne photometers.[74, 136] The principal results obtained are as follows.

* The most important exception is λ 6300-6364 (Seaton[135]).

The emission of $\lambda\,5577$ begins to appear between 85 and 90 km, is at its greatest between 94 and 99 km, and tails off to zero at 110 to 120 km (though in one case there was some evidence of emission above 143 km).

Ultraviolet emission near 2700 A, which is believed to be due to the Herzberg system of oxygen, has almost the same altitude distribution as has the green line.

In the three flights that were carried out, the maximum of the $\lambda\,5893$ luminosity was found to be at 85 km, 93 km, and 95 km, with the lower edge about 15 km below the maximum and the upper edge about the same above the maximum.

The position regarding $\lambda\,6300\text{-}6364$, the Meinel system of hydroxyl, and the continuum near 5300 A is still rather uncertain, since the filters employed did not isolate the different features fully. It seems likely, however, that the $\lambda\,6300\text{-}6364$ luminosity lies above the 163-km level (the highest level reached in the flight concerned), that the Meinel system originates between 56 km and about 100 km, and that the 5300-A continuum is emitted mainly from the 85- to the 110-km region.

The work done on the altitudes has been reviewed by Dalgarno.[137]

5.1.8 *Excitation Processes*

Various suggestions have been made regarding the source of the energy radiated in the nightglow. No attempt will be made to discuss them all fully.

If, in writing out a reaction, we give only the chemical symbol for an atom or molecule (other than polyatomic), we imply that we do not wish to specify the state.

5.1.8.1 *Incoming Particles*

Dauvillier[138] has proposed that the nightglow is caused by particles entering the atmosphere from extraterrestrial space. Several mechanisms may be envisaged which might conceivably give rise to an incident stream carrying sufficient energy (cf. Seaton[135]).

Though Dauvillier's proposal has some attractive aspects, incoming particles certainly cannot yield the major contribution to the nightglow, since, if they did, its spectrum would be very different from what it actually is: thus, small meteors would give their own characteristic spectrum: again, fast electrons, protons, or hydrogen atoms would give a spectrum similar to that of auroras. The possibility of a significant contribution to the more readily excited features is not of course excluded.

Great interest is attached to incoming particles from the solar gas because of Chapman's hypothesis[139] that they are of importance in the thermal economy of the upper atmosphere. In some calculations on the thermal economy Nicolet[140] has tentatively supposed that the inward energy flux associated with these particles may be of the order 0.6 erg/cm² sec or 4×10^{11} ev/cm² sec. If this were the case a significant contribution to λ 6300-6364 would be expected; indeed, it would be surprising that the feature is not stronger than it is (cf. Table IV) and that it does not exhibit more Doppler broadening than it does (cf. § 5.1.3). It is doubtless unrealistic to assume that the inward energy flux is uniform over the earth's surface. The geomagnetic field probably confines the incoming particles to high latitudes. Such confinement would make the effect on λ 6300-6364 more pronounced.

Blackett[141] has drawn attention to the fact that cosmic rays cause the emission of Cerenkov radiation in passing through the lower atmosphere. This radiation forms a continuum covering the transparent region of the spectrum with intensity approximately inversely proportional to the wavelength. The energy flux at sea level has been estimated by Blackett to be only about 2.3×10^6 ev/cm² sec, which is very much less than the energy flux from the main nightglow. Using a photomultiplier with its cathode at the focus of a parabolic mirror, Galbraith and Jelley[142] have detected light pulses and by means of an array of Geiger-Muller counters have shown them to be correlated with cosmic rays. They have also carried out polarization, directional, and other studies. Cerenkov radiation is strongly suggested.

Secondary effects resulting from cosmic rays may also lead to appreciable emission. The (0, 0) band, λ 3994, of the First Negative system of nitrogen would be expected to be one of the strongest features excited by the electrons liberated. Meinel[55] has estimated that a photon intensity of some $10^6/cm^{-2}$ sec^{-1} might ensue and has pointed out that this is of the order required for the feeble nightglow feature which has been attributed to this band.

According to Götz,[117] bright nights are caused by the incidence of solar and meteoric particles.

5.1.8.2 *Atmospheric Motions*

The possibility that atmospheric turbulence is in some way responsible for the nightglow has been put forward tentatively by de Jager,[143] who finds that the rate of viscous dissipation of the energy is adequate. It is not apparent, however, how the energy could become sufficiently concentrated to be available for producing excitation. As Seaton[135] has pointed out, the largest individual velocities reported for turbulent elements are not appreciably in excess of 300 m/sec, which corresponds to a kinetic energy of only 0.01 ev in the case of either an oxygen or nitrogen molecule, whereas excitation requires 2 ev and more.

According to Wulf[144] the nightglow is at least partially a manifestation of an electrical discharge caused by potential differences generated by zonal horizontal ionospheric winds cutting the vertical component of the earth's magnetic field. Wulf believes that the winds responsible for the separation of charge involved blow in the D and E regions and that the return path in which the postulated discharge occurs lies at an altitude of perhaps about 200 km. He has not yet developed his idea quantitatively. Even if a discharge actually does take place, it could account for only a few of the observed nightglow features. From the excitation functions and abundances concerned, it may readily be seen that the rate of formation of $O(^1D)$ would be considerably greater than that of $O(^1S)$ and many orders of magnitude greater than that of $Na(^2P)$; yet the average intensity of λ 6364-6300 is less than that of λ 5577 and about the same as that of λ 5893. Deactivating collisions might partly remove the discrepancy, but it is clear that the suggestion[144] that all three features are excited by discharge action cannot be accepted.

5.1.8.3 *Ionospheric Processes*

An obvious possibility is that part of the nightglow results from the recombination of the charged particles in the ionosphere. Some difficulty arises from the observed absolute intensities. Taking the maximum electron concentration in the F layer at midnight to be 2.5×10^5 cm^{-3} (a representative value), and taking the scale height to be 70 km, we find that the total number of electrons in the layer is only some 5×10^{12} cm^{-2}; and there are fewer electrons in the E and D layers. Negative ions are unlikely to be appreciably more, and may well be much less, abundant. Now, during the course of a 12-hour night, the number of photons emitted in the red lines is about 9×10^{12} cm^{-2} (cf. Table IV); a comparable number are emitted in the green line, the yellow doublet, the Herzberg system, and the continuum; and a far greater number are emitted in the Atmospheric system and in the Meinel system (§ 5.1.6). Since the intensities do not fall off markedly during the night, it may be concluded that there are not enough charged particles in the E and D layers to maintain any of the emissions, and that there are not enough even in the F layer to maintain the two strong systems. The position regarding the weaker spectral features is rather uncertain. At one time, many writers considered the F layer to be an inadequate reservoir of charged particles. It may in fact be just sufficient, however, since (1) a single recombination may give rise to several photons; (2) the charged particles may be more numerous than estimated, as full allowance may not have been made for those above the peak of the layer; (3) replenishment by some agency may conceivably take place at night. In view of the evidence on the altitudes (§ 5.1.7), it is apparent that the F layer may be invoked only in the case of the red lines.

Radiative recombination is not a sufficiently specific process to lead predominantly to the red lines; and in any event it is much too slow (Bates *et al.*[145]). Ionic recombination usually takes place along a few favored reaction paths (all exothermic to an appreciable extent) and may have a very large rate coefficient. It cannot be important in the present connection, however, as theoretical investigations (Bates and Massey[146]) indicate that it causes the disappearance of only a small fraction of the limited supply of charged particles.

Dissociative recombination in oxygen is rapid, and it has been suggested that

$$O_2^+(X\ ^2\Pi_g) + e \to O + O(^1D) \tag{5.10}$$

may be partly responsible for the red lines, the O_2^+ ions involved being formed either by charge transfer (Bates and Massey,[146] Nicolet[147])

$$O^+(^4S) + O_2(X\ ^3\textstyle\sum_g^-) \to O(^3P) + O_2^+(X\ ^2\Pi_g) \tag{5.11}$$

or by ion-atom interchange (Bates[148])

$$O^+(^4S) + O_2(X\ ^3\textstyle\sum_g^-) \to O_2^+(X\ ^2\Pi_g) + O(^3P). \tag{5.12}$$

The suggestion has been re-examined critically by Chamberlain,[149] who found that he could satisfactorily account for the observational results by making plausible but arbitrary assumptions about the rate coefficients and about certain atmospheric parameters. Brief mention may be made of two of these assumptions.

One assumption is that collisional deactivation of $O(^1D)$ atoms is unimportant in the F layer. This is consistent with conclusions reached by Seaton[150] in a theoretical study concerned mainly with collisional deactivation in auroras. It must be borne in mind, however, that any $O(^1D)$ atoms freed in dissociative recombination have probably considerable kinetic energy initially; and in consequence the chance of deactivation in the first few collisions suffered may be greater than supposed.

The second assumption is that the process

$$O_2^+(X\ ^2\Pi_g) + e \to O + O(^1S) \tag{5.13}$$

is very slow in comparison with reaction (5.10), as otherwise there would be conflict with the results of the rocket scientists (§ 5.1.7). It may be recalled that reaction (5.13) was invoked by Nicolet[147] to explain the presence of the green line in the nightglow (at the time when many erroneously believed the seat of the luminescence to lie in the F layer) and in addition was invoked by Seaton[151] to explain the intensity of the green line near the base of auroras. Since

$$NO^+(X\ ^1\textstyle\sum{}^+) + e \to N + O(^1S) \tag{5.14}$$

is strongly endothermic, the possibility of unwanted green-line emission would not arise if NO^+ were the most active molecular ion in the F layer.*

* Rocket experiments[150a] have shown that much NO^+ is present.

If the upper atmosphere were at a sufficiently high temperature, the red lines would be emitted as a result of excitation by direct electron impact

$$e + O(^3P) \rightarrow e + O(^1D). \tag{5.15}$$

Quantal calculations by Seaton[152] give the rate coefficient concerned to be about 1×10^{-19} cm^3 sec at 1000°K, 3×10^{-16} cm^3/sec at 1500°K, 2×10^{-14} cm^3/sec at 2000°K, 2×10^{-13} cm^3/sec at 2500°K, and 1×10^{-12} cm^3/sec at 3000°K. In view of the moderate temperature indicated by the observed Doppler width of the red lines (§ 5.1.3), it may hence be seen that the process cannot be important. This unimportance must be ensured by any acceptable model of the upper atmosphere. The condition is not very stringent.

It has been proposed[32] that the nightglow continuum may be due to radiative attachment

$$O(^3P) + e \rightarrow O^-(^2P) + h\nu \tag{5.16}$$

in the F and E layers. Since then, however, Smith and Branscomb[153] have shown that the electron affinity of atomic oxygen is only 1.46 ev, from which it follows that the peak of the continuum resulting from reaction (5.16) must lie near 8000 A, which is much too far in the red. The width of this continuum (defined as the wavelength distance between the positions of half-maximum intensity) must be quite narrow: for example, it would be about 200 A if the temperature were 500°K. An integrated photon intensity of only some 10^7 cm^{-2} sec^{-1} would be expected. Clearly another source must be sought for the nightglow continuum.

An electron liberated in associative detachment

$$O^-(^2P) + O(^3P) \rightarrow O_2 + e \tag{5.17}$$

may have as much as 3.6 ev kinetic energy. It may therefore excite atomic oxygen through reaction (5.15) and thus contribute to the red lines. An upper limit to the contribution is set by the rate of formation of the negative ions, which is of the order of 10^7 cm^{-2} sec^{-1}. Many of the electrons are probably given less than the maximum kinetic energy, as the oxygen molecules formed in reaction (5.17) may be in high rotational-vibrational levels or in electronically excited levels.

5.1.8.4 *Chemical Processes*

In 1931 Chapman[106] drew attention to the vast amount of chemical energy that is stored in the region near the 100-km level by the oxygen dissociated by photoaction and suggested that, in the course of the association that must be occurring to preserve the equilibrium, some of this energy is released as radiation. The number of free oxygen atoms is of the order of 5×10^{18} cm^{-2}, and it does not diminish significantly during the dark hours, so the reservoir is indeed large and has a continued existence. Further, the rate at which energy is converted from one form to another is very rapid, the mean number of dissociations, and therefore of associations, being of the order of 10^{12} cm^{-2} sec^{-1}. The potential at which oxygen atoms can supply energy is 5.11 ev. What would appear to be an extremely promising source for the nightglow is thus presented. A possible auxiliary source, which can supply energy at a potential of 9.76 ev, is provided by the dissociated nitrogen.

It is convenient to divide the various chemiluminescent processes which may take place into four main groups.

1. Since normal oxygen atoms can approach each other along the appropriate potential energy curves, oxygen molecules in the X $^3\sum_g^-$, a $^1\varDelta_g$, b $^1\sum_g^+$, $^1\sum_u^-$, $^3\varDelta_u$, and A $^3\sum_u^+$ states * can be formed through simple three-body association:

$$O(^3P) + O(^3P) + M \rightarrow O_2(X \, ^3\textstyle\sum_g^- \, a \, ^1\varDelta_g, \, b \, ^1\sum_g^+, \, ^1\sum_u^-, \, ^3\varDelta_u, \, A \, ^3\sum_u^+) + M \quad (5.18)$$

and, since the transitions concerned are optically allowed, oxygen molecules in the same states may also be formed at an appreciable (though probably slower) rate by radiative association:

$$O(^3P) + O(^3P) \rightarrow O_2(X \, ^3\textstyle\sum_g^-, \, a \, ^1\varDelta_g, \, b \, ^1\sum_g^+, \, ^1\sum_u^-, \, ^3\varDelta_u, \, A \, ^3\sum_u^+) + h\nu. \quad (5.19)$$

These association processes are generally regarded as the main processes opposing dissociation, so their combined rates would be expected to be of the order of 10^{12} cm^{-2} sec^{-1}. There seems no reason to suppose that the ground state, X $^3\sum_g^-$, is populated preferentially to any very marked extent. Hence it would seem that there should be intense emission from the excited a $^1\varDelta_g$, b $^1\sum_g^+$, $^1\sum_u^-$, $^3\varDelta_u$, and A $^3\sum_u^+$ states. The infrared Atmospheric system a $^1\varDelta_g \rightarrow X$ $^3\sum_g^-$ lies in a crowded and difficult spectral region. Of the others anticipated, only the main Atmospheric system, b $^1\sum_g^+ \rightarrow X$ $^3\sum_g^-$, and the Herzberg system, A $^3\sum_u^+ \rightarrow X$ $^3\sum_g^-$, have been identified with certainty. Their photon intensities are much less than 10^{12} cm^{-2} sec^{-1}. In contrast to other theories which have been advanced, the chemical theory is thus immediately able to account for the nightglow bands being strong. The difficulty rather is in understanding why they are not stronger than they are. Perhaps entry into the excited states may be hindered by the potentials along which the approach must be made being repulsive at large internuclear distances. It is just conceivable, too, that the rate of direct association is not so great as supposed—though the dissociation rate (from which this rate was obtained) can scarcely have been overestimated, and the equating of the two rates is justified unless indirect association (through, for example, some catalytic action) is unexpectedly rapid. According to Bates,[156] a possible explanation is that collisional deactivation through atom-atom interchange may be quite effective, a free oxygen atom displacing one of the atoms

* The unlettered $^1\sum_u^-$ and $^3\varDelta_u$ states are the states predicted theoretically by Moffit[154] and discovered experimentally by Herzberg.[155]

comprising an oxygen molecule in a state α to form an oxygen molecule in a lower state, β, thus

$$O(^3P) + O_2(\alpha) \rightarrow O_2(\beta) + O(^3P). \qquad (5.20)$$

Band systems emitted from molecules formed by association are in general highly developed. The fact that the (0, 1) band is the only member of the atmospheric system found in the nightglow spectrum might therefore appear peculiar. It has been suggested[80] that the transfer of electronic energy through

$$O_2(b\,^1\textstyle\sum_g^+, v \nRightarrow 0) + O_2(X\,^3\textstyle\sum_g^-, v = 0) \rightarrow O_2(X\,^3\textstyle\sum_g^-, v \nRightarrow 0) + O_2(b\,^1\textstyle\sum_g^+,$$
$$v = 0) \quad (5.21)$$

may be partly responsible for the absence of bands originating from excited vibrational levels.

2. The energy that becomes available when association takes place may be used in producing electronic excitation of a third atom or molecule. Chapman[106] has attributed the presence of the green and red lines to this mechanism, the specific processes advocated being

$$O_2 + O(^1S) \qquad (5.22)$$
$$3O(^3P) \Big\langle$$
$$O_2 + O(^1D). \qquad (5.23)$$

The rate coefficients are unknown, but it is not unreasonable to assume that they are high enough, since the intensity requirement necessitates that only a minute fraction of the triple collisions lead to excitation.

Chapman's suggestion regarding the green line has been widely accepted. In spite of the efforts of many workers, no plausible alternative has been discovered.

Like process (5.22), process (5.23) must be most effective at an altitude of about 100 km where the atomic oxygen concentration is greatest. It hence cannot account for the red lines which are now known to originate from much higher in the atmosphere (§ 5.1.7).

Irrespective of the occurrence of process (5.23) and of other excitation processes, the rate of formation of $O(^1D)$ atoms in the neighborhood of the 100-km level must be considerable, since the ^1D term is entered when the green line is emitted. Some deactivation process must therefore be operative. From the quantal calculations of Seaton[152] it may readily be seen that

$$e + O(^1D) \rightarrow e + O(^3P) \qquad (5.24)$$

is unimportant. The deactivation must be brought about in collisions with neutral particles. Several authors (Bates and Dalgarno,[157] Seaton[135]) have drawn attention to the fact that

$$O(^1D) + O_2(X\,^3\textstyle\sum_g^-, v = 0) \rightarrow O(^3P_2) + O_2(b\,^1\textstyle\sum_g^+, v = 2) \qquad (5.25)$$

is in almost exact energy resonance and have suggested that it may be responsible for the suppression of the red lines. The inverse process

$$O(^3P_2) + O_2(b\,^1\textstyle\sum_g^+, v = 2) \rightarrow O(^1D) + O_2(X\,^3\textstyle\sum_g^-, v = 0) \qquad (5.26)$$

must be taken into account. Its effectiveness in hindering the deactivation depends on the rate at which the $O_2(b\,^1\sum_g^+, v = 2)$ molecules are removed by collision processes like (5.20) and (5.21) and by spontaneous radiative transitions.

Several processes of the same type as (5.22) and (5.23) may be envisaged. Nicolet[157a] has suggested that the Vegard-Kaplan system, if present in the nightglow, may arise from

$$O(^3P) + N(^4S) + N_2(X\,^1\textstyle\sum_g^+) \rightarrow NO(X\,^2\Pi) + N_2(A\,^3\textstyle\sum_u^+). \qquad (5.27)$$

Associating oxygen atoms do not provide energy in sufficiently large quanta for the excitation of this system.

3. Strong continua may be emitted in radiative association. It has been estimated[80] that the intensity in photons per square centimeter per second resulting from

$$2O(^3P) \rightarrow O_2 + h\nu \qquad (5.28)$$

is of the order of 3×10^{31} times the numerical value of the rate coefficient involved. An appreciable intensity will ensue unless the rate coefficient is very small.

Several authors[80, 157a, 158] have suggested that

$$O(^3P) + NO(X\,^2\Pi) \rightarrow NO_2 + h\nu \qquad (5.29)$$

may contribute to the nightglow. Stewart[159] has shown that the continuum due to this process has a short wavelength limit between 3700 and 3800 A and rises to a flat maximum between 5400 and 5600 A.

Pressman et al.[160] arranged for 18.5 pounds of nitric oxide (that is, 1.7×10^{26} molecules of the gas) to be released from a rocket at an altitude of 106 km. As expected, an intense emission ensued. A spectroscopic examination indicated that the radiation was continuous, and process (5.29) was presumed responsible. The glow was estimated to have had an initial intensity of -2 visual magnitudes (equivalent to a total photon emission rate of about 6.7×10^{21} sec^{-1}). It grew in size and became fainter. An area of the sky equivalent to that of three or four moons was covered when the glow finally faded away, 10 minutes after the release. Pressman et al. suggested that process (5.29) was accompanied by

$$NO_2 + O(^3P) \rightarrow NO(X\,^2\Pi) + O_2(b\,^1\textstyle\sum_g^+) \qquad (5.30)$$

in which nitric oxide was re-formed. They suggested also that the decay of the glow was due to the removal of nitric oxygen by

$$NO(X\,^2\Pi) + N(^4S) \rightarrow N_2 + O(^3P, ^1D). \qquad (5.31)$$

Taking the rate coefficient for this process to be 10^{-12} cm^3/sec (Harteck[161]), they deduced that the atomic nitrogen concentration was of the order of 10^{10} cm^{-3}. As they stressed, however, their interpretation of the results is tentative.

In another rocket experiment designed to give information on the composition of the upper atmosphere, ethylene (which causes chemiluminescence in the presence of either atomic nitrogen or atomic oxygen) was released at 105 km and at 143 km (Zelikoff *et al.*[162]). Two glows, slightly different in color were observed. Unfortunately, the interpretation of the results is not so simple as had been hoped.

4. Two-body chemical processes of the substitution type

$$XY + Z \rightarrow X' + YZ' \tag{5.32}$$

are undoubtedly important, for only they could cause the observed emission from the rarer constituents.

Pointing out that the sodium in the upper atmosphere must continually be being oxidised and reduced, Chapman[163] suggested that the D doublet might be excited in the cycle through

$$\mathrm{NaO}(X\,{}^2\Pi) + \mathrm{O}({}^3P) \rightarrow \mathrm{O}_2(X\,{}^3\textstyle\sum_g^-) + \mathrm{Na}({}^2P) \tag{5.33}$$

According to Bawn and Evans,[164] however, the dissociation energy of NaO is at least 3.1 ev, in which case (5.33) would be endothermic by 0.1 ev or more; and Ogawa[165] reports that he has conducted experiments which show that the process does not occur. Alternative possibilities are (Bates and Nicolet[133])

$$\mathrm{NaH}(X\,{}^1\textstyle\sum) + \mathrm{O}({}^3P) \rightarrow \mathrm{OH}(X\,{}^2\Pi) + \mathrm{Na}({}^2P) \tag{5.34}$$

and (Bates[80])

$$\mathrm{NaH}(X\,{}^1\textstyle\sum) + \mathrm{H}({}^2S) \rightarrow \mathrm{H}_2(X\,{}^1\textstyle\sum_g^+) + \mathrm{Na}({}^2P) \tag{5.35}$$

both of which are known to be exothermic.

From a comparison of the intensity of the emission from sodium clouds ejected from night-flown rockets in winter and summer, Bedinger *et al.*[166] have concluded that the seasonal variation in the intensity of the $\lambda\,5893$ in the nightglow is to be attributed to a seasonal variation in the amount of atmospheric sodium. The sodium seeding experiments have raised several interesting photochemical problems. Their main value, however, has been in connection with wind studies (Manring *et al.*[166a]).

Bates and Nicolet[167] and Herzberg[168] have independently advocated that the Meinel hydroxyl system arises from the sequence

$$\mathrm{OH}(X\,{}^2\Pi) + \mathrm{O}({}^3P) \rightarrow \mathrm{H}(1\,{}^2S) + \mathrm{O}_2(X\,{}^3\textstyle\sum_g^-) \tag{5.36a}$$

$$\mathrm{H}(1\,{}^2S) + \mathrm{O}_3 \rightarrow \mathrm{O}_2(X\,{}^3\textstyle\sum_g^-) + \mathrm{OH}(X\,{}^2\Pi,\ v \leqslant 9). \tag{5.36b}$$

The energy available is insufficient to excite the levels with vibrational quantum number 10 or higher (from which no emission is observed). This natural avoidance of unwanted excitations was originally put forward as evidence favoring the view that process (5.36a) is the process actually operative, but, as Krassovsky[168a] has pointed out, if $OH(X\,^2\Pi,\ v \geqslant 10)$ molecules were in fact formed, they would be removed rapidly by

$$OH(X\,^2\Pi, v \geqslant 10) + O_2(X\,^3{\textstyle\sum_g^-}) \rightarrow H(1\,^2S) + O_3 \qquad (5.37)$$

Nevertheless, there can be little doubt but that the theory is correct: certain arguments that have been advanced against it have been answered by Bates and Moiseiwitsch;[168b] and positive support is provided by the laboratory work of McKinley and his associates,[169] which shows that a mixture of ozone and atomic hydrogen emits the Meinel hydroxyl system with an intensity distribution similar to that in the nightglow, and also that the reaction involved is as rapid as is required. There is no reason to suppose that the close energy balance causes the level with vibrational quantum number 9 to be preferentially populated as some workers have supposed.

Two-body processes may also contribute to emission from the main constituents: for example, Nicolet[157a] has suggested that process (5.30) may be partly responsible for the emission of the Atmospheric system.

5.2 Twilightglow

During the twilight periods certain spectral features are emitted more strongly than during the dark hours. It is with these features that the present section is concerned. A useful review has been given by Chamberlain.[169a]

5.2.1 $\lambda\,5893$ of NaI

As discovered independently by Currie and Edwards,[170] Cherniev and Vuks,[171] and Bernard,[23] the intensity of $\lambda\,5893$ is greatly enhanced at twilight. The explanation which immediately presents itself is that there is resonance scattering of solar radiation by free sodium atoms:

$$\left.\begin{array}{l} Na(^2S) + h\nu(\lambda\,5893) \rightarrow Na(^2P) \\ Na(^2P) \rightarrow Na(^2S) + h\nu(\lambda\,5893) \end{array}\right\} \qquad (5.38)$$

An alternative explanation which has been advocated by Vegard[172] is that the excited atoms are released in the photodissociation of some compound of the element. In support of this it was claimed[173] that a comparison of zenith and horizon measurements shows that the effective shadow of the earth is about 44 km above the surface, from which it was inferred that the solar radiation responsible for the twilight flash is screened by the ozone layer and therefore lies in the range 2000 to 3000 A. Dufay[174] has established, however, that the correct interpretation of the measurements is that the ill-defined effective shadow reached to only about 25 km; and, taking account of ozone absorption and Rayleigh scattering, he has demonstrated that such a shadow is consistent with λ 5893 being the active solar radiation.

Bricard and Kastler[175] have studied the absorption of the D doublet by a sodium vapor cell kept at various temperatures and from their results have been able to show that the temperature of the emitting atoms in the atmosphere must be about $240° \pm 50°$K. This favors the resonance scattering theory, since the fragments of a molecule which has suffered photodissociation in general have considerable kinetic energy initially. Any doubt remaining was removed in 1949 when Bricard et al.[176] proved that the λ 5893 twilight emission is polarized. The extent of the polarization for an observing direction making a right angle with the direction of the sun was found to be about 9 % as predicted, with resonance scattering assumed. Photodissociation would of course yield no polarization.

The variation is as would be expected. In the case of the morning twilight, for example, the intensity first increases as the sun approaches the horizon, so that the solar radiation can reach more and more sodium without attenuation in the lower atmosphere; it next reaches a plateau, and finally decreases again (Blamont[177]), this decrease being due to absorption of the solar radiation by sodium on the dayward side (Chamberlain[178]). The behavior during evening twilight is similar but reversed in time.

Observations by Bricard and Kastler,[175] Swings and Nicolet,[179] and Hunten[180] in the northern hemisphere and by Mayaud and Robley[181] in the southern hemisphere show that the intensity is greater in winter than in summer. Striking fluctuations about the mean occur. There appears to be no correlation between these fluctuations and magnetic activity.[180]

Swings and Nicolet[179] have found that the emission at sunrise tends to be rather stronger than at sunset. They comment that the emission is rather irregular as if the sodium distribution were patchy.

The abundance and distribution of the sodium is of considerable interest. By studying high-dispersion stellar spectrograms for indications of telluric absorption, Sanford[182] was able to show that the total number of free sodium atoms present at night does not exceed 1×10^{10} cm^{-2}. Further information may be obtained from twilight studies.

If we assume that the layer is optically thin, it may readily be seen that the D_1 or D_2 photon emission per illuminated sodium atom is given by

$$\mathscr{P}(D_1 \text{ or } D_2) = \frac{8\pi^2 e^2 \nu^2}{mc^3} f\Omega r \exp\left(-\frac{h\nu}{k\theta}\right) \text{ sec}^{-1} \qquad (5.39)$$

where f is the oscillator strength and ν is the frequency of the particular line of the doublet being considered, and where θ is the effective temperature of the solar radiation, Ω is its dilution, and r is the fraction by which its intensity at photon energy, $h\nu$, is reduced by the presence of a Fraunhofer line. Taking f_1 to be 0.33, f_2 to be 0.66, θ to be 6000°K, Ω to be 5.4×10^{-6}, r_1 to be 0.058, and r_2 to be 0.052 (Shane[183]), and assigning to the other quantities their standard values, we find that

$$\mathscr{P}(D_2)/\mathscr{P}(D_1) = 1.8, \quad \mathscr{P}(D_1) + \mathscr{P}(D_2) = 1/\text{sec}. \tag{5.40}$$

When bathed in solar radiation, atomic sodium is thus an extremely powerful source of the D doublet. An elementary calculation shows that the D doublet should be at least about a hundred times as intense as any of the other sodium doublets. In harmony with this, none of these others has been detected in the twilightglow. It is interesting to note that $\lambda\,3303, 4\,^2P \to 3\,^2S$ has been observed as a very weak feature in the spectrum of the glow from an artificial sodium cloud in the sunlit part of the atmosphere (Cooper et al.,[184] Vassy and Vassy[184a]).

Several writers have discussed the observational data, using the formula based on simple resonance scattering. Bricard and Kastler[175] and Barbier[185] deduced that the abundance of free sodium atoms in winter is rather less than the limit (1×10^{10} cm^{-2}) set by the work of Sanford. Hunten and Shepherd[186] investigated the distribution. They found that the concentration of free sodium atoms is greatest at 85 ± 3 km, that below this level it falls off quite rapidly, and that above, up to at least 100 km and probably to 115 km, it falls off with a scale height of 7.5 ± 2 km. Hunten[180] slightly revised the estimate of the altitude of the peak concentration to 84.5 ± 5 km. He reports that the seasonal change in this altitude is not more than 1 or 2 km. It may be remarked that 85 km is the lowest altitude from which emission has been observed from clouds of sodium ejected from rockets during twilight flights (Bedinger et al.[187]). Dufay and Tcheng[188] and Barbier and Roach[189] have independently reported that there is occasionally a slight enhancement, even when the sun is so far below the horizon that only the atmosphere at very great altitudes is illuminated. It was inferred that between the 200-km and 600-km levels the scale height describing the atomic sodium distribution may be as much as 250 km. This is difficult to credit. Further work is required.

In 1956 Hunten[190] drew attention to an interesting discrepancy between prediction based on single scattering and observation. Consider how the intensity of the twilight plateau depends on the total sodium abundance. As the abundance is increased, the intensity first increases in proportion, but it naturally does not continue to do so after the layer has ceased to be optically thin—owing to resonance absorption, it begins to increase less rapidly than in proportion to the abundance, and when the number of sodium atoms is about 10^{10} cm^{-2} it passes through a maximum. Some of the intensities recorded during the winter months were noticed to exceed the maximum permitted by the theory. Hunten suggested that multiple scattering must be important. Stimulated by this, Chamberlain[191] carried out detailed calculations using Chandresekhar's treatment of radiative transfer in a finite atmosphere. He found that the maximum intensity discrepancy was reduced by the inclusion of allowance for multiple scattering. Later he, Hunten and Mack[192] succeeded in eliminating it completely by taking account of the hyperfine structure of the D lines. The final theory also avoids inconsistencies between the computed and observed D_2/D_1 ratio which had been pointed out by Hunten. Table VI shows the satisfactory accord which Jones

TABLE VI

Sodium Abundance

From A. V. Jones and D. H. McPherson, *J. Atmos. Terr. Phys.* **12**, 166 (1958)

	Number of free sodium atoms (in units of $10^9/cm^2$)	
Period	From D_2/D_1 ratio	From intensity of twilight plateau
August–September	3.4 ± 1.8	2.5 ± 1.0
December–February	5.0 ± 2.0	5.5 ± 2.3
May–June	$0.7 \left\{ \begin{array}{c} + 1.0 \\ - 0.7 \end{array} \right.$	1.8 ± 0.6

and McPherson[193] find between the abundance of sodium as determined from measurements of this ratio, and as determined from measurements of the intensity of the twilight plateau. It may be mentioned here that Scrimger and Hunten[194] have made abundance determinations during the day from observations on the absorption of solar radiation by the sodium in the atmosphere. Their results are in excellent agreement with those obtained from the twilight studies.

The fraction of the sodium which is in the free state cannot be calculated at present because of the lack of much of the necessary data on rate coefficients. A few exploratory investigations have, however, been performed.[163, 195, 196] Oxidation occurs through

$$Na(^2S) + O_2(X\,^3\textstyle\sum_g^-) + M \rightarrow NaO_2 + M \qquad (5.41)$$

which Bawn and Evans[164] have shown to be extremely rapid, and through

$$Na(^2S) + O_3 \rightarrow NaO + O_2. \qquad (5.42)$$

Reduction occurs through such processes as

$$NaO_2 + O(^3P) \to NaO + O_2 \tag{5.43}$$

and

$$NaO(X\ ^2\Pi) + O(^3P) \to Na + O_2. \tag{5.44}$$

Qualitatively, it is apparent that the element must be mainly in the free state at great altitudes.

Photoionization,

$$Na(^2S) + h\nu \to Na^+(^1S) + e \tag{5.45}$$

tends to reduce the number of neutral atoms. It is opposed by several recombination processes of which

$$Na^+(^1S) + O^-(^2P) \to Na + O \tag{5.46}$$

is thought to be the most effective in the upper part of the region in which sodium can be detected. The rate coefficient for reaction (5.45) is about $1 \times 10^{-5}/\mathrm{sec}$ (Bates and Seaton[197]), and that for reaction (5.46) is probably of the order of 10^{-8} cm^3/sec (Bates and Boyd[198]). Hence the day equilibrium value of the ratio of the concentration of sodium ions to the concentration of sodium atoms is given by

$$n(Na^+)/n(Na) \simeq 10^3/n(O^-) \tag{5.47}$$

and may thus exceed unity. The two processes concerned are very slow, however, and consequently equilibrium can scarcely be reached. The degree of ionization is undoubtedly less than was originally supposed.

Various authors[163, 192] have speculated on the origin of the atmospheric sodium. The amount is so minute that there are many sources to be considered. Among those suggested are volcanic dust, salt from oceanic spray, meteors, and interplanetary matter. It would be surprising if traces of other metals did not also occur. Jones[199] has in fact reported the detection of the H and K lines of CaII (λ 3933.7 and λ 3968.5) in the twilightglow. He found suggestive evidence for a correlation with meteor showers. Supporting evidence has been obtained by Dufay.[199a] A feature near 6708 A was discovered during the IGY by Delannoy and Weill[199b] and by Gadsden and Salmon.[199c] It is identified by them with the resonance doublet of lithium. Barbier *et al.*,[199d] assuming resonance scattering to be the mechanism involved, estimated the ratio of the number of free lithium atoms to the number of free sodium atoms to be 6×10^{-3}, which they judged consistent with a meteoric origin. As is now realized, however, much lithium was released as a result of nuclear explosions. Gadsden and Salmon mention that observations carried out in Antarctica showed that the intensity of λ 6708 became comparable with that of λ 5839 during August, 1958 (in which month there was a nuclear explosion at high altitudes). From this they estimated that the ratio of free lithium atoms to free sodium atoms was then as high as 5×10^{-2} (compared with 2×10^{-3} in meteors and 2×10^{-5} in sea water). By September the estimated ratio had fallen by a factor of about 10. Working at Saskatoon Jones [199e] found the ratio to be only 4.5×10^{-4} in January 1959. This last is the only reliable determination. As Donahue[199f] has emphasized the others are untrustworthy since they are based only on the *relative* intensities of the resonance doublets. The abundances are not in general proportional to the intensities (see above) and therefore an *absolute* determination of intensity is essential.

Though some of the arguments put forward have been questioned by Harang[199g] it seems probable that contamination of the atmosphere by bomb tests was responsible for the lithium first detected (Odishaw,[199h] Barber[199i]). There may, however, also be an appreciable natural source of the element.

From their inability to detect the resonance doublet of potassium, λ 7665-7699, Lytle and Hunten[199j] inferred that the ratio of the number of free sodium atoms to the number of free potassium atoms is greater than 10 and is thus greater than the ratio of the abundances of the two elements in any of the obvious sources other than sea spray. This does not prove that sea spray must be the source, since photochemical reactions in the upper atmosphere might cause the fraction of sodium which is in the form of free atoms to differ greatly from the corresponding fraction of potassium.

5.2.2 λ 6300-6364 and λ 5577 of OI

When exposed to sunlight, oxygen atoms may be excited through the transitions $^3P \rightarrow {}^1D$ and $^3P \rightarrow {}^1S$ and may hence emit the red and green lines. For the former, the process is primarily one of resonance scattering (though there is a small contribution from cascading), whereas for the latter it is one of fluorescent scattering. Since the oscillator strengths involved are known from quantal calculations (Garstang[200]), the photon emission rates per illuminated atom, $\mathscr{P}(\lambda)$, may readily be obtained. If the distribution among the levels of the ground term is taken to be that appropriate to a temperature of 200°K and if collisional deactivation is ignored, it is found[157] that

$$\left. \begin{array}{c} \mathscr{P}(6300) = 3\mathscr{P}(6364), \quad \mathscr{P}(6300) + \mathscr{P}(6364) = 7.4 \times 10^{-10}/\text{sec} \\ \mathscr{P}(5577) = 3.5 \times 10^{-12}/\text{sec} \end{array} \right\} \quad (5.48)$$

The results are not very sensitive to the assumed temperature. At high temperatures the ground term of atomic energy may be treated as degenerate. The values of photon emission rates in the red and green lines are then 0.8 and 2.0 times those just cited.

An enhancement of the red lines during twilight was discovered in 1936 by Currie and Edwards[170] and by Cabannes and Garrigue.[201] Since then the phenomenon has been extensively studied (Elvey and Farnsworth,[98] Elvey,[202] Dufay and Tcheng,[188] Barbier[185, 203]). It is difficult to distinguish the evening enhancement for long after the sun falls below the horizon because of the superposition of the decay of the nocturnal emission. Some observers have claimed that the morning enhancement can be followed from shortly after midnight. The early part of the slow rise in intensity from the minimum near midnight should probably not be regarded as a true twilight effect, however. Indeed, doubts have been expressed as to whether any true twilight effect exists. Barbier[203] considers that these doubts have been answered by his analysis of observational data which shows that for angles of solar depression up to 28° to 30° the intensity at fixed zenith angle is greatest at the azimuthal angle corresponding to the direction of the sun.

Table VII gives average values of the absolute intensity of the enhanced part of the red lines. Barbier[203] reports that there are abnormal periods during which the intensity may be several times the average.

TABLE VII

Enhancement of Red Lines at Zenith Angle of 75°

From D. Barbier, *Ann. Géophys*, **15**, 179 (1959)

θ^a	15°	16°	17°	18°	20°	22°	24°	26°	28°	30°
A^a	Intensity in units of 10^6 photons/cm² oblique column									
0	735	600	490	390	230	130	85	60	35	10
30°	490	390	290	230	150	100	75	50	25	0
60°	260	150	85	60	50	35	25	15	10	0

[a] θ is the angle of depression of the sun, and A is the azimuthal angle measured from the subsolar line.

Koomen *et al.*[204] have succeeded in following the morning twilight to an angle of solar depression of 10° with the aid of a birefringent filter photometer. They found the enhancement was still increasing at this depression, even though the earth's shadow line in visible light cut the observing direction (zenith angle 75°) at an altitude of only 64 km. Hence the excitation mechanism can scarcely involve solar radiation in the visible part of the spectrum.

Using a Fabry-Perot interferometer Wark[205] has carried out temperature determinations from College, Alaska (65°N) at a time when twilight conditions favorable for the study existed at midnight. He found that the enhanced red lines are emitted from a region of the atmosphere at about 750°K.

As was early realized, resonance scattering is insufficient to account for the enhancement. Much of its potential contribution is suppressed by collisional deactivation which is rapid near the 100-km level where atomic oxygen is most abundant (Seaton[150]).

17

Bates[206] has drawn attention to several possible alternative processes including in particular photodissociation in the Schumann-Runge continuum:

$$O_2(X\,^3\textstyle\sum_g^-) + h\nu \to O(^3P) + O(^1D). \tag{5.49}$$

The rate coefficient is about 1.56×10^{-6}/sec when the solar radiation is unattenuated (Nicolet and Mange[207]). Using molecular oxygen concentrations recommended by Nicolet, Barbier[203] carried out calculations on the contribution of process (5.49) to the red lines. He obtained fair, but not conclusive, agreement with the observational results. One rather unsatisfactory feature is that, according to the theory, the main emission comes from a region which, on the model atmosphere adopted, is at a much higher temperature than the 750°K indicated by the measurements of Wark.

Chamberlain[149] has proposed that dissociative recombination, reaction (5.10), may be responsible for the twilight as well as for the nocturnal emission. The proposal has been demonstrated to be at least plausible as far as the evening effect is concerned, but it has not yet been developed to give an acceptable account of the morning effect.

According to Dufay et al.[208] the green line is sometimes slightly enhanced in the evening twilight, the intensity being perhaps twice as great when the depression of the sun is between 12° and 16° as it is at the commencement of the night. The effect is described as being very irregular.

Using equation (5.48) and noting that the solar radiation involved, $\lambda\,2970$, is much weakened in passing through the lower atmosphere, it may be shown that the enhancement due to fluorescent scattering is too slight to account for the observations reported. No other mechanism has been suggested.

Koomen et al.[204] have carried out a few twilight observations on the green line with their birefringent filter photometer. They did not detect an enhancement. Measurements made during a total solar eclipse have also failed to reveal any change in the intensity of the line that could be attributed to the change in the illumination of the atmosphere.[209]

5.2.3 $\lambda\,5199$ of NI

While studying the zodiacal light Courtès[25] detected a feature near $\lambda\,5199$ just after sunset on three consecutive evenings, attributing it to $^2D \to\,^4S$, $\lambda\,5198.5\text{-}5200.7$ of NI. Subsequently, Dufay[26, 210] investigated this feature in some detail. He discovered that it may also be emitted at sunrise but is feebler then; that, though it appears infrequently in winter, it is normally present in summer during the twilight periods and during the early part of the night, its photon intensity (which exhibits no correlation with magnetic activity) being variable but averaging about 2×10^7 cm^{-2} sec^{-1} (for a vertical column); and that the altitude of the emissive region is about 100 km or greater. By showing the wavelength to be about 5199.5 ± 0.2A he also provided support for the identification proposed by Courtès, about which, however, Chamberlain and Meinel[35] have expressed some doubts.

Dufay[26] proposed that the presence of λ 5199 results partly from

$$N(^4S) + h\nu(\lambda\,5199) \rightarrow N(^2D) \tag{5.50}$$

but mainly from

$$N(^4S) + h\nu(\lambda\,3466) \rightarrow N(^2P) \tag{5.51}$$

followed by

$$N(^2P) \rightarrow N(^2D) + h\nu(\lambda\,10{,}400). \tag{5.52}$$

Since the radiative life of $N(^2D)$ is approximately 26 hours (Garstang[200]), the emission may continue after sunset. This proposal has been criticized by Bates[211] on the grounds that, when allowance is made for collisional deactivation, the number of free nitrogen atoms required to explain the observed intensity is improbably high. The latest estimate, due to Seaton,[135] gives the number required to be 2×10^{19} cm^{-2}. Bates[211] has suggested that dissociative recombination

$$N_2^+(X\,^2\textstyle\sum_g^+) + e \rightarrow N + N(^2D) \tag{5.53}$$

may be the source of the excited atoms.

5.2.4 Band Systems

In 1933 Slipher[212] recorded that the First Negative system of nitrogen is emitted for a short time during morning and evening twilight. If it may be assumed that the solar radiation involved is not strongly absorbed in passing through the lower part of the atmosphere, then it may be inferred from the observations (Dufay and Dufay,[213] Dufay,[214] Swings and Nicolet[179]) that the emission is mainly from a layer near the 100-km level. The intensity of the so-called flash is extremely variable and appears to be correlated with magnetic activity.[213-215] Swings and Nicolet[179] report that it is about the same in the morning as in the evening.

It has been shown[215a] that the resonance scattering process

$$\left.\begin{aligned} N_2^+(X\,^2\textstyle\sum_g^+) + h\nu &\rightarrow N_2^+(B\,^2\textstyle\sum_u^+)\\ N_2^+(B\,^2\textstyle\sum_u^+) &\rightarrow N_2^+(X\,^2\textstyle\sum_g^+) + h\nu \end{aligned}\right\} \tag{5.54}$$

is very effective, the photon yield per illuminated ion* being as much as 0.1 sec^{-1}. An immediate deduction is that N_2^+ ions form but a small fraction

---

* The yield cited here is based on the value of the oscillator strength calculated by Bates[215a] rather than on that calculated by Shull[215b] (cf. Bates[80]) since (fortuitously) the former value is in good agreement with the measurement of Bennett and Dalby[215c] whereas the latter is not.

of the total ion content of the upper atmosphere, since otherwise the flash would be extremely intense. Doubtless the rarity of these ions is due mainly to the rapidity with which they are removed through dissociative recombination.

Slight enhancements of the (0, 1) band of the main Atmospheric system of oxygen[34, 103] and of the Meinel hydroxyl system[103] have been reported. Jones and Harrison[215d] have found that the (0, 1) band of the infrared Atmospheric system of oxygen appears in the spectrum of the evening (but not the morning) twilight. They attribute the emission to

$$O_2(X\,{}^3\textstyle\sum_g^-) + h\nu \rightarrow O_2(a\,{}^1\varDelta_g) \tag{5.55}$$

or to

$$O({}^3P) + O_3 \rightarrow 2O_2(a\,{}^1\varDelta_g). \tag{5.56}$$

5.3 Dayglow

Observations on the dayglow have until recently been impracticable because of the dominance of Rayleigh scattering by the lower atmosphere. Though the technical difficulties are grave, the development of the rocket as a research tool has rendered it possible to carry out measurements from altitudes above which the air is too tenuous for such scattering to be appreciable. Little success has yet been achieved. An integrated photon intensity of more than 10^{14} cm^{-2} sec^{-1} in the range between 4300 and 6400 A was first announced.[216] This was shown to be impossibly high both by purely theoretical considerations (Bates and Dalgarno[157]) and by an analysis of data on the brightness of the sky in a total solar eclipse (Morozov and Shklovsky[217]). In a later rocket flight[218] exposures were made with stereocameras at altitudes between 80 and 220 km. No luminosity could be detected. From this, Berg[218] concluded that the dayglow is at most only about one-thousandth as bright as it was originally reported to be.

The spectrum of the dayglow would be expected to be similar to, but richer than, that of the twilightglow. Bates and Dalgarno[157] have discussed the various processes likely to contribute. Detailed calculations on resonance scattering by atomic sodium have been performed by Donahue[219] and by Brandt and Chamberlain,[220] and detailed calculations on various processes leading to the emission of λ 6300-6364 have been carried out by Brandt.[221]

Acknowledgments

It is a pleasure to thank Drs. J. W. Chamberlain, A. Dalgarno, D. M. Hunten, and F. E. Roach for several helpful comments on the original manuscript, and Dr. J. Mazur for his assistance with the references.

References

1. See C. T. Elvey, *Astrophys. J.* **111**, 432 (1950).
2. J. W. Chamberlain, *Astrophys. J.* **121**, 277 (1955).
3. M. Dufay and J. Dufay, *Ann. Géophys.* **11**, 209 (1955).
4. H. W. Babcock, *Publ. Astron. Soc. Pacific* **51**, 47 (1939).
4a. J. W. Chamberlain, *Astrophys. J.* **128**, 713 (1958).
5. J. Cabannes and J. Dufay, *Ann. Géophys.* **1**, 1 (1944).
6. M. K. V. Bappu, *Astrophys. J.* **111**, 201 (1950).
7. J. Cabannes, J. Dufay, and M. Dufay, *C. R. Acad. Sci. (Paris)* **230**, 1233 (1950).
8. J. Dufay and M. Dufay, *C. R. Acad. Sci. (Paris)* **232**, 426 (1951).
9. A. B. Meinel, *Astrophys. J.* **111**, 555 (1950).
10. J. W. Chamberlain and F. L. Roesler, *Astrophys. J.* **121**, 541 (1955).
11. V. I. Krassovsky, *Dokl. Acad. Nauk SSSR* **66**, 53 (1949); *in* "The Airglow and the Aurorae" (E. B. Armstrong and A. Dalgarno, eds.), p. 86, Pergamon, London, 1956.
12. H. P. Gush and A. Vallance Jones, *J. Atmos. Terr. Phys.* **7**, 285 (1955).
13. D. Barbier, *Ann. Géophys.* **11**, 181 (1955).
14. W. W. Campbell, *Astrophys. J.* **2**, 162 (1895).
15. E. Wiechert, *Physik. Z.* **3**, 365 (1901–02).
16. V. M. Slipher, *Astrophys. J.* **49**, 266 (1919).
17. Lord Rayleigh, *Proc. Roy. Soc.* A**131**, 376 (1931).
18. H. D. Babcock, *Astrophys. J.* **57**, 209 (1923).
19. J. Cabannes and J. Dufay, *in* "The Airglow and the Aurorae" (E. B. Armstrong and A. Dalgarno, eds.), p. 73, Pergamon, London, 1956.
20. J. C. McLennan and G. M. Shrum, *Proc. Roy. Soc.* A**106**, 138 (1924); **108**, 501 (1925); J. C. McLennan, J. H. McLeod, and W. C. McQuarrie, *ibid.* **114**, 1(1927); J. C. McLennan, *ibid.* **120**, 327 (1928); J. C. McLennan and H. J. C. Ireton, *ibid.* **129**, 31 (1930).
21. V. M. Slipher, *Publ. Astron. Soc. Pacific* **41**, 262 (1929).
22. F. Paschen, *Z. Physik.* **65**, 1 (1930).
23. R. Bernard, *C. R. Acad. Sci. (Paris)* **206**, 908 (1938); *Z. Physik.* **110**, 291 (1938); *Astrophys. J.* **89**, 133 (1939).
24. J. Cabannes, J. Dufay, and J. Gauzit, *C. R. Acad. Sci. (Paris)* **206**, 870 (1938); **206**, 1525 (1938); *Astrophys. J.* **88**, 164 (1938).
25. G. Courtès, *C. R. Acad. Sci. (Paris)* **231**, 62 (1950).
26. M. Dufay, *C. R. Acad. Sci. (Paris)* **233**, 419 (1950).
27. A. B. Meinel, *Astrophys. J.* **111**, 433 (1950).
27a. V. S. Prokudina, *in* "Spectral, Electrophotometrical and Radar Researches of Aurorae and Airglow", p. 43. Acad. Sci. USSR, Moscow, 1959.
27b. I. S. Shklovsky, *Planet. Space Sci.* **1**, 63 (1959); see also J. C. Brandt and J. W. Chamberlain, *Astrophys. J.* **130**, 670 (1959).
28. E. T. Byram, T. A. Chubb, H. Friedman, and J. Kupperian, *in* "The Threshold of Space" (M. Zelikoff, ed.), p. 203, Pergamon, London, 1957; J. Kupperian, E. T. Byram, T. A. Chubb, and H. Friedman, *Ann. Géophys.* **14**, 329 (1958).
29. G. Déjardin, *Rev. Mod. Phys.* **8**, 55 (1936); *in* "Emission Spectra of the Night Sky and Aurorae," p. 3, Physical Society, London, 1948.
30. G. Frongia, *Nuovo Cim.* **16**, 360 (1939).
31. R. W. B. Pearse, *Repts. Progr. in Phys.* **9**, 42 (1942–33); *in* "Emission Spectra of the Night Sky and Aurorae," p. 12, Physical Society, London, 1948.
32. A. Kastler, *Ann. Géophys.* **2**, 315 (1946).

33. P. Swings, *in* "Atmospheres of the Earth and Planets" (G. P. Kuiper, ed.), p. 159, Univ. Chicago Press, Chicago, 1948.
34. A. B. Meinel, *Repts. Progr. in Phys.* **14**, 121 (1951).
35. J. W. Chamberlain and A. B. Meinel, *in* "The Earth as a Planet" (G. P. Kuiper, ed.), p. 514, Univ. Chicago Press, Chicago, 1954.
36. J. Dufay, *C. R. Acad. Sci. (Paris)* **213**, 284 (1941).
37. G. Herzberg, *Naturwissenschaften* **20**, 577 (1932).
38. G. Herzberg, *Canad. J. Phys.* **30**, 185 (1952).
39. H. P. Broida and A. G. Gaydon, *Proc. Roy. Soc.* A**222**, 181 (1954); A. G. Gaydon *in* "The Airglow and the Aurorae" (E. B. Armstrong and A. Dalgarno, eds.), p. 262, Pergamon, London, 1956.
40. P. Swings, *Astrophys. J.* **97**, 72 (1943).
41. J. Dufay and G. Déjardin, *Ann. Géophys.* **2**, 249 (1946).
42. D. Barbier, *Ann. Astrophys.* **10**, 47 (1947).
43. J. Dufay, *Ann. Géophys.* **3**, 1 (1947).
44. A. B. Meinel, *Publ. Astron. Soc. Pacific* **60**, 373 (1948); *Trans. Amer. Geophys. Union* **31**, 21 (1950).
45. J. Kaplan, *Nature* **159**, 673 (1947).
46. R. W. Nicholls, *in* "The Airglow and the Aurorae" (E. B. Armstrong and A. Dalgarno, eds.), p. 302, Pergamon, London, 1956.
47. A. B. Meinel, *Astrophys. J.* **112**, 464 (1950).
48. J. Kaplan, *Nature* **135**, 229 (1935).
49. J. Cabannes and J. Dufay, *C. R. Acad. Sci. (Paris)* **200**, 1504 (1935).
50. J. W. Chamberlain and N. J. Oliver, *J. Geophys. Res.* **58**, 457 (1953).
51. J. W. Chamberlain and N. J. Oliver, *Astrophys. J.* **118**, 197 (1953).
52. D. Barbier, *C. R. Acad. Sci. (Paris)* **237**, 599 (1953).
53. D. Barbier and D. R. Williams, *J. Geophys. Res.* **55**, 401 (1950).
54. M. Dufay, *C. R. Acad. Sci. (Paris)* **239**, 533 (1954).
55. A. B. Meinel, *Astrophys. J.* **118**, 200 (1953).
56. A. B. Meinel, *Astrophys. J.* **111**, 207, 555 (1950).
57. G. Herzberg, "Spectra of Diatomic Molecules," 2nd edn., Van Nostrand, New York, Macmillan, London, 1950.
58. W. S. Benedict, E. K. Plyler, and C. J. Humphreys, *J. Chem. Phys.* **21**, 398 (1953).
59. G. Déjardin, J. Janin, and M. Peyron, *C. R. Acad. Sci. (Paris)* **234**, 1866 (1952).
60. R. C. Herman and G. A. Hornbeck, *Astrophys. J.* **118**, 214 (1953).
61. G. E. Kron, *Publ. Astron. Soc. Pacific* **62**, 264 (1950).
62. J. Dufay, *Ann. Géophys.* **7**, 1 (1951).
63. J. W. Chamberlain and N. J. Oliver, *Phys. Rev.* **90**, 1118 (1953).
64. N. I. Fedorova, *Astron. J. USSR* **34**, 247 (1957); *Ann. Géophys.* **14**, 365 (1958).
65. C. T. Elvey, P. Swings, and W. Linke, *Astrophys. J.* **93**, 337 (1941).
66. J. Stebbins, A. E. Whitford, and P. Swings, *Phys. Rev.* **66**, 225 (1944); *Astrophys. J.* **101**, 39 (1945).
67. Y. Andrillat, *J. Phys. Radium* **17**, 442 (1956).
67a. J. W. Chamberlain and C. A. Smith, *J. Geophys. Res.* **64**, 611 (1959).
67b. M. Dufay, *Ann. Géophys.* **15**, 134 (1959).
68. F. W. P. Götz and M. Nicolet, *J. Geophys. Res.* **56**, 577 (1951).
69. R. Sloan, J. H. Shaw, and D. Williams, *J. Opt. Soc. Amer.* **45**, 455 (1955); R. M. Goody and W. T. Roach, *Quart. J. Roy. Meteorol. Soc.* **82**, 217 (1956); D. E. Burch and J. H. Shaw, *J. Opt. Soc. Amer.* **47**, 227 (1957).

69a. N. N. Shefov, *in* "Spectral, Electrophotometrical and Radar Researches of Aurorae and Airglow", p. 25, Acad. Sci. USSR, Moscow, 1959.

70. Lord Rayleigh, *Nature* **106**, 8 (1920).

71. J. Dufay, *C. R. Acad. Sci. (Paris)* **176**, 1290 (1923).

72. D. Barbier, J. Dufay, and D. Williams, *Ann. Astrophys.* **14**, 399 (1951).

73. F. E. Roach and A. B. Meinel, *Astrophys. J.* **122**, 530 (1955).

74. J. P. Heppner and L. H. Meredith, *J. Geophys. Res.* **63**, 51 (1958).

75. D. Barbier, *Ann. Astrophys.* **10**, 141 (1947).

76. R. Robley, *Ann. Géophys.* **13**, 222 (1957).

77. I. A. Khvostikov, *Dokl. Acad. Nauk SSSR* **21**, 322 (1938); **27**, 219 (1940).

78. J. Bricard and A. Kastler, *C. R. Adac. Sci. (Paris)* **224**, 1555 (1947); *Ann. Géophys.* **3**, 38 (1947); *in* "Emission Spectra of the Night Sky and Aurorae," p. 70, Physical Society, London, 1948; *Ann. Géophys.* **6**, 226 (1950).

79. D. R. Bates, *J. Atmos. Terr. Phys.* **6**, 171 (1955).

80. D. R. Bates, *in* "The Earth as a Planet" (G. P. Kuiper, ed.), p. 576, Univ. Chicago Press, Chicago, 1954.

81. L. Spitzer, *in* "The Atmospheres of the Earth and Planets" (G. P. Kuiper, ed.), p. 213, Univ. Chicago Press, Chicago, 1948.

82. E. B. Armstrong, *J. Atmos. Terr. Phys.* **3**, 274 (1953).

83. D. Q. Wark and J. M. Stone, *Nature* **175**, 254 (1955).

84. E. B. Armstrong, *J. Phys. Radium* **19**, 358 (1958); *J. Atmos. Terr. Phys.* **13**, 205 (1959).

85. J. Cabannes and J. Dufay, *Rev. Opt.* **35**, 103 (1956).

86. A. B. Meinel, *Astrophys. J.* **112**, 120 (1950).

87. J. Dufay and M. Dufay, *C. R. Acad. Sci. (Paris)* **232**, 426 (1951).

88. J. W. Chamberlain and N. J. Oliver, *Phys. Rev.* **90**, 1118 (1953).

88a. A. V. Mironov, V. S. Prokudina, and N. N. Shefov, *Ann. Géophys.* **14**, 364 (1958); F. K. Shuyskaya, *in* "Spectral, Electrophotometrical and Radar Researches of Aurorae and Airglow", p. 45, Acad. Sci. USSR, Moscow, 1959.

89. J. W. Chamberlain, *Astrophys. J.* **119**, 328 (1954).

90. P. Swings, *Astrophys. J.* **97**, 72 (1943).

91. D. Barbier, *C. R. Acad. Sci. (Paris)* **224**, 635 (1947).

92. J. Dufay and Tcheng Mao-Lin, *Ann. Géophys.* **2**, 189 (1946).

93. F. E. Roach and H. B. Pettit, *J. Geophys. Res.* **56**, 325 (1951).

94. H. B. Pettit, F. E. Roach, P. St. Amand, and D. R. Williams, *Ann. Géophys.* **10**, 326 (1954); F. E. Roach, *ibid.* **11**, 214 (1955).

95. S. F. Rodionov, E. N. Pavlova, and E. V. Rdultovskaya, *Dokl. Acad. Nauk SSSR* **66**, 55 (1949).

96. J. V. Karandikar, *Indian J. Phys.* **8**, 547 (1934).

97. H. B. Pettit and E. R. Manring, *Ann. Géophys.* **11**, 377 (1955).

98. C. T. Elvey and A. H. Farnsworth, *Astrophys. J.* **96**, 431 (1942).

99. D. Barbier, *in* "The Airglow and the Aurorae" (E. B. Armstrong and A. Dalgarno, eds.), p. 38, Pergamon, London, 1956.

100. E. R. Manring and H. B. Pettit, *in* "The Threshold of Space" (M. Zelikoff, ed.), p. 58, Pergamon, London, 1957; *J. Geophys. Res.* **63**, 39 (1958).

101. D. Barbier, *C. R. Acad. Sci. (Paris)* **245**, 1559 (1957).

102. D. Barbier, *Ann. Astrophys.* **16**, 96 (1953); **17**, 97 (1954).

103. P. Berthier, *Ann. Géophys.* **12**, 113 (1956).

104. C. T. Elvey, *Astrophys. J.* **97**, 65 (1943).

105. E. B. Armstrong, *in* "The Airglow and the Aurorae" (E. B. Armstrong and A. Dalgarno, eds.), p. 63, Pergamon, London, 1956.

106. S. Chapman, *Proc. Roy. Soc.* A**132**, 353 (1931); *Phil. Mag.* **23**, 657 (1937).

107. Lord Rayleigh and H. S. Jones, *Proc. Roy. Soc.* A**151**, 22 (1935).

108. J. Dufay and Tcheng Mao-Lin, *Ann. Géophys.* **3**, 153 (1947).

108a. D. Barbier, *Ann. Géophys.* **15**, 414 (1959).

109. J. Cabannes, J. Dufay, and Tcheng Mao-Lin, "Relations entre les Phénoménes Solaires et Géophysique," p. 207, Centre Nationale de la Recherche Scientifique, Paris, 1947.

110. P. St. Amand, *Ann. Géophys.* **11**, 450 (1956).

111. D. Barbier, *C. R. Acad. Sci. (Paris)* **244**, 2077 (1957).

112. D. F. Martyn and O. O. Pulley, *Proc. Roy. Soc.* A**154**, 455 (1936).

113. S. K. Mitra, *Nature* **155**, 786 (1945); D. F. Martyn, *J. Geophys. Res.* **57**, 144 (1952).

114. Lord Rayleigh, *Proc. Roy. Soc.* A**131**, 376 (1931).

115. C. Störmer, *Astrophys. Norveg.* **3**, 373 (1941).

116. Tcheng Mao-Lin and J. Dufay, *Cahiers Phys.* **14**, 63 (1943).

117. F. W. P. Götz, "Relations entre les Phénoménes Solaires et Géophysique," p. 241, Centre Nationale de la Recherche Scientifique, Paris, 1947.

118. P. Abadie, A. Vassy, and R. Vassy, *Ann. Géophys.* **1**, 189 (1945).

119. D. Barbier, *C. R. Acad. Sci. (Paris)* **244**, 1945 (1957), and private communication.

120. D. Barbier and H. B. Pettit, *Ann. Géophys.* **8**, 232 (1952).

120a. F. E. Roach, J. W. McCaulley, and C. M. Purdy, *J. Res. Nat. Bur. Stand.* **63D**, 19 (1959).

120b. F. E. Roach, *Proc. I.R.E.* **47**, 267 (1959).

120c. T. Gold, *J. Geophys. Res.* **64**, 1219 (1959).

120d. F. E. Roach, E. Tandberg-Hanssen, and L. R. Megill, *J. Atmos. Terr. Phys.* **13**, 113 and 122 (1958).

120e. D. Barbier and J. Glaume, *Ann Géophys.* **15**, 266 (1959).

121. D. M. Hunten, F. E. Roach, and J. W. Chamberlain, *J. Atmos. Terr. Phys.* **8**, 345 (1956).

122. Lord Rayleigh, *Proc. Roy. Soc.* A**129**, 458 (1930).

122a. F. E. Roach, J. W. McCaulley, and E. Marovich, *J. Res. Nat. Bur. Stand.* **63D**, 15 (1959).

122b. D. Barbier, *Ann. Géophys.* (in press.)

123. D. Barbier, *in* "Vistas in Astronomy" (A. Beer, ed.), Vol. 2, p. 929, Pergamon, London, 1956.

124. A. W. Harrison and A. V. Jones, *J. Atmos. Terr. Phys.* **11**, 192 (1957).

124a. D. M. Hunten, *Ann. Géophys.* **14**, 167 (1958).

125. J. Dufay and Tcheng Mao-Lin, *Ann. Géophys.* **3**, 282 (1947).

126. D. Barbier, *Mém. Soc. Roy. Sci. Liège* **12**, 43 (1952).

127. F. E. Roach, H. B. Pettit, and D. R. Williams, *J. Geophys. Res.* **55**, 183 (1950).

128. M. Huruhata, *Rept. Ionosphere Res. Japan* **4**, 137 (1950).

129. D. Barbier, *in* "The Airglow and the Aurorae" (E. B. Armstrong and A. Dalgarno, eds.), p. 9, Pergamon, London, 1956.

130. D. Barbier and J. Glaume, *Ann. Géophys.* **13**, 317 (1957).

131. F. E. Roach, L. R. Megill, M. H. Rees, and F. Marovich, *J. Atmos. Terr. Phys.* **12**, 171 (1958).

132. D. Barbier, *C. R. Acad. Sci. (Paris)* **244**, 1809 (1957).

132a. B. B. Michnevich, *Prog. in Phys. (USSR)* **63**, 197 (1957).

133. D. R. Bates and M. Nicolet, *J. Geophys. Res.* **55**, 235 (1950).

134. D. R. Bates and A. Dalgarno, *J. Atmos. Terr. Phys.* **4**, 112 (1953).

135. M. J. Seaton, *Ann. Géophys.* **11**, 232 (1955).
136. O. E. Berg, M. J. Koomen, L. Meredith, and R. Scolnik, *J. Geophys. Res.* **61**, 302 (1956); M. J. Koomen, R. Scolnik, and R. Tousey, *ibid.* **61**, 302 (1956); *in* "The Threshold of Space" (M. Zelikoff, ed.), p. 217, Pergamon, London, 1956; R. Tousey, *Ann. Géophys.* **14**, 186 (1958).
137. A. Dalgarno, *Ann. Géophys.* **14**, 241 (1958).
138. A. Dauvillier, *Rev. Gén. Elect.* **31**, 303, 443, 477 (1932).
139. S. Chapman, *in* "The Threshold of Space" (M. Zelikoff, ed.), p. 65, Pergamon, London, 1956.
140. M. Nicolet, *Science* **127**, 1317 (1958).
141. P. M. S. Blackett, *in* "Emission Spectra of the Night Sky and Aurorae," p. 34, Physical Society, London, 1948.
142. W. Galbraith and J. V. Jelley, *Nature* **171**, 349 (1953); *J. Atmos. Terr. Phys.* **6**, 250, 304 (1955); J. V. Jelley, *Planet. Space Sci.* **1**, 105 (1959).
143. C. de Jager, *Mém. Soc. Roy. Sci. Liège* **12**, 223 (1952).
144. O. R. Wulf, *J. Geophys. Res.* **58**, 531 (1953).
145. D. R. Bates, R. A. Buckingham, H. S. W. Massey, and J. J. Unwin, *Proc. Roy. Soc.* **A170**, 322 (1939).
146. D. R. Bates and H. S. W. Massey, *Proc. Roy. Soc.* **A187**, 261 (1946); **192**, 1 (1947).
147. M. Nicolet, *Phys. Rev.* **93**, 633 (1954).
148. D. R. Bates, *in* "Solar Eclipses and the Ionosphere" (W. J. G. Beynon and G. M. Brown, eds.), p. 191, Pergamon, London, 1956.
149. J. W. Chamberlain, *Astrophys. J.* **127**, 54 (1958).
150. M. J. Seaton, *Astrophys. J.* **127**, 67 (1958).
150a C. Y. Johnson, E. B. Meadows and J. C. Holmes, *J. Geophys. Res.* **63**, 443 (1958).
151. M. J. Seaton, *J. Atmos. Terr. Phys.* **4**, 295 (1954).
152. M. J. Seaton, *Phil. Trans.* **A245**, 469 (1953).
153. S. J. Smith and L. M. Branscomb, *J. Res. Natl. Bur. Standards* **55**, 165 (1955).
154. W. Moffitt, *Proc. Roy. Soc.* **A210**, 224 (1952).
155. G. Herzberg, *Canad. J. Phys.* **31**, 657 (1953).
156. D. R. Bates, *J. Atmos. Terr. Phys.* **6**, 171 (1955).
157. D. R. Bates and A. Dalgarno, *J. Atmos. Terr. Phys.* **5**, 329 (1954).
157a. M. Nicolet, *in* "The Threshold of Space" (M. Zelikoff, ed.), p. 40, Pergamon, London, 1957.
158. V. I. Krassovsky, *Dokl. Acad. Nauk SSSR* **78**, 669 (1958).
159. D. T. Stewart, *J. Atmos. Terr. Phys.* **10**, 318 (1957).
160. J. Pressman, L. M. Aschenbrand, F. F. Marmo, A. S. Jursa, and M. Zelikoff, *J. Chem. Phys.* **25**, 187 (1956); *in* "The Threshold of Space" (M. Zelikoff, ed.), p. 235, Pergamon, London, 1957.
161. P. Harteck, *in* "The Threshold of Space" (M. Zelikoff, ed.), p. 32, Pergamon, London, 1957.
162. M. Zelikoff, F. F. Marmo, J. Pressman, E. R. Manring, L. M. Aschenbrand, and A. S. Jursa, *J. Geophys. Res.* **63**, 31 (1958).
163. S. Chapman, *Astrophys. J.* **90**, 309 (1939).
164. C. E. H. Bawn and A. G. Evans, *Trans. Faraday Soc.* **33**, 1571 (1937).
165. M. Ogawa, *Science of Light* **3**, 47 (1954).
166. J. F. Bedinger, E. R. Manring, and S. N. Ghosh, *J. Geophys. Res.* **63**, 19 (1958).
166a. E. Manring, J. F. Bedinger, H. B. Pettit, and C. B. Moore, *J. Geophys Res.* **64**, 587 (1959).
167. D. R. Bates and M. Nicolet, *J. Geophys. Res.* **55**, 301 (1950).

168. G. Herzberg, *J. Roy. Astron. Soc. Canada* **45**, 100 (1951).

168a. V. I. Krassovsky, *in* "The Airglow and the Aurorae" (E. B. Armstrong and A. Dalgarno, eds.), p. 197, Pergamon, London, 1956.

168b. D. R. Bates and B. L. Moiseiwitsch, *J. Atmos. Terr. Phys.* **8**, 305 (1956); **11**, 69 (1957).

169. J. D. McKinley, D. Garvin, and M. J. Boudart, *in* "The Airglow and the Aurorae" (E. B. Armstrong and A. Dalgarno, eds.), p. 264, Pergamon, London, 1956; D. Garvin and J. D. McKinley, *J. Chem. Phys.* **24**, 1256 (1956).

169a. J. W. Chamberlain, *Ann. Géophys.* **14**, 196 (1958).

170. B. W. Currie and H. W. Edwards, *Terr. Mag.* **41**, 265 (1936).

171. V. I. Cherniev and M. F. Vuks, *Dokl. Akad. Nauk SSSR* **14**, 77 (1937).

172. L. Vegard, "Relations entre les Phénoménes Solaires et Géophysiques," p. 254, Centre National de la Recherche Scientifique, Paris, 1947.

173. L. Vegard, E. Tönsberg, and G. Kvifte, *Geofys. Publ. (Oslo)* **18**, No. 4 (1951).

174. J. Dufay, *C. R. Acad. Sci. (Paris)* **225**, 690 (1947).

175. J. Bricard and A. Kastler, *Ann. Géophys.* **1**, 53 (1944).

176. J. Bricard, A. Kastler, and R. Robley, *C. R. Acad. Sci. (Paris)* **228**, 1601 (1949).

177. J. E. Blamont, *in* "The Airglow and the Aurorae" (E. B. Armstrong and A. Dalgarno, eds.), p. 99, Pergamon, London, 1956.

178. J. W. Chamberlain, *J. Atmos. Terr. Phys.* **9**, 73 (1956).

179. P. Swings and M. Nicolet, *Astrophys. J.* **109**, 327 (1949).

180. D. M. Hunten, *in* "The Airglow and the Aurorae" (E. B. Armstrong and A. Dalgarno, eds.), p. 114, Pergamon, London, 1956.

181. P. N. Mayaud and R. Robley, *Ann. Géophys.* **10**, 258 (1954).

182. R. F. Sanford, *Publ. Astron. Soc. Pacific* **62**, 272 (1950).

183. C. D. Shane, *Lick Observ. Bull.* **19**, 119 (1941).

184. C. D. Cooper, E. R. Manring, and J. D. Bedinger, *J. Geophys. Res.* **63**, 369 (1958).

184a. A. Vassy and É. Vassy, *C. R. Acad. Sci. (Paris)* **248**, 2235 (1959).

185. D. Barbier, *Ann. Géophys.* **4**, 193 (1948).

186. D. M. Hunten and G. G. Shepherd, *J. Atmos. Terr. Phys.* **5**, 58 (1954).

187. J. F. Bedinger, E. R. Manring, and S. N. Ghosh, *J. Geophys. Res.* **63**, 19 (1958).

188. J. Dufay and Tcheng Mao-Lin, *Ann. Géophys.* **2**, 189 (1946).

189. D. Barbier and F. E. Roach, *Trans. Amer. Geophys. Union* **31**, 13 (1950).

190. D. M. Hunten, *in* "The Airglow and the Aurorae" (E. B. Armstrong and A. Dalgarno, eds.), p. 183, Pergamon, London, 1956.

191. J. W. Chamberlain, *J. Atmos. Terr. Phys.* **9**, 73 (1956).

192. J. W. Chamberlain, D. M. Hunten, and J. E. Mack, *J. Atmos. Terr. Phys.* **12**, 153 (1958).

193. A. V. Jones and D. H. McPherson, *J. Atmos. Terr. Phys.* **12**, 166 (1958).

194. J. A. Scrimger and D. M. Hunten, *Canad. J. Phys.* **35**, 918 (1957).

195. D. R. Bates, *Terr. Mag.* **52**, 71 (1947).

196. D. M. Hunten, *J. Atmos. Terr. Phys.* **5**, 44 (1954).

197. D. R. Bates and M. J. Seaton, *Proc. Phys. Soc.* B**63**, 129 (1950).

198. D. R. Bates and T. J. M. Boyd, *Proc. Phys. Soc.* A**69**, 910 (1956).

199. A. V. Jones, *Nature* **178**, 276 (1956); *Ann. Géophys.* **14**, 179 (1958).

199a. M. Dufay, *Ann. Géophys.* **14**, 391 (1958).

199b. J. Delannoy and G. Weill, *C. R. Acad. Sci. (Paris)* **247**, 806 (1958).

199c. M. Gadsen and K. Salmon, *Nature* **182**, 1598 (1958).

199d. D. Barbier, J. Delannoy, and G. Weill, *C. R. Acad. Sci. (Paris)* **247**, 886 (1958).

199e. A. V. Jones, *Nature* **183**, 1315 (1959).

199f. T. M. Donahue, *Nature* **183**, 1480 (1959).

199g. G. Kvifte, *Nature* **183**, 1384 (1959).

199h. H. Odishaw, *Science* **128**, 1599 (1958).

199i. D. R. Barber, *Nature* **183**, 384 (1959).

199j. E. A. Lytle and D. M. Hunten, *J. Atmos. Terr. Phys.* **16**, 236 (1959)

200. R. H. Garstang, *in* "The Airglow and the Aurorae" (E. B. Armstrong and A. Dalgarno, eds.), p. 324, Pergamon, London, 1956.

201. H. Garrigue, *C. R. Acad. Sci.* (*Paris*) **202**, 1807 (1936); J. Cabannes and H. Garrigue, *ibid.* **203**, 484 (1936).

202. C. T. Elvey, *in* "Emission Spectra of the Night Sky and Aurorae," p. 16, Physical Society, London, 1948.

203. D. Barbier, *Ann. Géophys.* **15**, 179 (1959).

204. M. J. Koomen, D. M. Packer, and R. Tousey, *in* "The Airglow and the Aurorae" (E. B. Armstrong and A. Dalgarno, eds.), p. 355, Pergamon, London, 1956.

205. D. Q. Wark, *Nature* **178**, 689 (1956).

206. D. R. Bates, *in* "Emission Spectra of the Night Sky and Aurorae," p. 21, Physical Society, London, 1948.

207. M. Nicolet and P. Mange, *J. Geophys. Res.* **59**, 15 (1954).

208. J. Dufay and J. Gauzit, "Relations entre les Phénoménes Solaires et Géophysiques," p. 245, Centre National de la Recherche Scientifique, Paris, 1947; J. Dufay and M. Dufay, *C. R. Acad. Sci.* (*Paris*) **226**, 1208 (1948).

209. M. J. Koomen, C. Lock, D. M. Packer, R. Scolnik, and R. Tousey, *in* "The Airglow and the Aurorae" (E. B. Armstrong and A. Dalgarno, eds.), p. 135, Pergamon, London, 1956.

210. M. Dufay, *Mém. Soc. Roy. Sci. Liège* **12**, 141 (1952); *C. R. Acad. Sci.* (*Paris*) **236**, 2160 (1953).

211. D. R. Bates, *Ann. Géophys.* **8**, 194 (1952).

212. V. M. Slipher, *Monthly Not. Roy. Astron. Soc.* **93**, 857 (1952).

213. M. Dufay and J. Dufay, *C. R. Acad. Sci.* (*Paris*) **224**, 1834 (1947).

214. M. Dufay, *Ann. Phys.* **8**, 813 (1953).

215. M. Costello, H. Serson, R. Montalbetti, and W. Petrie, *Canad. J. Phys.* **32**, 562 (1954).

215a. D. R. Bates, *Proc. Roy. Soc.* A**196**, 562 (1949).

215b. H. Shull, *Astrophys. J.* **112**, 352 (1950); *ibid.* **114**, 546 (1952).

215c. R. G. Bennett and F. W. Dalby, *J. Chem. Phys.* **31**, 434 (1959).

215d. A. V. Jones and A. W. Harrison, *J. Atmos. Terr. Phys.* **13**, 45 (1958).

216. H. A. Miley, E. H. Cullington, and J. F. Bedinger, *Trans. Amer. Geophys. Union* **34**, 680 (1953).

217. V. M. Morozov and I. S. Shklovsky, *in* "The Airglow and the Aurorae" (E. B. Armstrong and A. Dalgarno, eds.), p. 201, Pergamon, London, 1956.

218. O. E. Berg, *J. Geophys. Res.* **60**, 271 (1955).

219. T. M. Donahue, *J. Geophys. Res.* **61**, 663 (1956).

220. J. C. Brandt and J. W. Chamberlain, *J. Atmos. Terr. Phys.* **13**, 90 (1958); J. C. Brandt, *ibid.* **13**, 100 (1958).

221. J. C. Brandt, *Astrophys. J.* **128**, 718 (1958).

Chapter 6

General Character of Auroras *

D. R. BATES

6.1 Appearance 269
6.2 Classification of Auroral Forms 271
6.3 Altitude 272
    6.3.1 Lower Border 273
    6.3.2 Luminosity Distribution and Upper Limit........................... 277
6.4 Other Features of the Geometry... 278
6.5 Geographical Distribution.. 280
6.6 Temporal Distribution.. 284
    6.6.1 Diurnal Occurrence... 284
    6.6.2 Yearly Occurrence.. 285
    6.6.3 Secular Occurrence... 286
6.7 Relation with Other Geophysical Phenomena............................. 288
    6.7.1 Magnetic Disturbances.. 288
    6.7.2 Earth Currents... 292
    6.7.3 Vertical Potential Gradient at Ground Level....................... 292
6.8 Motion of Aurora along Lines of Latitude............................... 293
    References... 294

Auroras are among the most conspicuous of natural phenomena. A major display gives as much illumination on the ground as does the full moon. The light may be white, green, yellow, blue, violet, or red. Some auroras appear quiescent; others change rapidly in brightness, color, position, and aspect. Though they have been seen from almost all parts of the globe, they are most frequent at high magnetic latitudes.

6.1 Appearance

The following is a selection from some descriptions of aurora published in 1879 in "Aurorae: Their Characters and Spectra." [1]

Aurora observed by Dr. Hayes; Port Foulbe, 6th January 1861

The darkness was so profound as to be oppressive. Suddenly, from the rear of the black cloud which obscured the horizon, flashed a bright ray. Presently an arch of many colours fixed itself across the sky, and the aurora gradually developed.

The space within the arch was filled by the black cloud; but its borders brightened steadily, though the rays discharged from it were exceeding capricious, now glaring

---

* The results of the International Geophysical Year (IGY), which are of special value in connection with the general character of auroras, were not available when this chapter was being written.

269

like a vast conflagration, now beaming like the glow of a summer morn. More and more intense grew the light, until, from irregular bursts, it matured into an almost uniform sheet of radiance. Towards the end of the display its character changed. Lurid fires flung their awful portents across the sky, before which the stars seemed to recede and grow pale.

The colour of the light was chiefly red; but every tint had its turn, and sometimes two or three were mingled; blue and yellow streamers shot across the terrible glare, or, starting side by side from the wide expanse of the radiant arch, melted into each other, and flung a strange shade of emerald over the illuminated landscape. Again this green subdues and overcomes the red; then azure and orange blend in rapid flight, subtle rays of violet pierce through a broad flash of yellow, and the combined streams issue in innumerable tongues of white flame, which mount towards the zenith.

Aurora observed by Mr. Capron; Guildford, 24th October 1870

At 6 p.m. indications of the coming display were visible in the shape of a bright silver glow in the north, which contrasted strongly with the opposite dark horizon. For two hours this continued, with the addition from time to time of a crimson glow in the north-east, and of streamers of phosphorescent cloud, shaped like horse-tails (very different from the more common auroral diverging streams of light), which floated upwards and across the sky from east to west to the zenith. At about 8 o'clock the display culminated; and few observers I should think ever saw a more lovely sky-picture. Two patches of intense crimson light about this time massed themselves on the north-east and north-west horizon, the sky between having a bright silver glow. The crimson masses became more attentuated as they mounted upwards; and from them there suddenly ran up bars or streamers of crimson and gold light, which, as they rose, curved towards each other in the north, and, ultimately meeting, formed a glorious arch of coloured light, having at its apex an oval white luminous corona or cloud of similar character to the phosphorescent clouds previously described, but brighter. At this time the spectator appeared to be looking at the one side of a cage composed of glowing red and gold bars, which extended from the distant parts of the horizon to a point over his head. Shortly after this the display gradually faded away, and at 9 o'clock the sky was of its usual appearance, except that the ordinary tint seemed to have more of indigo, probably by contrast with the marvellous colours which had so lately shone upon it.

Aurora observed by Lieut. Parr; Floeberg Beach, 19 February 1876

An aurora appeared shortly after 11 p.m. consisting of a bright arch, whose centre bore about E.S.E., and had an altitude of 5°, with a second broader and fainter arch about 7° above the first. These arches maintained their altitudes. The upper one remained at about the same intensity. However, the lower one varied considerably. It would gradually brighten, then send streamers up to the second, then break into light patches, and gradually fade away. This happened three or four times during the 40 minutes the display lasted. At times streamers would come up from the horizon to the lower arch and seemed to brighten it, but none of them extended beyond it. Neither did the streamers from the lower arch extend beyond the upper one. The aurora was slightly green in colour when brightest.

Descriptions such as these are not by themselves fully adequate. The beautiful paintings of Crowder, reproduced in color in an article by Gartlein,[2] supplement them admirably.

Observations on artificial auroras resulting from nuclear detonations at great altitudes have been reported by Cullington[2a] and Newman.[2b]

6.2 Classification of Auroral Forms

Though no two auroras are identical, there are a limited number of general types. The standard classification given below was drawn up by a Committee of the International Geodetic and Geophysical Union.[3] It should be noted that the various types are not sharply defined but merge into one another. Several may occur at the same time.

Homogeneous quiet arcs (HA) may be narrow or broad and may be almost uniform in brightness or patchy (perhaps even being split up into fibers). The upper border is usually diffuse, and the lower border sharp, giving the appearance of *a dark segment* between the arc and the horizon. In some instances the lower border is regular like a rainbow; in others it is irregular (in which case it is often very luminous and is often transformed soon afterward into rays). Several parallel arcs extending from horizon to horizon may occur. Such arcs may merge together, forming a large zone across the sky. When the arc is double, the upper arc may turn round at the eastern end (in the northern hemisphere) and continue as the lower arc. The color is usually greenish yellow or almost white.

Homogeneous bands (HB) have not the regular shape of arcs and are more rapidly moving. The lower border is commonly sharp but uneven. Sometimes the band consists of a segment of semicircular or ellipsoidal shape which is more luminous when viewed tangentially. It may possess folds and may be so broad that it resembles a hanging curtain. If it is broad it often develops into *bands with ray structure* (RB). Narrow bands also occur. In general the color is bluish white.

Pulsating arcs (PA) often stand isolated in the sky. The whole arc or part of it flashes up and disappears rhythmically with a period of several seconds. Bluish green is the usual color.

Diffuse luminous surfaces (DS) consist of residual luminosities resembling clouds which may cover much of the sky. They often occur after intense displays of rays and curtains. Their color may range from violet-white to red.

Pulsating surfaces (PS) are diffuse patches appearing and disappearing rhythmically with a period which may be less than a second or as much as a minute, but retaining their position and shape. Patches lying near the magnetic zenith may be comparatively sharp. The form often occurs in conjunction with a *flaming aurora* (F).

The poleward *glow* (G) is a white, greenish, or occasionally red luminosity near the horizon resembling the dawn. It may form the upper part of an arc whose lower border is underneath the horizon.

Rays (R) resemble searchlight beams. They may be short or long, narrow or broad, isolated or in great bundles. An important characteristic is that they always appear to converge toward the magnetic zenith. The color is usually greenish yellow but is sometimes red. Rays are often associated with other auroral forms.

An *arc with ray structure* (RA) arises when a homogeneous arc which for a rather long time has remained quiet becomes sharp and luminous along its lower border and then changes rapidly into an arc of rays.

Bands with ray structure (RB) resemble homogeneous bands but are composed of a number of rays either close together or somewhat scattered. A band which is near the magnetic zenith may have the form of a corona.

A *drapery* (D) consists of a band made up of long rays and having the appearance of a curtain (which, if near the magnetic zenith, may be fanlike in form, owing to perspective).

A *corona* (C) is formed by bands, draperies, or rays which seemingly converge on the magnetic zenith. It is not necessarily complete.

A *flaming aurora* (F) often appears after an intense display of rays and curtains and is often followed by the formation of a corona. It is a characteristic rapidly moving type. Strong waves of light travel upward one after the other in the direction of the magnetic zenith. These waves may be of the form of detached arcs, the direction of motion being normal to the arcs; or they may be compared with invisible waves which in their passage illuminate broad rays and patches, making them appear and disappear rhythmically.

6.3 Altitude

Long before the beginning of the present century investigations on the altitudes of aurora were carried out by scientists such as Mairan, Bergmann, Cavendish, and Dalton (cf. Capron,[1] Chapman and Bartels,[4]). It was not until after the pioneer work of Störmer[5] in 1910, however, that accurate determinations began to be made. Thanks mainly to his continued efforts[6-9] and to the efforts of other Norwegians, notably Vegard and Krogness[10] and Harang and Tönsberg,[11] much reliable information is now available. In addition to these studies in Norway, studies have been made in Canada by McLennan *et al.*,[12] Currie and Edwards,[13] Stagg,[14] and McEwen and Montalbetti,[14a] in Alaska by Fuller and Bramhall,[15] and in New Zealand by Geddes.[16]

The location of an aurora is determined from photographs of it taken simultaneously from two or more stations in telephonic or radio communication.

Störmer's network consisted of eight stations. The lengths of the base lines range from 27 km to 259 km. Some of the longer ones lie approximately along a magnetic meridian. These base lines are then approximately perpendicular to the arcs and bands, which facilitates precise measurements.

The images of the stars on a plate fix the astronomical orientation; and by comparing plates obtained at different stations the parallactic shift and hence the position of an auroral feature can be found with the aid of trigonometry. Detailed accounts of the procedure have been given by Harang[17] and Störmer.[18] Graphical and instrumental aids are employed extensively to ease the labor that is involved.

6.3.1 *Lower Border*

The lower border of an aurora is usually the part which is the most clearly defined. Because of this, it is the part for which the best statistical data on altitudes are available.

6.3.1.1 *Combined Data*

Figure 1 shows the distribution of the altitudes of the lower borders, $h(l)$, for all forms obtained by combining the measurements of Störmer[7] at Oslo

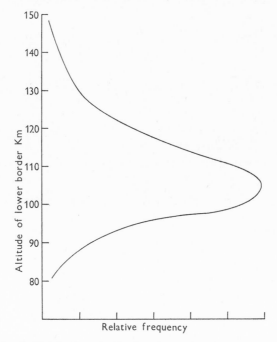

FIG. 1. Distribution of altitudes of lower borders of auroras.

and Bossekop, of Vegard and Krogness[10] at Haldde, and of Harang and Tönsberg[11] at Tromsö. The undulations in the curves usually displayed are probably not significant. A sharp double peak is sometimes shown.

18

Consistent with the measurements, it is convenient in general theoretical discussions to adopt 105 km as the typical value of $h(l)$ and to regard 90 km and 125 km as limits between which $h(l)$ lies in the majority of cases. Aurora for which $h(l)$ is smaller than 90 km or greater than 125 km are not, of course, uncommon.

A firm lower limit cannot be given, but it may be said that cases in which $h(l)$ is 80 km or less are rare. At Tromsö in 1932 Harang and Bauer[19] found an intense arc with crimson base to have an altitude of only 65 to 70 km. This is the most extreme case which can be regarded as being well established.

Instances have been reported of aurora occurring near ground level and even of aurora accompanied by a swishing or rustling noise. The observational evidence has been reviewed by Chapman.[20] He did not consider that it should be discarded completely. It is, however, very difficult to accept low and audible aurora. The effects seen and heard have probably other explanations (cf. Chapman and Bartels[4]).

It is doubtful if an upper limit to $h(l)$ exists. If the probable occurrence of aurora too feeble to be photographed is ignored, however, it would seem that values exceeding 200 km are very infrequent except in the special case of rays located in the sunlit portion of the atmosphere. Störmer[21] has found that these tend to end on or just above the earth's shadow line and has found also that for some $h(l)$ is as great as 600 km. It is to be noted that a ray which disappears on reaching the shadow line may reappear lower down. Such a ray consisting of two luminous parts, one situated in sunlight and another, along the continuation of the same line, in darkness, is termed a *divided ray*. It would seem as if the solar radiation sensitizes the atmosphere and thereby renders visible a part of the ray that would otherwise be invisible.

6.3.1.2 *More Detailed Examination of Data*

It is natural to inquire whether $h(l)$ depends on the type of the aurora, its distance from the magnetic axis, and other such factors. Much effort has been devoted to inquiries of this nature.

The number of factors on which $h(l)$ might conceivably depend is considerable; there is the possibility of unsuspected correlations between them; and the statistical analysis of the data has been, of necessity, rather crude. Caution must therefore be exercised regarding the reality of some of the suggested trends.

The distributions of $h(l)$ for the main types of aurora have been investigated by Vegard and Krogness[10] and others. It is doubtful if the differences between the individual distribution curves obtained and the combined distribution curve shown in Fig. 1 are significant except in the case of rays for which the distribution curve appears to fall off relatively slowly at great altitudes.

Some mean values of $h(l)$ are given in Table I. The dependence on auroral type is not very pronounced.

There is convincing evidence that $h(l)$ and the intensity are inversely correlated: for example, Störmer[6] has found that $h(l)$ averages 113 km and 101 km for draperies of feeble and strong intensity, and Harang[22] has found that it averages 114 km and 95 km for arcs of feeble and strong intensity. This very marked effect (confirmed by McEwen and Montalbetti[14a]) should be taken into account in investigations on other possible effects. Unfortunately it has usually been ignored.

TABLE I

Data on Mean Altitudes of Lower Borders of Auroras

(Values for $h(l)$ in kilometers, with number of cases studied in parentheses)

Auroral type	Southern Norway		Northern Norway Vegard and Krogness[c]
	Störmer[a]	Störmer[b]	
HA	104 (41)	107 (290)	109 (355)
RA	101 (32)		107 (888)
HB	94 (10)		
PA	88 (4)	} 103 (430)	
PS	93 (19)		106 (160)
DS	88 (46)	94 (158)	
R	127 (52)		113 (61)
RB	103 (126)	96 (405)	} 110 (409)
D	104 (64)		

[a] C. Störmer, *Geofys. Publ. (Oslo)* **18**, No. 7 (1953).
[b] C. Störmer, *Terr. Mag.* **51**, 501 (1946); **53**, 251 (1948).
[c] L. Vegard and O. Krogness, *Geofys. Publ. (Oslo)* **1**, No. 1 (1920).

From an analysis he carried out in 1937 Egedal[23] concluded that $h(l)$ falls throughout the night, the diminution in the interval from 3 hours after sunset to 8 hours being found to be about 15 km, using the data of Störmer,[6] and to be about 10 km, using the data of Vegard and Krogness.[10] It is claimed that the trend occurs both in the combined data and in the data for the principal auroral types.* Störmer[8] re-investigated the matter in 1948 and also examined whether there is a dependence on the distance, θ, from the magnetic axis. His results are shown in Table II (partially as an illustration of the type of data used in the analysis). Except in the case of the HA form they give some support to the conclusion of Egedal. There appears to be a

* Confining their attention to weak auroras, however, McEwen and Montalbetti[14a] found no significant diurnal change in $h(l)$.

TABLE II

Variation of Altitude, h(l), of Lower Border of Aurora with Distance, θ, from the Magnetic Axis and with Local Time of Occurrence

From C. Störmer, *Terr. Mag.* **53**, 251 (1948)

(Values for h(l) in kilometers, with number of cases studied in parentheses)

Distance from magnetic axis	Local time (hours)												Mean time of occurrence	
	18	19	20	21	22	23	00	01	02	03	04	05	Mean	(hours)
Homogeneous quiet arcs (HA)														
θ < 24°	— (0)	96 (3)	— (0)	113 (3)	111 (2)	110 (1)	— (0)	102 (3)	105 (1)				105 (13)	22.2
24° < θ < 26°		108 (1)	101 (7)	109 (22)	109 (37)	107 (20)	108 (47)	111 (10)	114 (3)				108 (147)	22.8
26° < θ < 28°		99 (6)	107 (11)	107 (18)	106 (16)	102 (24)	106 (11)	103 (15)	114 (3)				105 (104)	22.4
28° < θ		105 (3)	104 (17)	— (0)	101 (1)	119 (5)	— (0)	— (0)	— (0)				107 (26)	20.5
Mean		101 (13)	104 (35)	108 (43)	108 (56)	106 (50)	108 (58)	106 (28)	113 (7)				107 (290)	
Pulsating arcs (PA) and pulsating surfaces (PS)														
θ < 24°	— (0)	— (0)	— (0)	— (0)	— (0)	— (0)	102 (1)	— (0)	83 (2)	81 (2)	— (0)		88 (5)	02.0
24° < θ < 26°	— (0)	— (0)	— (0)	— (0)	— (0)	99 (1)	87 (5)	85 (7)	94 (13)	88 (5)	— (0)		90 (31)	01.5
26° < θ < 28°	— (0)	111 (3)	111 (22)	93 (12)	100 (1)	91 (21)	91 (11)	83 (1)	— (0)	— (0)	— (0)		98 (71)	21.7
28° < θ	104 (2)	104 (11)	109 (56)	108 (134)	104 (2)	101 (41)	104 (49)	104 (4)	— (0)	99 (21)	100 (3)		106 (323)	21.9
Mean	104 (2)	106 (14)	110 (78)	107 (146)	103 (3)	98 (63)	101 (66)	91 (12)	93 (15)	96 (28)	100 (3)		103 (430)	
Diffuse luminous surfaces (DS) (red ones excluded)														
θ < 24°	— (0)	— (0)	— (0)	— (0)	— (0)	— (0)	97 (1)	— (0)	105 (5)	— (0)	— (0)	— (0)	87 (9)	02.7
24° < θ < 26°	— (0)	— (0)	— (0)	— (0)	— (0)	— (0)	93 (3)	93 (18)	94 (30)	86 (8)	89 (3)	— (0)	90 (48)	02.0
26° < θ < 28°	— (0)	— (0)	— (0)	106 (13)	— (0)	— (0)	92 (13)	91 (10)	— (0)	83 (19)	— (0)	— (0)	96 (68)	00.5
28° < θ	96 (4)	108 (4)	— (0)	102 (9)	93 (4)	93 (4)	95 (6)	93 (4)	— (0)	100 (2)	— (0)	97 (2)	98 (33)	22.2
Mean	96 (4)	108 (4)	— (0)	104 (22)	93 (4)	93 (4)	93 (23)	92 (32)	95 (35)	85 (29)	89 (3)	97 (2)	94 (158)	
Bands with ray structure (RB)														
θ < 24°			98 (4)	105 (6)	105 (3)	108 (1)	98 (2)	92 (1)	88 (1)	96 (2)	98 (5)		100 (25)	23.5
24° < θ < 26°		104 (3)	101 (15)	106 (30)	105 (14)	105 (24)	98 (14)	85 (9)	— (0)	80 (16)	91 (1)		99 (123)	22.9
26° < θ < 28°		104 (3)	104 (22)	110 (5)	103 (22)	103 (22)	96 (46)	85 (17)	81 (13)	88 (8)	— (0)		95 (178)	23.1
28° < θ		— (0)	— (0)	93 (17)	95 (2)	88 (7)	91 (6)	88 (7)	87 (2)	87 (30)	84 (1)		90 (79)	24.5
Mean		104 (3)	102 (41)	102 (58)	101 (61)	102 (61)	96 (68)	83 (34)	82 (16)	85 (56)	95 (7)		96 (405)	

tendency for $h(l)$ to be a decreasing function of θ for the RB form and to be an increasing function of θ for PA, PS, and DS forms. Further work is, however, required. It is sometimes asserted that when θ is large so also in general is $h(l)$—that is, aurora at low latitudes are in general at great altitudes. Chamberlain and Meinel[24] consider that the assertion is incorrect. They suggest that it originates from the fact that observational selection at low latitudes weighs heavily in favor of aurora at great altitudes (since these can be seen even if located at high latitudes where the main auroral activity occurs).

Harang[25] has investigated whether $h(l)$ is influenced by the position relative to the earth's shadow line. He reports that on an average $h(l)$ is slightly greater for aurora on the sunlit side than for aurora on the dark side. Moreover, he considers that the effect is not merely statistical. On one occasion he had the opportunity of making measurements on a 800-km-long arc one half of which was illuminated and the other half of which was not.[26] He reports that in passing from the dark side of the shadow line to the sunlit side $h(l)$ increased steadily from 100 km to 120 km or rather more. It may be noted that the apparent sensitization effect mentioned in 6.3.1.1 in connection with rays would tend to cause $h(l)$ to decrease during the passage.

According to Egedal[27] and Harang,[22] $h(l)$ depends on the hour angle of the moon, the mean being perhaps about 5 km smaller at ebb tide than at flood tide. Additional evidence is very desirable. Great care must be taken in the choice of the measurements to be used in the analysis.

6.3.2 Luminosity Distribution and Upper Limit

Harang[28] has carried out careful photometric measurements to determine how the intensity of the emitted light varies with the altitude of the emitting region of an aurora. He found it convenient to characterize the luminosity distribution by the distances t_l^n and t_u^n between the level of maximum intensity and the two levels at which the intensity is a fraction, n, of the maximum, the subscript l referring to the level in the *lower* part of the aurora and the subscript u to the level in the *upper* part. Table III gives the mean values of these parameters for aurora located at various levels. It is seen that the intensity falls off more rapidly in the region below the maximum than in the region above, and that the rate at which it falls off is a decreasing function of the altitude of the level at which the maximum occurs.

Owing to the gradualness of the diminution of the intensity the altitude, $h(u)$, of the upper limit of an aurora is usually rather indefinite. As an indication of the values that arise it may be mentioned that Vegard and Krogness[10] find that $h(u)$ averages 143 km for the HA, 174 km for the RA, 176 km for the RB and D, and 250 km for the R form. The means may be greatly exceeded: for example, Störmer[29] has reported faint arcs reaching above the 200-km level and red rays with summits between the 600-km and 700-km levels. These were in the dark part of the atmosphere. In the illuminated part the extreme altitudes are even greater: thus Störmer has observed a sunlit arc having its upper portion at an altitude which he measured to be about 450 km; and he has also observed sunlit rays apparently stretching to an altitude of 1100 km.

TABLE III

Luminosity Distribution in Aurora

From L. Harang, *Geofys. Publ. (Oslo)* **16**, No. 6 (1946); *Terr. Mag.* **51**, 381 (1946)

Altitude of level where maximum occurs (km)	Auroral type	$t_l^{\frac{2}{3}}$ (km)	$t_l^{\frac{1}{2}}$ (km)	$t_l^{\frac{1}{3}}$ (km)	$t_u^{\frac{2}{3}}$ (km)	$t_u^{\frac{1}{2}}$ (km)	$t_u^{\frac{1}{3}}$ (km)
100		5.3	6.8	8.2	9.2	13.5	18.6
110		5.7	7.2	8.8	10.3	15.2	20.8
120	Arcs and draperies	6.7	8.8	10.1	12.1	18.4	24.7
130		8.2	11.0	12.3	14.3	22.0	29.3
140		10.3	13.4	15.3	17.2	25.5	33.8
150		13.8	18.0	22.7	21.8	30.8	41.2
160		19.6	27.6	35.0	(33.0)	(46.0)	(60.0)
185	Normal rays	43	53	62	46	61	79
270	Sunlit rays	76	103	135	87	117	146

6.4 Other Features of the Geometry

A detailed study has not yet been made of the horizontal dimensions of aurora, so that only some isolated items of information can be given. Arcs may be as much as 1000 km in length. Little is known about their widths. What is perhaps the most important item concerns rays: Vegard[30] has found that these may have a cross-sectional diameter of 0.5 km or even less. This is of considerable theoretical interest. (See § 7.4.3.)

Arcs lie almost along circles of magnetic latitude, but (in the northern hemisphere) their western ends are slightly closer to the axis point than are their eastern ends. Vegard and Krogness[10] have found that the magnetic azimuth, a_m, of the mean direction of arcs is 101° at Haldde, and Currie and Edwards[13] that it is 99° at Chesterfield Inlet. Values similarly slightly above 90° have been obtained at most other stations.[17, 18, 31]

The directions of the arcs in a given locality show a certain scatter. Let x be the angle an arc makes with the mean direction, and let D be the value of $|\cos x|$ averaged over all arcs. Noting that, if the directions of the arcs were random, then D would be $2/\pi$ or 0.635, Vegard and Krogness[10] introduced as a measure of the scatter the number

$$G = (D - 0.635)/0.365. \tag{6.1}$$

Clearly if there were no scatter G would be unity, and if there were complete scatter it would be zero. For the arcs at Haldde, Vegard and Krogness found G to be 0.90; but for those at Fort Conger (which is near the axis point) they found it to be vanishingly small, indicating the absence of a preferred direction.

Some of the earlier results show a pronounced diurnal variation (cf. Vegard[31]). Harang,[22] too, reports that at Tromsö a_m decreases by about 15° during the period from 16 hours to midnight (when the rate of decrease is the most rapid). It was at first thought (Currie and Jones[32]) that a diurnal variation also appears in the results obtained from several Canadian stations.

TABLE IV

Angles of Azimuth and Elevation for the Auroral and Magnetic Zeniths

Station	Angle of azimuth		Angle of elevation		Number of observations
	Auroral	Magnetic	Auroral	Magnetic	
Haldde[a]	− 2.7°	− 2.5°	75.4°	76.7°	11
Oslo[b]	− 9.8°	− 9.7°	70.0°	70.8°	9

[a] L. Vegard and O. Krogness, *Geofys. Publ.* (*Oslo*) **1**, No. 1 (1920).
[b] C. Störmer, *Geofys. Publ.* (*Oslo*) **4**, No. 7 (1926).

Jensen and Currie[33] although not seeking to discredit the work of the Norwegian scientists, now consider that this is at least doubtful. In their view the supposed diurnal variation at the Canadian stations disappears if the analysis of the data is carried out in a manner that takes account of a seasonal variation which they claim to exist. According to them this seasonal variation is very marked: thus at Saskatoon they found that a_m passes through a maximum of about 115° in February and through a minimum of 90° or rather less in October and November.

In view of the large systematic variations that are suggested it is clear that the averaged values of a_m and the values of G given in the literature require critical examination.

The alignment effect is exhibited by other auroral forms. It seems, however, that the mean directions and the extents of the scatter are not the same: thus, for draperies at Haldde, Vegard and Krogness[10] found a_m and G to be 133° and 0.44, which are considerably different from the corresponding values (cited above) for arcs.

Aurora having ray structure follow the magnetic lines of force closely not only in the horizontal plane but also in a vertical plane.

The direction of rays is determined by the position of the auroral zenith or corona (to which they appear to converge). This position may be measured with high precision. The auroral zenith is found almost to coincide with the magnetic zenith (that is, the point where the celestial sphere is intersected by the direction of the magnetic lines of force for the locality). Table IV gives values of the angles of azimuth and elevation for the auroral and magnetic zeniths at Haldde and at Oslo. As can be seen, the auroral and magnetic azimuths are essentially equal, but the auroral elevation is about 1° less than the magnetic elevation.

The position of the auroral zenith appears to vary slightly with time during a strong display (Störmer[34]).

6.5 Geographical Distribution

In past surveys of the geographical distribution an aurora was always assigned not only to the place where it was overhead but to all stations from which it was seen. It is important to bear this in mind when studying the results of such surveys, for the lower border of an aurora at the mean altitude of 105 km may be visible from as far away as 1000 km. Aurora observed from low and moderate latitudes are generally on the poleward side of the zenith.

The parts of the earth between geomagnetic latitudes 60° and the poles are termed the *auroral regions*; the parts between geomagnetic latitudes 45° and 60° the *subauroral belts*; and the part between geomagnetic latitudes 45° S and 45° N the *minauroral belt*. Included in the auroral regions are the *auroral zones* (where auroras are most frequent) and the *auroral caps* (the polar regions within the auroral zones).

Using his catalog[35] of aurora recorded in the northern hemisphere during the years 1700 to 1872, Fritz[36] in 1881 computed the average frequency of nights on which aurora could be seen from various stations, expressing it as M nights per year. Many of the stations were in effective operation only during part of the chosen period. Since auroral activity fluctuates considerably from year to year, it was necessary to correct the values of M obtained directly from these stations. The corrections were found by using the records from Central Europe (which cover the entire period) and assuming that the relative frequency with which aurora can be observed at different stations is the same at all epochs.

From his reduced data Fritz prepared his well-known chart showing lines of constant M or *isochasms*. These lines approximate to concentric circles about the magnetic axis point. The reports of arctic observers led Fritz to believe that M does not increase toward a single polar maximum but that instead it passes through a maximum, the angular distance of which from the axis point averages 23°. This belief was confirmed by the work of Sverdrup,[37] who from observations carried out during the drift of the *Maud* concluded that of the aurora visible from a point on Fritz's line of maximum M approximately half appear in the northern segment of the sky and approximately half in the southern segment.

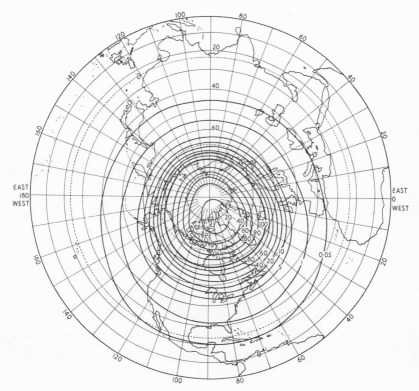

FIG. 2. Estimated percentage frequency of days with occurrence of aurora, clear nights, northern hemisphere. After E. H. Vestine, *Terr. Mag.* **49**, 77 (1944).

In 1944 Vestine[38] prepared a revised chart of isochasms in the northern hemisphere using, in addition to the data of Fritz, data obtained between 1871 and 1942 (which period includes the 1882–83 and 1932–33 Polar Years). He paid special attention to the region near and within the peak isochasm, since the original chart is here deficient. For this region corrections such as were applied by Fritz, to reduce the data to a common epoch, were judged to be undesirable, since the secular variation in the auroral frequency at high latitudes is smaller in amplitude than, and different in phase from, the corresponding variation at low latitudes (§ 6.6.3.1).

Unlike Fritz, Vestine did not ignore the fact that clouds often obscure aurora that would otherwise be visible and, using the admittedly very incomplete meteorological information available, estimated the percentage of nights aurora would be seen if all nights were clear.

Figure 2 reproduces the chart finally obtained. It is to be noted that the percentage is 100 on the peak isochasm. As Vestine points out, the similarity between the isochasms and the curves of equal geomagnetic disturbance is very striking.

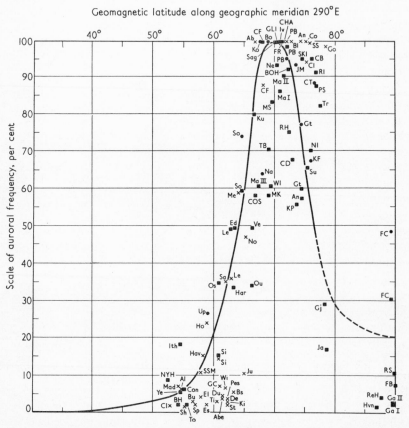

FIG. 3. Estimated average auroral percentage frequency, clear nights, meridian 290° E, adjusted to circular zone, maximum auroral display in geomagnetic latitude 69° N. After E. H. Vestine, *Terr. Mag.* **49**, 77 (1944).

In 1958 Hultqvist[38a] computed the isochasms assuming that they are projections on the surface of circles in the equatorial plane along magnetic lines of force (Alfvén[38b]). His results suggested that the isochasms of Vestine[38] lie about 4° too far north in the region of Hudson Bay. Information obtained during the IGY (Gartlein[38c]) confirms that this is indeed the case (Hult-qvist[38d], Vestine and Sibley[38e]).

The sharpness of the fall-off on either side of the peak is best seen from Fig. 3, which gives a plot of the isochasmic frequency along a geographic meridian. It should be borne in mind that the picture presented is necessarily over-simplified. Meek[39] reports that observations made over a period of a year in 1948–49 at Portage la Prairie and Baker Lake (geomagnetic latitude 59° N and 75° N) establish that there are definitely *two* peaks of occurrence of aurora in the night, one being at 65° N and the other at 68° N. He further reports that during the same period aurora were seen north of Portage la Prairie more frequently in the morning than in the evening, whereas they were seen north of Baker Lake more frequently in the evening than in the morning.

Observations in the Antarctic are naturally rather scarce. The first important study of the geographical distribution in the southern hemisphere was carried out in 1898 by Boller,[40] who made a crude estimate of the position of the main auroral zone. More refined estimates were made in 1931 and in 1939 by Davies and by Geddes and White.[41] In 1945 Vestine and Snyder[42] prepared a tentative chart of isochasms. As in the northern hemisphere the isochasms may be represented closely by a set of concentric circles about the magnetic axis point. Strong aurora appear to occur simultaneously in the two hemispheres.

In neither of the charts do the isochasms extend to the tropics, for aurora appear so rarely in this region that it has not been possible to assign a reliable value to the isochasmic frequency. Chapman[43] has given an account of some of the few such aurora known. As far as he could discover, the most extreme case on record is provided by the great aurora of the February 4, 1872, which was seen as far south as Aden, only 9° from the geomagnetic equator. Another remarkable case is mentioned by Chapman. On February 14, 1848, Hooker[44] from the east bank of Soane River at geomagnetic latitude 13° N observed an aurora with rays and arc. The rays crossed the zenith into the southern half of the sky, and the arc, which lay between the bearings W 20° S and N 50° E rose to an elevation of 20° above the horizon. On the night in question there was no world-wide auroral display. In connection with the first of these cases it may be noted that a sunspot maximum occurred half-way through 1871, and in connection with the second that one occurred at the beginning of 1848 (cf. Chapman and Bartels[4]).

A few aurora have been photographed from quite low latitudes: for example, the aurora of August 10, 1950, was photographed by Abbott[45] working in Spetsai, Greece.

Red arcs, too feeble to be seen, have been detected by Barbier[45a], Duncan,[45b] and Roach and Marovich,[45c] while carrying out photometric studies on the nightglow in middle latitudes. They appear to be not uncommon at least near sunspot maximum.

It would be of great value to have charts of *isoaurorals*, that is, charts showing the geographical distribution of the frequency of appearance of *overhead* aurora (Chapman[43]). Qualitatively it is obvious that the isoauroral frequency curve along a meridian lies below the corresponding isochasmic frequency curve at geomagnetic latitudes away from the main auroral zone.

In future work on the geographical distribution it is desirable that the various types of aurora should be treated separately. A significant dependence on the type may well exist. Aurora seen from low latitudes are often described as being red in color. This may be partially an altitude effect, but it may, however, be partially due simply to Rayleigh scattering, for such aurora usually appear close to the horizon. Another type effect reported is that pulsating aurora, at least as observed from College Alaska are seldom poleward of geomagnetic latitude 66° N, seemingly being concentrated between 63° N and 65° N (Heppner *et al.*[46]). Ray forms appear to extend about 2° of latitude further from the pole than do arc forms (Gartlein[46a]).

6.6 Temporal Distribution

6.6.1 *Diurnal Occurrence*

The dependence of the frequency of occurrence of aurora on the time of day has been investigated by Vegard,[47] Chree,[48] Sverdrup,[37] Lee,[49] Currie

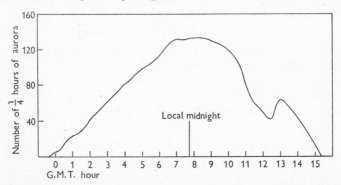

Fig. 4. Diurnal variation of auroral frequency at Fort Rae, September, 1932–March, 1933. From J. M. Stagg, "British Polar Year Expedition, Fort Rae, N.W. Canada, 1932–33," Vol. 1, p. 127, Royal Society, London, 1937.

and Edwards,[13] Fuller,[15] Stagg,[14] Stetson and Brooks,[50] Malville,[50a] and others.

It is found that the auroral frequency curve (cf. Fig. 4) passes through a main maximum, usually an hour or so in advance of local midnight. Strong rapidly moving forms have a tendency to favor the period before this maximum, and feeble quiet forms to favor the period after.

Vegard[47] considers that the scatter among the results from different stations is reduced if, in expressing the time, the reference meridian is chosen to be the magnetic rather than the geographic. According to him the main maximum occurs about 1.3 hours before magnetic midnight at the place of observation. The fuller information now available shows that this is far from being the case on the polar caps. Thus Malville[50a] reports that the time of the main maximum becomes earlier as the geomagnetic pole is approached, and at the South Pole is as much as nine hours in advance of geomagnetic midnight. As he points out the trend is in accord with Stormer's[18] line of precipitation for negative particles.

Many of the frequency curves (including the one depicted in Fig. 4) exhibit a subsidiary maximum in the early morning. There has been some doubt concerning the reality of this feature (cf. Hulburt[51]).

Aurora reflect radio waves (cf. Chapter 8). The property enables their diurnal distribution to be determined. This has been done by Currie et al.[52] using 56-Mc/sec and 106-Mc/sec waves as the probes. The derived curves are of the same general form as those based on ordinary visual observations. They show the disputed early morning peak. There is, however, little indication of this on the otherwise very similar curves obtained by Gerson.[53]

A major advantage of the radio method is that it is applicable throughout the full 24 hours. Currie et al. did not detect auroral echoes in any part of the daylight period other than the early morning. Though Gerson reports detecting them almost throughout the 24 hours, he agrees that the phenomenon is predominantly nocturnal.

6.6.2 Yearly Occurrence

Figure 5 shows how the 1267 aurora observed at Yerkes Observatory, Williams Bay (geomagnetic latitude 53° N), during the 55-year interval from 1897 to 1951 are distributed among the months, cognizance being taken of cloudiness and of the number of dark hours in each month (Meinel et al.[54]). As is apparent, the auroral frequency passes through maxima in the equinoctial months and through minima in the summer and winter months (just as does the magnetic disturbance[4]). This trend is exhibited in the records from other moderate- and low-latitude stations (Tromholt,[55] Lee,[49] Egedal,[56] Clayton[57]). It has also been found by Gerson,[58] using the radio method.

The dependence of the distribution on latitude alone is obscured by the change with latitude of the ratio of the lengths of day and night. If this change is ignored, as it usually is, then on going poleward the summer minimum becomes progressively deeper while the winter minimum becomes progressively shallower, disappears, and is replaced by a maximum which is then the only one in the distribution (Chree[59]).

Gartlein and Moore[60] have obtained some very interesting results from their study of overhead aurora in North America. They find that for such aurora the ratio of the mean of the numbers occurring in June and December to the mean of the numbers occurring in March and September is a steadily

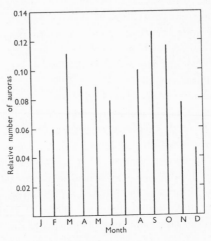

FIG. 5. Auroral frequency at Williams Bay corrected for cloudiness and number of dark hours in each month. From A. B. Meinel, B. J. Negaard, and J. W. Chamberlain, *J. Geophys. Res.* **59**, 407 (1954).

increasing function of geomagnetic latitude. In the region between geomagnetic latitudes 58° N and 60° N the level of activity appears to be constant throughout the year.

6.6.3 *Secular Occurrence*

6.6.3.1 *Solar Cycle*

The variation in the auroral frequency through the sunspot cycle is very marked at low geomagnetic latitudes, as has long been recognized (cf. Chree[59]). Stetson and Brooks[50] have presented an interesting plot of data obtained in the period 1885–1940 at Blue Hill near Boston (geomagnetic latitude 54° N). A noteworthy feature is the great differences between the magnitudes of the maxima in different 11.1-year periods. This is clearly exemplified in the historical records of aurora; thus aurora were seen in Rome eight times between 1786 and 1789 but were rare for the next forty years (Chapman and Bartels[4]). Again, examination of the Scandinavian catalogs shows that the greatest maximum in the numbers of aurora observed yearly from 1749 to

1877 was about three times the smallest maximum, the greatest being for 1872 and the smallest for 1818 (Chree[59]). It may be remarked, incidentally, that each of these maxima *followed* the nearest maximum in the sunspot number (which were in 1870 and 1816, respectively). The lag is characteristic. In general (cf. Stetson,[61] Clayton,[57] Meinel *et al.*[54]), the auroral curve, like the magnetic disturbance curve, reaches its maximum one or two years after the sunspot number curve reached its maximum, whereas the minima of all three curves tend to be closely coincident.

The correlation coefficients between sunspot and auroral numbers in corresponding years of different solar cycles are low. Using the Yerkes data, Meinel *et al.*[54] obtained a coefficient of 0.05 at the maximum of the cycle and a coefficient of 0.28 at the minimum.

The results of Paulsen and Arrhenius[62] and the observations carried out during the 1882–83 and 1932–33 Polar Years (cf. Vestine[38]) indicate that the great *increase* in the number of aurora seen at low latitudes after a sunspot maximum is accompanied by a distinct but less pronounced *decrease* in the number seen at high latitudes on the magnetic axis side of the peak isochasm. Vegard[63] attributed the behavior to expansion of the main auroral zone away from the axis at times of magnetic storms (which are most frequent after a sunspot maximum). Superimposed on the change caused by the expansion there is probably a general rise in the auroral frequency. The available evidence suggests that the auroral frequency near the peak isochasm is greater after sunspot maximum than at sunspot minimum (Vestine,[38] Vestine and Snyder[42]).

6.6.3.2 *Recurrence Tendencies and Relation with Sunspots*

Like magnetic disturbances auroras have a tendency to recur after a lapse about equal to the mean time (27.3 days) between successive passages of sunspots through the central meridian or mean *synodic* rotation period. (Fritz,[36] Sverdrup,[37] Dixon,[64]). Since aurora are more easy to see in the dark than in the full of the moon and since the lunar period is 29.5 days, it is clear that the apparent recurrence tendency is greater than the actual. Cognizance of this has not always been taken. On eliminating the influence of the moon by suitable statistical treatment of the data, Meinel *et al.*[54] discovered that, though there is indeed a tendency for aurora to recur after approximately 27 days, it is but slight. Unlike earlier workers (who did not eliminate the influence of the moon) they found no indication of the 27-day periodicity extending beyond a single solar rotation. They found also that there is quite a marked tendency for an aurora to be followed by another aurora within a few nights.

In connection with the results just reported it may be noted that, although large sunspots often survive several solar rotations, the flare actually associated with a spot has a life of less than the rotation period (cf. Kiepenheuer[65]).

Clayton [57] has made a statistical study of the association between aurora and sunspots. He found that most aurora occur about one and a half 24-hour days after a spot or group of spots crosses the central meridian;* that the area of spots preceding brilliant aurora is much larger than the area of spots preceding moderate aurora; and that the effectiveness of a spot of given size on the central meridian is a decreasing function of its distance from the center of the disk.

Several interesting and suggestive sequences of events are described in the literature.

The sequence occurring between the 23rd and 29th of March, 1940, is especially noteworthy. Accounts of the various aspects of it have been given by Rowland and others.[66] At 23d 11h 30m, a bright flare, extending over a group of spots which was at the time 3 days before central meridian passage, was observed in Hα light with the Greenwich spectrohelioscope. Its commencement was not detected, but the associated radio fade-out, lasting $1\frac{1}{4}$ hours, began at 23d 11h 8m. About 26 hours later, starting at 24d 13h 45m, there occurred one of the greatest magnetic storms known; and on the same evening a brilliant aurora was visible from England. At 27d 17h 10m a second flare covering the same group of spots as the first was observed. It was the brightest that had ever been observed at Greenwich. The start of the associated radio fade, which persisted for about 2 hours, was at 27d 16h 19m. Just 48 hours after this, at 29d 16h 0m, another magnetic storm began; and auroral activity was again seen from England that evening.

As a further example attention may be drawn to the accounts given by Richardson and by McNish[67] of the essentially similar sequence preceding the intense aurora of September 18, 1941.

Odishaw[67a] has given a brief survey of some of the relevant IGY work. Mention may be made of the great display of February 10-11, 1958, which is fully documented by Winckler et al.[67b].

6.7 Relation with Other Geophysical Phenomena

6.7.1 *Magnetic Disturbances*

Incidental mention has already been made of several similarities between the morphology of aurora and the morphology of magnetic disturbance. These strongly suggest that the two phenomena are connected.

Table V, which is based on an analysis by Chree[48] of observational data obtained at Cape Denison (67° S, 143° E) during the 1912–13 Australasian

---

* If the delay is taken to be simply the time primorary auroral particles take to travel from the sun to the earth, then the *mean* speed must be about 10^3 km/sec.

Antarctic Expedition, shows that there is undoubtedly a correlation. The auroral and magnetic character figures, A and C, give a measure of the degree of activity. Thus the auroral character figures 0, 1, and 2 signify, respectively, *no* aurora, a *faint* aurora, and a *very bright* aurora—Chree uses 0.5 for a *very faint* aurora and 1.5 for a *bright* aurora, but these intermediate cases have been excluded. Similarly the magnetic character figures 0, 1, and 2 signify respectively *quiet, moderately disturbed,* and *highly disturbed* conditions. As can be seen, auroral activity and magnetic activity tend to go together. This tendency is also apparent in the records obtained at other stations (cf. Lee,[49] Davies,[68] Currie and Edwards,[69] Stagg,[14] Meek,[70] Meinel *et al.*,[54] Barbier[45a]). With increasing K number[4] auroras go further from the poles and auroras at lower latitudes become brighter.

TABLE V

Incidence of Auroral and Magnetic Character Figures at Cape Denison

Auroral character figure	Magnetic character figure			Average
	C			
A	0	1	2	C
0	293	157	31	0.46
1	252	267	59	0.67
2	1	8	26	1.7_1
Average A	0.4_7	0.6_5	0.9_7	

It is difficult to find detailed associations between the two activities. Stagg[14] has carried out a careful study of the problem, using the data from Fort Rae (which is at geomagnetic latitude 68.9° N and is thus in the main auroral zone). The following are among the conclusions he reached.

1. Intense moving aurora with ray structure, especially if overhead, is often, but not invariably, accompanied by very large magnetic disturbance in which the meridian force components change by several hundred gammas in a few minutes. When a homogeneous arc is the only form, magnetic disturbance does not seem to occur, but the development of ray structure in such an arc often signals the appearance of oscillations in the field after a quiet period. Quick formation or bodily movement of draperies or bands with ray structure is more often accompanied by rapid field changes than is violent internal wave motion.

2. Though the most striking parts in an auroral display and the sharpest and greatest changes in the meridian force frequently coincide, there are occasions when they are out of phase. It may not be until after a very bright

19

corona has dispersed into draperies oriented along the magnetic prime vertical plane that the major changes occur.

3. Simultaneous activity on a large scale in the two phenomena are commoner in the early than in the late part of a protracted display. Again, when apparently equally intense and similarly structured and positioned aurora occur twice in a night, the magnetic disturbance at the time of the first is generally more than at the time of the second.

4. Disparity in the relative degrees of activity is evident not only between the earlier and later parts of the same night. Not infrequently a succession of outbursts of aurora repeatedly culminating in those forms with which the largest magnetic disturbance is usually associated is accompanied by almost insignificant magnetic disturbance. Conversely considerable magnetic disturbance may occasionally be in progress with no aurora of appreciable intensity visible.

5. Magnetic disturbances occurring during the hours of daylight are often not less great than, and apparently have no characteristics which distinguish them from, magnetic disturbances accompanying aurora.

6. Even given the position and other properties of an aurora, it does not seem possible to predict the seat and direction of the electric current system responsible for the changes in the field.

Some progress has been achieved by Meek,[39, 70] working at Saskatoon. This is southward from the main auroral zone, the geomagnetic latitude being 61° N. Meek's conclusions are based on observations during slight and moderate disturbances, for severe disturbances were rare during the period of the research.

Before summarizing the results it may be recalled that during a general disturbance many *increases* and *decreases* of the horizontal field, H, occur. These features are called positive and negative bays (cf. Chapman and Bartels[4]).

Numerous superimposed bays may be world-wide in effect, but individual bays are localized. The duration of a positive bay is less than an hour; that of a negative bay is usually less than 2 hours. There is a tendency for the former type to be centered around 20 h and for the latter type to be centered around 2 h. Almost all positive bays are followed by a negative bay, but on a particular night a negative bay is not necessarily preceded by a positive bay. During a positive bay the disturbance vector rotates anticlockwise, and during a negative bay it rotates clockwise (which rotations correspond, respectively, to eastward and westward movements of negative charge along the northern auroral zone).

The incidence and elevation of aurora were found to be closely associated with ΔH, the variation in the horizontal field: thus the observers log at Saskatoon shows that aurora was visible on only 30 % of quite clear nights ($\Delta H < 50\,\gamma$) and on such nights usually lay low on the northern horizon, whereas aurora was visible on every very disturbed clear night ($\Delta H > 300\,\gamma$) and on such nights always extended at least to the zenith.

Meek states that the sporadic E layer becomes increasingly prominent before the advent of a *positive* bay, and at the advent a bright auroral arc appears at an elevation usually not more than 10° and at an azimuth which is often slightly west of the magnetic north. Coincident with its appearance he obtains spasmodic echoes from the same part of the sky on frequencies between 10 Mc/sec and 18 Mc/sec, the range being 400 to 800 km. There is some evidence that D-region absorption increases slightly throughout the course of the bay and that so does the maximum reflection frequency from the sporadic E layer. The aurora usually remains approximately constant in position, but it may move northward. It decays in intensity and becomes more diffuse as the field returns to normal.

In the case of a *negative* bay the development is entirely different. Sometime before the commencement of such a bay (several hours before, if the bay is large) there is an augmentation of the sporadic E layer which becomes more uniform and of appreciable thickness. During this period aurora is usually seen in the north. When the bay begins, draperies and bands appear higher above the horizon. The maximum elevation reached is crudely dependent on ΔH, being about 60° if ΔH is 100 γ and about 90° if ΔH is 200 γ (which is in harmony with results obtained earlier by Rostad[71]). Owing to absorption, high-frequency radio echoes from above the base of the luminosity cannot be obtained during that part of a large bay when the field is greatly depressed with aurora overhead. The aurora and the absorption persist long after the peak of the bay is past. Eventually the former becomes diffuse and patchy and the latter becomes less severe, reception of echoes from the E and F layers being occasionally possible.

The intensity of aurora visible during either type of bay is related to the rate of change of the field.

Studies similar to those of Meek have been carried out by Heppner[72] at College, which is at a rather higher geomagnetic latitude (64.5° N) than Saskatoon. The conclusions reached are in general accord. Heppner reports that the switch from a positive to negative deviation common near midnight is coincident with a distinct discontinuity in the auroral activity. In some cases there is a northward recession and temporary disappearance of all auroral forms: in others there is a breakup of the arc into active rayed forms followed by diffuse aurora (diffuse surfaces, diffuse draperies, and pulsating diffuse forms) or directly into diffuse aurora, the breakup progressing with time from north to south. He further reports that the decay of the negative deviation occurs during diffuse and pulsating aurora and that if a short positive bay follows (as often happens) these sometimes persist through it and sometimes give place to a homogeneous arc. According to him there is some evidence that SSC's (world-wide sudden commencements followed by a period of storminess[4]) and the breakup of the original arcs are simultaneous events.

The relationship between auroral and magnetic activity has also been discussed by Gartlein[46a], Bless et al.,[72a] and Malville.[50a]

Accounts of the magnetic effects associated with artificial (nuclear) auroras have been given by Newman,[2b] Matsushita,[72b] Lawrie et al.,[72c] and Mason and Vitousek.[72d]

6.7.2 *Earth Currents*

Since earth currents are linked with changes in the geomagnetic field (cf. Chapman and Bartels[4]), they would naturally be expected to show an association with aurora. The existence of a close correlation has been verified directly by Rooney[73], Romick and Elvey,[73a] and others. Investigations on the very complicated relationship have not proved very rewarding and need not be discussed. Brief mention may, however, be made of the violence of the earth-current storms associated with auroral displays. At College, Rooney has recorded potential gradients of more than a hundred times the amplitude of the regular periodic variation, peaks in excess of a volt per kilometer being reached. Telegraphic communication is often affected, and damage may even be caused. Surges in the cables are usually noticeable many hours before the display they herald. This enables a warning to be sent to auroral field workers to be prepared to take observations.

6.7.3 *Vertical Potential Gradient at Ground Level*

As is well known, the earth is negatively charged. The vertical potential gradient at ground level averages about 100 volts/meter. It is not the same at all places, and at a given place it shows irregular fluctuations superimposed on diurnal and seasonal variations (cf. Gish[74]).

Several workers (Sherman,[75] Scholz[76]) have reported finding that the gradient is depressed when there is an auroral display, the high atmosphere apparently gaining negative charge. Though sharing the general scepticism about the validity of such claims, Sheppard[77] sought to test them while at Fort Rae, and from a statistical analysis of the data he concluded that the effect is probably real but small, the decrease in the gradient during an auroral display in general not exceeding about 10 volts/meter. The problem requires further investigation.

6.8 Motion of Aurora along Lines of Latitude

The fact that aurora may exhibit rapid latitudinal motion was realized by Tromholt[78] and other early writers. Störmer[6] appears to have been the first to carry out quantitative studies. Two examples from his more recent work may be cited. He records[29] that a red surface with summit at perhaps 700 km which was seen on January 25, 1938, was, at about 1 h, moving eastward at 1.7 km/sec; and again that a yellow-green cloudlike aurora at perhaps 106 km which was seen on January 3, 1940, was, at about 19 h moving westward, the mean speed being 0.5 km/sec and the speeds of different parts ranging between 0.2 km/sec and 0.8 km/sec. Similar results have been obtained by Krogness and Tönsberg.[79] Radio scientists have confirmed that east–west and west–east speeds of several kilometers per second are not uncommon (cf. Bullough and Kaiser[80]). These speeds are much greater than the wind speeds normally found (cf. Chapter 8). In view of this and in view of the lack of distortion shown by even lengthy rays and draperies, many authors consider that the latitudinal motion of aurora cannot be due to atmospheric motion but must instead be due to motion relative to the earth of the agency responsible for the excitation and ionization. This view is not shared by Meinel,[81] who argues that the apparent wind speeds indicated by ionospheric scintillation are in fact extremely high during auroral activity. As Kaiser[82] and others have emphasized, however, the speeds are sometimes in excess of the speed of sound, so it is not easy to attribute them to atmospheric motion; and further echoes from meteors in the vicinity of auroral ionization behave in the normal manner.

The number of cases so far studied is not large. Meinel and Schulte[83] measured the velocities of six auroras from Yerkes Observatory. They found that the velocities of the two which occurred before midnight were westward, whereas those of the four which occurred after midnight were eastward, and suggested the trend might be general. Noting that Roach et al.[84] report a similar midnight reversal of the drift of the airglow patches, they propose that the atmospheric motion hypotheses should be invoked. Though this last proposal does not command wide acceptance, there seems little doubt that the trend suggested is real. It has been noted by other visual observers (cf. Bless et al.[85]) and by radio scientists (cf. Kaiser,[82] Lyon and Kavadas,[85a]) but is of course of a statistical nature and is certainly not followed by all aurora (cf. Meek[86]).* Attention has been drawn (Meinel and Schulte,[83] Meinel[81]), to the striking resemblance the phenomenon bears to the reversal of the ionospheric current near midnight and noon during magnetic storms

---

* Kim and Currie[86a] have found that westward motions occur in the early evening and eastward motions in the late morning, but that motions in either direction may occur in the 4 hours around midnight. The speeds do not indicate a gradual slowing down of the westward motions prior to a change to eastward motions.

(Chapman,[87] Vestine[88]). There seems little doubt but that there exists a close relation between the auroral motion and the current system, negative charge being transported in the direction of the motion (Kaiser[82]). In harmony with this Malville[50a] finds that the auroral motions in the southern zone are in the same direction as in the northern zone.

Acknowledgment

It is a pleasure to thank Drs. J. W. Chamberlain, A. Dalgarno, D. M. Hunten, and F. E. Roach for helpful comments on the original manuscript, and Dr. J. Mazur for his assistance with the references.

References

1. J. R. Capron, "Aurorae: Their Characters and Spectra," Spon, London, 1879.
2. C. W. Gartlein, *Natl. Geograph. Mag.* **92**, 673 (1947).
2a. A. L. Cullington, *Nature* **182**, 1365 (1958).
2b. P. Newman, *J. Geophys. Res.* **64**, 923 (1959).
3. "Photographic Atlas of Auroral Forms," International Geodetic and Geophysical Union, Oslo, 1951; S. Chapman, *Ann. IGY* **4**, 41 (1957).
4. S. Chapman and J. Bartels, "Geomagnetism," Clarendon, Oxford, 1940.
5. C. Störmer, *Videnskapsselskapets-Skrifter I. Mat. Nat. Kl. Oslo* (1911).
6. C. Störmer, *Terr. Mag.* **18**, 133 (1913); **20**, 1, 158 (1915); **21**, 45, 153, 157 (1916); *Geofys. Publ. (Oslo)* **1**, No. 5 (1921).
7. C. Störmer, *Geofys. Publ. (Oslo)* **4**, No. 7 (1926).
8. C. Störmer, *Terr. Mag.* **51**, 501 (1946); **53**, 251 (1948).
9. C. Störmer, *Geofys. Publ. (Oslo)* **18**, No. 7 (1953).
10. L. Vegard and O. Krogness, *Geofys. Publ. (Oslo)* **1**, No. 1 (1920).
11. L. Harang and E. Tönsberg, *Geofys. Publ. (Oslo)* **9**, No. 5 (1932).
12. J. C. McLennan, H. S. Wynne-Edwards, and H. J. C. Ireton, *Canad. J. Res.* **A5**, 285 (1931).
13. B. W. Currie and H. W. Edwards, *Terr. Mag.* **39**, 293 (1934); B. W. Currie, *Canad. J. Phys.* **33**, 773 (1955).
14. J. M. Stagg, "British Polar Year Expedition, Fort Rae, N.W. Canada, 1932-33," Vol. 1, p. 127, Royal Society, London, 1937.
14a. D. J. McEwen and R. Montalbetti, *Canad. J. Phys.* **36**, 1593 (1958).
15. V. R. Fuller and E. H. Bramhall, *Misc. Publ. Univ. Alaska* **3**, (1937); V. R. Fuller, *Terr. Mag.* **36**, 297 (1931); **37**, 159 (1932); **38**, 207 (1933); **40**, 269 (1935).
16. M. Geddes, *New Zealand J. Sci. Tech.* **19**, 55 (1937); **20**, 289 (1939).
17. L. Harang, "The Aurorae," Chapman and Hall, London, 1951.
18. C. Störmer, "The Polar Aurorae," Clarendon, Oxford, 1955.
19. L. Harang and W. Bauer, *Gerlands Beitr. Geophys.* **37**, 109 (1932).
20. S. Chapman, *Nature* **127**, 341 (1931); **130**, 764 (1932).
21. C. Störmer, *Z. Geophys.* **5**, 177 (1929); **6**, 463 (1930); *Geofys. Publ. (Oslo)* **12**, No. 7 (1938); *Observatory* **67**, 161 (1947).
22. L. Harang, *Terr. Mag.* **50**, 297 (1950).
23. J. Egedal. *Météorologie* **13**, 301 (1937).
24. J. Chamberlain and A. B. Meinel, "The Earth as a Planet" (G. P. Kuiper, ed.), p. 514, Univ. Chicago Press, Chicago, 1954.
25. L. Harang, *Gerlands Beitr. Geophys.* **54**, 81 (1939).

26. L. Harang, *Terr. Mag.* **41**, 143 (1936); **42**, 55 (1937).

27. J. Egedal, *Nature* **124**, 913 (1929).

28. L. Harang, *Geofys. Publ. (Oslo)* **16**, No. 6 (1946); *Terr. Mag.* **51**, 381 (1946).

29. C. Störmer, *Geofys. Publ. (Oslo)* **13**, No. 7 (1942).

30. L. Vegard, *Phil. Mag.* **42**, 47 (1921).

31. L. Vegard, *in* "Terrestrial Magnetism and Electricity" (J. A. Fleminr, ed), McGraw-Hill, New York, 1939.

32. B. W. Currie and C. K. Jones, *Terr. Mag.* **46**, 269 (1941).

33. R. E. Jensen and B. W. Currie, *J. Geophys. Res.* **58**, 201 (1953).

34. C. Störmer, *Naturwissenschaften* **26**, 633 (1938).

35. H. Fritz, "Verzeichnis beobackteter Polarlichter," Gerolds Sohm in Comm, Vienna, 1873.

36. H. Fritz, "Das Polarlicht," Brockhaus, Leipzig, 1881.

37. H. U. Sverdrup, "Auroral Results, Maud Expedition 1918–1925," *Carnegie Inst. Wash. Publ.* No. **175**, 6 (1927).

38. E. H. Vestine, *Terr. Mag.* **49**, 77 (1944).

38a. B. Hultqvist, *Arkiv för geofysik* **3**, 63 (1958).

38b. H. Alfvén, "Cosmical Electrodynamics", Clarendon, Oxford, 1950.

38c. C. W. Gartlein, "U. S. Visual Observations News Letter", No. 18, Ithaca, 1959.

38d. B. Hultqvist, *Nature* **183**, 1478 (1959); see also *ibid.* **184**, 262 (1959).

38e. E. H. Vestine and W. L. Sibley, *J. Geophys. Res.* **64**, 1338 (1959).

39. J. H. Meek, *J. Geophys. Res.* **59**, 87 (1954). •

40. W. Boller, *Gerlands Beitr. Geophys.* **3**, 56, 550 (1898).

41. F. T. Davies, *Terr. Mag.* **36**, 199 (1931); M. Geddes, *ibid.* **44**, 189 (1939); M. Geddes and F. W. G. White, *ibid.* **44**, 367 (1939).

42. E. H. Vestine and E. J. Snyder, *Terr. Mag.* **50**, 105 (1945).

43. S. Chapman, *Proc. Indian Acad. Sci.* **37**, 175 (1953); *Ann. IGY* **4**, 25 (1957).

44. J. D. Hooker, "Himalayan Journals," Vol. 2, Murray, London, 1854.

45. W. N. Abbott, *J. Atmos. Terr. Phys.* **1**, 343 (1951); W. N. Abbott and S. Chapman, *ibid.* **14**, 111 (1959).

45a. D. Barbier, *Ann Géophys.* **14**, 334 (1958).

45b. R. A. Duncan, *Australian J. Phys.* **12**, 197 (1959).

45c. F. E. Roach and E. Marovich, *J. Res. Nat. Bur. Stand.* **63**D. (in press) (1959); *ibid.* **64**D.

46. J. P. Heppner, E. C. Byrne, and A. E. Belon, *J. Geophys. Res.* **57**, 121 (1952).

46a. C. W. Gartlein, *Ann. Géophys.* **15**, 31 (1959).

47. L. Vegard, *Phil. Mag.* **23**, 211 (1912).

48. C. Chree, *Proc. Phys. Soc.* **39**, 389 (1927).

49. A. W. Lee, "Auroral Observations at Lerwick Observatory 1924–29," Meteorology Office, Professional Notes, No. 56, London, 1930.

50. H. T. Stetson and C. F. Brooks, *Terr. Mag.* **47**, 21 (1942).

50a. J. M. Malville, *J. Geophys. Res.* **64**, 1389, (1959).

51. E. O. Hulburt, *Terr. Mag.* **36**, 23 (1931).

52. B. W. Currie, P. A. Forsyth, and F. E. Vawter, *J. Geophys. Res.* **58**, 179 (1953).

53. N. C. Gerson, *Proc. Phys. Soc.* B**68**, 408 (1955).

54. A. B. Meinel, B. J. Negaard, and J. W. Chamberlain, *J. Geophys. Res.* **59**, 407 (1954).

55. S. Tromholt, "Katalog der in Norwegen bis June 1878, beobackteten Nordlichter," Kristiania, Oslo, 1902.

56. J. Egedal, "Observations of Aurorae from Danish Light-Vessels during the Years 1897–1937," Publikationer fra Det Danske Meteorologiske Institut, Tillseg, Copenhagen, 1937.

57. H. H. Clayton, *Terr. Mag.* **45**, 13 (1940).

58. N. C. Gerson, *J. Atmos. Terr. Phys.* **6**, 263 (1955).
59. C. Chree, Aurora Polaris. *In* "Encyclopedia Britannica," 11th edn., Vol. 2, p. 927, New York, 1911.
60. C. W. Gartlein and R. K. Moore, *J. Geophys. Res.* **56**, 85 (1953).
61. H. T. Stetson, *Science* **90**, 482 (1939).
62. A. Paulsen, "Aurores borealis observees a Godthaab," Inst. Met. de Danemark, Copenhagen, 1891; S. Arrhenius, *Medd. Vatenskapsakad. Nobelinst.* **1**, No. 6 (1906).
63. L. Vegard, *Jahrb. Radioakt. Elektronik* **14**, 383 (1917); *Handbuch der Experimentalphysik* **25**, 385 (1928).
64. F. E. Dixon, *Terr. Mag.* **44**, 335 (1939).
65. K. O. Kiepenheuer, "The Sun" (G. P. Kuiper, ed.), p. 322, Univ. Chicago Press, Chicago, 1953.
66. J. P. Rowland, *Nature* **145**, 625 (1940); M. A. Ellison, *ibid.* **145**, 898 (1940); A. G. McNish, *Terr. Mag.* **45**, 359 (1940).
67. R. S. Richardson, *Terr. Mag.* **46**, 459 (1941); A. G. McNish, *ibid.* **46**, 461 (1941).
67a. H. Odishaw, *Science* **128**, 1599 (1958).
67b. J. R. Winckler, L. Peterson, R. Hoffman, and R. Arnoldy, *J. Geophys. Res.* **64**, 597 (1959).
68. F. T. Davies, *Terr. Mag.* **40**, 267, 456 (1935).
69. B. W. Currie and H. W. Edwards, *Terr. Mag.* **41**, 265 (1936).
70 J. H. Meek, *J. Geophys. Res.* **58**, 445 (1953).
71. A. Rostad, *Geofys. Publ. (Oslo)* **10**, No. 10 (1935).
72. J. P. Heppner, *J. Geophys. Res.* **59**, 329 (1954); **60**, 29 (1955).
72a. R. C. Bless, C. W. Gartlein, D. S. Kimball, and G. Sprague, *J. Geophys. Res.* **64**, 949 (1959).
72b. S. Matsushita, *Nature* **184**, B.A.33 (1959); *J. Geophys. Res.* **64**, 1149 (1959).
72c. J. A. Lawrie, V. B. Gerard, and P. J. Gill, *Nature* **814**, B.A.34 (1959).
72d. R. G. Mason and M. J. Vitousek, *Nature* **184**, B.A.52 (1959).
73. W. J. Rooney, *Terr. Mag.* **39**, 103 (1934).
73a. G. J. Romick and C. T. Elvey, *J. Atmos. Terr. Phys.* **12**, 283 (1958).
74. O. H. Gish, "Terrestrial Magnetism and Electricity" (J. A. Fleming, ed.), McGraw-Hill, New York, 1939.
75. K. L. Sherman, *Trans. Amer. Geophys. Union* **15**, 141 (1934).
76. J. Scholz, *Gerlands Beitr. Geophys.* **44**, 145 (1935).
77. P. A. Sheppard, "British Polar Year Expedition, Fort Rae, N.W. Canada 1932–33," Vol. 1, p. 309, Royal Society, London, 1937.
78. S. Tromholt, "Under the Rays of the Aurora Borealis," Sampson Low, Marston, Searle and Rivington, London, 1885.
79. O. Krogness and E. Tönsberg, *Geofys. Publ. (Oslo)* **11**, No. 8 (1936).
80. K. Bullough and T. R. Kaiser, *J. Atmos. Terr. Phys.* **5**, 189 (1954).
81. A. B. Meinel, *Astrophys. J.* **122**, 206 (1955).
82. T. R. Kaiser, *in* "The Airglow and the Aurorae" (E. B. Armstrong and A. Dalgarno, eds.), p. 156, Pergamon, London, 1956.
83. A. B. Meinel and D. H. Schulte, *Astrophys. J.* **117**, 454 (1953).
84. F. E. Roach, D. R. Williams, and H. B. Pettit, *Astrophys. J.* **117**, 456 (1953).
85. R. C. Bless, C. W. Gartlein, and D. S. Kimball, *Astrophys. J.* **122**, 205 (1955).
85a. G. F. Lyon and A. Kavadas, *Canad. J. Phys.* **36**, 1661 (1958).
86. J. H. Meek, *Astrophys. J.* **120**, 602 (1954).
86a. J. S. Kim and B. W. Currie, *Canad. J. Phys.* **36**, 160 (1958).
87. S. Chapman, *Proc. Roy. Soc.* A**115**, 242 (1927).
88. E. H. Vestine, "The Geomagnetic Field," Carnegie Institution, Washington, 1947.

Chapter 7

The Auroral Spectrum and its Interpretation

D. R. Bates

7.1 Identifications 298
    7.1.1 Lines from Incoming Particles...................................... 299
    7.1.2 Forbidden Lines.. 300
    7.1.3 Allowed Lines.. 302
    7.1.4 Molecular Band Systems... 303
7.2 Absolute Intensity.. 304
7.3 Relative Intensities.. 307
7.4 Variations in the Auroral Spectrum...................................... 310
    7.4.1 Altitude Effects... 310
    7.4.2 Latitude Effects... 312
    7.4.3 Type Effects... 313
    7.4.4 Temporal and Correlation Effects................................... 314
    7.4.5 Sunspot Cycle Effects.. 316
7.5 Theory of the Auroral Spectrum.. 316
    7.5.1 Primary Processes.. 316
    7.5.2 Secondary and Other Processes...................................... 322
    7.5.3 Individual Lines and Band Systems of the Atmospheric Constituents.... 324
7.6 Temperature 339
    7.6.1 Heating 343
7.7 Electric Fields... 343
    7.7.1 Rays... 344
    7.7.2 True Low-Latitude Auroras.. 347
    References.. 348

Experiments such as those carried out in 1872 by Ranyard[1] prove that the light emitted is unpolarized, so that the aurora must be self-luminous. Its spectrum shows discreet lines and bands. Toward the end of the last century Angstrom and others made wavelength measurements and conjectured as to the origin of the main features.[2] Because of the crudity of the instruments available and the paucity of the information concerning atomic and molecular spectra, this early work achieved little success and need not be reported. We shall not seek here to give a historical survey but shall confine ourselves to an account of the present state of knowledge. After reporting on the identifications and certain other aspects of the auroral spectrum we shall discuss the excitation mechanisms involved. The general subject has been developed rapidly in recent years. In most respects research on it is at a more advanced stage than is research on the airglow. There are several reasons for this: the aurora is much the brighter phenomenon and therefore the less difficult for observers to study; also, many of the collision processes concerned in it take place at comparatively high energies which greatly facilitates both laboratory and theoretical investigations on them.

7.1 Identifications

In 1953 Chamberlain and Oliver[3] compiled a useful list of auroral lines and bands based mainly on the researches of Vegard and Kvifte[4] (3100 to 8100 A), Barbier and Williams[5] (3100 to 5000 A), Dahlstrom and Hunten[6] (3800 to 7000 A), Meinel[7] (6200 to 8900 A), and Petrie and Small[8] (3300 to 8900 A). Table I gives this list, slightly revised and extended to take into account the later work of Chamberlain *et al.*,[9] Hunten,[10] Bagariazky and Fedorova,[11] Omholt,[12] and Harrison and Jones.[13] The features indicated by an asterisk (*) may well be present but have not yet been verified with certainty.

TABLE I

Auroral Spectrum

---

1. *Atomic Features*

Allowed Lines

HI: $2\ ^2P^0$—$3\ ^2D$ et al. ($H\alpha$); $2\ ^2P^0$—$4\ ^2D$ et al. ($H\beta$); $2\ ^2P^0$—$5\ ^2D$ et al. ($H\gamma$).

NaI: $3\ ^2\underline{S^*}$—$3\ ^2P^0$ (D doublet).

NI: $3s\ ^4P$—$3p\ ^4D^0$; $3s\ ^4P$—$3p\ ^4P^0$; $3s\ ^4\underline{P^*}$—$4p\ ^4P^0$; $3s\ ^4P$—$4p\ ^4S^0$;
       $3s\ ^2P$—$4p\ ^2S^0$; $3s\ ^2\underline{P^*}$—$3p'\ ^2D^0$; $3s\ ^2\underline{P^*}$—$3p'\ ^2P^0$.

NII: $2p^3\ ^1\underline{D^{0*}}$—$3p\ ^1P$; $3s\ ^3P^0$—$3p\ ^3D$; $3s\ ^3P^0$—$3p\ ^3P$; $3s\ ^3\underline{P^{0*}}$—$3p\ ^1D$;
       $3s\ ^1P^0$—$3p\ ^1P$; $3s\ ^1\underline{P^{0*}}$—$3p\ ^3D$; $3s\ ^1P^0$—$3p\ ^1D$; $3p\ ^1\underline{P^*}$—$3d\ ^3F^0$;
       $3p\ ^3D$—$3d\ ^3F^0$; $3p\ ^3\underline{D^*}$—$3d\ ^3D^0$; $3p\ ^3\underline{D^*}$—$3d\ ^3P^0$; $3p\ ^3\underline{S^*}$—$3d\ ^3P^0$;
       $3p\ ^3\underline{P^*}$—$3d\ ^3D^0$; $3p\ ^3\underline{P^*}$—$3d\ ^3P^0$.

OI: $3s\ ^5S^0$—$3p\ ^5P$; $3s\ ^5\underline{S^{0*}}$—$4p\ ^5P$; $3s\ ^3S^0$—$3p\ ^3P$; $3s\ ^3S^0$—$4p\ ^3P$;
       $3s\ ^3S^0$—$5p\ ^3P$; $3p\ ^5\underline{P^*}$—$5s\ ^5S^0$; $3p\ ^5P$—$4d\ ^5D^0$; $3p\ ^5\underline{P^*}$—$6s\ ^5S^0$;
       $3p\ ^5\underline{P^*}$—$5d\ ^5D^0$; $3p\ ^5\underline{P^*}$—$6d\ ^5D^0$; $3p\ ^3\underline{P^*}$—$3s'\ ^3D^0$; $3p\ ^3\underline{P^*}$—$5s\ ^3S^0$;
       $3p\ ^3\underline{P^*}$—$6s\ ^3S^0$.

OII: $3s\ ^4P$—$3p\ ^4D^0$; $3s\ ^4P$—$3p\ ^4P^0$; $3s\ ^4P$—$3p\ ^4S^0$; $3s\ ^2P$—$3p\ ^2D^0$;
       $3s\ ^2P$—$3p\ ^2P^0$; $3p\ ^4\underline{D^{0*}}$—$3d\ ^4F$; $3p\ ^4\underline{D^{0*}}$—$3d\ ^4P$; $3p\ ^4\underline{D^{0*}}$—$3d\ ^4D$;
       $3p\ ^4\underline{D^{0*}}$—$3d\ ^2F$; $3s'\ ^2\underline{D^*}$—$3p'\ ^2F^0$; $3s'\ ^2\underline{D^*}$—$3p'\ ^2D^0$; $3p\ ^4\underline{P^{0*}}$—$3d\ ^4P$;
       $3p\ ^4\underline{P^{0*}}$—$3d\ ^4D$; $3p\ ^4\underline{P^{0*}}$—$3d\ ^2F$; $3p\ ^2\underline{D^{0*}}$—$3d\ ^2D$; $3p\ ^4\underline{S^{0*}}$—$3d\ ^4P$;
       $3p\ ^4\underline{S^{0*}}$—$3d\ ^4D$; $3p\ ^2P^0$—$3d\ ^2D$.

Forbidden Lines

	$^2_1[\ \ ]$	$^3_1[\ \ ]$	$^3_2[\ \ ]$
NI:	$2p^3,\ ^4S^0$—$^2D^0$;	$2p^3,\ ^4S^0$—$^2P^0$;	$2p^3,\ ^2\underline{D^{0*}}$—$^2P^0$.
NII:			$2p^2,\ ^1D$—^1S.
OI:	$2p^4,\ ^3P$—^1D;		$2p^4,\ ^1D$—^1S.
OII:			$2p^3,\ ^2\underline{D^{0*}}$—$^2P^0$.

2. Molecular Features

N$_2$: $B\,^3\Pi_g \rightarrow A\,^3\Sigma_u^+$, First Positive: 0*0; 1–0; 2–0, 2–1; 3–0, 3–1, 3–2; 4*0, 4–1, 4–2; 5–1, 5–2, 5–3, 5*4; 6–2, 6–3, 6–4, 6*5; 7–3, 7–4, 7–5, 7*6; 8–4, 8–5, 8*6, 8*7; 9*4, 9*5, 9–6, 9–7, 9*8; 10–6, 10*7, 10*8, 10*9; 11*7, 11*8, 11*9, 11*10; 12–8, 12*9.

N$_2$: $C\,^3\Pi_u \rightarrow B\,^3\Pi_g$, Second Positive: 0–0, 0–1, 0–2, 0–3, 0*4; 1–0, 1–1, 1–2, 1–3, 1–4, 1–6; 2–1, 2–2, 2*3, 2–4, 2–5, 2–7; 3–2, 3–3, 3*4, 3–5, 3–7, 3–8; 4*4, 4*8.

N$_2$: $A\,^3\Sigma_u^+ \rightarrow X\,^1\Sigma_g^+$, Vegard-Kaplan: 0–10, 0*12; 1–9, 1–10, 1–11, 1–12, 1*13, 1*16; 2*10, 2*11, 2–12, 2–13, 2–14, 2*15; 3–13, 3–14, 3–15, 3*18; 4*11, 4*14; 5*15, 5*17.

N$_2^+$: $B\,^2\Sigma_u^+ \rightarrow X\,^2\Sigma_g^+$, First Negative: 0–0, 0–1, 0–2, 0–3, 0*4; 1–0, 1–1, 1–2, 1–3, 1–4, 1*5; 2–1, 2–2, 2–3, 2–4, 2–5; 3–2, 3*3, 3–4, 3–5; 4*6, 4–7; 5*6, 5*7; 6*7, 6*8.

N$_2^+$: $A\,^2\Pi_u \rightarrow X\,^2\Sigma_g^+$, Meinel Negative: 0–0; 1–0; 2–0; 3–0, 3–1; 4*0, 4–1, 4–2; 5*1, 5–2.

O$_2$: $A\,^1\Sigma_g^+ \rightarrow X\,^3\Sigma_g^-$, Atmospheric: 0–1; 1–1.

O$_2^+$: $b\,^4\Sigma_g^- \rightarrow a\,^4\Pi_u$, First Negative: 0–0, 0*1; 1–0, 1*1; 2–0.

A beautiful set of microphotometer tracings covering the spectral region between 3340 A and 9000 A is reproduced in "The Earth as a Planet." [14]

7.1.1 Lines from Incoming Particles

The presence of the Balmer lines of atomic hydrogen in the auroral spectrum was announced in 1939 by Vegard.[15] Rather more than a decade later Gartlein[16] fully established the correctness of the proposed identifications by showing that the features form a distinct group, their intensities relative to one another being always the same.

Both Vegard[17] and Gartlein[16] noted that the lines are broad and suggested that they must originate from incoming hydrogen rather than from atmospheric hydrogen. Proof of this was provided by Meinel,[18] who in 1950 obtained the spectra of an aurora in the direction of the magnetic zenith and found Hα to be Doppler-shifted. The extension of the violet wing of the line indicates that protons must be entering the atmosphere along the magnetic lines of force, some with a speed of at least 3300 km/sec. Only a lower limit to the speed can be inferred, since very fast protons have little chance of capturing an electron, and thus of being able to emit. In the case of auroras on the magnetic horizon, the Balmer lines, though not shifted, are broadened. This broadening strongly suggests that the protons spiral round the lines of force (Vegard[19]).

The atomic hydrogen emission varies greatly in intensity. This will be discussed later (§ 7.5).

Bernard[20] has claimed to have detected a number of lines of neutral and ionized helium in the auroral spectrum. Later workers (Barbier and Williams,[5] Meinel,[21] Chamberlain and Oliver[3]) agree, however, that the identifications advocated must be rejected. Mironov et al. [21a] have reported that HeI, $2s^3S - 2p^3P$, appeared strongly on a plate obtained during the IGY but it is likely that one of the hydroxyl bands of the nightglow was responsible for the spectral feature concerned.

According to Vegard,[22] Petrie and Small,[8] and Hunten,[10] the sodium D doublet is sometimes enhanced in high latitude auroras. A convincing explanation of the enhancement has not yet been given, but several authors have suggested that it may just conceivably be caused by emission due to incoming sodium ions. The element is, of course, one of great cosmic rarity: in the solar chromosphere, for example, sodium is less abundant than hydrogen by a factor of about 5×10^5 (Minnaert[23]). Appreciable enhancement of the D-doublet does not appear to occur in low latitude auroras. Manring and Pettit[23a] state that photometric measurements carried out in New Mexico during the aurora of February 10-11, 1958 show that though the intensity of λ 6300-6364 increased by a factor of almost a million that of the D-doublet remained at about the normal nightglow value.

There is no evidence for the incidence of any other species of heavy particle.

7.1.2 Forbidden Lines

Tables II and III give some relevant properties of the systems NI, NII, OI, OII, and OIII in their ground configurations. The values adopted for the transition probabilities and radiative lifetimes are those calculated by Garstang.[24]

As has long been recognized, the green λ 5577, $^1S \rightarrow {}^1D$ and red λ 6300-6364, $^1D \rightarrow {}^3P$ lines of OI are among the more prominent in the auroral spectrum. The ultraviolet line λ 2972, $^1S \rightarrow {}^3P$ naturally cannot be observed from below the ozone layer. Red auroras (known as type A) owe their color to λ 6300-6364. In such auroras the red color is sometimes restricted to the tops of the streamers.

The presence of the NI lines λ 3466, $^2P \rightarrow {}^4S$ and λ 5198-5201, $^2D \rightarrow {}^4S$ is also well established. Though the lines λ 10,395-10,404, $^2P \rightarrow {}^4S$ must be emitted, they have not yet been detected with certainty. Bagariazky and Fedorova[11] report, however, an anomalous increase of the intensity of the p_2 and P_2 lines of the (4-1) hydroxyl band (λ 10,392 and λ 10,416) during strong auroras. They believe this to be due to some additional emission and mention $^2P \to {}^4S$ as a possibility. Supporting evidence has been put forward by Harrison and Jones.[13]

Vegard and Kvifte,[4] Barbier and Williams,[5] and others have suggested that a faint feature near 3727 A may be due to λ 3726-3729, $^2D \to {}^4S$ of

TABLE II

Wavelengths and Transition Probabilities of Forbidden Lines between Levels of Ground Configurations of NI, NII, OI, OII, and OIII

	Multiplet			J's	Wavelength, λ (A)	Transition probability, A (sec^{-1})
NI:	$2p^3$,	$^2D \to {}^4S$,	$^2_1[$ $]$	$2\frac{1}{2} \to 1\frac{1}{2}$	5201	7.0×10^{-6}
				$1\frac{1}{2} \to 1\frac{1}{2}$	5198	1.6×10^{-5}
		$^2P \to {}^4S$,	$^3_1[$ $]$	$\frac{1}{2}, 1\frac{1}{2} \to 1\frac{1}{2}$	3466	5.4×10^{-3}
		$^2P \to {}^2D$,	$^3_2[$ $]$	$\frac{1}{2}, 1\frac{1}{2} \to 2\frac{1}{2}$	10395	4.6×10^{-2}
				$\frac{1}{2}, 1\frac{1}{2} \to 1\frac{1}{2}$	10404	3.3×10^{-2}
NII:	$2p^2$,	$^1D \to {}^3P$,	$^2_1[$ $]$	$2 \to 2$	6584	3.0×10^{-3}
				$2 \to 1$	6548	1.0×10^{-3}
				$2 \to 0$	6527	4.2×10^{-7}
		$^1S \to {}^3P$	$^3_1[$ $]$	$0 \to 2$	3071	$1 \cdot 6 \times 10^{-4}$
				$0 \to 1$	3063	3.4×10^{-2}
		$^1S \to {}^1D$,	$^3_2[$ $]$	$0 \to 2$	5755	1.1
OI:	$2p^4$,	$^1D \to {}^3P$,	$^2_1[$ $]$	$2 \to 2$	6300	6.9×10^{-3}
				$2 \to 1$	6364	2.2×10^{-3}
				$2 \to 0$	6392	1.1×10^{-6}
		$^1S \to {}^3P$,	$^3_1[$ $]$	$0 \to 2$	2958	3.7×10^{-4}
				$0 \to 1$	2972	7.8×10^{-2}
		$^1S \to {}^1D$,	$^3_2[$ $]$	$0 \to 2$	5577	1.3
OII:	$2p^3$,	$^2D \to {}^4S$,	$^2_1[$ $]$	$2\frac{1}{2} \to 1\frac{1}{2}$	3729	4.1×10^{-5}
				$1\frac{1}{2} \to 1\frac{1}{2}$	3726	1.3×10^{-4}
		$^2P \to {}^4S$,	$^3_1[$ $]$	$\frac{1}{2}, 1\frac{1}{2} \to 1\frac{1}{2}$	2470	4.6×10^{-2}
		$^2P \to {}^2D$,	$^3_2[$ $]$	$\frac{1}{2}, 1\frac{1}{2} \to 2\frac{1}{2}$	7319	9.2×10^{-2}
				$\frac{1}{2}, 1\frac{1}{2} \to 1\frac{1}{2}$	7330	7.0×10^{-2}
OIII:	$2p^2$,	$^1D \to {}^3P$,	$^2_1[$ $]$	$2 \to 2$	5007	2.1×10^{-2}
				$2 \to 1$	4959	7.1×10^{-3}
				$2 \to 0$	4932	1.9×10^{-6}
		$^1S \to {}^3P$,	$^3_1[$ $]$	$0 \to 2$	2331	7.1×10^{-4}
				$0 \to 1$	2321	2.3×10^{-1}
		$^1S \to {}^1D$,	$^3_2[$ $]$	$0 \to 2$	4363	1.6

OII, though the transition probability involved is only 7.7×10^{-5} sec^{-1} (cf. Table II). Petrie[25] has criticized the attribution, since he failed to find λ 7319-7330 $^2P \to {}^2D$ (for which the transition probability is 1.6×10^{-1} sec^{-1}) even on heavily exposed plates; and, as he stated, selective excitation would scarcely be anticipated. The problem has been discussed further by Seaton,[26] who concludes that Petrie is probably correct.* It should not be inferred that λ 7319 to 7330 is necessarily absent. Chamberlain and Roesler[27] have pointed out that blending with certain airglow features would make this multiplet difficult to recognize unless strong; Omholt[12] has tentatively claimed to have detected it on spectra from high altitudes, and Dufay[27b] has observed it to be prominent in the spectra of low latitude auroras. As will be seen later (§ 7.5.3.3) the complete absence of λ 7319-7330 would be rather surprising. According to Belon and Clark[27c] both multiplets were in the

TABLE III

Excitation Potentials and Radiative Lifetimes of Terms of Ground Configurations of NI, NII, OI, OII, and OIII

Term	Excitation potential (ev)	Lifetime (sec)	Excitation potential (ev)	Lifetime (sec)	Excitation potential (ev)	Lifetime (sec)
	NI		OII			
^2P	3.56	12	5.00	4.8		
^2D	2.37	9.4×10^4	3.31	1.3×10^4		
^4S	0	—	0	—		
	NII		OI		OIII	
^1S	4.04	0.90	4.17	0.73	5.33	0.55
^1D	1.89	250	1.96	110	2.50	36
^3P	0	—	0	—	0	—

spectrum of the type A aurora of February 10-11, 1958.

Petrie[25] has found a weak feature which he believes may be λ 5755, $^1S \to {}^1D$ of NII, which has a transition probability of 1.1 sec^{-1}. As he remarks, the identification is not inconsistent with the apparent absence of λ 6548-6584, $^1D \to {}^3P$, since this has the much lower transition probability of 4.0×10^{-3} sec.$^{-1}$ Dufay[27b] has detected λ 5755 in the emission from low latitude auroras.

There is no evidence for the presence of the forbidden lines of OIII. As need scarcely be said, NIII does not possess low-lying metastable levels.

7.1.3 *Allowed Lines*

Though several lengthy lists of proposals were published, generally accepted identifications of allowed lines were not made until 1948, when

* Wallace[27a] has since established the presence of the multiplet in the spectrum of a type A aurora.

Meinel[28] successfully explored the infrared region. Considerable progress has since been made.

Inspection of Table I reveals an interesting contrast: whereas the initial levels of the OI lines involve a number of different orbitals, most of the NI, NII, and OII lines originate from levels with the excited electron in one of only two orbitals—in $3p$ or $4p$ for NI and in $3p$ or $3d$ for NI and OII. Many lines not included in Table I have been identified in the spectra of type A auroras (cf. Wallace,[27a] Belon and Clark[27c]).

Various OIII and NIII lines have been listed by Vegard and Kvifte,[4] but all are blended with other features, and the proposed identifications are rejected by most observers. Petrie and Small[29] give a table of thirteen unidentified features which appear sharp and which they consider may be atomic in origin. They do not regard as convincing the proposal[30, 31] that some of them are due to the β system of nitric oxide.

7.1.4 Molecular Band Systems

7.1.4.1 Oxygen

The $(0, 1)$ or Kaplan-Meinel band of the Atmospheric system $b\,^1\Sigma_g^+ \to X\,^3\Sigma_g^-$ was discovered in the auroral spectrum by Meinel[7]. As in the case of the nightglow, the $(0, 0)$ band is absorbed and cannot be detected. Members of other sequences were at first thought to be absent, but in 1954 Chamberlain et al.[9] established that the $(1, 1)$ band is also emitted and is in fact about half as intense as the $(0, 1)$ band.

In seeking to identify auroral band systems it is important that comparison should be made not with laboratory spectra but with synthetic spectra,[30, 31] the profiles corresponding to the expected low rotational temperature being computed from the molecular constants (with allowance for the finite width of the slit of the apparatus). The realization of this by Nicolet[30] enabled him to recognize bands of the First Negative system $b\,^4\Sigma_g \to a\,^4\Pi_u$ in spectra obtained by Vegard and Kvifte.[4] Later work by Vegard,[17] Dahlstrom and Hunten,[6] and Gartlein and Sherman[32] confirmed the identification. Dahlstrom and Hunten[6] have suggested that the system is mainly responsible for the dark red color of the lower border of certain auroras. These auroras are referred to as type B. According to Dahlstrom and Hunten, they are simply auroras which penetrate into the region of molecular oxygen.

Murcray[33] has reported that an aurora apparently caused an enhancement of the emission in the 9.6-μ ozone band. If confirmed, the effect will be of interest in that the atmospheric region concerned must be at quite a low altitude.

7.1.4.2 Nitrogen

A large number of bands of the First Positive system, $B\,^3\Pi_g \to A\,^3\Sigma_u^+$, have been identified (cf. Vegard and Kvifte,[4] Gartlein and Sprague,[34]

Harrison and Jones[13]). Those in the infrared are among the strongest in the auroral spectrum. The system is very highly developed emissions from levels with v' up to 12 having been detected.

Vegard[22] has attributed the redness of the base of type B auroras to an enhancement of the First Positive system. The view of Dahlstrom and Hunten has already been mentioned (§ 7.1.4.1). Doubtless both the systems in question contribute to the red sensation (Hunten[10]).

The Second Positive system, $C\,^3\Pi_u \to B\,^3\Pi_g$, is prominent in the ultra-violet part of the spectrum (cf. Vegard and Kvifte,[4] Barbier and Williams,[5] Petrie and Small[8]). Though some of the members are blended with other features, the progressions for which v' is 0, 1, 2, and 3 certainly occur. The progression for which v' is 4 may be present. Higher progressions are probably too feeble to be observed.

It is well established that at least the $v' \leqslant 3$ progressions of the forbidden Vegard-Kaplan system, $A\,^3\sum_u^+ \to X\,^1\sum_g^+$, are emitted from auroras.[4, 5, 8] Few members of the lowest progression have been detected, but, as Chamberlain and Meinel[14] point out, this may be due to blending. The intensity distributions through the other progressions have been estimated by Barbier and Williams.[5] They are in fair accord with what would be expected from the relevant Franck-Condon factors as calculated by Jarmain et al.[35]

The First Negative system, $B\,^2\sum_u^+ \to X\,^2\sum_g^+$, is emitted strongly, the (0, 0) band at $\lambda\,3914$ being especially intense.[4, 5, 8] Members of progressions with v' up to at least 3 have been identified. The system gives rise to the blue color of sunlit auroras. Its presence in the spectrum of the night sky provides a useful indication of auroral activity.

Many of the infrared auroral features which were at one time assigned to the First Positive system are now known to belong to the Meinel Negative system.[7] The vibrational numeration in Table I is that favored by Meinel[36] and Douglas.[37] Its correctness has been questioned,[11] but it is confirmed by the detection of an intense auroral feature at the predicted position, 1.11 μ of the strong (0, 0) band (Harrison and Jones[13]).

7.2 Absolute Intensity

Considering radiation of wavelength λ, let $B(\lambda)$ be the angular surface brightness in photons/cm^2 sterad. The photon emission rate from a column 1 square centimeter in cross section lying along the line of sight is given by

$$\psi(\lambda) = 4\pi B(\lambda). \tag{7.1}$$

If t is the effective path length in kilometers, then

$$P(\lambda) = 10^{-5}\,\psi(\lambda)/t \tag{7.2}$$

is the emission rate in photons/cm³ sec, which is a quantity of great physical interest. Seaton[38] suggests that for high-latitude auroras t is of the order of unity.

The apparent visual brightness may be expressed in terms of $\psi_v(5550)$, the equivalent photon emission rate at the wavelength of maximum visual sensitivity. According to Seaton, about half the visual brightness is due to the oxygen green line; that is,

$$\psi(5577) \simeq \tfrac{1}{2}\psi_v(5550). \tag{7.3}$$

It is convenient to take $\psi(5577)$ as a measure of the visual brightness. The first estimates of this photon emission rate for auroras of various international brightness coefficients (cf. Chapman et al.[39]) were made by Seaton. They are given in Table IV, the unit used being the kilorayleigh (kR) (that is, 10^9 photons/cm² sec).

TABLE IV

Absolute Intensities and International Brightness Coefficients

International brightness coefficient	Description	Ψ (5577) (kilorayleighs)	
		Seaton[a]	Hunten[b]
—	Extreme lower limit, brightness of night sky	0.4	—
I (weak or faint)	Brightness of Milky Way	2	1
II (medium)	Brightness of moonlit cirrus clouds	10	10
III (bright)	Brightness of moonlit cumulus	100	100
IV (very bright)	Illumination equals that of full moon	5000	1000
—	Extreme upper limit, brightness of full moon	5×10^6	—

[a] M. J. Seaton, *J. Atmos. Terr. Phys.* **4**, 285 (1954).
[b] D. M. Hunten, *J. Atmos. Terr. Phys.* **1**, 141 (1955).

Omholt,[40] working at Tromsö, has carried out photometric measurements on $\lambda\,4278$, the (0, 1) band of the N_2^+ First Negative system, which he finds to be 0.4 times as intense as $\lambda\,5577$, so that

$$\psi(5577) = \frac{5577}{4278 \times 0.4}\,\psi(4278)$$

$$= 3.3\,\psi(4278) \tag{7.4}$$

His results are given in Table V. They suggest that the higher values of Seaton are rarely (or never) encountered. Measurements made at College,

Alaska, by Barbier and Pettit[41] and by Ashburn[42] and at Saskatoon by Hunten[10] suggest the same. Hunten has proposed a slight revision of Seaton's scale (cf. Table IV).

TABLE V

Measured Absolute Intensities in Auroras of Various Forms

From A. Omholt, *J. Atmos. Terr. Phys.* **5**, 243 (1954)

Auroral form	ψ (4278) (kilorayleighs)	Estimated length of column (km)	P (4278)* (10^4 cm^{-3} sec^{-1})
Faint arc	4	10	0.4
Weak pulsating surfaces	2	10	0.2
Medium rays	6–12	1	6–12
Medium arcs	15–32	10	1.5–3.2
Strong rays	32	1	32
Strong arcs	67	10	6.7
Lower border of strong drapery	90	5	18
Very bright display in rapid movement	150	10	15
Band in rapid movement (strongest aurora measured)	200	10	20

* The full photon emission rate in the N_2^+ First Negative system, P (1st Neg.), is 6.5 times P (4278).

The Balmer lines are naturally of special interest. Chamberlain[43] has estimated $\psi(H\alpha)$ to have been about 3 kR in a moderately brilliant arc at

TABLE VI

Photon Emission Rates in Type B Aurora, International Brightness Coefficient IV

From D. M. Hunten, *J. Atmos. Terr. Phys.* **7**, 141 (1955)

Wavelength (A)	Identification	$\psi(\lambda)$ (kR)
6875	N_2 First Pos. (3, 0)	250
6789	(4, 1)	290
6705	(5, 2)	230
6624	(6, 3)	190
6545	(7, 4)	110
6469	(8, 5)	110
6130	N_2^+ Meinel Neg. (4, 0)	26
6000	O_2^+ First Neg. (0, 0), (1, 1)	34
5577	$\frac{3}{2}$[OI]	(1000)
5228	N_2 First Neg. (0, 3)	21
3914	N_2^+ First Neg. (0, 0)	(1000)
3805	N_2 Second Pos. (0, 2)	31

the zenith. Photometric measurements by Hunten[10] have shown that $\psi(H\beta)$ was at least 2 kR in a type B aurora of international brightness coefficient IV, viewed 45° from the zenith. Incidentally, in the same aurora, Hunten observed that a feature which he believes to have been the D doublet of sodium was very intense, $\psi(5893)$ being about 16 kR. Table VI gives photon emission rates for other prominent features in this aurora.

Although agreeing that the Balmer lines sometimes attain the intensities cited in the preceding paragraph Galperin[43a] considers these occasions unusual. He finds that $\psi(H\alpha)$ rarely exceeds 200 R.

7.3 Relative Intensities

It is obvious from the different colors of auroras that the relative intensities of the various spectral features are not always the same. This section is concerned with the information available on representative mean values.

Auroras are often observed at low angles of elevation so that the light traverses a long path through the atmosphere. In consequence, the absorption and scattering suffered may be considerable and if not taken properly into account may lead to grave errors in the estimated intensities in the violet and ultraviolet regions. Observers attempt to correct for the effect, but inconsistencies in many of the results given show that they have not always been completely successful or that instrumental and calibration errors are greater than supposed (cf. Bates[44]). Some of the published altitude and latitude variations are consequently open to suspicion.

Band systems provide a useful means of judging the accuracy attained. The relative intensities $I(v', v'')$ in a v'' progression are independent of the source of excitation. If $I_O(v', v'')$ denote the reported auroral intensities and $I_T(v', v'')$ the theoretical or laboratory intensities, the ratio

$$R(v', v'') = I_T(v', v'')/I_O(v', v'') \qquad (7.5)$$

should therefore remain constant through such a progression. Reliable data on $I_T(v', v'')$ being available, a check on $I_O(v', v'')$ can thus be obtained.

Seaton[38] has carried out a critical examination of the values of $I_O(v', v'')$ given by Vegard and Kvifte[4] for bands of the N_2^+ First Negative and N_2 Second Positive systems, taking $I_T(v', v'')$ for the former system from averaged theoretical and laboratory data compiled by Bates,[44] and taking $I_T(v', v'')$ for the latter system to be as calculated by Nicholls.[45] On plotting $\log [R(v', v'')]$ against λ, the wavelength of the band concerned, he found that the points for a given v'' progression lie along a straight line of nonzero slope, and that the lines for all progressions in both systems are approximately parallel. He attributed the fact that the common slope is nonzero to some systematic error, and from his plots derived the factor f_λ by which I_O, the reported relative intensity of a spectral feature, should be multiplied to get

I_C, the true relative intensity. In the ultraviolet region f_λ is large: thus f_{3150} is 100 and f_{4000} is 10, if the scale is so adjusted that f_{5577} is close to unity. Most relative intensity measurements published before 1955 must be similarly corrected.

In view of the unexpectedly large magnitude of f_λ, Seaton investigated the possibility of self-absorption being important. He found that in the case of the First Negative system of nitrogen it becomes significant only if $n(N_2^+)$ exceeds 4×10^8 cm^{-3}, which is most unlikely. There is no reason to expect that self-absorption is significant for the Second Positive system of nitrogen. The band profiles published by Vegard and Tönsberg[46] and others do not show any indication of the phenomenon.

If the values of f_λ obtained as described are accepted and applied to the data of Vegard and Kvifte,[4] it is found that $I(3466)$ * averages about $1.2 \, I(5577)$, where $\lambda 3466$ is $^3_1[NI]$ and that $I(3914)$ and $I(3371)$ both average about $5I(5577)$, where $\lambda 3914$ and $\lambda 3371$ are the (0, 0) bands of the N_2^+ First Negative and N_2 Second Positive systems. As has already been mentioned (§ 7.2), Omholt[40] finds that $I(4278)$ is about $0.4I(5577)$, which corresponds to $I(3914)$ being $1.5I(5577)$, since it follows from the Franck-Condon factors † concerned that $I(3914)/I(4278)$ is approximately 3.8, irrespective of the source. In fair agreement with this, Hunten's measurements[10] give $I(3914)$ to be about $1.1I(5577)$; and in less satisfactory agreement Rees's measurements[47a] give $I(3914)$ to be about $0.5I(5577)$. The value of $I(3914)$ first quoted may thus be too high. It would not be surprising if the "f_λ-corrected" mean intensities of Vegard and Kvifte were in error by a factor of 2 or even slightly more.

Intensity determinations have been made on both the observed bands of the O_2 Atmospheric system. As already noted, Chamberlain et al.[9] judge that the $\lambda 7708$ (1, 1) band is about half as strong as the $\lambda 8645$ (0, 1) band. Averaging of some results of Omholt indicates that $I(7708)$ is $0.08 \, I(5577)$. If it were not for absorption, the intensity of the unobserved $\lambda 7619(0, 0)$ band would be considerable: thus with the calculated Franck-Condon factors[47] it may be seen that $I(7619)$ would be about $23I(8645)$ and hence about $4I(5577)$, fluorescent scattering (cf. § 5.1.3) being neglected, since it can scarcely be appreciable in auroras.

The intensities of the forbidden red lines of oxygen are related by

$$I(6364) = \tfrac{1}{3}I(6300) \tag{7.6}$$

(cf. Table II). They are usually of the same order as that of the green line. Owing to the great variations that occur, a more precise simple statement cannot be made here (cf. § 7.4).

* Here and in the remainder of the chapter, the subscript C is omitted as unnecessary, all relative intensities cited being corrected as far as possible.

† A useful set of tables of Franck-Condon factors has been compiled by Nicholls.[47]

Hunten[10] has remarked that on photographic spectra $\lambda\,5198\text{-}5201$, $^2_1$[NI] is almost as strong as $\lambda\,5228$, the (0, 3) band of the N_2^+ First Negative system, but that on photoelectric spectra it has never appeared, though it would probably have done so if it were one-tenth as strong as the band. The proposed explanation is that $\lambda\,5198\text{-}5201$ is indeed as feeble as the photoelectric spectra indicate but that it is emitted for a much longer time than the other radiations and therefore appears on the photographic spectra. It may be noted that $I(5228)$ equals $0.033I(3914)$.

The feature at 7325 A which Omholt[12] has attributed to $\lambda\,7319\text{-}7330$, $^3_2$[OII] is apparently observable only in the higher parts of auroras, and there

TABLE VII

Relative Intensities of Some Allowed OI and NI Lines

Wavelength (A)	Identification	Vegard and Tönsberg[a]	Meinel[b]	Omholt[c]
7774	OI $3s\ ^5S^0$—$3p\ ^5P$	1.00	1.00	1.00
7992	OI $3p\ ^3P$—$3s'\ ^3D^0$	0.34	0.15	0.20
8447	OI $3s\ ^3S^0$—$3p\ ^3P$	0.72	1.5	1.8
8187			0.15	0.08
8216	NI $3s\ ^4P$—$3p\ ^4P^0$	0.24	0.23	0.13
8243			0.05	
8682	NI $3s\ ^4P$—$3p\ ^4D^0$		7.2	
8704			3.8	

[a] L. Vegard and E. Tönsberg, *Geofys. Publ. (Oslo)* **18**, No. 8 (1952).
[b] A. B. Meinel, *Astrophys. J.* **113**, 583 (1951).
[c] A. Omholt, *J. Atmos. Terr. Phys.* **10**, 320 (1957).

$I(7325)$ is about $0.1I(5577)$. No information seems to have been published on the relative intensity of $\lambda\,5755$, $^3_2$[NII], but it is certainly low.

Table VII gives the results of some measurements by Vegard and Tönsberg,[48] Meinel,[7] and Omholt[12] on the relative intensities of allowed OI and NI lines, the scale for each set being chosen so that $I(7774)$ is unity. The differences between corresponding entries may be at least partly real. Thus Petrie and Small,[29] who have also measured the relative intensities of a number of lines, comment that $I(8447)/I(7774)$ varies considerably from one spectrum to another; they state that it always exceeds unity,* averages 1.5, and is as great as 3 in some instances.

There is considerable uncertainty on how to relate the entries in Table VII to the intensity of some standard feature, such as the green line. Vegard

* In view of this statement it is presumed that an earlier measurement by Petrie[49] giving the ratio as 0.3 is now regarded as unreliable.

and Tönsberg[48] give the opinion that $I(7774)$ is 0·3 $I(5577)$. Taking $I(6300 +$ 6364) to be 0·4 $I(5577)$, as it is in the brighter parts of most auroras, Percival and Seaton[50] judge that Meinel's result[7] that $I(7774)/I(6300 +$ 6364) is 0.7 provides some confirmation of this. The red lines appear to be unusually weak in Meinel's spectrum, however. Further, Omholt[12] finds that $I(7774)$ is only about 0.08$I(5577)$, and Bagariazky[50a] that $I(8447)$ is rather less than 0.07 $I(3914)$.

Observers agree that the allowed lines of OII are less prominent in the aurora than those of OI, but that the allowed lines of NII are more prominent than those of NI. This is in accord with laboratory experience on the excitation of the spectra of oxygen and nitrogen.

7.4 Variations in the Auroral Spectrum

7.4.1 *Altitude Effects*

Figure 1 shows the variation with angle of elevation of the intensities of selected features in the spectrum of a quiet arc observed by Meinel[51] on the north magnetic horizon from Williams Bay (geomagnetic latitude 53° N). Attention is drawn to several points.

1. The allowed emissions from the atmospheric constituents (λ 7774 and λ 8446 of OI, First Positive system of N_2, First and Meinel Negative systems of N_2^+) have almost the same luminosity-altitude curve. According to Vegard[52] and Omholt,[12] slight differences occur. The following are placed in the reported order of increasing rate of fall-off of intensity with altitude: allowed OI lines, N_2^+ First Negative system; allowed NI lines, N_2 First Positive system; N_2^+ Meinel Negative system.

2. The maximum of the curve for $H\alpha$ lies at a slightly lower level than the maximum of the main curve, and the fall-off above it is much more rapid than in the case of the main curve. In contrast, Vegard[53, 54] states that at Tromsö (geomagnetic latitude 67° N), the Balmer lines are stronger in the upper part of auroras than in the lower; and Galperin[54a] also finds this to be the case at Loparskaya (geomagnetic latitude 63° N).

3. The λ 6300 maximum occurs at a somewhat greater altitude. It is remarkably broad.

4. Above the maximum the λ 5577 curve follows the main curve; below it follows the λ 6300 curve.

5. Both λ 6300 and λ 5577 increase in intensity relative to the allowed emissions in the region below the maximum. The behavior suggests that at the lower altitudes conditions are especially favorable for the formation of $O(^1D)$ and $O(^1S)$. Harang[55, 56] at Tromsö, who has also investigated the distribution of emissions in arcs, found, however, that $I(6300)$ decreases

much more rapidly at the lower border than does $I(5577)$ and that this intensity decreases slightly less rapidly than does $I(3914)$. Vegard[52] and

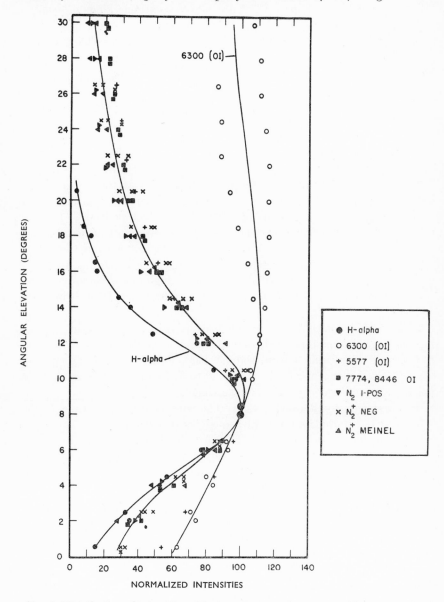

FIG. 1. Distribution of intensities of features in auroral spectrum. All are normalized to an arbitrary value of 100 at the elevation of the maximum Hα intensity. After A. B. Meinel, *Mém. Soc. Roy. Sci. Liège* **12**, 203 (1952).

Omholt[12] agree that $I(5577)/I(3914)$ is somewhat greater near the lower limit of an aurora than it is near the upper.

Krassovsky[56a] and Galperin[43a,54a] describe two extreme kinds of spectra. In high altitude auroras of red type A the spectra are characterized by the prominence of the OI, OII, NI and NII lines (especially λ 6300-6364 and other strongly forbidden lines) and by the relative weakness of the band systems (other than the N_2^+ First Negative system). Low altitude yellow-green auroras have spectra dominated by λ 5577 and the band systems. Hydrogen lines appear much more often in the first kind of spectra than in the second.

Petrie (cf. Seaton[26]) states that the intensity ratio $I(6300 + 6364)/I(5577)$ is about 0.40 for the region between the base and the level of maximum luminosity of steady homogeneous arcs (100 to 110 km). According to Vegard,[57] it generally averages between 1.0 and 1.4 at the upper border (near the 130-km level). The trend (cf. Vegard[22, 52]) is in harmony with Fig. 1 and with the work of Harang.[56] It must, however, be stressed that the ratio is extremely variable. On one evening Vegard and Tönsberg[58] found that it exceeded 6 in a red type A aurora, and on the next evening they found that λ 6300-6364 was scarcely detectable in a red type B aurora. According to Vegard,[59] $I(6300 + 6364)/I(5577)$ may be as high as 80; the lowest value that appears to be given in the literature is 0.05 (quoted by Swings and Meinel[60]).

It has been claimed[61] that λ 6300-6364 is enhanced in sunlit auroras, but, as Vegard[62] has remarked, the enhancement is mainly simply a manifestation of the altitude effect. Seaton[63] has pointed out that the evidence for the assertion that red sunlit rays tend to end on the earth's shadow line (as do blue sunlit rays[64]) is quite unconvincing.

Measurements by Bernard[65] show that with increasing altitude λ 3466, $^3_1[NI]$ and the (forbidden) Vegard-Kaplan system become more prominent relative to the allowed emissions. The altitude variation of the (forbidden) O_2 Atmospheric system seems to be between that of the N_2 First Positive system and that of the N_2^+ First Negative system (Omholt[12]).

The main altitude effects described clearly indicate that collisional deactivation of metastable atoms and molecules is important in the auroral region.

7.4.2 Latitude Effects

The intensity of the hydrogen emissions relative to the allowed atmospheric emissions increases with decreasing latitude. Vegard and Kvifte[66] have measured $I(H\beta)/I(4709)$ at Oslo (geomagnetic latitude 60° N) and at Tromsö (geomagnetic latitude 67° N). They report that on an average this ratio is about 0.7 at the former station and about 0.1 at the latter.

According to Vegard,[52, 54] $I(5577)/I(4278)$, $I(6300 + 6364)/I(4278)$, and $I(5198 + 5201)/I(4278)$ are also greater at Oslo than at Tromsö by factors of about 1.7, 3.4, and 3.7, respectively.* Red type A auroras are more frequent and more pronounced as regards color at Oslo than at Tromsö. The forbidden lines are relatively strong in these. Vegard[54] has observed one in which $I(5577)/I(4278)$ was more than twenty times as great as the usual value (though Omholt[67], Rees,[47a] and Murcray[67a] have found that in general this ratio varies very little from one aurora to another, irrespective of the type).

Spectra have been obtained from stations at low geomagnetic latitudes by Rayleigh,[68] Slipher,[69] Götz,[70] Dufay et al., [71-73] Barbier,[74] Dufay and Moreau,[75] and Dufay.[27b] In general, they refer to the upper parts of auroras at high latitudes. The characteristics associated with great altitudes are exhibited. Thus Götz[70] reports that $I(6300 + 6364)/I(5577)$ may be 10 or even greater, in harmony with which Dufay and Moreau[75] find that λ 6300-6364 may be of the order of 300 times as intense as in the nightglow, whereas Dufay and Tcheng[73] find that λ 5577 is usually not more than a few times as intense. For the aurora of February 10-11, 1958 $I(6300 + 6364)/I(5577)$ was as great as 3×10^3 according to the photometric measurements of Manring and Pettit.[23a] Again, λ 5198-5201 may appear quite strongly. Dufay and Tcheng[73] have estimated that its intensity may be perhaps 0.015 that of λ 6300-6364; and Götz[70] has observed that it may persist for hours after the disappearance of λ 5577. A feature of special interest is the high vibrational development of the N_2^+ First Negative system (Rayleigh,[68] Dufay,[72] Barbier,[74] Mironov et al.[21a]). Much detailed information on low-latitude auroras is contained in a paper by Barbier,[75a] which appeared in 1958.

Duncan[75b] states that observations made near Sydney (geomagnetic latitude 42° S.) during one aurora show that the zenith λ 6300 emission was about 30 % plane polarized with magnetic vector north-south. The effect is puzzling.

7.4.3 Type Effects

The intensity of the hydrogen emission depends very markedly on the auroral type. At moderate and low latitudes where it is strongest in quiet arcs and weakest in rayed structures (cf. Meinel,[76] Dahlstrom and Hunten[6]). Fan and Schulte[77] have reported that quiet arcs at Williams Bay (geomagnetic latitude 53° N) always show Hα, but rayed structures never. Interesting quantitative information on the intensity of the hydrogen emission relative

* Part of the reported effect may arise from experimental errors. The existence of such errors is revealed by the claim that $I(4708)/I(4278)$ and $I(3914)/I(4278)$ depend on latitude (which is of course impossible, since λ 4708, λ 4278, and λ 3914 originate from the same vibrational level).

to the N_2^+ First Negative emission has been obtained by Omholt,[67] also working at Williams Bay. He reports that in arcs $I(H\beta)/I(4709)$ ranges from 0.2 to 0.7 or even to rather higher. One particular aurora was studied in some detail. Just after the first arc broke up and showed ray structure, $I(H\beta)/I(4709)$ was about 0.25 in the more homogeneous auroral *background*. The ratio slowly decreased to 0.15 to 0.10 over a period of about half an hour. In the ray structure and in the flaming and pulsating aurora which followed, it was less than 0.05 and may well have been zero. The picture is complicated by some observations carried out at Saskatoon (geomagnetic latitude 61° N) by Hunten,[10] which gave $I(H\beta)/I(4709)$ to range from 0.01 to 0.15 in normal auroras, but gave it to be as high as 250 in a flickering aurora and as high as 65 in faint, very active rays.* Photoelectric measurements by Montalbetti[78a] suggest that there is no systematic relationship between the various auroral types and the hydrogen emission at places within the auroral zone.

It may be mentioned that many years ago Vegard[79] concluded that isolated rays cannot be due to incoming hydrogen. He argued that rays are so narrow (§ 6.6.4) that they could not contain the spiral orbits of particles other than electrons unless the kinetic energy associated with the component of velocity perpendicular to the magnetic field vector were only a few kiloelectron volts, which is most unlikely.

There is some evidence that the D doublet of sodium is strong both in red type A (λ 6300-6364) auroras (Vegard[54]), and in red type B (O_2^+ First Negative, N_2 First Positive) auroras (Hunten[10]).

In sunlit auroras the N_2^+ First Negative system is enhanced relative to the other features and shows high vibrational development (Störmer[80]). Other type effects involving the main atmospheric constituents have been described (cf. Vegard,[62] Harang[81]), but mention of them will not be made here as they are likely to remain of little interest until auroral theory is very much more advanced than it is at present.

7.4.4 *Temporal and Correlation Effects*

The Balmer lines have a tendency to be most prominent in the early part of a display (Petrie and Small,[8] Meinel,[51] Gartlein[82]). Their intensities may be greatest several hours in advance of the full auroral development (Romick and Elvey[82a]). Indeed, Galperin[43a] refers to cases in which the hydrogen emission began before any auroral forms could be detected visually and had faded away before the main display burst into view. Gartlein[82] has also

---

* Furthermore, Chamberlain[78] has reported that the great aurora of March 2, 1957, which covered most of the sky at Williams Bay, showed strong hydrogen lines when only draperies or other active rayed structures were apparent.

commented that the general luminescence may continue long after the Balmer lines have become too feeble to be observed. According to Veller[82b] the decrease of the hydrogen emission through a display is less marked at high latitudes than at low latitudes.

Meinel[51] reports that the intensities of the Balmer lines and that of the N_2^+ First Negative system are closely correlated through an auroral display, but that there is no such correlation with the intensity of λ 6300-6364 or with that of the N_2 First Positive system. Presumably there is also no such correlation with the intensity of the Meinel Negative system, since Fan and Schulte[77] find that this system and the N_2 First Positive system vary together.

According to Vegard,[54] λ 6300-6364 and λ 5198-5207 tend to be enhanced relative to the allowed spectral features in an aurora in which the Balmer lines are strong. The association may in part be simply a manifestation of the altitude and latitude effects.

Work by Ashburn[83] shows that the major pulsations of the N_2^+ First Negative system are matched quite closely by pulsations in λ 5577, which follow with a time lag of about half a second. Omholt and Harang[84] also studied these emissions in pulsating or moving forms. They demonstrated that their results are consistent with the assumption that the rates of formation of the excited particles concerned are proportional, the time lag arising simply because, whereas $N_2^+(B\,^2\Sigma_u^+)$ radiates almost instantaneously $OI(^1S)$ has an appreciable life. The deduced values of this life range from 0.45 to 0.75 second. Pointing out that the upper of these values almost coincides with the radiative life (cf. Table IV), Omholt and Harang attributed the occurrence of lower values to collisional deactivation.

Omholt[85] makes the interesting comment that the time lag can be easily observed visually and appears to be the most important cause of the shift in color in rapidly changing auroras.

The Vegard-Kaplan system may have quite a long time lag. Hunten[10] has observed it to be unusually prominent in the afterglow of an aurora. He inferred that the life of the $N_2(A\,^3\Sigma_u^+)$ molecules must be at least 20 or 30 seconds. A marked time lag also occurs in the λ 5198-5201 emission (cf. §§ 7.3 and 7.4.2).

A series of spectroscopic observations of importance in connection with theories * of the origin of auroras has been carried out by Montalbetti and Jones[86] at Saskatoon (geomagnetic latitude 61° N) and Churchill (geomagnetic latitude 70° N). These stations straddle the northern auroral zone (geomagnetic latitude 67° N).

In examining their results for a diurnal variation, Montalbetti and Jones discovered that there is a tendency for $H\alpha$ to appear strongly before midnight

* A critical account of the various theories has been given by Chamberlain.[78]

at Saskatoon and after midnight at Churchill. As they point out, this is exactly opposed to the predictions of Martyn's theory.[87]

Montalbetti and Jones also studied the relation between the emission of the hydrogen lines and magnetic activity. Consistent with Martyn's theory they found that at Saskatoon the $H\alpha$ intensity tends to increase with increase of magnetic activity (perhaps passing through a maximum), whereas at Churchill it tends to decrease. The general picture suggested is of an auroral zone which has strong hydrogen emission on its southern flank and which moves away from the pole when magnetic conditions become disturbed.

7.4.5 Sunspot Cycle Effects

Vegard[62] finds that red type A auroras have a tendency to occur near sunspot maximum and red type B auroras have a tendency to occur near sunspot minimum.

7.5 Theory of the Auroral Spectrum

The occurrence of Doppler-shifted Balmer lines in the spectrum signifies that incoming protons must be at least partially responsible for auroras. We shall first consider the direct effect of these protons and of the hydrogen atoms formed from them by electron capture. Shklovsky[87a] has pointed out that some captures must occur in interplanetary space and has estimated that the flux of neutral hydrogen atoms in the incident stream is 0.01 to 0.03 times the flux of protons. He suggests that these neutral hydrogen atoms may reach low geomagnetic latitudes and thus be of special importance.

7.5.1 Primary Processes

7.5.1.1 Penetration of the Primary Stream

Adopting the model of the upper atmosphere recommended in 1952 by the Rocket Panel,[88] Bates[89] computed the equivalent path lengths of air at STP that must be traversed to reach various levels and hence, using laboratory range data, constructed a graph of incident proton energy, $\mathscr{E}_i$, versus altitude of penetration, $h(p)$, for the special case in which there is no spiraling round the magnetic lines of force. According to this graph $\mathscr{E}_i$ is 5 kev if $h(p)$ is 135 km, is 15 kev if $h(p)$ is 125 km, is 200 kev if $h(p)$ is 105 km, is 1000 kev if $h(p)$ is 90 km, and is 4000 kev if $h(p)$ is 75 km.* When spiraling occurs, the value of $\mathscr{E}_i$ corresponding to a given value of $h(p)$ is of course greater than that cited, the equivalent path length of air traversed being

* It may be recalled that the main auroral region lies between 90 and 125 km (cf. § 6.3).

greater than assumed. As is now realized, the Rocket Panel's model is inaccurate. It will therefore be necessary to repeat the computations when the structure of the upper atmosphere in the auroral zone is properly determined.

Heavier systems have not so much penetrating power as have protons of the same incident energy. The effect is not very marked: for example, the lowest level reached by a 200-kev α-particle is only 2 or 3 km above the lowest level reached by a 200-kev proton.

If they have the same incident energy, electrons have very much more penetrating power than protons. On the other hand, if they have the same incident velocity, they have very much less penetrating power (cf. Table VIII).[90]

TABLE VIII
Comparison of Ranges of Protons and Electrons
N. N. Das Gupta and S. K. Ghosh, *Rev. Mod. Phys.* **18**, 225 (1946).

Protons			Electrons		
Speed (10⁴ km/sec)	Energy (kev)	Range (cm in air at STP)	Speed (10⁴ km/sec)	Energy (kev)	Range (cm in air at STP)
0.25	33	0.05	3	2.6	0.04
0.5	130	0.2	6	11	0.2
1	520	0.8	12	47	3.4
2	2,100	7.5	18	130	18
3	4,700	30	24	340	83
5	13,000	190	27	660	220
10	53,000	3000	29.7 (= 0.99c)	3100	1300

7.5.1.2 *Hydrogen Emission*

An incoming proton may pick up an electron in a collision with an atom or molecule of one of the atmospheric constituents:

$$H^+ + M \rightarrow H(n, l) + M^{+\prime}. \tag{7.7}$$

The hydrogen atom formed, which quickly cascades to the ground state if not initially in this state, undergoes further collisions. In these it may be excited:

$$H(1s) + M \rightarrow H(n, l) + M' \tag{7.8}$$

or it may be ionized:

$$H(1s) + M \rightarrow H^+ + e + M' \tag{7.9}$$

(after which the sequence may be repeated). Processes (7.7) and (7.8) may lead to the radiation of the Balmer lines; and process (7.9) influences the intensity indirectly, since it and process (7.7) together control the H^+/H ratio in the stream.

Quantal calculations on the capture process (7.7) for the case in which M is a hydrogen atom have been carried out by Bates and Dalgarno;[91] and similar calculations on the excitation process (7.8) and the loss process (7.9) have been carried out by Bates and Griffing.[92] With the results of these as a guide and with certain additional experimental data it is possible to estimate the cross-section energy curves relevant for the treatment of the passage of a H^+–H stream through air. Proceeding in this way, Chamberlain[43] and Bates[89] independently concluded that the number of $H\alpha$ photons emitted per stream particle is approximately 50, provided $\mathscr{E}_i$, the incident energy, is above about 100 kev. The corresponding numbers of $H\beta$ and $H\gamma$ photons are 11 and 3 respectively, if the Balmer decrement $I_\alpha: I_\beta: I_\gamma$ is 3.34:1.00:0.33 as calculated by Chamberlain.[43], *

With the aid of the values of the photon yields just quoted, estimates may be made of the incident proton flux, F, if the absolute intensity of one of the Balmer lines is known. The two auroras mentioned at the end of § 7.4.3 will serve as examples. It may readily be seen that in the case of the moderately brilliant arc F must have been about 6×10^7 cm^{-2} sec^{-1} (as was first pointed out by Chamberlain); and that in the case of the red type B aurora of international brightness coefficient IV F must have been at least about 1×10^9 cm^{-2} sec.$^{-1}$

Almost all the $H\alpha$ emission occurs after the energy of the protons has been reduced to 100 kev. The remaining range is then only about 0.1 cm of air at STP. Hence for an aurora at, for example, the 105-km level, the emission might be expected to be confined to an altitude interval of less than 3 km. The observed luminosity-altitude distribution for $H\alpha$, though sharper than the main luminosity-altitude distribution (cf. § 7.4.1), is not sharp enough to be consistent with such an interval.

A similar apparent anomaly arises in connection with the main luminosity-altitude distribution itself, if incident protons are taken to be the cause of auroras. This distribution may readily be computed, since the Bragg curve for excitation must be closely the same form as the known Bragg curve for ionization. Assuming that the primary auroral particles are homogeneous in energy and follow rectilinear paths, Bates and Griffing[93] found that the predicted distributions are much narrower than the distributions observed by Harang,[55] except for high auroras.

The finite width in latitude of auroras magnifies their apparent vertical extent. This is not taken into account in the luminosity-altitude distributions published by the observers. Griffing and Stewart[94] investigated the effect

* Galperin[43a] reports that observations in the Soviet Union indicate that Chamberlain overestimates the decrement.

and concluded that it is insufficient to bring about harmony between the observations and predictions either in the special case of Hα or in the case of the other emissions.

As pointed out by Bates and Griffing,[93] harmony could be achieved by arbitrarily postulating that the incident protons have an energy spread.

There is another discrepancy which can also be resolved by the same postulate as was suggested earlier by Shklovski.[95] This discrepancy concerns the Hα profile from an aurora in the magnetic zenith. The maximum of the profile observed by Meinel[51] is at a Doppler displacement corresponding to a velocity of about 500 km/sec, whereas if the protons were monoenergetic the maximum would lie at about 2000 km/sec (cf. Chamberlain[43]). The energy spread required by the postulate is, however, unattractively great. To explain the Hα profile it is necessary to suppose that a considerable fraction of the incident protons have energies as low as about 1 kev; and as has already been noted (§ 7.5.1.1), the penetration of the stream indicates that some have energies at least about one hundred times this.

An alternative approach was therefore explored by Chamberlain,[96] who abandoned the artificial assumption that the particles follow rectilinear paths and instead assumed that they have a dispersal in direction and travel down the magnetic lines of force in spiral orbits. Using the same cross-section energy curves as in his earlier work on the photon yield, he carried out computations on the Hα profile and demonstrated that, if the dispersal were suitably chosen, the observations of Meinel would be reproduced. In addition, the discrepancies connected with the luminosity-altitude distributions would be reduced (Chamberlain,[96] Omholt[97]).

The concept of spiraling was not of course new—Vegard[62] had made extensive use of it many years earlier in his researches on auroral forms. As already mentioned (§ 7.1.1), direct evidence for it is provided by the fact that the Balmer lines are broadened in the spectrum obtained from an aurora on the magnetic horizon. Omholt[97] investigated this quantitatively. He discovered that the dispersal in direction which had been chosen to account for the magnetic zenith results is difficult to reconcile with the magnetic horizon results (Meinel,[51] Vegard and Kvifte[98]), the computed profile being much too broad.

Recognizing that the observations cannot be explained by invoking either an energy spread or a dispersal in direction alone, Chamberlain[78, 99] turned to the possibility of invoking both effects. He found this very promising. Taking the z (polar) axis parallel to the magnetic lines of force and letting the incident flux of protons crossing unit area in the xy plane with energy between $\mathscr{E}_i$ and $\mathscr{E}_i + d\mathscr{E}_i$ and in solid angle $d\Omega$ about a direction θ be $\mathscr{F}(\mathscr{E}_i, \theta)d\mathscr{E}_i\,d\Omega$, he demonstrated that quite satisfactory agreement with the observations can be obtained by taking

$$\mathscr{F}(\mathscr{E}_i, \theta) = \text{Const } \cos^2\theta/\mathscr{E}_i^{\frac{3}{2}}. \tag{7.10}$$

The functional dependence on $\mathscr{E}_i$ is entirely arbitrary, but that on θ has some theoretical justification. Significant error may have been introduced by the adoption of the Rocket Panel's model atmosphere and more especially by the use of approximate cross-section energy curves. If correct, equation (7.10) is likely to be of great significance in connection with the origin of the primary auroral protons. In order that it may be properly tested, and perhaps refined, further and more precise measurements on luminosity-altitude distributions and line profiles at different latitudes are required. Considerable uncertainty remains. It should be noted, for instance that Shklovsky[87a] reports that the profiles obtained in the Soviet Union (cf. Galperin[54a]) do not show as much Doppler shift as found by Meinel.

Although it necessitates a little anticipation, we shall now examine the important question: "Are the incoming protons the dominant cause of any or all auroras?" As pointed out by Omholt,[67] useful evidence is provided by the intensities of the Balmer lines relative to the N_2^+ First Negative system.

Consider the case of a normal arc at the 105-km level. If we remember that the photon yield in Hβ is 11 per proton (see above) and that the energy required to penetrate to the 105-km level is about 200 kev (§ 7.5.1.1), it is apparent that the energy flux carried by the incident protons is $A[(2 \times 10^5)/11]I(\mathrm{H}\beta)$ ev/cm^2 sec, where A is a constant depending on the geometry of the aurora. Since each ion pair formed requires the expenditure of about 35 ev, the rate of ionization $\mathscr{I}_P$ due directly or indirectly to the incident protons, must be approximately $A[(2 \times 10^5)/11 \times 35]I(\mathrm{H}\beta)$ cm^{-2} sec^{-1} or $500\ AI(\mathrm{H}\beta)$ cm^{-2} sec^{-1}.

The emission of the N_2^+ First Negative system by auroras is undoubtedly due to the simultaneous ionization and excitation of nitrogen molecules in fast collisions (see § 7.5.3.7). Stewart[100] has determined the cross section describing the fast collisions giving rise to the $(0, 2)$ band $\lambda\, 4709$. Over a considerable energy range the cross section he obtains is smaller by a factor of 450 than the full ionization cross section as measured by Tate and Smith.[101] Allowing for the oxygen content of the air, we hence may see that the total rate of ionization, $\mathscr{I}_T$, is perhaps $600\ AI(4709)$ cm^{-2} sec^{-1}.

It follows from the two preceding paragraphs that, if $\mathscr{I}_P$ is to equal $\mathscr{I}_T$, then $I(\mathrm{H}\beta)/I(4709)$ must be about unity. This may sometimes be the case at low latitudes (§ 7.4.3), but at high latitudes the ratio is in general considerably smaller (§ 7.4.2). In spite of the crudity of the calculations, which did not take account of the implications of equation (7.10), it seems probable that, although incident protons may conceivably be the dominant cause of some low-latitude auroras, they cannot be the dominant cause of most high-latitude auroras.

Hunten's discovery that in certain cases $I(\mathrm{H}\beta)/I(4709)$ is as high as 250 (§ 7.4.3) is very interesting. A conceivable explanation is that in such cases there is an unusually large number of relatively low-energy incident protons (or hydrogen atoms). Line profiles would be informative.

7.5.1.3 *Helium Lines*

It is of some importance to know whether the failure of observers to detect helium lines signifies that the incoming stream does not contain an appreciable fraction of helium nuclei.

Laboratory work was at first thought to indicate that a He^{++}–He^{+}–He beam passing through air would not in fact give appreciable emission of the helium lines; and a detailed comparison of spectra obtained from the beam with spectra obtained from auroras was judged to provide positive evidence for the presence of a considerable fraction of helium nuclei in the incoming stream.[102] These inferences have been shown to be unjustified, however (Bates,[89] Fan[103]).

The processes governing the emission of the helium lines have been discussed by Bates,[104] but they form a rather complicated set, and it is scarcely feasible at present to make quantitative predictions on photon yields per incident helium ion. Fan[103] deduced from his experiments that $\lambda\,5876$, HeI, $3\,^3D \to 2\,^3P$ would be detectable if the ratio of helium ions to protons in the incoming stream were 0.1 or higher. Further work is required.

7.5.1.4 *Excitation and Ionization of Atmospheric Constituents by H^+–H Shower*

The amount of energy expended for each primary ion produced is about 70 ev. Hence a 200-kev particle gives rise to some 3×10^3 primary ions before being brought to rest. The number of primary excitations is probably comparable.

After the energy is reduced to below about 50 kev, capture becomes important and provides a new source of ions. Unlike the protons, the hydrogen atoms may cause spin-reversal transitions. The total number of these capture and spin-reversal processes has been assessed to be of the order of 1×10^3 per incident proton. Provided $\mathscr{E}_i$, the incident energy, is high the dependence on it is slight.

7.5.1.5 *Nuclear Reactions*

The excitation energy of the lowest level of N^{14} is 2.3 Mev. In some auroras $\mathscr{E}_i$ exceeds this. Colgate[105] considers that an observable γ-ray flux should result from

$$N^{14}(p, p')N^{14*}, \quad N^{14*} \to N^{14} + \gamma. \tag{7.11}$$

He estimates that the number of γ-particles per proton stopped is approximately

$$10^{-5}\,\mathscr{E}_i^2 \,. \quad (3\ \mathrm{Mev} < \mathscr{E}_i < 30\ \mathrm{Mev}). \tag{7.12}$$

21

7.5.2 *Secondary and Other Processes*

7.5.2.1 *Electrons*

Because of their initial kinetic energy, some of the electrons freed by the incident protons and by the hydrogen atoms formed by capture, and some of the electrons stripped from these fast-moving atoms, may cause excitation and ionization. Some quantal calculations relating to the energy distribution of the ejected electrons have been carried out by Bates *et al.*[106] It has been estimated that the secondary excitation is about thrice the primary and that the secondary ionization is about the same as the primary. These estimates may be in error by a factor of 2 or even rather more. The importance of the secondary processes relative to the primary is sensitive to the nature of the transition being greater for a spin-reversal transition having a small energy defect than for a non-spin-reversal transition having a large energy defect.

Ejection from atoms and molecules is not the only possible source of energetic electrons. Indeed, the argument given toward the end of § 7.5.1.2 suggests that there is a more important source, at least in high-altitude auroras.

Energetic electrons may be incident on the atmosphere according to many of the theories of the origin of auroras. Again, they may result from discharge action in the atmosphere, as has been suggested by a number of people (cf. Chamberlain[78]).

Evidence for the existence of energetic electrons has been obtained. Using rocket-borne instruments, Meredith *et al.*[107] have detected soft radiation above the 50-km level in the auroral zone. They at first judged this radiation to be the high-energy tail of a stream of primary electrons, but later Van Allen and Kasper[108] found it to be X-radiation, which may plausibly be attributed to bremsstrahlung of primary electrons.* Van Allen[110] has estimated the energy of the assumed electrons to be 10 to 100 kev and the flux to be 10^6 to 10^8 cm^{-2} sec^{-1}. The X-radiation is strongly peaked in the auroral zone. Winckler *et al.*,[111] however, have observed bursts of X-radiation, correlated in time with visible auroras in balloon flights over Minneapolis (geomagnetic latitude 55° N). They report that these bursts usually occur when an homogeneous arc develops ray structure or when rays grow stronger in intensity. From measurements made during a balloon flight from Churchill (geomagnetic latitude 70° N), Anderson[111a] established a detailed connection between the appearance of X-radiation and storm-type decreases in the local geomagnetic field. In contrast to what was observed at Minneapolis, he found no detailed connection with visual auroras.

---

* Van Allen *et al.*[109] surmise that the high-intensity radiation observed from satellites 1958 α and γ is closely related.

At the Fifth General Assembly of CSAGI, Moscow, 1958, preliminary results on the detection of the charged particles themselves were presented by McIlwain[112] and by Meredith *et al.*[113] The observations were made by means of equipment flown on rockets from Churchill. Both energetic electrons and energetic ions were detected. The energetic electrons were much the more important in the auroras (rayed and diffuse) penetrated. They appeared to be confined to within visible auroras. In contrast, the energetic ions were found to have a constant flux over quite large areas—in one flight, for example, the flux (and ion energy spectrum) remained constant while the rocket traversed a horizontal distance of 40 km and passed out of a rayed structure.

7.5.2.2 *Radiation*

The influence of the incident solar radiation must be taken into account in the case of auroras located above the earth's shadow line (see § 7.5.3.7.1).

Radiation emitted by an aurora may produce secondary effects. Some of it must cause photodissociation (see § 7.5.3.1.2), and some of it must cause photoionization (see § 7.5.3.7). Degradation through fluorescent scattering must also take place (see § 7.5.3.1.2).

7.5.2.3 *Processes Occurring at Thermal Energies*

The effectiveness of certain processes is increased by the changes in the upper atmosphere brought about by an aurora. Bates *et al.*[114] have pointed out that the additional ionization produced leads to more rapid recombination and that a significant contribution to the luminescence may result (see § 7.5.3.1.2). They argued that in equilibrium the rate at which the free charges disappear must equal the rate at which they are liberated, and that this is considerable is apparent from the high intensity in the N_2^+ First Negative system (which is emitted after simultaneous excitation and ionization (see § 7.5.3.7)). Several supporting arguments have been advanced (Seaton,[26] Bates[89]). The mean photon yield per recombination is unfortunately unknown.

The electrons present in the auroral region may also be of importance in that they may contribute to the collisional deactivation of metastable atoms and molecules.

Collisions between metastable and normal atoms and molecules may result in some redistribution of the excitation energy. In general, conversion of excitation energy, other than rotational, into translational energy (thus preventing the emission of radiation) is not readily brought about in thermal encounters, but deactivation of metastable molecules by atom-atom interchange[115] may be important.

The extent to which auroras cause local alterations in the chemical composition of the atmosphere is difficult to estimate. One of the possibilities is that the abundance of atomic nitrogen is augmented by impact dissociation and more especially by dissociative recombination

$$N_2^+ + e \to N' + N''. \tag{7.13}$$

Using the intensity of the N_2^+ First Negative system (Table V) as an indicator of the ionization rate (cf. § 7.5.3.7), and hence of the rate of (7.13), we see that on some occasions the nitrogen atom yield must be of the order of 10^8 cm^{-3} sec^{-1}. The time a given volume of air is in the reactive zone may be too short, however, to allow very much accumulation to take place.[89]

7.5.3 *Individual Lines and Band Systems of the Atmospheric Constituents*

Many scientists have discussed the processes likely to be responsible for the main auroral emissions, but much remains to be done before a detailed theory can be presented. Such a theory must necessarily be complicated, for it is apparent from the altitude and latitude effects and from the rapid changes of color that occur that a number of processes normally proceed at comparable rates, that these rates vary relative to one another, and that deactivation is important. A full quantitative treatment would require much more data on the cross sections of the pertinent collision mechanisms than at present available.

Notation

Processes of the type

$$X + M \to X + M' \tag{7.14}$$

where X is an energetic electron, hydrogen atom, or (in the case of a non-spin-change transition), proton, and M is a target system frequently arise in the discussion. For brevity we do not display the three possibilities. Instead, we refer to them by the same equation number and indicate whether the incident particle being considered is an electron, hydrogen atom, or proton by placing after this number the letters e, h, or p, respectively. Not all the free electrons have sufficient kinetic energy to produce excitation or ionization. We refer to those which have as *active*, and to those which do not have as *passive*. The number density of active electrons we denote by $n(e|A)$, but we do not introduce any special symbol for the number density of passive electrons, as this is not appreciably different from $n(e)$, the number density of all electrons (Bates[44]).

If in writing out a reaction we give only the chemical symbol for an atom or molecule (other than polyatomic), we imply that we do not wish to specify the electronic state or states.

7.5.3.1 *Forbidden OI Lines*

The prominence of the forbidden oxygen lines in the auroral spectrum led early workers to seek some unusual excitation mechanism. Vegard,[62] for example, sought to invoke

$$N_2(A\,^3\textstyle\sum_u^+) + O_3 \to N_2(X\,^1\textstyle\sum_g^+) + O_2(X\,^3\textstyle\sum_g^-) + O(^1D \text{ or } ^1S) \tag{7.15}$$

or

$$N_2(A\,^3\textstyle\sum_u^+) + O(^3P) \to N_2(X\,^1\textstyle\sum_g^+) + O(^1D \text{ or } ^1S). \tag{7.16}$$

Neither of these processes is at all plausible, and in any event there is no reason to suppose that the processes which immediately suggest themselves,

$$e + O(^3P) \rightarrow e + O(^1D) \tag{7.17e}$$

and

$$e + O(^3P) \rightarrow e + O(^1S) \tag{7.18e}$$

are not responsible for the major part of the λ 6300-6364 and λ 5577 emission.[114] To illustrate the position, suppose that the energy of every active electron is 10 ev. If we take the cross section–energy curves for (7.17e) and (7.18e) to be as computed by Seaton,[116] it may readily be shown that in this hypothetical case the rates of population of the ^1D and ^1S terms are $4 \times 10^{-9} n(O) \, n(e \mid A) \, \text{cm}^{-3} \, \text{sec}^{-1}$, and $7 \times 10^{-10} n(O) \, n(e \mid A) \, \text{cm}^{-3}$ sec^{-1}, respectively. At the 105-km level, where $n(O)$ is perhaps $1 \times 10^{12} \, \text{cm}^{-3}$, these rates are $4 \times 10^3 \, n(e \mid A) \, \text{cm}^{-3} \, \text{sec}^{-1}$ and $7 \times 10^2 \, n(e \mid A) \, \text{cm}^{-3} \, \text{sec}^{-1}$ and are thus large (cf. Tables IV and V), even when $n(e \mid A)$ is quite small.

In harmony with observation (§ 7.4.1), the red lines would be expected to be more intense than the green line at great altitudes, collisional deactivation being there unimportant. The value of the ratio of the intensities naturally depends on the unknown energy distribution of the active electrons.

Red patches 200 to 400 km wide are sometimes observed at altitudes between 300 and 700 km (Störmer[64]). They appear to persist for several minutes—that is, for about the radiative life time of $O(^1D)$. Seaton[63] has suggested that this may not be a coincidence. According to him, a red patch may result from the λ 6300-6364 emission from atoms left in the wake of a rapidly moving ray.

7.5.3.1.1 *Deactivation*. At moderate and low altitudes possible deactivation of $O(^1D)$ and $O(^1S)$ must be considered. Since the radiative life of $O(^1D)$ is much longer than that of $O(^1S)$ (cf. Table III), the red lines are likely to be suppressed to a greater extent than the green line, which is what is indicated by the observations (§ 7.4.1).

It is convenient to derive here a general formula concerning relative intensities (cf. Seaton[26]). Consider a system such as OI, OII, OIII, NI, or NII, with three terms in the normal configuration, 1 denoting the ground term, and 2 and 3 the metastable terms (taken in order of increasing energy). Let $n(X_p)$ be the number density in p per cubic centimeter, S_{pq} be the rate of excitation from p to q per cubic centimeter per second and A_{qp} and d_{qp} be the respective probabilities per second of the reverse transition taking place spontaneously and through collisional deactivation. The equations of equilibrium are then

$$\{A_{32} + A_{31} + d_{32} + d_{31}\}n(X_3) = S_{13} + S_{23} \tag{7.19}$$

$$S_{23} + \{A_{21} + d_{21}\}n(X_2) = S_{12} + \{A_{32} + d_{32}\}n(X_3). \tag{7.20}$$

If $n(X_2)$ is sufficiently small, as is generally the case, S_{23} may be ignored, and therefore

$$n(X_2)/n(X_3)$$

$$= \frac{A_{31} + A_{32} + d_{32} + d_{31}}{A_{21} + d_{21}} \left\{ \frac{S_{12}}{S_{13}} + \frac{A_{32} + d_{32}}{A_{31} + A_{32} + d_{31} + d_{32}} \right\}. \quad (7.21)$$

The intensity ratio

$$I(\lambda_{21})/I(\lambda_{32}) = \lambda_{32} A_{21} n(X_2)/\lambda_{21} A_{32} n(X_3) \qquad (7.22)$$

can hence in principle be calculated.

By combining (7.21) and (7.22) and substituting numerically from Tables II and III, it may be seen that, if d_{32} may be neglected (as is almost certainly the case), then

$$I(6300 + 6364)/I(5577) = r_c + r_d \qquad (7.23)$$

where

$$r_c = \frac{0.88}{1 + 110 d_{21}}, \; r_d = 0.94 \frac{S_{12}}{S_{13}} \times \frac{1 + 0.73 d_{31}}{1 + 110 d_{21}}. \qquad (7.24)$$

The term r_c arises from the contribution to the red lines due to the excitation of $O(^1S)$ followed by *cascading* with the emission of the green line, and the term r_d arises from the contribution due to the *direct* excitation of $O(^1D)$. In the absence of deactivation $I(6300 + 6364)/I(5577)$ would clearly be 0.88 or higher. Furthermore, the lower limit would be reached only in the unlikely event of S_{12}/S_{13} being zero. As Seaton has pointed out, S_{12}/S_{13} would be expected to be considerably greater than unity, since the excitation of $O(^1D)$ is favored compared with that of $O(^1S)$, both because of the statistical weights (w_2 is 5 and w_3 is 1), and because of the excitation potentials (1.96 ev for ^1D against 4.17 ev for ^1S).

Since $I(6300 + 6364)/I(5577)$ may be as low as 0.05 in auroras (cf. § 7.4.1), deactivation of $O(^1D)$ atoms must be very important.* The work of Omholt and Harang[84] (cf. § 7.4.4) provides evidence that $O(^1S)$ atoms are subject to some deactivation. We shall now consider the deactivation processes that might be operative.

The suggestion has been made[26] that there may be significant deactivation by oxygen negative ions through

$$O(^1D) + O^-(^2P) \rightarrow O(^3P) + O(^3P) + e. \qquad (7.25)$$

This seems most unlikely. Even if the associated rate coefficient were 10^{-9} cm^{-3} sec^{-1}, the concentration $n(O^-)$ would have to be some 10^8 cm^{-3}

---

* In addition, nightglow studies have shown that the emission of the red lines from the atmospheric region below about 100 km is suppressed (§ 5.1.7).

for the contribution to d_{21} to be 10^{-1} sec^{-1}. Now the coefficient for ionic recombination,

$$O^-(^2P) + X^+ \rightarrow O + X \qquad (7.26)$$

can scarcely be less than 10^{-9} cm^{-3} sec^{-1} and is probably more (cf. Bates and Boyd[117]). Hence the establishment of the concentration cited would require the rate of formation of O^- to be 10^7 cm^{-3} sec^{-1} or higher. There does not appear to be any process which could satisfy this requirement.

Electrons may make superelastic collisions with metastable oxygen atoms

$$O(^1D) + e \rightarrow O(^3P) + e \qquad (7.27)$$

$$O(^1S) + e \rightarrow O(^1D) + e \qquad (7.28)$$

$$O(^1S) + e \rightarrow O(^3P) + e. \qquad (7.29)$$

Seaton[26, 116] has calculated the associated deactivation coefficients by quantal methods, finding d_{21} to be $1.6 \times 10^{-9}n(e)$ in the temperature region of interest and d_{31} and d_{32} to be somewhat smaller. Using his results and taking S_{12}/S_{13} to be 5 (or greater), Seaton demonstrated that the observed values of $I(6300 + 6364)/I(5577)$ in bright auroras can be explained by the action of (7.27), provided the electron concentration, $n(e)$, is 7×10^7 cm^{-3} (or greater) at the lower border and is 2×10^7 cm^{-3} (or greater) at the upper border.

If (7.27) were responsible for the deactivation, the intensity ratio would depend on $n(e)$ and therefore on the luminosity of the aurora. Bright auroras are usually chosen for spectrophotometric measurements, but, as Seaton[116] recognized, it is unlikely that such a dependence would have escaped detection if it existed. Omholt[119] has advanced the criticism that the values of $n(e)$ demanded are unacceptably high (cf. § 7.5.3.7). Higher values would be needed if (7.28) and (7.29) were to be invoked to account for the observed behavior of the green line (§ 7.4.4).

The considerations indicated in the last paragraph, together with the fact that nightglow studies (§ 5.1.7) have shown that the emission of the red line from the atmospheric region below about 100 km is suppressed in spite of the effective absence of free electrons, led Seaton[118] to explore the possibility of deactivation in collisions with neutral atoms and molecules.

For the sake of definiteness S_{12}/S_{13} and its dependence on the altitude had to be fixed at an early stage of the investigation. The measurements on $I(6300 + 6364)/I(5577)$ can be interpreted simply when deactivation is unimportant. From them Seaton inferred that S_{12}/S_{13} is about 10 at great altitudes. He discussed two models consistent with this: model A, S_{12}/S_{13} independent of altitude; model B, S_{12}/S_{13} about 40 below 110 km, falling linearly with altitude to about 10 at 135 km and constant thereafter. Case A was designed to represent an aurora in which the excitation is mainly produced by electrons ejected by fast primary particles, and case B to represent an aurora of the discharge type (see § 7.7). Table IX gives values of the deactivation parameters, d_{21} and d_{31}, consistent with the auroral observations (including those of Omholt and Harang on the green line, § 7.4.4). For reference purposes it also gives the particle concentrations $n(O)$, $n(O_2)$, and $n(N_2)$ adopted by Seaton in his discussion. The required value of the rate coefficient of any deactivation process proposed may be obtained by dividing d_{21} (or d_{31}) by the particle concentration of the appropriate species.

TABLE IX

$O(^1D)$ and $O(^1S)$ Deactivation Parameters

From M. J. Seaton, *Astrophys. J.* **127**, 67 (1958).

Altitude (km)	d_{21} (sec^{-1})		d_{31} (sec^{-1})	Particle concentrations (cm^{-3})		
	Case A[a]	Case B[b]	Cases A and B	$n(O)$	$n(O_2)$	$n(N_2)$
100	1.3	3.3	2.3	1.8×10^{12}	2.4×10^{12}	1.4×10^{13}
105	0.45	1.8	1.3	2.0×10^{12}	5.4×10^{11}	7.4×10^{12}
110	0.23	0.91	0.6	1.2×10^{12}	1.6×10^{11}	3.7×10^{12}
120	0.09	0.24	0.1	3.3×10^{11}	3.0×10^{10}	9.2×10^{11}
130	0.05	0.09		1.1×10^{11}	1.0×10^{10}	3.1×10^{11}
140	0.03	0.03		4.5×10^{10}	3.8×10^{9}	1.2×10^{11}
160	0.01_4	0.00_7		1.0×10^{10}	9.0×10^{8}	2.7×10^{10}

[a]Allowed to fall off with altitude less rapidly than as the gas density.
[b]Chosen to be proportional to the gas density.

The possibility of significant deactivation in collisions with oxygen atoms may be dismissed with some confidence. Collisions with oxygen molecules seem much more promising. According to the measurements of Vegard and Kvifte,[120] the rate coefficients for

$$O(^1D) + O_2(X\,^1\textstyle\sum_g^+) \to O(^3P) + O_2 \qquad (7.30)$$

and

$$O(^1S) + O_2(X\,^1\textstyle\sum_g^+) \to O(^1D \text{ or } {}^3P) + O_2 \qquad (7.31)$$

are only of the order of 10^{-15} cm^{-3} sec.$^{-1}$ Should this be the case, both processes could be ignored (cf. Table IX). Seaton, however, considers it possible that the rate coefficients are much greater than those found by Vegard and Kvifte. Special interest is attached to

$$O(^1D) + O_2(X\,^1\textstyle\sum_g^+, v = 0) \to O(^3P_2) + O_2(b\,^1\textstyle\sum_g^+, v = 2) \qquad (7.32)$$

because of the essentially exact energy resonance. The effectiveness of (7.32) is reduced by the reverse process. This reverse process is hindered if the

$O_2(b\,{}^1\sum_g^+, v = 2)$ molecules are removed by deactivating collisions or by the emission of radiation. Seaton has shown that removal by the emission of radiation causes the *effective* rate coefficient of (7.32) to increase with altitude as required in case A (cf. Table IX), and by arbitrarily assigning favorable values to various unknowns he has shown also that the process might account for the magnitude of d_{21} at the greater altitudes. Success so attained has, of course, little real significance. Even if the detailed proposals put forward should prove to be incorrect, however, it is not improbable that (7.32) is important in some region of the atmosphere. It may be noted that suppression of the red lines would be accompanied by enhancement of the O_2 Atmospheric system.

Molecular nitrogen possesses no terms of low excitation potential, so that deactivation through

$$O({}^1D) + N_2(X\,{}^1\textstyle\sum_g^+) \rightarrow O({}^3P) + N_2(X\,{}^1\textstyle\sum_g^+) \tag{7.33}$$

$$O({}^1S) + N_2(X\,{}^1\textstyle\sum_g^+) \rightarrow O({}^3P) + N_2(X\,{}^1\textstyle\sum_g^+) \tag{7.34}$$

or

$$O({}^1S) + N_2(X\,{}^1\textstyle\sum_g^+) \rightarrow O({}^1D) + N_2(X\,{}^1\textstyle\sum_g^+) \tag{7.35}$$

involves the conversion of electronic energy into vibrational energy and is hence likely to proceed slowly. Furthermore (7.33) and (7.34) violate Wigner's spin conservation rule. It may be seen from Table IX that (7.33) could give the dominant contribution to d_{21} in case A only if its rate coefficient increased from about 1×10^{-13} cm^{-3} sec^{-1} at 100 km to about 5×10^{-13} cm^{-3} sec^{-1} at 160 km, and in case B only if its rate coefficient were about 2.5×10^{-13} cm^{-3} sec^{-1} at all altitudes;* and it may be seen also that (7.34) and (7.35) together could give the dominant contribution to d_{31}, cases A and B, only if the sum of their rate coefficients were about 1.5×10^{-13} cm^{-3} sec^{-1}. These values seem rather high but cannot be excluded in the present state of knowledge.

Much remains to be done before the problem of the deactivation of $O({}^1D)$ and $O({}^1S)$ in auroras can be regarded as satisfactorily solved.

7.5.3.1.2 *Excitation Other Than Through Electron Impact with Atomic Oxygen.* It must not be assumed that (7.17e) and (7.18e) give rise to the entire λ 6300-6364 and λ 5577 emissions. From the estimates given in § 7.5.1.4 it seems not unlikely that the relative contribution from (7.17h) and (7.18h) is by no means negligible when the energy of the incident protons is low. Ionic[121, 122] and dissociative[114] recombination are other possibilities. Seaton[26] has suggested that the latter is responsible for the increased

---

* Since the rate coefficients would be expected to be rapidly increasing functions of the temperature and therefore of the altitude, the required behavior in case A is easier to accept than that in case B.

prominence of λ 6300-6364 and λ 5577 below the maximum of the main luminosity (§ 7.4.1). In the same connection Bates[89] has drawn attention to

$$X + O_2(X\,{}^3\Sigma_g^-) \to X + O({}^1D) + O({}^3P) \qquad (7.36ehp)$$

pointing out that the cross section must be large, since the corresponding optical transition, $X\,{}^3\Sigma_g^- \to B\,{}^3\Sigma_u^-$, is strong. Doubtless

$$X + O_2(X\,{}^3\Sigma_g^-) \to X + O({}^1S) + O \qquad (7.37ehp)$$

also occurs (cf. Tanaka[123]).

Meinel[51] has reported that the red lines appear to be emitted from a large region of the sky. It has been tentatively proposed[89] that this phenomenon may be due to the auroral ultraviolet radiation being absorbed in the Schumann-Runge continuum:

$$O_2(X\,{}^3\Sigma_g^-) + h\nu \to O({}^1D) + O({}^3P) \qquad (7.38)$$

and in the Hartley continuum:

$$O_3 + h\nu \to O({}^1D) + O_2(X\,{}^3\Sigma_g^-). \qquad (7.39)$$

Deactivation may make the degradation to λ 6300-6364 rather inefficient.

7.5.3.2 *Forbidden NI lines*

Seaton[26] has shown that the presence of λ 5198-5201 and λ 3466 in the spectra of high-latitude auroras cannot be attributed to

$$e + N({}^4S) \to e + N({}^2D \text{ or } {}^2P) \qquad (7.40e)$$

(cf. § 7.7.2), the calculated intensities being too low unless the unacceptable assumption is made that the nitrogen is almost completely dissociated. Clearly (7.40h) may also be dismissed.

The most attractive possibilities would seem to be

$$N_2^+(X\,{}^2\Sigma_g^+) + e \to N + N({}^2D \text{ or } {}^2P) \qquad (7.41)$$

and

$$X + N_2(X\,{}^1\Sigma_g^+) \to X + N + N({}^2D \text{ or } {}^2P). \qquad (7.42ehp)$$

Reliable estimations of the intensities resulting from these cannot be given.

Deactivation is again important and exerts the same type of influence as it does in the case of the forbidden oxygen lines (Barbier[74]). Using (7.21) and (7.22) and neglecting the d_{31} and d_{32} terms (though he considers this may not be entirely justified), Seaton[26] finds

$$I(5198 + 5201)/I(3467) = \frac{10}{1 + 9.6 \times 10^4\,d_{21}}\left\{\frac{S_{12}}{S_{13}} + 0.94\right\}. \qquad (7.43)$$

According to him the rate coefficient for

$$N({}^2D) + e \to N({}^4S) + e \qquad (7.44)$$

is approximately 0.52 times that for (7.27), and therefore is about 5×10^{-10} cm^{-3} sec^{-1} at an electron temperature of 500°K. Even if $n(e)$ were only 10^5 cm^{-3}, the contribution of (7.44) to d_{21} would thus be 5×10^{-5} sec.$^{-1}$ It may be seen from (7.43) that this contribution alone would make $I(5198 + 5201)/I(3467)$ smaller by a factor of about 6 than it would be if d_{21} were zero. Deactivation through collisions with neutral atoms and molecules may also be important. The pertinent rate coefficients are not known.

7.5.3.3 *Forbidden OII and NII lines*

The presence of $\lambda\,7319\text{-}7330$ of OII in the auroral spectrum would be expected,[114] for there can be little doubt but that

$$X + O(^3P) \rightarrow X + O^+(^2P) + e \qquad (7.45ehp)$$

proceeds at a rate within an order of magnitude of the rate for the corresponding process believed to be responsible for the intense N_2^+ First Negative system (see § 7.5.3.7). Unless $n(e)$ is very high indeed, electron deactivation would not lead to severe suppression.

It is not unlikely that the emission of $\lambda\,5755$ of NII is due to

$$X + N_2(X\,^1\textstyle\sum_g^+) \rightarrow X + N + N^+(^1S) + e. \qquad (7.46ehp)$$

A plausible alternative has never been proposed. Electron deactivation can scarcely be very important.

7.5.3.4 *Permitted OI, OII, NI, and NII Lines*

It is not unnatural to suppose in the first instance that the emission of the permitted OI and OII lines results mainly from the neutral atoms being struck by fast electrons (and perhaps by other fast particles). The supposition is not necessarily correct.

Percival[124] has carried out quantal calculations on the cross sections for

$$e + O(^3P) \rightarrow e + O(3p\,^3P) \qquad (7.47e)$$

and

$$e + O(^3P) \rightarrow e + O(3p\,^5P). \qquad (7.48e)$$

Using the results obtained, which are admittedly of low precision, he and Seaton[50] have estimated that the ratio of the intensity of $\lambda\,8446$, OI, $3p^3P \rightarrow 3s^3S$ to that of $\lambda\,7774$, OI, $3p^5P \rightarrow 3s^5S$ would be more than 3 if only electron excitation were operative. The observed ratio, which is reported to vary, may be as low as unity (cf. § 7.3). Though (7.47e) and (7.48e) are thus not favored, Percival and Seaton do not exclude the possibility that the discrepancy arises simply from inaccuracies in the calculated cross sections. There is another discrepancy which they consider cannot be dismissed. They estimate that collisions between electrons and oxygen atoms would give $I(7774)/I(5577)$ to be much less than 0.1, whereas the observed ratio is about 0.3, according to them. As indicated in §7.3, however, the observed ratio may in fact be smaller than supposed by Percival and Seaton —it may perhaps be only about 0.08, so that the discrepancy may be less serious than imagined.

Percival and Seaton are of the opinion that oxygen molecules are the target systems, as in

$$X + O_2(X\ ^3\textstyle\sum_g^-) \to X + O' + O''. \tag{7.49ehp}$$

Data on the cross sections involved are lacking, so that an appraisal cannot be made, but the relatively low abundance of oxygen may well cause difficulties. Moreover, the hypothesis does not seem to be in harmony with the observed very slow fall-off with altitude of the intensities of the allowed lines (cf. § 7.4.1).

Swings[125] has pointed out that, owing to a wavelength coincidence the Lyβ radiation $\lambda\,1026$ emitted from the primary stream can bring about the photoexcitation process

$$O(^3P) + h\nu \to O(3d\ ^3D) \tag{7.50}$$

and, since this may be followed by

$$O(3d\ ^3D) \to O(3p\ ^3P) + h\nu(\lambda\ 11{,}260) \tag{7.51}$$

he suggested that $\lambda\,8446$ might be appreciably augmented. The suggestion has been investigated in detail by Omholt.[126] On carrying out the necessary calculations, taking account of the Doppler width of the Lyβ radiation, of its absorption by molecular oxygen, and of

$$O(3d\ ^3D) \to O(^3P) + h\nu(\lambda\ 1026) \tag{7.52}$$

he finds that the augmentation is negligible.

Excitation of the permitted OI lines in dissociative recombination is energetically impossible. It may, however, occur in ionic recombination processes such as

$$O^+(^4S) + O^-(^2P) \to O' + O'' \tag{7.53}$$

which may be very rapid. The photon yield is difficult to estimate but must be less than the negative ion yield from

$$O(^3P) + e \to O^-(^2P) + h\nu. \tag{7.54}$$

Taking the attachment coefficient to be 1×10^{-15} cm^{-3} sec^{-1} (Smith and Branscomb[127]), $n(O)$ to be 1×10^{12} cm^{-3}, and $n(e)$ to be 2×10^7 cm^{-3}, we find that the rate of formation of O$^-$ ions is 2×10^4 cm^{-3} sec.$^{-1}$ Some of those formed may disappear not by ionic recombination but by associative detachment:

$$O^-(^2P) + O(^3P) \to O_2 + e. \tag{7.55}$$

The rate at which this process proceeds is not known reliably.

Little can be said regarding the permitted OII lines, since information is not available on the cross sections for the simultaneous excitation and ionization of oxygen atoms:

$$X + O(^3P) \rightarrow X + O^{+\prime} + e. \qquad (7.56ehp)$$

It may be necessary to consider

$$X + O_2(X\,^3\textstyle\sum_g^-) \rightarrow X + O' + O^{+\prime} + e \qquad (7.57ehp)$$

and

$$H^+ + O(^3P) \rightarrow H' + O^{+\prime} \qquad (7.58)$$

if (7.56ehp) should prove to be too inefficient. Neither of these alternatives is attractive.

The permitted NI and NII lines probably arise from fast collisions with nitrogen molecules:

$$X + N_2(X\,^1\textstyle\sum_g^+) \rightarrow X + N' + N'' \qquad (7.59ehp)$$

$$X + N_2(X\,^1\textstyle\sum_g^+) \rightarrow X + N' + N^{+\prime} + e. \qquad (7.60ehp)$$

If these processes are indeed responsible for the emission, many of the lines should be broad.

7.5.3.5 O_2 Systems.

As already mentioned, (7.32) may contribute to the Atmospheric system; and impact excitation

$$X + O_2(X\,^3\textstyle\sum_g^+) \rightarrow X + O_2(b\,^1\textstyle\sum_g{}^+) \qquad (7.61eh)$$

must occur. It is difficult to judge which process is the more important.

The relative numbers $r(v')$ in the different vibrational levels are of interest. According to Chamberlain et al.[9] their observational results require that $r(1)/r(0)$ is about 0.025; and presumably $r(2)/r(0)$ is still smaller. Process (7.32) populates the 2-level preferentially. With the computed Franck-Condon factors (Nicholls[47]), it may be shown that, if process (7.61) alone were operative, then $r(1)/r(0)$ would be about 0.07 and $r(2)/r(0)$ would be almost zero. Both processes thus tend to lead to a greater development of the system than is observed. There is not necessarily any anomaly, however, for it is possible that vibrational deactivation of $O_2(b\,^1\textstyle\sum_g^+)$ proceeds rapidly (§ 5.1.8.4).

Impact excitation would also be expected to lead to the infrared Atmospheric system. It would not lead to systems such as that of Herzberg, the required change in the internuclear separation for bands in the visible region being too great.

7.5.3.6 N_2 Systems

There seems no reason to suppose that the presence of the Vegard-Kaplan and First and Second Positive systems cannot be attributed to

$$X + N_2(X\,^1\textstyle\sum_g^+) \rightarrow X + N_2(A\,^3\textstyle\sum_u^+, B\,^3\Pi_g, \text{ or } C\,^3\Pi_u) \qquad (7.62eh)$$

One would expect (7.62e) to be the more effective. Gartlein and Sprague[34] have claimed that the rotational temperature indicated by the First Positive system is rather higher than usual when the Balmer lines are strong, which might suggest that (7.62h) is important. The validity of their claim has, however, been questioned by Chamberlain and Meinel.[14]

Since the excitation involves spin reversal, the dependence of the cross section on the energy of the electron is very different from what it is in the case of the excitation of the band systems of the molecular ions. As Rypdal and Vegard[128] have pointed out, the intensities of the N_2 systems relative to the N_2^+ systems must therefore be sensitive to the energy distribution of the active electrons so that pronounced variations would be expected. Deactivation of $N_2(A\,^3\textstyle\sum_u^+)$ must also contribute to the multifariousness of the auroral spectrum. It is doubtless responsible for the increase with altitude of the ratio of the intensity of the Vegard-Kaplan system to that of the main allowed emissions (Seaton[26]). The suggestion has been made (Bates[115]) that atom-atom interchange

$$N_2(A\,^3\textstyle\sum_u^+) + O(^3P) \to NO(X\,^2\Pi) + N(^4S) \qquad (7.63)$$

may be quite effective in bringing about deactivation. Another process which must be borne in mind is

$$N_2(A\,^3\textstyle\sum_u^+) + e \to N_2(X\,^1\textstyle\sum_g^+) + e. \qquad (7.64)$$

The rate coefficients of (7.63) and (7.64) and the radiative life of the metastable molecule are all unknown.

Assuming (7.62e) to be the excitation process operative, Bates[44] calculated the relative rates of entry into different v' levels of $N_2(C\,^3\Pi_u)$. These relative rates, $g(v')$, naturally depend on the vibrational temperature, T_V, of the normal molecules. It is possible to derive $g(v')$ from the observed relative intensities of the bands in the auroral spectrum. With the aid of the calculated values T_V may hence in principle be deduced. The method is of course applicable to any allowed system. In the case of the Second Positive system the deduced T_V is rather sensitive to the adopted relative intensities. The relative intensities obtained by Vegard and Kvifte[4] have been analyzed by several authors.[44, 129] They yield an unacceptably high value of T_V, which might suggest that the assumption that (7.62e) is responsible for the excitation of the Second Positive system is incorrect. There are inconsistencies, however, which show them to be untrustworthy.[44] Later measurements by Petrie and Small[29] and by Hunten and Shepherd[130] are more reliable. They are consistent with T_V being any value less than about 1000°K. Results at variance with those of Petrie and Small and of Hunten and Shepherd have been obtained by Omholt.[131] Until they are checked it is scarcely worth speculating on the explanation of the difference. There is slightly stronger evidence for the existence of a similar difference with the N_2^+ First Negative system. The tentatively proposed explanation (§ 7.5.3.7) cannot readily be applied to the case of the N_2 Second Positive system, since the excitation of this system by proton impact is forbidden.

Since many of the bands of the First Positive system are obscured by other spectral features, their relative intensities are poorly determined. Petrie and Small[29] and Omholt[12] deduced values of $g(v')$, but no interesting inferences have been drawn.

7.5.3.7 O_2^+ and N_2^+ Systems

The O_2^+ First Negative system and the N_2^+ First and Meinel Negative systems almost certainly result from fast encounters involving the parent neutral molecules:

$$X + O_2(X\,^3\textstyle\sum_g^-) \rightarrow X + O_2^+(b\,^4\textstyle\sum_g^-) + e \qquad (7.65ehp)$$

$$X + N_2(X\,^1\textstyle\sum_g^+) \rightarrow X + N_2^+(B\,^2\textstyle\sum_u^+) + e \qquad (7.66ehp)$$

$$X + N_2(X\,^1\textstyle\sum_g^+) \rightarrow X + N_2^+(A\,^2\Pi_u) + e. \qquad (7.67ehp)$$

Some authors have urged that the molecular ions are the target systems, but arguments based on relative abundances show that this is normally not the case.[44]

According to Shklovski[132] the N_2^+ First Negative system arises not from (7.66ehp) but from

$$H^+ + N_2(X\,^1\textstyle\sum_g^+) \rightarrow H(1s) + N_2^+(B\,^2\textstyle\sum_u^+) \qquad (7.68p)$$

for which the cross section is quite large (cf. Carleton and Lawrence[133]). The discussion in § 7.5.1.4 indicates, however, that the yield is probably less than the yield even from other primary collisions alone, except when the incident energy is low. The position regarding the corresponding capture processes leading to the emission of the O_2^+ First Negative system and the N_2^+ Meinel Negative system is similar. Shklovsky[87a] considers that the incident energies are in general lower than is suggested in § 7.5.1.1.

Table X gives the results of some calculations by Bates[44] on the relative rates of population of different vibrational levels of N_2^+, $B\,^2\sum_u^+$ due to (7.66e) and due to

$$e + N_2^+(X\,^2\textstyle\sum_g^+) \rightarrow e + N_2^+(B\,^2\textstyle\sum_u^+). \qquad (7.69e)$$

Values of $g(v')$ have been derived from the measurements of Vegard and Kvifte[4] on the relative intensities of the bands of the N_2^+ First Negative system in high-latitude auroras. To reconcile them with either of the sets in Table X, an absurdly high T_V would have to be assumed.[44] Similar measurements have been made by Petrie and Small.[29] The relative intensities they obtained differ considerably from those obtained by Vegard and Kvifte and are undoubtedly much more accurate. Using them, Petrie and Small found $g(0):g(1):g(2)$ to be 1.00:0.15:0.02. On referring to Table X it may be seen that, if (7.66e) is taken to be the excitation process, then T_V is required to be rather over 1000°K, which is lower than the value apparently indicated by the measurements of Vegard and Kvifte, but is still higher than could be accepted. Hunten[10] has also carried out relative intensity determinations, finding $g(0):g(1)$ to be $1.00:0.11_3$, which is consistent with any value of T_V less than about 700°K. It is uncertain whether the difference between the results of Petrie and Small and those of Hunten is real or is merely due to experimental error. If the difference is real, then presumably the excitation processes operative were not the same. One possibility is that electrons alone were responsible for the excitation in the auroras studied by Hunten, whereas heavy particles gave an important contribution in the auroras

TABLE X

Calculated Relative Rates of Population of Various Vibrational Levels of N_2^+, $B\ ^2\Sigma_u^+$ by Electron Impact with (a) N_2, $X\ ^1\Sigma_g^+$ and (b) N_2^+, $X\ ^2\Sigma_g^+$

| Case | Rate at vibrational temperature (°K) of: | | | | | |
	0°	500°	1000°	2000°	4000°	6000°
(a) $v' = 0$	1.00	1.00	1.00	1.00	1.00	1.00
1	0.11	0.11	0.13	0.26	0.47	0.60
2	0.00	0.00	0.01	0.07	0.22	0.36
(b) $v' = 0$	1.00	1.00	1.00	1.00	1.00	1.00
1	0.40	0.40	0.41	0.46	0.57	0.66
2	0.09	0.09	0.12	0.21	0.36	0.47

studied by Petrie and Small (cf. Bates[44]). It would be of interest, in this connection, to know if the results show any dependence on whether or not the Balmer lines are present.*

It may be noted that neither the relative population rates obtained by Petrie and Small nor those obtained by Hunten can be reconciled with (7.69e) as the excitation process. As mentioned at the beginning of the section, there are other reasons for believing that (7.69e) is in general very much less effective than is (7.66e).

In the course of investigations in the infrared spectral region Hunten[133b] noticed variations in the relative intensities of the (1, 0) and (2, 1) bands of the Meinel Negative system which suggest that one or the other of these

* Since this was written Clark and Belon[133a] have reported finding some evidence for a positive correlation between the extent of the vibrational development and the intensity of the hydrogen emission. Further observational work is needed.

bands is excited by a highly selective process. As he recalled, Omholt[12] has pointed out that

$$O^+(^2D) + N_2(X\ ^1\textstyle\sum_g^+, v = 0) \to O(^3P) + N_2^+(A\ ^2\Pi_u, v = 1)$$

is in almost exact energy balance and has supposed that it may be important. Quantal studies (cf. Bates and Lynn[133c]) indicate that such *accidental* resonance does *not* lead to large cross sections in the case of charge exchange.

If it is accepted that the N_2^+ First Negative system is emitted after simultaneous ionization and excitation of molecular nitrogen and if K is taken as the ratio of the total rate of ionization to the rate at which (7.66ehp) proceeds, it is apparent that in equilibrium

$$n(e) = \{KP(\text{1st Neg.})/\alpha)\}^{\frac{1}{2}} \tag{7.70}$$

where as usual $n(e)$ is the electron concentration, α is the effective recombination coefficient, and P (1st Neg.) is the photon emission rate. This equation was used in 1954 by Seaton[38] and by Omholt[40] in their discussions on auroral ionization. At that time direct information on K was lacking, and consequently only a lower limit to $n(e)$ could be derived.

The cross section for (7.66e) has now been measured in the laboratory by Stewart.[100] Since the total ionization cross section has long been known from the work of Tate and Smith,[101] K may be calculated. A value of about 20 is obtained. Accepting this and taking P (1st Neg.) to be about $5 \times 10^5/$ cm^{-3} sec^{-1} in a strong arc (cf. Table V) and α (which is still very uncertain) to be 1×10^{-7} cm^{-3} sec^{-1}, we find that $n(e)$ is about 1×10^7 cm^{-3}.

Bates[89] has pointed out that auroras free electrons deep in the atmosphere owing to the emission of Lyα radiation, λ 1216, which can penetrate to the D region and can ionize nitric oxide. The effect has been investigated in detail by Omholt.[126] He found that it may make an appreciable contribution to polar blackouts. Chapman and Little[134] have drawn attention to the probable importance of the ionizing effect of the X-radiation generated by the primary electrons (§ 7.5.2.1).

7.5.3.7.1 *Sunlit Auroras*. The prominence of the N_2^+ First Negative system in the spectrum of a sunlit aurora has been shown by Bates[135] to be due simply to the resonance scattering of solar radiation:

$$\left.\begin{array}{l} N_2^+(X\ ^2\textstyle\sum_g^+) + h\nu \to N_2^+(B\ ^2\textstyle\sum_u^+) \\ N_2^+(B\ ^2\textstyle\sum_u^+) \to N_2^+(X\ ^2\textstyle\sum_g^+) + h\nu \end{array}\right\} \tag{7.71}$$

It is estimated* that the photon yield per illuminated N_2^+ ion Y (1st Neg.), is about 0.1 sec^{-1}. Because of the considerable magnitude of this yield N_2^+ ions are remarkably effective in, as it were, sensitizing the atmosphere. Their effectiveness is illustrated by the divided auroras discovered by Störmer.[64] In these the section above the earth's shadow line is rendered

* See footnote in § 5.2.4.

luminous by the resonance scattering in the sensitized part of the atmosphere along the ray; the section immediately below the shadow line is dark because the relative inefficiency of excitation by collisions is such that at the small gas density prevailing no detectable emission results; and the third section, luminous like the first, is due to collisional excitation, eventually becoming effective as in ordinary auroras.

The high sunlit auroras which stretch to about the 1000-km level are of special interest because of the hope that they may provide information concerning the atmosphere at extreme altitudes. From the fact that they are bright enough to be detected it has been estimated that in them $n(N_2^+)$ must be at least some 10^2 cm^{-3}. The assumption should not be made that the N_2^+ ions are necessarily formed locally. They may actually be formed at much lower altitudes, since the very long mean free path in the region concerned gives rise to the possibility of a rapid upward drift due to diffusion and perhaps electrical forces.[136]

Sunlit rays are usually a faint grayish color, but a few have been described as being a deep blue-violet (Störmer[64]). Assuming this to be a true color sensation, Seaton[38] considers that for such cases the effective photon intensity in the N_2^+ First Negative system exceeds 10^{11} cm^{-2} sec^{-1} and hence, on allowing for atmospheric absorption, that ψ (1st Neg.) exceeds 10^{12} cm^{-2} sec^{-1}. If the thickness of the ray is 1 km, $n(N_2^+)$ would have to be at least 2×10^7 cm^{-3} for such a yield; and $n(e)$ would also have to be at least this value, since the negative ion-to-electron ratio is certainly small in sunlit rays.

Calculations on the relative intensities of the bands have been carried out by Bates.[89, 135] The problem is rather more complicated than the corresponding problem encountered in the case of emission due to electron impact, for it cannot be assumed that the distribution among the vibrational levels of the ground state is determined by the temperature. Changes in the vibrational quantum numbers may occur when an ion absorbs or emits. As a result, even if initially all the ions were in the zeroth vibrational level they would become distributed among the other vibrational levels, an equilibrium distribution being rapidly reached in which the numbers entering any level balance those leaving. At low altitudes vibrational deactivation may proceed quite rapidly through

$$N_2^+(X\,^2{\textstyle\sum}_g^+, v \neq 0) + N_2(X\,^1{\textstyle\sum}_g^+, v = 0) \to N_2(X\,^1{\textstyle\sum}_g^+, v \neq 0)$$
$$+ N_2^+(X\,^2{\textstyle\sum}_g^+, v = 0) \quad (7.72)$$

and in ion-atom interchange collisions, but at great altitudes the process is unimportant. Consequently the equilibrium distribution among the vibrational levels is not the same at all altitudes.

Table XI compares the calculated (Bates[135]) and observed (Störmer[80]) relative intensities of some bands in high sunlit rays. The agreement is quite satisfactory. Jones and Hunten[136a] have pointed out that the observed relative intensities were not corrected for the overlapping of neighbouring bands so that the true extent of the vibrational development was not as great as supposed. They believe that the correction required (which depends on the rotational temperature) is considerable. If this is the case it would seem that the radiative equilibrium assumed in the original calculations was not reached. Jones and Hunten attribute the lack of equilibrium to the very rapid removal of N_2^+ ions through dissociative recombination.

TABLE XI

Relative Intensities in High Sunlit Rays

Blue-violet group			Blue group		
Band	Predicted intensity	Observed intensity	Band	Predicted intensity	Observed Intensity
(0, 1) λ 4278	100	100	(0, 2) λ 4709	100	100
(1, 2) λ 4236	51	59	(1, 3) λ 4652	74	97
(2, 3) λ 4199	24	35	(2, 4) λ 4600	78	85

It may be noted here that the intensity distribution characteristic of sunlit rays is also characteristic of auroras seen from low latitudes. These latter are usually at great altitudes. Many of them are therefore likely to be in the illuminated part of the atmosphere. This may be the explanation of the intensity distribution. The aurora of the April 17 and 18, 1947, which Barbier[74] observed from a low-latitude station, was originally stated to be in the dark portion of the atmosphere (cf. Bates[135]), so that it did not seem that scattering by ions could be invoked, and to account for the intensity distribution the possibility of excitation by heavy-particle collisions was tentatively suggested. It has since transpired, however (cf. Seaton[63]), that it is not known with certainty in which portion of the atmosphere the aurora lay.

In addition to causing scattering of the First Negative system N_2^+ ions cause scattering of the Meinel Negative system, which should therefore also be enhanced in sunlit auroras. Should the number density of metastable nitrogen molecules, $N_2(A\ ^3\Sigma_u^+)$, be sufficient, scattering by them would lead to an appreciable enhancement of the First Positive system.[137]

7.6 Temperature

Apart from some early work by Vegard and Harang[138] in which the order of interference was insufficient (Spitzer[139]), little attempt appears to have been made to determine the temperature in the auroral region from the Doppler widths of forbidden lines. Armstrong[140] has attacked the problem with modern interferometric techniques. From a study of $\lambda\,5577$ he obtained temperatures ranging from 310° to 500°K above faint auroral arcs (perhaps between 115 and 155 km).[141] Mulyarchik[141a] obtained temperatures less than about 400°K in a similar study. Measurements he made on $\lambda\,6300$ indicated approximately 1000°K except in the case of an intense type A aurora (presumably at a great altitude) where they indicated 2500°K or higher.

Much more effort has been devoted to the determination of the rotational temperatures. Unfortunately, the results are in poor accord, those obtained by the Norwegians being peculiar and different from those obtained by other workers.

From the remarks in § 5.1.3 it is apparent that the rotational temperature, T_R, indicated by a band of a forbidden system must be the same as the ordinary translational temperature, T_T, up to well above the 100-km level. In the case of an allowed system it cannot be assumed that the two temperatures are identical, since emission occurs before collisions can establish equipartition of energy. It is necessary to consider whether the excitation mechanism operative disturbs the original equipartition.

Electron impact does not change the total angular momentum of the target system appreciably, so that the distribution among the rotational levels of the excited states corresponds to that for thermal equilibrium in the ground state (Branscomb[142]).

In calculating T_R one must therefore use B'' the rotational constant for the ground state, rather than B', the rotational constant for the excited state. The correction introduced by the difference between B' and B'' is usually small.

The interpretation of T_R becomes uncertain if the excitation is by heavy-particle impact (cf. Carleton,[143] Roesler et al.[144]).

Most of the temperature determinations have been made from bands of the N_2^+ First Negative system. Within the R branch of one of these bands the intensity, $I_{K'}$, corresponding to the rotational quantum number, K', is given by

$$\left.\begin{array}{l} I_{K'} = CK' \exp[-\kappa K'(K'+1)] \\ \kappa = h^2/8\pi^2 JkT_R \end{array}\right\} \tag{7.73}$$

where C is some constant, J is the moment of inertia of the ions, and the other symbols have their customary significance. The graph of $\log\,[I_{K'}/K']$ versus $K'(K'+1)$ is a straight line from the slope of which κ and hence T_R, the rotational temperature, can immediately be obtained. An alternative but less reliable procedure is to find the position of the peak of the R branch. If K'_m is the rotational quantum number of the line at the peak, then

$$\kappa = 1/K'_m(2K'_m + 1). \tag{7.74}$$

Vegard and his associates[98, 145, 48, 54,] have taken a large number of spectra from which they have been able to determine the smoothed profiles of a few of the bands with some accuracy. A relatively high-dispersion instrument, acquired in 1950, gave partial separation of the individual lines. The results were not affected significantly. In the latest paper[54] it is reported that T_R is about 220°K. This is what would be expected for the region from which the most intense emission usually originates—that is, the region near the 105-km level. It is also reported that T_R does not increase with altitude, which is in conflict with the conclusions reached from all other evidence. A conceivable explanation of the anomaly is that stray light from strong auroras at about 105 km was not properly eliminated.

TABLE XII

Rotational Temperature and Auroral Class, λ 3914

From G. G. Shepherd and D. M. Hunten, *J. Atmos. Terr. Phys.* **6,** 328 (1955)

Auroral class	Rays and draperies	Homogeneous and ray bands	Red type B
	Number of observation		
	34	104	30
Temperature class	Percentage of type in temperature class		
High (275°–465°K)	85	26	10
Average (221°–274°K)	9	48	37
Low (150°–220°K)	6	26	53

Shepherd and Hunten[146] have also made temperature determinations from the profiles of unresolved bands. Their work is superior to that of the Norwegians in that they used a rapid scanning spectrometer by which a range of 50 A could be covered in only 10 seconds. Moreover, they reduced the basic data in a more refined manner. As they point out, the height of the unresolved profile at any wavelength depends on the line spacing at that wavelength as well as on the line intensity. The line spacing along the R branch is not constant. To allow for this, Shepherd and Hunten multiplied the profile height by a factor proportional to the local line spacing. Neglect of the correction makes the temperature too low, the error being only 40° at 250°K, but being 400° at 1000°K.

During six observing nights Shepherd and Hunten made a total of 180 temperature determinations. The values they obtained ranged from 150° to 465°K, the mean being 258°K.

In fifteen cases the altitude as well as the temperature was measured. When plotted, the results show a considerable scatter. Shepherd and Hunten suggest that this scatter may be at least in part real. It is so great that the results cannot be regarded as providing proof that the mean temperature-altitude curve has a positive gradient. Very suggestive evidence of such a gradient is, however, provided by Table XII, in which the auroras observed are classified and the percentage of each class having high medium, and low temperatures is given. As can be seen, rays and draperies which tend to have more than the average altitude give mainly high temperatures, whereas the red type B auroras which tend to have less than the average altitude give mainly low temperatures.

From spectra in which the lines forming the R branches of the $\lambda\,3914$ and $\lambda\,4278$ bands were partially resolved, Petrie[147] derived values of T_R in the range $450°$ to $700°$K. These values apparently refer to the summits of visible auroras.

In 1953 fully resolved spectra of bands of the N_2^+ First Negative system were obtained.[148] Jones and Harrison[149] have carried out a detailed study of such spectra. In making plots of $\log(I_{K'}/K')$ versus $K'(K' + 1)$, they found that it was not always possible to draw a single straight line through all the points. They attributed this to nonuniformity of the temperature of the luminous region. At small K' the intensities are controlled by the strong emission from the low-temperature region near the 105-km level; but at large K' the intensities may be appreciably enhanced by even faint emission from the high-temperature region at great altitudes. Jones and Harrison determined T_R both from the intensities at small K' and from those at large K'. They obtained differences of up to about $100°$K and concluded that in the auroral region T_R varies from below $250°$K to above $390°$K. Because of the long exposures required, it was not possible to investigate single auroral features whose altitude could be measured.

Some progress in this direction has been made by Montalbetti,[150] who has found that at Churchill the average temperature for strong auroras is $250° \pm 23°$K and for weak auroras is $335° \pm 52°$K. From the difference in the average altitudes of strong and weak auroras as determined by the Norwegian observers, Montalbetti inferred that the temperature gradient is about $6°$K/km.

Unfortunately, comparatively little work has been done on the forbidden band systems. As the spectroscopic studies have been unaccompanied by altitude determinations, the results serve only to indicate the temperature range in the auroral region of the upper atmosphere. A temperature as low as $200°$K has been deduced from measurements on the (0, 1) band of the O_2 Atmospheric system (Chamberlain et al.[9]); and one as high as $850°$K has been deduced from measurements on bands of the Vegard-Kaplan system (Petrie[147]). The first of these temperatures refers to the base of an aurora, and the second to the summit.

Important studies of the N_2^+ First Negative system in sunlit auroras have been carried out by Hunten and his associates. One spectra[150a] gave T_R to be $1060° \pm 100°K$ near the 250 km level; another [136a,150b] gave it to be approximately $2200°K$ in the 400 to 500 km region. The first of these values is almost certainly the same as the local translational temperature. It is difficult to decide whether or not the second is also the same. Account must be taken of the conversion of vibrational energy (which may be high) into rotational energy in ion-atom interchange collisions; and again account must be taken of the possibility that the N_2^+ ions involved may have acquired rotational energy from translational energy due to an electric field.

7.6.1 *Heating*

It is natural to inquire if the upper atmosphere is heated to a significant extent by auroras either in the immediate vicinity of a display or globally.

According to the estimates in § 7.5.3.7, the rate of ionization in a strong arc is approximately 10^7 cm^{-3} sec^{-1}. The amount of energy dissipated locally for each ion formed can scarcely differ by any considerable factor from 8 ev. If the particle concentration at the altitude of the arc is taken to be 4×10^{12} cm^{-3}, it may be seen that the rate of gain of thermal energy per gas atom or molecule must be about 2×10^{-5} ev/sec, which corresponds to a heating rate of about $5°K$/min. Because of winds a given volume of air cannot remain in the active zone for long, and consequently the rise in temperature is likely to be small.

Thermal energy is given to the air in a vertical column through a strong arc at a rate of perhaps about 4×10^{14} ev/cm^2 sec (mainly near the 105-km level). For comparison it may be noted that the mean thermal energy which photoionization supplies to the region above the base of the F_1 layer is judged to be more than 1×10^{10} ev/cm^2 sec at the equator, even at the minimum of the sunspot cycle.[151] If we bear in mind that visible auroras cover only a very minute fraction of the earth's surface, it would seem unlikely that they are of importance in the thermobalance of the upper atmosphere. A heat source at great altitudes is what is needed to account for the temperature gradient.

7.7 Electric Fields

A number of scientists (cf. Alfvèn,[152] Lebedinsky,[153] Wulf,[154] Vestine[155]) have speculated on the possibility of auroral displays being at least partially due to discharge action, but only Chamberlain[156] and Seaton[63] have attempted to discuss the resulting emission in any detail, and we shall confine ourselves here to giving an account of their investigations.

7.7.1 *Rays*

Homogeneous arcs and long thin rays appear to be the two extreme types of aurora, and it is not unlikely that the theoretical descriptions of them are simpler and more fundamental than the theoretical description of any intermediate type.

The presence of Doppler-shifted Balmer lines in their spectra indicates that arcs are closely associated with incoming protons, but there are reasons for believing that such protons cannot be directly responsible for rays (§ 7.4.3). It is conceivable that rays are due to incoming electrons. Though he does not disprove this, Chamberlain[156] considers it more probable that rays are simply discharges through the atmosphere. His development of the hypothesis is briefly as follows.

Assuming the existence of an electric field, X, Chamberlain first calculated the approximate energy distribution of the electrons, taking into account elastic collisions with gas atoms and molecules, and taking into account inelastic collisions leading to excitation of $O(^3P)$ to $O(^1D$ or $^1S)$ or leading to ionization of any of the constituents. He did this by solving numerically the integrodifferential equation of Smit[157] which governs the distribution. To simplify the solution he took the elastic cross section, $Q(\text{el})$, to be a constant which he put equal to πa_0^2 or 8.8×10^{-17} cm^2 (which is actually too low; cf. Massey and Burhop[158]) and took the mean free path of the electrons to be

$$\lambda = 1/n(\text{at})Q(\text{el}) \tag{7.75}$$

where $n(\text{at})$ is the number density of *atoms* (free and combined together). The distribution is governed by the energy

$$\epsilon = eX\lambda \tag{7.76}$$

gained by an electron in falling through the field a distance equal to one mean free path.

For a given distribution the rate coefficients s_{12}, s_{21}, s_{13}, and s_{ion}, describing, respectively, excitation to and deactivation of $O(^1D)$, excitation to $O(^1S)$, and ionization, may readily be computed. Some results are displayed in Table XIII.

Using the approximate method due to Morse *et al.*[159] Chamberlain also calculated u, the mean drift velocity along the field (Table XIII). He found that the associated current density, $\mathscr{J}$, could with sufficient accuracy be expressed as

$$\mathscr{J} = 1.3 \times 10^7 \, \epsilon^3 \, en(e) \tag{7.77}$$

where ϵ is in electron volts and $n(e)$, as usual, is the electron concentration.

Taking $\mathscr{J}$ to be constant along the ray, Chamberlain next investigated how $n(e)$ must vary if the luminosity is also to be constant along the ray (as it approximately is). He took the $\lambda\,5577$ photon emission rate to be a measure of the luminosity and arbitrarily assumed it to be 1.1×10^6 cm^{-3} sec^{-1} (which in the case of a ray of radius 50 meters corresponds to a surface brightness in $\lambda\,5577$ about twenty-seven times that of the zenith nightglow). To avoid the relative intensity of $\lambda\,6300\text{-}6364$ being unacceptably great (cf. Table XIII), he assumed 0.32 ev to be the minimum value of ϵ in the ray (this minimum being attained at the base of the ray). He further assumed that collisional deactivation of $O(^1S)$ may be neglected, so that each $O(^1S)$ atom yields 0.94 $\lambda\,5577$ protons. When ϵ is 0.32, s_{13} is 3.0×10^{-12} cm^{-3} sec^{-1} (Table XIII). If the base of the ray is at 120 km, where $n(O)$ is 3.9×10^{11} cm^{-3}

TABLE XIII

Rate Coefficients and Mean Drift Velocity

From J. W. Chamberlain, *in* "The Airglow and the Aurorae"(E. B. Armstrong and A. Dalgarno, eds.), p. 206, Pergamon, London, 1956.

ϵ (ev)	s_{12} (cm^3/sec)	s_{21} (cm^3/sec)	s_{13} (cm^3/sec)	$s_{1\text{on}}$ (cm^3/sec)	s_{12}/s_{13}	u (10^7 cm/sec)
0.10	5.4×10^{-11}	6.5×10^{-9}	4×10^{-15}	—	13,000	—
0.32	4.6×10^{-10}	7.4×10^{-9}	3×10^{-12}	2.6×10^{-16}	150	0.60
0.50	$1.0_6 \times 10^{-9}$	8.4×10^{-9}	2.3×10^{-11}	3.8×10^{-14}	46	0.84
1.00	2.5×10^{-9}	7.5×10^{-9}	1.9×10^{-10}	1.2×10^{-11}	13	1.24
10.0	3.5×10^{-9}	6.0×10^{-9}	5.0×10^{-10}	2.8×10^{-9}	7	6.8

according to the Rocket Panel's model which was used by Chamberlain, it follows from the $\lambda\,5577$ photon emission rate equation

$$0.94\,s_{13}n(e)n(O) = 1.1 \times 10^6 \text{ cm}^{-3}\text{ sec}^{-1} \tag{7.78}$$

that $n(e)$ is there 1×10^6 cm^{-3}. Hence from (7.77) $\mathscr{J}$ is 6×10^{12} electrons cm^{-2} sec^{-1} and

$$n(e)\epsilon^{\frac{2}{3}} = 4.6 \times 10^5 \text{cm}^{-3} \text{ (ev)}. \tag{7.79}$$

If it is accepted that (7.78) and (7.79) remain valid above the base of the ray (because of the constancy of the current and of the $\lambda\,5577$ luminosity) $n(e)$ and ϵ (and thus X) may be computed as a function of $n(O)$ or of z, the altitude. Chamberlain's results are given in Table XIV. As is seen, the required $n(e)$ is a decreasing function of the altitude, which is not attractive. The model ray has a luminosity which is constant over a gas density range of a factor of 30 (or over an altitude range of 40 km). Constancy over a more extended range is not easy to achieve. For the ray to stretch further downward, ϵ— and $n(e)$—would have to change very slowly indeed; and it is scarcely possible for it to stretch further upward with undiminished intensity in $\lambda\,5577$, since s_{13} becomes so insensitive to ϵ that the effect of the decrease of $n(O)$ with altitude cannot be compensated.

In Chamberlain's model, deactivation of $O(^1D)$ by electrons is unimportant. Deactivation by some other species of particle must, however, be very effective if the ratio of the intensity of λ 6300 to λ 5577 is to be as observed.

TABLE XIV

Parameters of Ray along which λ 5577 Luminosity is Constant

From J. W. Chamberlain, *in* "The Airglow and the Aurorae" (E. B. Armstrong and A. Dalgarno, eds.), p. 206, Pergamon, London, 1956.

ϵ (ev)	$n(e)$ (10^6 cm^{-3})	$n(O)$ (10^{10} cm^{-3})	$n(at)$ (10^{11} cm^{-3})	z (km)	λ (km)	X (volts/km)
0.32	1.00	39	20	120	0.057	5.6
0.50	0.71	7.3	3.7	137	0.31	1.6
1.00	0.48	1.3	0.65	160	1.75	0.57

Table XV shows the required values of σ_2, the fraction of oxygen atoms leaving the ^1D term by deactivating collisions, and of

$$d_{21} = \kappa n(X) \qquad (7.80)$$

where κ is the rate coefficient describing the deactivation process, and $n(X)$ is the number of the particles involved in this process. It is seen that $d_{21}/n(at)$ is almost constant and is quite large (cf. Table IX of § 7.5.3.1.1).

TABLE XV

Rates of Collisional Deactivation of $O(^1D)$ and of Ionization in Ray

From J. W. Chamberlain, *in* "The Airglow and the Aurorae" (E. B. Armstrong and A. Dalgarno, eds.), p. 206, Pergamon, London, 1956.

z (km)	Assumed $I(6300)/I(5577)$	σ_2	d_{21}	$d_{21}/n(at)$ (10^{-13} cm^3/sec)	Ionization rate $n(at)n(e)S_{Ion}$ (cm^{-3} sec^{-1})
120	1.00	0.99	0.98	4.9	5.2×10^2
160	2.74	0.73	0.025	3.9	3.8×10^5

Also included in Table XV are the calculated values of the ionization rates in the upper and lower parts of the ray. These rates should be indicative of the intensities of systems like the N_2^+ First Negative. The theory predicts that the emission of such systems is confined to moderate and great altitudes and that their intensities relative to the intensity of λ 5577 should be very dependent on excitation conditions. This is not in harmony with the observations of Omholt[67] (§ 7.4.2).

Equating the ionization rate to the recombination rate gives that in equilibrium

$$n(e)_{eq} = n(at)s_{ion} \alpha \qquad (7.81)$$

where α, as usual, is the effective recombination coefficient. An empirical fit to the figures in Table XIII yields

$$s_{ion} \simeq 2 \times 10^{-11} \epsilon^{10} \quad (0.32 \leqslant \epsilon \leqslant 1.0). \qquad (7.82)$$

By combination with (7.79) and substitution in (7.81) it may be seen that

$$n(e) \simeq 4 \times 10^{14}[n(at)/\alpha]^{\frac{1}{16}} \text{ cm}^{-3}. \qquad (7.83)$$

Evaluation of (7.83) gives that $n(e)_{eq}$, which is clearly extremely insensitive to $n(at)$ and to α, is approximately 10^6 cm^{-3}—slightly above the values of $n(e)$ for a constant luminosity (Table XIV). The time required for ionization equilibrium to be reached is estimated to be about a minute. Suppose that the electron concentration is initially small everywhere. After a ray is formed it increases, approaching equilibrium. When the values in Table XIV are passed, the electric field diminishes and the ray fades (unless, as Chamberlain thinks is not unlikely, the excess ionization in the ray is dissipated by diffusion or winds).

Chamberlain has made tentative suggestions regarding the origin of the electric field but has not attempted to develop them quantitatively.

7.7.2 *True Low-Latitude Auroras*

A theoretical study of the type of world-wide auroral activity seen on rare occasions from geomagnetic latitudes as low as 20° has been carried out by Seaton.[63]

Because of the extensive observational data on it, the great display of September 18 and 19, 1941, was chosen for detailed examination. The principal spectral characteristics to be explained are the great intensity and development of the N_2^+ First Negative system, the high value of the $I(6300)/I(5577)$ ratio, and the presence of λ 5198-5201 of NI (cf. § 7.4.2). As far as can be judged, the base of the emitting region was at 200 km or above.

Seaton attributes the N_2^+ First Negative system to resonance scattering in the sunlit part of the atmosphere (cf. § 7.5.3.7) and from the estimated intensity concludes that $n(N_2^+)$ was about 3×10^2 cm^{-3}. He points out that $n(e)$ must have been greater than this but that radio measurements show that it did not exceed 10^4 cm^{-3}. A value between 10^3 cm^{-3} and the upper limit just cited would appear reasonable.

The remaining spectral features are typical of low-energy electron excitation. Seaton considers that electrons involved gained their energy from electric fields producing current systems flowing through the upper atmosphere.

Dismissing collisional deactivation of $O(^1D)$ and $O(^1S)$ as unimportant in the altitude region concerned, he found that the parameter, ϵ (defined in § 7.7.1), must have been about 1 for consistency with the observed $I(6300)/I(5577)$ ratio. Using the excitation rates given in Table XIII, he further found that if $n(e)$ is 3×10^3 cm^{-3} the absolute intensities obtained are of the required order. It is to be noted from (7.77) that the adopted values of $n(e)$ and ϵ correspond to a current density of 4×10^{10} electrons/cm^2 sec, or (integrating through a 100-km thick sheet) to a total current of 0.06 amp/cm.

Seaton also investigated the excitation of λ 5198-5201, which he took to occur through collisions between electrons and nitrogen atoms, the ionization rate being too low for dissociative recombination to be appreciable. He neglected deactivation by other heavy particles but took account of deactivation by electrons. The determination of $n(N)/n(O)$ was his main object. As he pointed out, the number of atoms entering the long-lived ^2D term cannot be taken to equal the number leaving. Adopting

$$s_{12}(O) = 2.0 \times 10^{-9} \text{ cm}^3/\text{sec}, \quad s_{12}(N) = 4.0 \times 10^{-9} \text{ cm}^3/\text{sec},$$
$$s_{21}(N) = 3.9 \times 10^{-9} \text{ cm}^3/\text{sec} \quad (7.84)$$

and, assuming the excitation to be zero initially and constant thereafter, he showed that

$$n(N)/n(O) = 0.3 \frac{1 + 3.8 \times 10^{-4}n(e)}{1 - (1/B)[1 - \exp(-B)]} \frac{\int_0^t I(5198 + 5201)dt}{\int_0^t I(6300)dt} \quad (7.85)$$

where

$$B = 1.04 \times 10^{-5}[1 + 3.8 \times 10^{-4} n(e)]t \quad (7.86)$$

where t is in seconds. The precise value of $n(e)$ is of little moment, provided it does not exceed about 10^4 cm^{-3}. Applying (7.85) to the observational data of Dufay and Tcheng,[73] Seaton deduced $n(N)/n(O)$ to be about 0.15 in the atmospheric region concerned. Further theoretical work is needed.

Acknowledgments

It is a pleasure to thank Drs. J. W. Chamberlain, A. Dalgarno, D. M. Hunten, and F. E. Roach for several helpful comments on the original manuscript, and Dr. J. Mazur for his assistance with the references.

References

1. A. C. Ranyard, *Nature* **7**, 201 (1872).
2. J. R. Capron, "Aurorae: Their Characters and Spectrum," Spon, London, 1879.
3. J. W. Chamberlain and N. J. Oliver, *J. Geophys. Res.* **58**, 457 (1953).
4. L. Vegard and G. Kvifte, *Geofys. Publ. (Oslo)* **16**, No. 7 (1945).
5. D. Barbier and D. R. Williams, *J. Geophys. Res.* **55**, 401 (1950).

6. C. E. Dahlstrom and D. M. Hunten, *Phys. Rev.* **84,** 378 (1951).

7. A. B. Meinel, *Astrophys. J.* **113,** 583 (1951).

8. W. Petrie and R. Small, *Astrophys. J.* **116,** 433 (1952).

9. J. W. Chamberlain, C. Y. Fan, and A. B. Meinel, *Astrophys. J.* **120,** 560 (1954).

10. D. M. Hunten, *J. Atmos. Terr. Phys.* **7,** 141 (1955).

11. B. A. Bagariazky and N. I. Fedorova, *in* "The Airglow and the Aurorae" (E. B. Armstrong and A. Dalgarno, eds.), p. 174, Pergamon, London, 1956; B. A. Bagariazky, *Izvest. Akad. Nauk SSSR Ser. Geofys.* No. 4 (1957).

12. A. Omholt, *J. Atmos. Terr. Phys.* **10,** 320 (1957).

13. A. W. Harrison and A. V. Jones, *J. Atmos. Terr. Phys.* **11,** 192 (1957).

14. J. W. Chamberlain and A. B. Meinel, *in* "The Earth as a Planet" (G. P. Kuiper, ed.), p. 514, Univ. Chicago Press, Chicago, 1954.

15. L. Vegard, *Nature* **114,** 1089 (1939).

16. C. W. Gartlein, *Trans. Amer. Geophys. Union* **31,** 18 (1950).

17. L. Vegard, *Ann. Géophys.* **6,** 157 (1950).

18. A. B. Meinel, *Phys. Rev.* **80,** 1096 (1950); *Astrophys. J.* **113,** 50 (1951).

19. L. Vegard, *Geofys. Publ. (Oslo),* **18,** No. 5 (1952).

20. R. Bernard, *in* "Emission Spectra of the Night Sky and Aurorae," p. 93, Physical Society, London, 1948.

21. A. B. Meinel, *Repts. Prog. in Phys.* **14,** 121 (1951).

21a. A. V. Mironov, V. S. Prokudina, and N. N. Shefov, *in* "Spectral, Electrophotometrical and Radar Researches of Aurorae and Airglow", p. 20, Acad, Sci. USSR, Moscow, 1959.

22. L. Vegard, *in* "Emission Spectra of the Night Sky and Aurorae," p. 82, Physical Society, London, 1948.

23. M. Minnaert, *in* "The Sun" (G. P. Kuiper, ed.), p. 88, Univ. Chicago Press, Chicago, 1953.

23a. E. R. Manring and H. B. Pettit, *J. Geophys. Res.* **64,** 149 (1959).

24. R. H. Garstang, *Monthly Not. Roy. Astron. Soc.* **111,** 115 (1951); *Astrophys. J.* **115,** 506 (1952); *in* "The Airglow and the Aurorae" (E. B. Armstrong and A. Dalgarno, eds.), p. 324, Pergamon. London, 1956.

25. W. Petrie, *Phys. Rev.* **87,** 1002 (1952).

26. M. J. Seaton, *J. Atmos. Terr. Phys.* **4,** 295 (1954).

27. J. W. Chamberlain and F. L. Roesler, *Astrophys. J.* **121,** 541 (1955).

27a. L. Wallace, *J. Atmos. Terr. Phys.* (in press).

27b. M. Dufay, *Ann. Géophys.* **15,** 134 (1959).

27c. A. E. Belon and K. C. Clark, *J. Atmos. Terr. Phys.* **16,** 220 (1959).

28. A. B. Meinel, *Publ. Astron. Soc. Pacific* **60,** 357 (1948).

29. W. Petrie and R. Small, *Canad. J. Phys.* **31,** 911 (1953).

30. M. Nicolet, *in* "Emission Spectra of the Night Sky and Aurorae," p. 105, Physical Society, London, 1948.

31. M. Nicolet and R. Dogniaux, *J. Geophys. Res.* **55,** 21 (1950).

32. C. W. Gartlein and D. F. Sherman, *Mém. Soc. Roy. Sci. Liège* **12,** 187 (1952).

33. W. B. Murcray, *Nature* **180,** 139 (1957).

34. C. W. Gartlein and G. Sprague, *Mém. Soc. Roy. Sci. Liège* **12,** 191 (1952).

35. W. R. Jarmain, P. A. Fraser, and R. W. Nicholls, *Astrophys. J.* **118,** 229 (1953).

36. A. B. Meinel, *Astrophys. J.* **114,** 431 (1951).

37. A. E. Douglas, *Astrophys. J.* **117,** 380 (1953).

38. M. J. Seaton, *J. Atmos. Terr. Phys.* **4,** 285 (1954).

39. S. Chapman *et al., Ann. IGY* **4,** 41 (1957).

40. A. Omholt, *J. Atmos. Terr. Phys.* **5**, 243 (1954).
41. D. Barbier and H. Pettit, *Ann. Géophys.* **8**, 232 (1952).
42. E. V. Ashburn, *J. Atmos. Terr. Phys.* **6**, 67 (1955).
43. J. W. Chamberlain, *Astrophys. J.* **120**, 360 (1954).
43a. G. I. Galperin, *Planet. Space Sci.* **1**, 57 (1959).
44. D. R. Bates, *Proc. Roy. Soc.* A**196**, 217 (1949).
45. R. W. Nicholls, *Phys. Rev.* **77**, 421 (1950).
46. L. Vegard and E. Tönsberg, *Geofys. Publ. (Oslo)* **11**, No. 2 (1935).
47. R. W. Nicholls, *in* "The Airglow and the Aurorae" (E. B. Armstrong and A. Dalgarno, eds.), p. 302, Pergamon, London, 1956.
47a. M. H. Rees, *J. Atmos. Terr. Phys.* (in press).
48. L. Vegard and E. Tönsberg, *Geofys. Publ. (Oslo)* **18**, No. 8 (1952).
49. W. Petrie, *J. Geophys. Res.* **55**, 143 (1950).
50. I. C. Percival and M. J. Seaton, *in* "The Airglow and the Aurorae" (E. B. Armstrong and A. Dalgarno, eds.), p. 244, Pergamon, London, 1956.
50a. B. Y. Bagariazky, *Ann. Géophys.* **14**, 366 (1958).
51. A. B. Meinel, *Mém. Soc. Roy. Sci. Liège* **12**, 203 (1952).
52. L. Vegard, *Geofys. Publ. (Oslo)* **12**, No. 14 (1940).
53. L. Vegard, *Geofys. Publ. (Oslo)* **19**, No. 4 (1955).
54. L. Vegard, *Geofys. Publ. (Oslo)* **19**, No. 9 (1956).
54a. G. I. Galperin, *Ann. Géophys.* **14**, 363 (1958).
55. L. Harang, *Geofys. Publ. (Oslo)* **16**, No. 13 (1946); *Terr. Mag.* **51**, 381 (1946).
56. L. Harang, *J. Atmos. Terr. Phys.* **9**, 157 (1956); *Geofys. Publ. (Oslo)* **20**, No. 5 (1958).
56a. V. I. Krassovsky, *Ann. Géophys.* **14**, 356 (1958).
57. L. Vegard, *Nature* **141**, 200 (1938); *Geofys. Publ. (Oslo)* **12**, No. 5 (1938).
58. L. Vegard and E. Tönsberg, *Geofys. Publ. (Oslo)* **13**, No. 5 (1941).
59. L. Vegard, *Geofys. Publ. (Oslo)* **20**, No. 4 (1958).
60. P. Swings and A. B. Meinel, *in* "The Atmospheres of the Earth and Planets" (G. P. Kuiper, ed.), 2nd edn., p. 159, Univ. Chicago Press, Chicago, 1952.
61. C. Störmer, *Geofys. Publ. (Oslo)* **12**, No. 7 (1930).
62. L. Vegard, *in* "Terrestrial Magnetism and Electricity" (J. A. Fleming, ed.), p. 573, McGraw-Hill, New York, 1939.
63. M. J. Seaton, *in* "The Airglow and the Aurorae" (E. B. Armstrong and A. Dalgarno, eds.), p. 225, Pergamon, London, 1956.
64. C. Störmer, *Geofys. Publ. (Oslo)* **13**, No. 7 (1942).
65. R. Bernard, *Ann. Astrophys.* **4**, 31 (1941).
66. L. Vegard and G. Kvifte, *Geofys. Publ. (Oslo)* **19**, No. 2 (1954).
67. A. Omholt, *Astrophys. J.* **126**, 461 (1957).
67a. W. B. Murcray, *J. Geophys. Res.* **64**, 955 (1959).
68. Lord Rayleigh, *Proc. Roy. Soc.* A**101**, 114 (1922).
69. V. M. Slipher, *Monthly Not. Roy. Astron. Soc.* **93**, 664 (1933).
70. F. W. P. Götz, *Naturwissenschaften* **29**, 690 (1941); *Experientia* **3**, 185 (1947).
71. J. Dufay, J. Gauzit, and Tcheng Mao-Lin, *Cahiers Phys.* **1**, 59 (1941).
72. J. Dufay, *Cahiers Phys.* **1**, 71 (1941).
73. J. Dufay and Tcheng Mao-Lin, *Cahiers Phys.* **2**, 52 (1942).
74. D. Barbier, *Ann. Géophys.* **3**, 227 (1947); "Relations entre les Phénoménes Solaires et Géophysiques," p. 182, Centre National de la Recherche Scientifique, Paris, 1947.
75. M. Dufay and G. Moreau, *Ann. Géophys.* **13**, 153 (1957).

75a. D. Barbier, *Ann. Géophys.* **14**, 334 (1958).

75b. R. A. Duncan, *Planet. Space Sci.* **1**, 112 (1959).

76. A. B. Meinel, "Proceedings of the Conference on Auroral Physics, London, Ontario, July, 1951" (N. C. Gerson, ed.), p. 75, Airforce Cambridge Research Center, Cambridge, Massachusetts, 1954.

77. C. Y. Fan and D. H. Schulte, *Astrophys. J.* **120**, 563 (1954).

78. J. W. Chamberlain, *Advances in Geophys.* **4**, 109 (1958).

78a. R. Montalbetti, *J. Atmos. Terr. Phys.* **14**, 200 (1959).

79. L. Vegard, *Phil. Mag.* **42**, 47 (1921).

80. C. Störmer, *Nature* **142**, 1034 (1938); *Terr. Mag.* **44**, 7 (1939).

81. L. Harang, "The Aurorae," Chapman and Hall, London, 1951.

82. C. W. Gartlein, *Mém. Soc. Roy. Sci. Liège* **12**, 195 (1952).

82a. G. J. Romick and C. T. Elvey, *J. Atmos. Terr. Phys.* **12**, 283 (1958).

82b. A. E. Veller, *Ann. Géophys.* **14**, 323 (1958).

83. E. V. Ashburn, *J. Geophys. Res.* **60**, 205 (1955).

84. A. Omholt and L. Harang, *J. Atmos. Terr. Phys.* **7**, 247 (1955).

85. A. Omholt, *in* "The Airglow and the Aurorae" (E. B. Armstrong and A. Dalgarno, eds.), p. 178, Pergamon, London, 1956.

86. R. Montalbetti and A. V. Jones, *J. Atmos. Terr. Phys.* **11**, 43 (1957).

87. D. F. Martyn, *Nature* **167**, 92 (1951).

87a. I. S. Shklovsky, *Ann. Géophys.* **14**, 414 (1958).

88. The Rocket Panel, *Phys. Rev.* **88**, 1027 (1952).

89. D. R. Bates, *Ann. Géophys.* **11**, 253 (1955).

90. N. N. Das Gupta and S. K. Ghosh, *Rev. Mod. Phys.* **18**, 225 (1946).

91. D. R. Bates and A. Dalgarno, *Proc. Phys. Soc.* A**65**, 919 (1952); **66**, 972 (1953).

92. D. R. Bates and G. W. Griffing, *Proc. Phys. Soc.* A**66**, 961 (1953); A**67**, 663 (1954); A**68**, 90 (1955).

93. D. R. Bates and G. W. Griffing, *J. Atmos. Terr. Phys.* **3**, 212 (1953).

94. G. W. Griffing and A. L. Stewart, *J. Atmos. Terr. Phys.* **4**, 339 (1954).

95. I. S. Shklovski, *Dokl. Acad. Nauk SSSR* **81**, 367 (1951).

96. J. W. Chamberlain, *Astrophys. J.* **120**, 360 (1954).

97. A. Omholt, *J. Atmos. Terr. Phys.* **9**, 18 (1956).

98. L. Vegard and G. Kvifte, *Geofys. Publ. (Oslo)* **18**, No. 3 (1951).

99. J. W. Chamberlain, *Astrophys. J.* **126**, 245 (1957).

100. D. T. Stewart, *Proc. Phys. Soc.* A**69**, 437 (1956).

101. J. T. Tate and P. T. Smith, *Phys. Rev.* **39**, 270 (1932).

102. C. Y. Fan and A. B. Meinel, *Astrophys. J.* **118**, 205 (1952).

103. C. Y. Fan, *in* "The Airglow and the Aurorae" (E. B. Armstrong and A. Dalgarno, eds.), p. 276, Pergamon, London, 1956; *Phys. Rev.* **103**, 1740 (1956).

104. D. R. Bates, *in* "The Airglow and the Aurorae" (E. B. Armstrong and A. Dalgarno eds.), p. 251, Pergamon, London, 1956.

105. S. A. Colgate, *Phys. Rev.* **99**, 665 (1955).

106. D. R. Bates, M. R. C. McDowell, and A. Omholt, *J. Atmos. Terr. Phys.* **10**, 51 (1957).

107. L. H. Meredith, M. B. Gottlieb, and J. A. Van Allen, *Phys. Rev.* **97**, 201 (1955).

108. J. A. Van Allen and J. E. Kasper, *Bull. Amer. Phys. Soc.* **1**, 230 (1956).

109. J. A. Van Allen, G. H. Ludwig, E. C. Ray, and C. E. McIlwain, *Jet Propulsion* **23**, 588 (1958); *IGY Satellite Rept. Ser.* No. 3, 73 (1958).

110. J. A. Van Allen, *Proc. Natl. Acad. Sci.* **43**, 57 (1957).

111. J. R. Winckler, L. Peterson, R. Arnoldy, and R. Hoffman, *Phys. Rev.* **110**, 1221 (1958).

111a. K. A. Anderson, *Phys. Rev.* **111**, 1397 (1958).

112. C. E. McIlwain, *IGY Rocket Rept. Ser.* No. **1**, 164 (1958).

113. L. H. Meredith, L. R. Davis, J. P. Hoeppner, and O. E. Berg, *IGY Rocket Rept. Ser.* No. **1**, 169 (1958).

114. D. R. Bates, H. S. W. Massey, and R. W. B. Pearse, *in* "Emission Spectra of the Night Sky and Aurorae," p. 97, Physical Society, London, 1948.

115. D. R. Bates, *J. Atmos. Terr. Phys.* **6**, 171 (1955).

116. M. J. Seaton, *Phil. Trans. Roy. Soc.* A**245**, 469 (1953).

117. D. R. Bates and T. J. M. Boyd, *Proc. Phys. Soc.* A**69**, 910 (1956).

118. M. J. Seaton, *Astrophys. J.* **127**, 67 (1958).

119. A. Omholt, *J. Atmos. Terr. Phys.* **7**, 73 (1955).

120. L. Vegard and G. Kvifte, *Geofys. Publ.* (*Oslo*) **17**, No. 1 (1947).

121. S. N. Ghosh, *Proc. Natl. Inst. Sci. India* **12**, 405 (1946).

122. S. K. Mitra, *Nature* **157**, 692 (1946).

123. Y. Tanaka, *J. Chem. Phys.* **20**, 1728 (1952).

124. I. C. Percival, *Proc. Phys. Soc.* A**70**, 241 (1957).

125. P. Swings, *in* "The Airglow and the Aurorae" (E. B. Armstrong and A. Dalgarno, eds.), p. 249, Pergamon, London, 1956.

126. A. Omholt, *J. Atmos. Terr. Phys.* **9**, 28 (1956).

127. S. J. Smith and L. M. Branscomb, *J. Res. Natl. Bur. Standards* **55**, 165 (1955).

128. R. Rypdal and L. Vegard, *Geofys. Publ.* (*Oslo*) **12**, No. 12 (1940).

129. A. Omholt, *J. Atmos. Terr. Phys.* **5**, 63 (1954).

130. D. M. Hunten and G. G. Shepherd, *J. Atmos. Terr. Phys.* **6**, 64 (1955).

131. A. Omholt, *J. Atmos. Terr. Phys.* **6**, 61 (1955).

132. J. S. Shklovski, *Dokl. Acad. Nauk SSSR* **81**, 525 (1951).

133. N. P. Carleton and T. R. Lawrence, *Phys. Rev.* **109**, 1159 (1958).

133a. K. C. Clark and A. E. Belon, *J. Atmos. Terr. Phys.* **16**, 205 (1959).

133b. D. M. Hunten, *Ann. Géophys.* **14**, 167 (1958); see also A. W. Harrison and A. V. Jones, *J. Atmos. Terr. Phys.* **13**, 291 (1959).

133c. D. R. Bates and N. Lynn, *Proc. Roy. Soc.* A**253**, 141 (1959).

134. S. Chapman and C. G. Little, *J. Atmos. Terr. Phys.* **10**, 20 (1957).

135. D. R. Bates, *Proc. Roy. Soc.* A**196**, 562 (1949).

136. D. R. Bates, *in* "Rocket Exploration of the Upper Atmosphere" (R. L. F. Boyd and M. J. Seaton, eds.), p. 347, Pergamon, London, 1954.

136a. A. V. Jones and D. M. Hunten, *Canad. J. Res.* **38**, (in press) (1960).

137. D. R. Bates and A. E. Witherspoon, *Monthly Not. Roy. Astron. Soc.* **112**, 101 (1952).

138. L. Vegard and L. Harang, *Geofys. Publ.* (*Oslo*) **11**, No. 1 (1934); **11**, No. 15 (1937).

139. L. Spitzer, *in* "The Atmospheres of the Earth and Planets" (G. P. Kuiper, ed.), p. 213, Univ. Chicago Press, Chicago, 1949.

140. E. B. Armstrong, *in* "The Airglow and the Aurorae" (E. B. Armstrong and A. Dalgarno, eds.), p. 366, Pergamon, London, 1956.

141. E. B. Armstrong, *J. Atmos. Terr. Phys.* **13**, 205 (1959).

141a. T. M. Mulyarchik, *in* "Spectral, Electrophotometrical and Radar Researches of Aurorae and Airglow," p. 41, Acad. Sci. USSR, Moscow, 1959.

142. L. M. Branscomb, *Phys. Rev.* **79**, 619 (1950).

143. N. P. Carleton, *Phys. Rev.* **107**, 110 (1957).

144. I. L. Roesler, C. Y. Fan, and J. W. Chamberlain, *J. Atmos. Terr. Phys.* **12**, 200 (1958).

145. L. Vegard, E. Tönsberg, and G. Kvifte, *Geofys. Publ.* (*Oslo*) **18**, No. 4 (1951).

146. G. G. Shepherd and D. M. Hunten, *J. Atmos. Terr. Phys.* **6**, 328 (1955).
147. W. Petrie, *J. Atmos. Terr. Phys.* **4**, 5 (1953).
148. A. V. Jones, D. M. Hunten, and G. G. Shepherd, *Astrophys. J.* **118**, 350 (1953).
149. A. V. Jones and A. W. Harrison, *J. Atmos. Terr. Phys.* **6**, 336 (1955).
150. R. Montalbetti, *Canad. J. Phys.* **35**, 831 (1957).
150a. E. A. Lytle and D M Hunten, *Canad. J. Res.* **38**, (in press) (1960).
150b D. M. Hunten, H. J. Koenig, and A. V. Jones, *Nature* **183**, 453 (1959).
151. D. R. Bates, *Proc. Phys. Soc.* B**64**, 805 (1951); *Proc. Roy. Soc.* A**236**, 206 (1956).
152. H. Alfvén, "Cosmical Electrodynamics," Clarendon, Oxford, 1950.
153. A. J. Lebedinsky, *Dokl. Acad. Nauk SSSR* **86**, 913 (1952); *in* "The Airglow and the Aurorae" (E. B. Armstrong and A. Dalgarno, eds.), p. 222, Pergamon, London, 1956.
154. O. R. Wulf, *J. Geophys. Res.* **58**, 531 (1953).
155. E. H. Vestine, *J. Geophys. Res.* **58**, 539 (1953); **59**, 93 (1954).
156. J. W. Chamberlain, *in* "The Airglow and the Aurorae" (E. B. Armstrong and A. Dalgarno, eds.), p. 206, Pergamon, London, 1956.
157. J. A. Smit, *Physica* **3**, 543 (1936).
158. H. S. W. Massey and E. H. S. Burhop, "Electronic and Ionic Impact Phenomena," Clarendon, Oxford, 1952.
159. P. M. Morse, W. P. Allis, and E. S. Lamar, *Phys. Rev.* **48**, 412 (1935).

Chapter 8

Radar Studies of the Aurora

HENRY G. BOOKER

8.1 Introduction 355
8.2 Pulse Radar Experiments.. 356
    8.2.1 Radar Observations of the Aurora................................. 357
8.3 Analysis of Observations in Terms of Azimuth........................... 359
8.4 The Distribution of Auroral Echoes with Range......................... 360
8.5 Analysis of Auroral Echoes in Terms of Height......................... 360
8.6 Diurnal, Seasonal, and Sunspot Cycle Variations of Auroral Echoes.......... 362
8.7 Motion Associated with Auroral Echoes.................................. 362
8.8 Frequency Dependence of Auroral Echoes................................. 366
8.9 Polarization of Auroral Echoes... 366
8.10 The Importance of Approximate Perpendicularity between the Earth's
    Magnetic Field and the Radius from the Radar to the Aurora.............. 366
8.11 Theories of Auroral Radar Echoes...................................... 369
8.12 The Cause of Movement in the Location of Auroral Echoes................ 373
    References 374

8.1 Introduction

During the past twenty-five years, and more especially in the past ten years, a new means of investigating the aurora has become available. Whatever causes excitation of atoms and molecules during auroras also causes ionization, and the presence of ionization can be detected by using radio waves. The effect of the aurora on radio propagation was observed in 1933 by Sir Edward Appleton in an expedition to Tromsö, Norway, as part of the program for the second International Polar Year.[1] Since then, phenomena believed to be associated with the aurora have frequently been observed with conventional ionospheric radio sounders operating in the frequency range from 1 to 20 Mc/sec, particularly in Norway,[2] in Germany,[3] in Canada,[4,5] and in Alaska;[6-8] observations[9] have also been made by means of an oblique incidence ionospheric sounder. To obtain reliable echoes from auroral ionization, it is, however, best to operate in the frequency range from 20 to 800 Mc/sec. Below 20 Mc/sec attenuation is troublesome, and above 800 Mc/sec backscattering is weak and no echoes have so far been reported with confidence.

The fact that radio echoes from the aurora were possible was known twenty years ago to radio amateurs operating on frequencies of 28, 50, and 144 Mc/sec. They obtained unusual, and often distorted, communication by pointing their directional antennas northward instead of at each other.[10]

Since then, the aurora has been investigated by radar methods using various frequencies between 30 and 800 Mc/sec. Auroral radar echoes in this frequency range were first obtained by Harang and Stoffregen at Tromsö, Norway.[11] After World War II, they were obtained more or less accidentally at Manchester, England,[12] and Ottawa, Canada,[13] by equipment erected to examine echoes from meteor trails. Since then, auroral radars have been in use at a number of other locations: Kiruna, Sweden;[14] Saskatoon, Canada;[15] Ithaca, New York;[16] Oslo and Tromsö, Norway;[17] South Dartmouth, Massachusetts;[18] and Fairbanks, Alaska.[19-21] Agreement between observations made by various workers at different locations is good, but there is no corresponding agreement concerning the interpretation of these observations. First, in §§ 8.2 to 8.10 the known facts will be summarized, after which in §§ 8.11 and 8.12 an account will be given of theories which have been suggested to explain them.

8.2 Pulse Radar Experiments

The radars used for investigating echoes from the aurora have generally been of fairly high power with rather long pulse lengths. Larger antenna gains have usually been possible at the higher frequencies. At 30 Mc/sec the

TABLE I
Radar Parameters

Frequency (Mc/sec)	30	56	72	106	398
Location	Kiruna, Sweden	Saskatoon, Canada	Manchester, England	College, Alaska	College, Alaska
Magnetic dip (degrees)	77	77	69	77	77
Peak power (kw)	100	50	10	100	60
Pulse duration (μsec)	40	60	40	100	400–900
Antenna gain	8	20	90	120	4000
Receiver sensitivity (watts)	3×10^{-14}	5×10^{-13}	2×10^{-14}	10^{-13}	10^{-16}

typical antenna is a three-element Yagi with a gain of about 8. At 400 Mc/sec, however, the antennas have been 60-foot paraboloids with a gain of 4000 and a beam width of about 3 degrees between half-power points. Typical parameters are listed in Table I. With radar parameters of the type indicated, azimuth resolution is poor at 30 Mc/sec but quite good at 400 Mc/sec. In the UHF band some degree of resolution in height is also possible, amounting perhaps to 10 km.

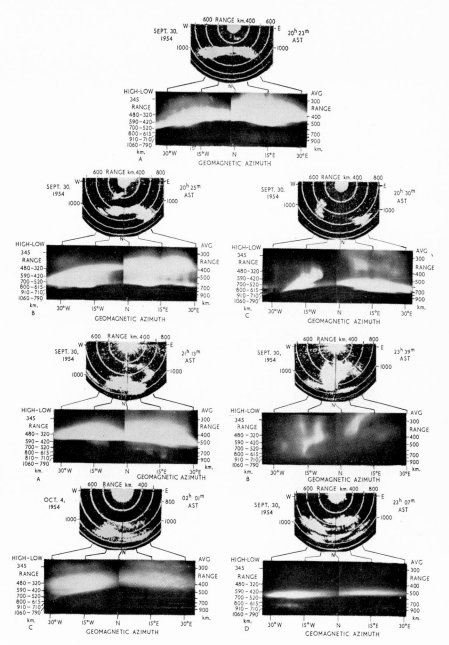

FIG. 1. Photographs of visible aurora compared with simultaneous 106–Mc/sec radar echoes at College, Alaska. From K. L. Bowles, *J. Geophys. Res.* **59**, 553 (1954); Research Report EE248, Cornell University, Ithaca, New York, 1955.

[*To face page* 356

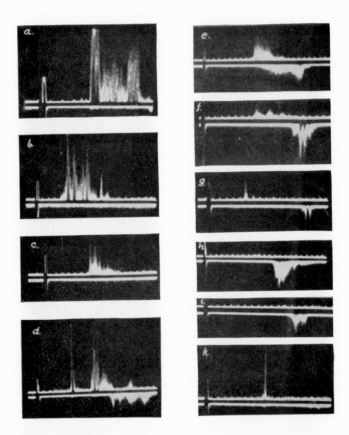

FIG. 2. Echoes on two frequencies received simultaneously on a double-beam oscillo-graph in Norway. The upper trace shows echoes on 35 Mc/sec, and the lower trace shows echoes on 74 Mc/sec. The pips on the upper trace indicate 50-km range marks. From L. Harang and V. Landmark, *J. Atmos. Terr. Phys.* **4**, 322 (1954).

The range resolution of auroral radars has varied from more than 100 km down to a few kilometers. Many observers have classified echoes into diffuse echoes and discrete echoes depending on whether they were or were not resolved in range by the equipment in use. The radars employed here had such different range resolutions that there is not much uniformity in use of the terms discrete echoes and diffuse echoes. In all probability most echoes observed by workers at Manchester, and classified by them into discrete and diffuse echoes, would be classified by the Stanford Research Institute observers at College, Alaska, as discrete echoes. On the other hand, what the Stanford observers refer to as a weak diffuse echo covers a considerable part of the sky and has probably never been observed at Manchester.

8.2.1 Radar Observations of the Aurora

In describing radar observations of the aurora it is convenient to begin with observations made by Bowles[20] at College, Alaska, on 106 Mc/sec. Like all the other observers, he found that auroral echoes came predominantly from low angles of elevation in a quadrant bisected by magnetic north. If visible aurora existed overhead or to the south, no radar echoes could be obtained from it. No difficulty was experienced, however, in obtaining echoes from auroral forms at low angles of elevation to the north.

When echoes were being obtained from visible aurora to the north, the radar echoes were displayed on a plan position indicator, and simultaneous photographs of the northern sky were made. The radio and visual observations were then correlated in the manner shown in Fig. 1. It is convenient to compare the northward-looking auroral photograph with a photograph of the corresponding display on the plan position indicator of the radar, oriented with its magnetic north at the bottom for the following reason. The lower edges of auroral forms generally occur in the vicinity of 100 km, so that height on the photograph corresponds approximately to range on the plan position indicator, and the two corresponding photographs should look roughly alike. Examination of Fig. 1 shows that a significant, but not perfect, correlation exists between visible auroral forms and radar echoes. It must be remembered, however, that this kind of correlation applies only in the northern quadrant. Elsewhere, including vertically overhead, existence of visible aurora does not usually lead to detectable radar echoes.

If the direction of the radar beam is held fixed in the direction of magnetic north, the presence of auroral echoes in this direction may be detected and the time variation of their ranges may be studied. Experiments of this kind were made by Currie et al.[15] at a frequency of 106 Mc/sec at Saskatoon, Canada. They found that individual echoes were usually short-lived, typical durations being measured in minutes, and that their ranges frequently changed at rates of the order of 500 to 1000 m sec.[-1]

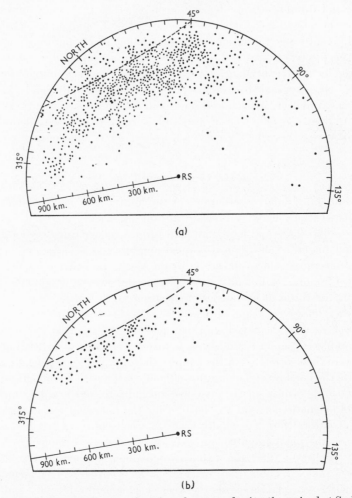

(a)

(b)

FIG. 3. Mass plots of echoes as a function of range and azimuth received at Saskatoon, Canada, (a) on 56 Mc/sec and (b) on 106 Mc/sec, simultaneously. The position of the auroral zone of maximum auroral frequency is shown by the dashed lines. From B. W. Currie, T. A. Forsyth, and F. E. Vawter, *J. Geophys. Res.* **58**, 179 (1953).

All auroral echoes have a complex structure and fade up and down rapidly. The probability distribution of amplitude is approximately Rayleigh, indicating that the echo is formed from many contributions combining in approximately random phase. In Fig. 2 are shown amplitude-range displays made simultaneously at 35 and 74 Mc/sec in Norway by Harang and

Landmark.[17] The upper trace, for which amplitude is recorded vertically upward, refers to 35 Mc/sec and the lower trace, for which amplitude is recorded vertically downward, refers to 74 Mc/sec. The beam angles of the antennas used at the two frequencies were the same, and they were mounted at the same height above ground. Echoes were frequently seen at 35 Mc/sec at times when there were no echoes at 74 Mc/sec, and occasionally the reverse was true. When echoes were seen simultaneously at both frequencies, the range on the higher frequency was generally greater than the range on the lower.

8.3 Analysis of Observations in Terms of Azimuth

The tendency for auroral echoes to occur only in the northern quadrant has been demonstrated by Hellgren and Meos[14] at Kiruna, Sweden, on a

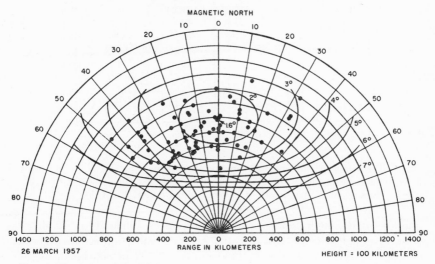

FIG. 4. Mass plot of 398-Mc/sec echoes as a function of range and azimuth, College, Alaska, March 26, 1957. The points represent observations. The curves are derived from theory, as explained in § 8.10. From R. L. Leadabrand, L. Dolphin, and A. M. Peterson, I. R. E. Transactions on Antennas and Propagation, $AP-7$, 127 (1959).

frequency of 30.3 Mc/sec; at Saskatoon, Canada,[15] on frequencies of 56 and 106 Mc/sec; and at College, Alaska,[22] on a frequency of 51.7 Mc/sec. The results from Saskatoon[15] are shown in Fig. 3, in which the dashed curve shows the position of the auroral zone of maximum frequency. It should be understood that, at all of these locations, visual aurora frequently occurred to the south of the radar, but radar echoes were not then obtained. To clinch this point Dyce[22] made observations on 51.9 Mc/sec at Point Barrow, Alaska, where most of the visible aurora is seen to the south of the observing station. He found that, even when most of the visible aurora is to the south of the station, radar echoes come predominantly from low angles of elevation in a generally northerly direction.

Leadabrand et al.,[19] observing at a frequency of 398 Mc/sec at College, Alaska, have shown that the azimuth restriction on the directions of auroral echoes extends into the UHF band. Figure 4 is typical of their results.

8.4 The Distribution of Auroral Echoes with Range

Harang and Landmark[17] in Norway examined the way in which the amplitude of echoes on 35 and 74 Mc/sec depended on their range. Their results are shown in Fig. 5. They also showed that the frequency of occurrence of echoes depended on their range, as shown in Fig. 6. Similar results were

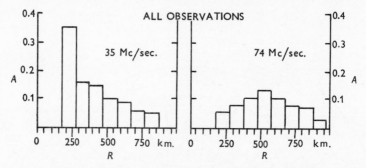

Fig. 5. The amplitude of echoes as a function of range on 35 and 74 Mc/sec in Norway. The columns indicate the mean value of amplitudes, A, as a function of the range, R. From L. Harang and V. Landmark, J. Atmos. Terr. Phys. 4, 322 (1954).

obtained by Bullough and Kaiser[23] at Manchester, England, on 72 Mc/sec, and workers in Sweden,[14] Canada,[15] and Alaska[22] found that echoes generally occur in the range from 500 to 1000 km, with 700 to 800 km being the commonest value. At lower frequencies, somewhat shorter ranges occur, but ranges of the order of 100 km are never observed.

8.5 Analysis of Auroral Echoes in Terms of Height

The only observers who have been able to sweep in elevation a beam sufficiently narrow to make direct observations of the height of auroral echoes are Leadabrand et al.[19] Their observations were made at College, Alaska, with a 3-degree beam at a frequency of 398 Mc/sec. Their observations for a period of 2 days are shown in Fig. 7. Heights are distributed from 75 to 135 km, the most frequent height being 110 km. The height of maximum response from an auroral arc varied with the azimuth from

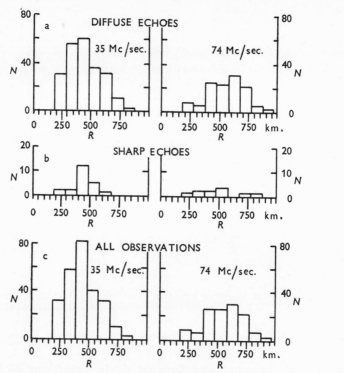

FIG. 6. Frequency of occurrence of echoes on 35 and 74 Mc/sec as a function of range, Norway. The columns indicate the number, N, of echoes observed for each 50-km increase in range, R. From L. Harang and V. Landmark, *J. Atmos. Terr. Phys.* **4**, 322 (1954).

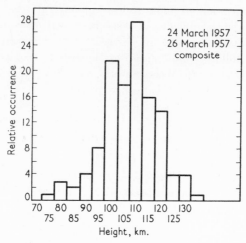

FIG. 7. Frequency of occurrence of echoes at 398 Mc/sec as a function of height for March 24 and 26, 1957, College, Alaska. From R. L. Leadabrand, L. Dolphin, and A. M. Peterson, I. R. E. Transactions on Antennas and Propagation, *AP—7*, 127 (1959).

magnetic north. A minimum height was obtained in the direction of magnetic north, and the height increased with angle from magnetic north as shown in Fig. 8.

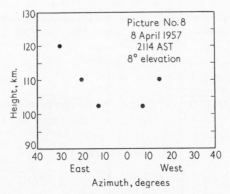

FIG. 8. Predominant height of reflection as a function of azimuth measured from magnetic north for auroral arcs to the north of College, Alaska, measured at 398 Mc/sec. Distance of arc to the north is 580 km. From R. L. Leadabrand, L. Dolphin, and A. M. Peterson, I. R. E. Transactions on Antennas and Propagation, *AP—7*, 127 (1959).

8.6 Diurnal, Seasonal, and Sunspot Cycle Variations of Auroral Echoes

Auroral echoes are more common at sunspot maximum than at sunspot minimum. They are more common at the equinoxes than at the solstices.

The diurnal variation of radar echoes of auroral type is particularly interesting in view of the difficulty of observing visual aurora during daylight. The diurnal variation observed by Currie *et al.*[15] at Saskatoon, Canada, is shown in Fig. 9. Bullough and Kaiser[23] at Manchester, England, and Fricker *et al.*,[18] at South Dartmouth, Massachusetts, have found much the same kind of diurnal variation. It appears that echoes of auroral type are predominantly a nighttime phenomenon. Under conditions of auroral disturbance, however, it is quite common for echoes to occur before sunset. Quite reliable warning of the occurrence of visible aurora on a particular evening can, indeed, be obtained from radio observations made during the preceding afternoon.

8.7 Motion Associated with Auroral Echoes

Bullough and Kaiser[23] found that, when the locations of auroral echoes moved, it was generally along a line of constant magnetic latitude in either the westerly or easterly direction. To observe these velocities over a period of time they pointed a 72-Mc/sec radar on an azimuth 50 degrees west of magnetic north, and observed the rates of change of the ranges of echoes. In

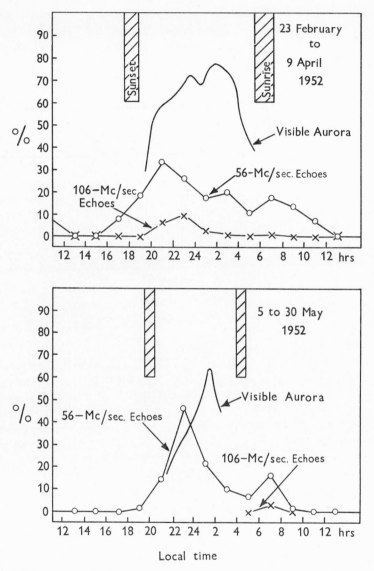

Fig. 9. Diurnal variations of 106-Mc/sec echoes, 56-Mc/sec echoes, and visible aurora at Saskatoon, Canada. From B. W. Currie, T. A. Forsyth, and F. E. Vawter, *J. Geophys. Res.* **58**, 179 (1953).

this way they obtained, over a period of time, the radial velocities shown in Fig. 10. Motion was generally to the west during the early part of the night and to the east during the later part of the night. The change in direction occurred between 1900 and 0400 hours local time, the average time of reversal being around 2200 hours local time. Toward the beginning and end of the night velocities were generally of the order of 700 m sec^{-1}, but individual velocities in excess of 1000 m sec^{-1} were observed.

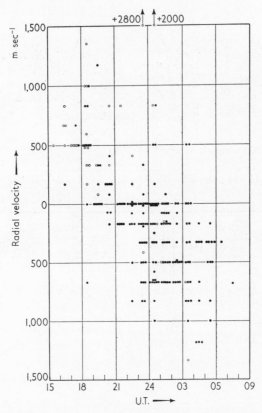

FIG. 10. Radial velocities measured from the rate of change of individual echo features seen with an antenna pointing 50 degrees west of magnetic north at Manchester, England, 1949–53. Open circles refer to diffuse echoes, and solid circles to discrete echoes. From K. Bullough and T. R. Kaiser, *J. Atmos. Terr. Phys.* **5,** 189 (1954); **6,** 198 (1955).

Another method of studying motions associated with auroral echoes is to measure their Doppler shift and Doppler spread. Bowles[20] and Nichols[21] used low-power continuous-wave transmitters to make measurements of this kind. By means of a spectrum analyzer the spectrum of both the transmitted wave and the received echo may be presented as shown in Fig. 11. The Doppler shift and the Doppler spread are usually of the same order of magnitude and are proportional to the transmitted frequency. Nichols,

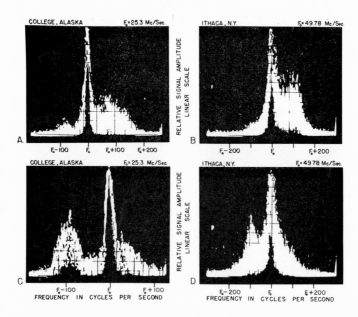

FIG. 11. Radiofrequency spectra of transmitted frequency, F_0, and auroral echoes, showing Doppler shift and Doppler spread. From K. L. Bowles, *J. Geophys. Res.* **59**, 553 (1954); Research Report EE248, Cornell University, Ithaca, New York, 1955.

[*To face page* 364

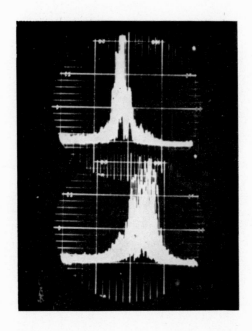

FIG. 12. Doppler shift in opposite directions in the spectra of auroral echoes received on antennas 30 degrees west of magnetic north and 30 degrees east of magnetic north at College, Alaska, 41 Mc/sec. The central vertical line represents the transmitted frequency, and the side of a large square corresponds to a frequency shift of 50 sec⁻¹. From B. Nichols, *J. Atmos. Terr. Phys.* **11**, 292 (1957); Scientific Report No. 1, Contract AF19 (604)–1857, Geophysical Institute of Alaska, 1957.

operating at College, Alaska, on frequencies of 41 and 106 Mc/sec used a pair of antennas, one directed 30 degrees west of magnetic north and the other directed 30 degrees east of magnetic north. With this arrangement he was able to obtain Doppler shifts in opposite directions on the two antennas, as shown in Fig. 12. In this diagram the central vertical line corresponds to the transmitted frequency, and the side of a large square corresponds to a frequency shift of 50 sec^{-1}. This he interpreted as indicating motion along a magnetically east-west line. The velocities observed in this way over a period of time are shown in Fig. 13. Motion was predominantly to the east in the

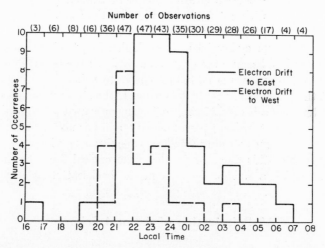

FIG. 13. Nocturnal variations of drift motions to east and west measured by the Doppler shift technique. From B. Nichols, *J. Atmos. Terr. Phys.* **11**, 292 (1957); Scientific Report No. 1, Contract AF19 (604)–1857, Geophysical Institute of Alaska 1957.

early part of the night and predominantly to the west in the late part of the night. Velocities were of the order of 700 m sec^{-1}, with individual values in excess of 1000 m sec^{-1}.

Bowles[20] made use of a keyed continuous-wave, or pulse Doppler, radar so that simultaneous observations could be made of Doppler shift and range. In this way he was able to compare the velocity deduced from the time-rate-of-change of range with the velocity deduced from the Doppler shift. He found that, although the two velocities were broadly of the same order of magnitude, significant differences existed in the numerical values. He even quotes cases in which the signs of the two velocities were different.

The drift speeds associated with auroral echoes are high compared with wind speeds deduced from the movement of meteoric trails. Such trails seen by auroral radars during auroral displays[20, 23] give normal wind speeds of the order of 50 m sec^{-1}.

8.8 Frequency Dependence of Auroral Echoes

No adequate measurements have been made of the frequency dependence of auroral echoes, although the matter has been discussed by Harang and Landmark,[17] Forsyth and Vogan,[24] and Leadabrand *et al.*[19] Measurements of the variation in the strength of auroral echoes with radio frequency require absolute measurements by a series of radar equipments operated at the same location and looking at the same auroral echo at the same time. Even then there is doubt as to whether the target is filling the volume illuminated by the various radars to the same extent. In principle this difficulty could be avoided by using radars on different frequencies having the same beam angles and the same pulse lengths. In practice, however, this is not feasible over the whole range of frequency involved. At the higher frequencies a narrow-beam antenna is required because the echoes are weak; at the lower frequencies a narrow-beam antenna would be too expensive to build. All that can safely be said at the present time is the following. If the strength of echoes is expressed in terms of a backscattering coefficient measured per unit volume of atmosphere, per unit incident power density, and per unit solid angle, then the coefficient becomes steadily smaller as the frequency increases from 30 to 400 Mc/sec. In this range of frequency no critical frequency has been reported at which a sudden decrease in the backscattering coefficient is noticed.

8.9 Polarization of Auroral Echoes

A number of observers have examined the polarization of auroral echoes and in all cases have found it to be closely identical with the transmitted polarization. Some minor exceptions at 34 Mc/sec are mentioned by Harang and Landmark.[17]

8.10 The Importance of Approximate Perpendicularity between the Earth's Magnetic Field and the Radius from the Radar to the Aurora

Before the observations concerning the restriction in azimuth and range of auroral echoes described in §§ 8.3 and 8.4 had been made, the possible existence of such a restriction had been predicted by Chapman.[25] Bearing in mind the ray structure along the earth's magnetic field frequently seen in visible aurora, he suggested that auroral ionization might be aligned along the earth's magnetic field. This should lead to a situation in which echoes are strongest when the aurora is viewed perpendicular to the lines of the earth's magnetic field. He worked out the geometry of this idea for various locations of the radar, and his calculations have been extended by Cain[26], Booker *et al.*[16] and Fricker *et al.*[18] It followed from Chapman's theory that auroral radar echoes should be most easily obtained by radars located in regions where the magnetic dip is of the order of 70 to 75 degrees, because a perpendicular is then possible from the radar onto the lines of the earth's magnetic field with the height of its foot near 100 km. For a magnetic dip as high as 80 degrees auroral echoes would be impossible on Chapman's theory because perpendiculars from the radar onto the lines of force of the earth's magnetic field would have their feet below the ionosphere.

The observations described in §§8.3 and 8.4 show that Chapman's theory requires modification and yet contains an important element of truth. These observations may be summarized by saying that the vast majority of auroral echoes come from a point where the radius from the radar makes with the direction of the earth's magnetic field an angle within a few degrees of the perpendicular. To appreciate this it is necessary to be able to make calculations of the off-perpendicular angle associated with an auroral target at any relevant point in the ionosphere. A complete set of such calculations appropriate to a series of different heights and to observations from College, Alaska (magnetic dip 77 degrees) have been made by Leadabrand et al.[19] Some of their results are shown in Fig. 14; Fig. 14a refers to targets at a height of 80 km. For a target at this height, magnetically due north of College, at a range of 570 km, the radial from College makes with the direction of the earth's magnetic field an angle that is off-perpendicular by about 0.1 degree. The contours shown in Fig. 14a are the loci of points where the off-perpendicular angle for targets at a height of 80 km have the values 1 degree, 2 degrees, 3 degrees, 4 degrees, and 5 degrees. Figure 14b shows similar results for a target height of 100 km. For targets at 150 km, the off-perpendicular angle cannot be less than 4.8 degrees, and this occurs for a target magnetically due north of College at a range of 930 km. Superimposed upon the observations of auroral echoes shown in Fig. 4 are the off-perpendicular angle contours for a height of 100 kilometers taken from Fig. 14b. It is clear that the region from which auroral echoes are obtained is the region for which the off-perpendicular angle is within a few degrees of zero.

It would be interesting to know by how many degrees the off-perpendicular angle must be increased from zero in order to reduce the strength of the echo by 3 decibels, and to know how this angle varies with frequency. It is difficult to derive this information from the data so far available because of the transient nature of individual auroral echoes and because of large differences in the antenna gains and pulse lengths of the radars. Examination of published results suggests, however, that permissible off-perpendicular angles are somewhat greater at low frequencies than at high frequencies. This is particularly noticeable if the Saskatoon observations at 56 Mc/sec shown in Fig. 3a are compared with the simultaneous observations at 106 Mc/sec shown in Fig. 3b.

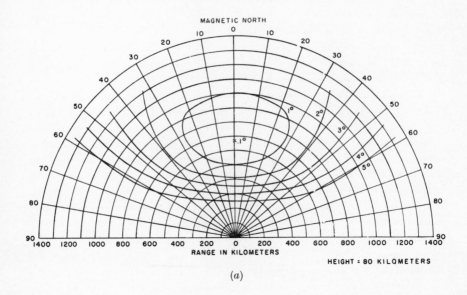

(a)

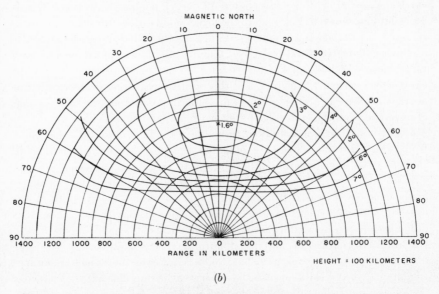

(b)

FIG. 14. Contours of constant off-perpendicular angle for assumed constant reflection heights at College, Alaska (magnetic dip 77 degrees). Reflection height is (a) 80 km, (b) 100 km. From R. L. Leadabrand, L. Dolphin, and A. M. Peterson, I. R. E. Transactions on Antennas and Propagation, *AP—7*, 127 (1959).

8.11 Theories of Auroral Radar Echoes

It has been suggested by Booker[27] that the modification of Chapman's theory required to explain the observations described in §§8.3 and 8.4 involves consideration of columns of ionization fairly restricted in length and aligned along the earth's magnetic field. Columns of length S would give satisfactory echoing properties at wavelength λ over angles up to $\lambda/(2S)$ from the perpendicular to the column. This would permit some deviation from the normality condition to exist and would make it possible for these deviations to be greater at longer wavelengths. Booker therefore supposed that the aspect sensitivity of auroral echoes is to be explained in terms of columns of ionization, parallel to the earth's magnetic field, but restricted in length. Even without detailed calculations one can see that, in order to explain the observations, this length must be a few wavelengths at a frequency of the order of 30 Mc/sec. Column lengths of the order of a few tens of meters are therefore indicated, with column diameters small in comparison.

The model of ionization density in an aurora considered by Booker is one in which the electron concentration is underdense in the sense that the plasma frequency is less than the radio wave frequency in the VHF and UHF bands. In this ionization he supposed that there are irregularities that are nonisotropic, with an axis of symmetry parallel to the earth's magnetic field. The correlation distance L along the earth's magnetic field is supposed to be large compared to the correlation distance T transverse to the earth's magnetic field. The problem is to ascertain what values of L and T are required to explain the facts concerning auroral echoes.

The upshot of the calculations[27] is that the strength and aspect sensitivity of auroral echoes can be explained if: (1) the mean electron density corresponds to a plasma frequency of around 10 Mc/sec; (2) there are irregularities in electron density axially symmetrical about the earth's magnetic field and having a gaussian autocorrelation function; (3) the correlation distance along the earth's magnetic field is around 10 meters; (4) the correlation distance transverse to the earth's magnetic field is around 10^{-1} meter or less; and (5) the mean square fractional deviation of electron density is of the order of 10^{-3}.

If auroral echoes are due to irregularities in auroral ionization with a scale along the earth's magnetic field of the order of 10 meters and a scale transverse to the earth's magnetic field of the order of 10^{-1} meter or less, it is necessary to explain the origin of such irregularities. Booker[28] has suggested that they are due to turbulence. A size spectrum of irregularities is associated with turbulence, and it is the smallest irregularities that would be principally involved in a backscattering phenomenon. Booker has made tentative estimates of the size and shape of small-scale irregularities in electron density due to turbulence at E-region levels. The results are plotted in Fig. 15. The curve marked L shows how the scale, along the earth's magnetic field, of irregularities in electron density associated with the small eddies varies with height. The curve marked T shows how the scale of these irregularities perpendicular to the earth's magnetic field varies with height. At a height of 110 km the values of L and T shown in Fig. 15 are of the same order of magnitude as those deduced in the preceding section from study of auroral backscattering. The curve marked l in Fig. 15 shows how the mean

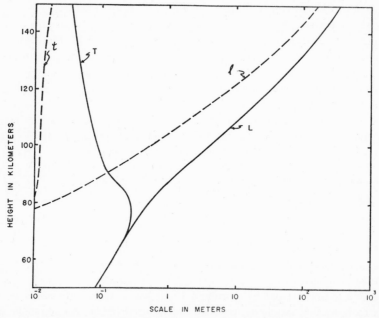

Fig. 15. Variation with height of scales L and T of irregularities of electron density along and across the earth's magnetic field according to Booker [*J. Geophys. Res.* **61**, 673 (1956)]. Curves l and t indicate the minimum possible values of L and T based on the electronic mean free path and gyroradius, respectively.

free path of electrons varies with height in the atmosphere. This is the minimum scale along the earth's magnetic field that could be associated with turbulence. The curve marked t shows how the minimum possible scale perpendicular to the earth's magnetic field varies with height; this is influenced by the gyroradius of electrons in the presence of the earth's magnetic field.

In connection with the height variations of L and T shown in Fig. 15 it is appropriate to consider some height observations made by Leadabrand et al.[19] at 398 Mc/sec. For two particular widespread echoes they found that

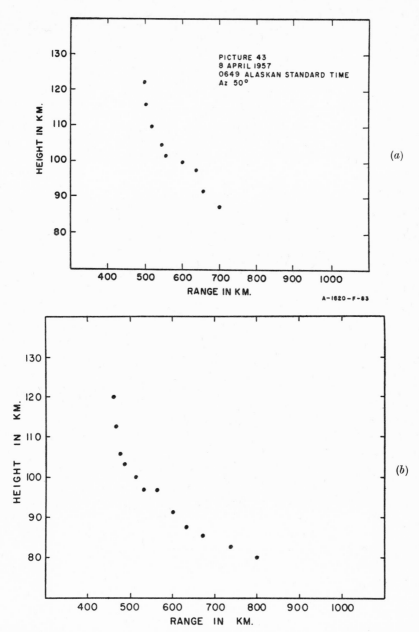

FIG. 16. Height of lower edge of echo as a function of range on 398 Mc/sec at College, Alaska, April 8, 1957, bearing approximately 20 degrees east of magnetic north: (a) 0649, (b) 0711, Alaska standard time. From R. L. Leadabrand, L. Dolphin, and A. M. Peterson, I. R. E. Transactions on Antennas and Propagation, *AP—7*, 127 (1959).

the height of the lower edge varied with range in the manner illustrated in Figs. 16a and 16b. If these data are replotted to indicate variation of off-perpendicular angle with height, we obtain the circles shown in Fig. 17. It is also possible to use results such as those of Fig. 8 which show how the maximum response varies with the height along an auroral arc, the minimum height occurring where the arc is magnetically due north. If these observations are replotted to show off-perpendicular angle as a function of height, we obtain the dots plotted in Fig. 17. All these observations may therefore

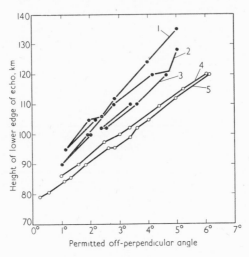

FIG. 17. Permitted off-perpendicular angle as a function of height, derived from data presented in Fig. 16 (circles) and presented in part Fig. 8 (dots).

be explained in terms of a variation of permitted off-perpendicular angle as a function of height between 80 and 130 km. It seems safe to deduce that the observations of Leadabrand *et al.* indicate that the scattering properties of auroral ionization vary with height in the region between 80 and 130 km. The most obvious interpretation of the data shown in Fig. 17 is that the scale of irregularities along the earth's magnetic field decreases with height. This interpretation would imply that, at a height of 130 km, the scale of irregularities of electron density along the earth's magnetic field becomes comparable with the mean free path of the electrons. The variation with height in the scattering properties of auroral ionization may, however, well be of a more complicated character, involving a variation with height in the intensity of the irregularities. Whether the height variations of L and T shown in Fig. 15 are feasible would require some reworking of the theory, and it might be appropriate to replace the gaussian autocorrelation function with an autocorrelation function more representative of turbulence.

Workers at Manchester, England, and Saskatoon, Canada, have regarded their observations of auroral radar echoes in the VHF band as implying overdense ionization in the aurora at the frequency of observation. Overdense ionization at frequencies of 56 and 106 Mc/sec at Saskatoon and of 72 Mc/sec at Manchester requires a state of affairs quite different from that envisaged in the theory of Booker,[27] where it was assumed that the ionization density involved in auroral ionization corresponds to a plasma frequency of less than 30 Mc/sec. The arguments against plasma frequencies of the order of 100 Mc/sec or more in the aurora are:

1. Sporadic E echoes seen on ionospheric recorders under auroral conditions do not usually involve cut-off frequencies much in excess of 10 Mc/sec.

2. The absorption experienced in auroral latitudes does not require plasma frequencies much in excess of 10 Mc/sec.

3. Observations of auroral radar echoes between 30 and 800 Mc/sec have shown no indication of the presence of a critical frequency in this range.

4. The auroral plasma frequencies that can be conveniently explained in terms of incoming protons and electrons are of the order of 10 Mc/sec.

It seems undesirable, therefore, to assume, unless it is strictly necessary, that plasma frequencies in auroral ionization are radically in excess of 10 Mc/sec. Overdense ionization at a frequency of 100 Mc/sec would require auroral ionization densities about 100 times what seems reasonable. At 800 Mc/sec overdense ionization would require auroral ionization densities between 1000 and 10,000 times what seems reasonable. For a contrary point of view, however, the reader is referred to Forsyth and Vogan.[24]

Currie *et al.*[15] at one time sought to explain the aspect sensitivity of auroral echoes in terms of an absorbing layer on the under side of auroral ionization. Although such an absorbing blanket could in principle explain the absence of echoes at vertical incidence, it cannot explain the now well-established absence of echoes to the south in the presence of visible aurora to the south. Furthermore the ionization densities required are high.

Harang and Landmark[17] sought to explain the echoes that they received during auroras as backscattering from rough ground mirrored in auroral sporadic E ionization. This explanation was disproved by McNamara and Currie[29] and has been abandoned by the original authors at frequencies above 30 Mc/sec, so far as the majority of their echoes are concerned. Echoes of the type contemplated by Harang and Landmark do, however, occur in the HF band.

8.12 The Cause of Movement in the Location of Auroral Echoes

The easterly or westerly movement of auroral targets with speeds of the order of 500 to 1000 m sec^{-1} cannot possibly be due to wind. These speeds are in excess of the velocity of sound and are about a power of 10 greater than reasonable wind speeds or than wind speeds simultaneously observed from the movement of meteor trails. Auroral ionization could, however, move under the influence of an electric field. In combination with the earth's magnetic field, auroral ionization would move eastward under the influence of an electric field directed toward the equator, and westward under the influence of one directed toward the pole. The velocity would be of the order of E/B, where E is the horizontal electric field and B is the vertical component of the earth's magnetic field. To explain in this way a drift velocity of the order of 600 m sec^{-1} would require an electric field of the order of 3×10^{-2} volts per meter or 3 kv per degree of magnetic latitude. The electric potential in the E region of the ionosphere would have to decrease toward the pole in the early part of the night and toward the equator in the later part of the night.

It would not be necessary for the apparent position of a block of auroral ionization to move at the same speed as the irregularities of ionization density within it, because the former could be affected by changes in the position of the exciting mechanism. In these circumstances the velocity given by the rate of change of radar range could differ from the velocity given by a Doppler measurement. There is nothing inexplicable, therefore, in the observations of Bowles[20] that simultaneous measurements of these velocities are not identical.

Deductions concerning the electric field existing in the E region of the ionosphere can be made not only by measuring electronic drifts but also by measuring the variations in the earth's magnetic field at the ground. A close relation should exist therefore between the drift motion observed in auroral ionization and the associated variations in the earth's magnetic field. A start has been made on studies of this type by Meek.[4]

References

1. E. V. Appleton, R. Naismith, and L. J. Ingram, *Phil. Trans. Roy. Soc.* A**236**, 191 (1937).
2. L. Harang, "The Aurorae," Chapter 8, Wiley, New York, 1951.
3. G. Leighauser and B. Beckmann, *Z. Tech. Physik.* **18**, 290 (1937); W. Dieminger and H. Plendl, *Hochfrequenztech.* **51**, 117 (1938); R. Eyfrig, G. Goubau, Th. Netzer, and J. Zenneck, *ibid.* **51**, 149 (1938); B. Beckmann, W. Menzel, and F. Vilbig, *Telegraphen-Fernsprch. u. Funk-Tech.* **27**, 245 (1938); **28**, 130, 425 (1939).
4. J. H. Meek, *J. Geophys. Res.* **54**, 330 (1949); **58**, 445 (1953).
5. J. H. Meek, *J. Geophys. Res.* **57**, 177 (1952).
6. J. P. Heppner, E. C. Byerne, and A. E. Belon, *J. Geophys. Res.* **57**, 121 (1952).
7. V. Agy, *J. Geophys. Res.* **59**, 267 (1954); **59**, 499 (1954).
8. R. W. Knecht, *J. Geophys. Res.* **61**, 51 (1956).
9. A. M. Peterson and R. L. Leadabrand, *J. Geophys. Res.* **59**, 306 (1954); S. Stein, *ibid.* **63**, 391 (1958).

10. R. K. Moore, *J. Geophys. Res.* **56,** 97 (1951).
11. L. Harang and W. Stoffregen, *Hochfrequenztech.* **55,** 105 (1940).
12. A. Aspinall and G. S. Hawkins, *J. Brit. Astron. Assoc.* **60,** 130 (1950).
13. D. W. R. McKinley and P. M. Millman, *Canad. J. Phys.* **31,** 171 (1953).
14. G. Hellgren and J. Meos, *Tellus* **4,** 249 (1952).
15. B. W. Currie, T. A. Forsyth, and F. E. Vawter, *J. Geophys. Res.* **58,** 179 (1953).
16. H. G. Booker, C. W. Gartlein, and B. Nichols, *J. Geophys. Res.* **60,** 1 (1955).
17. L. Harang and V. Landmark, *J. Atmos. Terr. Phys.* **4,** 322 (1954).
18. S. J. Fricker, R. P. Ingalls, M. L. Stone, and S. T. Wang, *J. Geophys. Res.* **62,** 527 (1957).
19. R. L. Leadabrand, L. Dolphin, and A. M. Peterson, I. R. E. Transactions on Antennas and Propagation, *AP—7,* 127 (1959).
    (602)–1462, Stanford Research Institute, 1957.
20. K. L. Bowles, *J. Geophys. Res.* **59,** 553 (1954); Research Report EE248, Cornell University, Ithaca, New York, 1955.
21. B. Nichols, *J. Atmos. Terr. Phys.* **11,** 292 (1957); Scientific Report No. 1, Contract AF19 (604)–1859, Geophysical Institute of Alaska, 1957.
22. R. B. Dyce, *J. Geophys. Res.* **60,** 317 (1955); *QST* p. 11 (January, 1955).
23. K. Bullough and T. R. Kaiser, *J. Atmos. Terr. Phys.* **5,** 189 (1954); **6,** 198 (1955).
24. T. A. Forsyth and E. L. Vogan, *J. Atmos. Terr. Phys.* **10,** 215 (1957).
25. S. Chapman, *J. Atmos. Terr. Phys.* **3,** 1 (1952).
26. J. C. Cain, *J. Geophys. Res.* **58,** 377 (1953).
27. H. G. Booker, *J. Atmos. Terr. Phys.* **8,** 204 (1956).
28. H. G. Booker, *J. Geophys. Res.* **61,** 673 (1956).
29. A. G. McNamara and B. W Currie, *J. Geophys. Res.* **59,** 279 (1954).

Chapter 9

The Ionosphere

J. A. Ratcliffe and K. Weekes

9.1 Introduction 378
    9.1.1 Purpose of the Chapter 378
    9.1.2 Nomenclature 379
    9.1.3 Bibliography 379
    9.1.4 The Plan of the Chapter 380
9.2 Theory of the Origin and Shape of Layers of Electrons 380
    9.2.1 The Production of Electrons 380
    9.2.2 The Loss of Electrons 383
    9.2.3 Layers in Equilibrium 387
    9.2.4 Time-Varying Layers 388
    9.2.5 Vertical Movements of Electrons 389
9.3 The Ionosphere as a Dynamo and a Motor 392
    9.3.1 The Atmospheric Dynamo 392
    9.3.2 The Tensor Conductivities 393
    9.3.3 The Atmospheric Motor 397
9.4 Theory of Wave Propagation through the Ionosphere 397
    9.4.1 The Penetration Frequency 397
    9.4.2 The $h'(f)$ Curves or Ionograms, and $N(h)$ Curves 398
    9.4.3 More Detailed Wave Theory 400
    9.4.4 The "Whistler Mode" of Propagation 401
    9.4.5 Absorption 402
9.5 The Undisturbed D Region 403
    9.5.1 Introduction 403
    9.5.2 Experimental Methods for Investigating the D Region 404
    9.5.3 Anomalous Winter Absorption 408
    9.5.4 The D Region and Solar Activity 408
    9.5.5 The Electron Content of the D Region 409
    9.5.6 Recombination in the D Region 412
    9.5.7 Negative Ions in the D Region 413
9.6 The Undisturbed E Layer 414
    9.6.1 Approximate Behavior 414
    9.6.2 Complications in the Penetration of the E Layer 414
    9.6.3 Tabulated Critical Frequencies 416
    9.6.4 The Shape and Height of the E Layer 416
    9.6.5 Intensity of the Ionizing Radiation 417
    9.6.6 Detailed Diurnal Variations and Vertical Movements 417
    9.6.7 The E Layer at Night 418
    9.6.8 Sporadic E (Es Ionization) 419
9.7 The Undisturbed $F1$ Layer (or Ledge) 425
    9.7.1 The Appearance of the $F1$ Ledge 425
    9.7.2 Approximate Behavior of the Critical Frequency, $fF1$ 425
    9.7.3 Departures from Simple Behavior 426

9.8 The Undisturbed $F2$ Layer 427
    9.8.1 Anomalous Critical Frequency, $fF2$................................. 427
    9.8.2 Electron Profiles [$N(h)$ Curves]..................................... 432
    9.8.3 Solar Cycle Variations.. 433
    9.8.4 Effects of Eclipses.. 434
    9.8.5 Above the Peak of the $F2$ Layer.................................. 434
    9.8.6 Outline Theory of the F Layer................................... 435
    9.8.7 Evidence for Vertical Movements................................. 437
    9.8.8 Theories of Movements... 439
9.9 The Collision Frequency of Electrons..................................... 441
    9.9.1 Measurements of Effective Collision Frequency...................... 442
    9.9.2 Interpretation of the Measured Values............................. 443
    9.9.3 Comparison of Theory and Experiment............................ 444
9.10 Horizontal Irregularities and Movements................................. 445
    9.10.1 Experimental Evidence... 445
    9.10.2 Sizes of Irregularities 446
    9.10.3 Irregular Movements.. 446
    9.10.4 Regular Horizontal Movements or Drifts.......................... 447
    9.10.5 Spread-F Echoes.. 450
9.11 Disturbances and Storms in the Ionosphere.............................. 450
    9.11.1 Two Types of Disturbance...................................... 450
    9.11.2 Sudden Ionosphere Disturbances (S.I.D.)......................... 451
    9.11.3 Ionosphere Storms.. 452
    9.11.4 Theories of Ionosphere Storms.................................. 455
    9.11.5 The Disturbance of February 23, 1956........................... 456
References.. 456

9.1 Introduction

9.1.1 *Purpose of the Chapter*

The purpose of this chapter is to give an account of what is known about the ionosphere as a result of radio-wave sounding conducted from the ground. Investigations of this kind have covered a very wide range, and it would be neither possible nor proper to discuss them all in detail here. We shall, instead, try to give a critical account of present-day facts and the theories based on them. The conclusions will be our own and would not necessarily be agreed by all workers. In particular it will be noticed that, in discussing some aspects of the work, we feel a little less certain about the conclusions than some authors might. It seems to us proper, at this stage, to be cautious about accepting conclusions until they have been shown to be compatible with all the known facts.

In addition to its use in general investigations of the ionosphere, radio-wave sounding has been intensively used for the investigations of the aurora and of ionized meteor trails. The results of these two more specialized investigations are fully described in Chapters 8 and 11; they will be referred to here only when necessary.

The results obtained recently with rockets and artificial satellites are complementary to those derived from radio-wave soundings. They are discussed fully in Chapters 3 and 4.

9.1.2 Nomenclature

Students of the upper atmosphere have divided it into "zones," "spheres," or "regions" for the purpose of nomenclature. Some of these have been mentioned in Chapters 1 and 2, where the word "ionosphere" has been introduced. For the purpose of the present chapter we shall follow the recommendations of a committee of the Institute of Radio Engineers[244] and define the ionosphere to be "the part of the earth's upper atmosphere where ions and electrons are present in quantities sufficient to affect the propagation of radio waves (at present thought to be above 50 km)." It usually extends from about 50 km up to great heights but may sometimes extend lower down. Again according to the recommendations of the Committee the ionosphere is divided into the regions called D, E, and F, defined so that the part of the ionosphere below 90 km is called the D region, that between 90 and 160 km the E region, and that above 160 km the F region. It was once thought that there were distinct layers of electrons in the different regions, and these were named * the D, E, and F layers according to the level at which their peaks occurred. It has since been realized, largely as the result of measurements made with rockets,[134, 234] that these layers are not necessarily characterized by a maximum, but are sometimes marked only by a "ledge," where the gradient is small. It will prove convenient, nevertheless, to write of an E layer, although its "peak" may scarcely show on a curve in which electron density is plotted against height. If there is need to write of more than one layer or ledge inside a single region, they will be numbered 1, 2, ..., from below, so that we shall write, for example, of the F1 ledge below the F2 layer. To avoid confusion we shall adhere strictly to this nomenclature for the D region, because, as we shall show, there is no clear evidence for the existence of a D layer having a peak of electron density in the D region.

9.1.3 Bibliography

The literature of the ionosphere consists of some thousands of papers, and it would clearly be impossible to list them all. We have chosen to refer to

* Appleton[298] has stated that in his early work he was accustomed to write E for the electric field of the wave reflected from the first layer he recognized. Later, when he recognized a second layer, at a greater height, he wrote F for the field of the wave reflected from it. Still later he conjectured that there might be a third layer, lower than either of them, so he decided to name the first two layers E and F, and the possible lower one D, thereby leaving earlier letters of the alphabet for other possible undiscovered layers lower still.

those which we consider to be the first, or the leading papers on a topic, and to later papers, preferably of a review nature, which contain comprehensive lists of references. As far as possible we have avoided the mention of names in the text. References 7, 8, 187, 219, and 262 are of a general nature and deal with several of the topics discussed in this chapter.

9.1.4 *The Plan of the Chapter*

In §§ 9.2, 9.3, and 9.4 we shall summarize the results of theories concerning the production and movements of layers of electrons, the flow of currents in them, and the passage of radio waves through them. In the succeeding sections we shall discuss what is known about the electron distribution in the D, E, and F regions separately. In § 9.9 we summarize our knowledge of collision frequencies, and in § 9.10 we explain that the ionosphere has an irregular horizontal structure and discuss the results of investigating the movements of the irregularities. In § 9.11 we discuss the different kinds of ionosphere disturbance and their effects on the different regions. These are related to the disturbances of the geomagnetic field, and the phenomena of the aurora, discussed more fully in Chapters 10 and 8.

We shall not discuss details of experimental methods or of theories; these can be found in the references cited. Occasional reference will be made to what is known of the physics of the sun, and of solar ionizing radiations, but the details of these topics are dealt with in Chapter 4.

9.2 Theory of the Origin and Shape of Layers of Electrons

9.2.1 *The Production of Electrons*

As an ionizing radiation penetrates from outside deeper and deeper into the atmosphere, it encounters a greater and greater density of gas and hence produces more and more electrons in each unit volume. The radiation is, however, absorbed in the process, and below a certain height the rate at which its intensity decreases as it travels downward is greater than the rate at which the gas density increases, so that the rate of production of electrons decreases as we go lower. There is thus a level at which the rate of production is greatest, and it is determined jointly by the absorbability of the radiation and by the gradient of the gas density.

The general problem of calculating the rate of production at each level, for an atmosphere containing many gases, and a solar spectrum spread over a wide range of wavelengths, is quite complicated. It is, however, useful to study the simplified problem which arises when there is one gas with an absorption coefficient independent of wavelength. In discussing this problem Chapman[74] supposed that the atmosphere consisted of a single gas of molecular weight M at a uniform temperature, T, in equilibrium under the action of gravity over a flat earth, so that the density, ρ, was given, as a function of the height, h, above some arbitrary zero, by $\rho = \rho_0 \exp(-h/H)$, where $H = RT/Mg$ is the scale height. He then supposed that an ionizing radiation in which there was a power flux I_∞ per unit area was incident from above at an angle χ and showed that, in each unit volume, electrons would be produced at a rate, q, which had a peak * at a height, h_m, given by

$$\exp(h_m/H) = \rho_0 A H \sec \chi \tag{9.1}$$

where A is the mass absorption coefficient of the radiation. If, now, heights are measured from h_m as a zero and are expressed in terms of H as a unit,

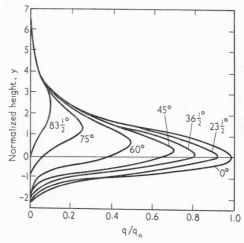

Fig. 1. The normalized rate of production of electrons (q/q_0) plotted against the normalized height, y [see equation (9.4)] for different values of the solar zenith angle, χ.

through a quantity $z = (h - h_m)/H$, and if B electrons are produced when unit energy is absorbed, then q is given at all heights by the expression

$$q = q_m \exp[1 - z - \exp(-z)] \tag{9.2}$$

where

$$q_m = \frac{B I_\infty \cos \chi}{H \exp(1)}. \tag{9.3}$$

Equation (9.2) shows that the production function, $q(z)$, expressed in the normalized form, has the same shape for all radiations, gases, and angles of incidence. It is represented in Fig. 1 by the curve labeled $\chi = 0$.

---

* It is convenient to use the word "peak" to indicate the maximum of any quantity when considered as a function of height, so that $dN/dh = 0$ at the peak.

It is sometimes convenient to express heights in terms of their (normalized) distance above $h_m(0)$, the height of the peak when $\chi = 0$. For this purpose we write

$$\exp[h_m(0)/H] = A\rho_0 H$$

and
$$y = [h - h_m(0)]/H \tag{9.4}$$

and we find

$$q(y) = q_0 \exp[1 - y - \sec \chi \exp(-y)] \tag{9.5}$$

where

$$q_0 = BI_\infty/H \exp(1) \tag{9.6}$$

is the peak value of q when $\chi = 0$, so that, from (9.3)

$$q_m = q_0 \cos \chi. \tag{9.7}$$

Curves to show $q(y)/q_0$ for different values of χ are plotted in Fig. 1. If any one of these curves is plotted in terms of the normalized height, z, according to (9.2) it will take the form shown for $\chi = 0$.

It is important to notice, from (9.1) and (9.3), that the height, h_m, of the peak of production is determined by the absorption coefficient (A), the scale height (H), the density (ρ_0) of the gas at the reference level, and the angle of incidence (χ), but not by the intensity, I_∞, of the incident radiation; whereas the magnitude, q_m, of the peak rate of production depends on the incident intensity (I_∞), the scale height (H), and χ.

Some modifications of the simple theory of Chapman are important. In one[74] the flat earth is replaced by a spherical one, with the result that the mass of gas between a height, h, and the sun is no longer $\rho H \sec \chi$ but is $\rho H \, \mathrm{Ch}(\chi, H)$, where $\mathrm{Ch}(\chi, H)$ is a function of χ and H which has been tabulated.[312] Correspondingly, $\sec \chi$ in (9.1) and (9.3) is replaced by $\mathrm{Ch}(\chi, H)$. For $\chi < 75°$, $\mathrm{Ch}(\chi, H) \risingdotseq \sec \chi$, and (9.1) and (9.3) are sufficiently exact, but for larger values of χ, such as occur near sunrise and sunset, it is necessary to use the more complicated forms.

The theory has also been extended[202] to deal with gases which are not at the same temperature at all heights. If the temperature is proportional to the height, so that

$$H = H_0 + \gamma h$$

it has been shown that (9.7) takes the modified form

$$q_m = q_0(\cos \chi)^{1+\gamma}. \tag{9.8}$$

In the simple theory of Chapman it is supposed that the only process by which the radiation is absorbed is the ionizing process itself. Circumstances may, however, arise in which a radiation capable of ionizing gas A is also absorbed by gas B, but without ionizing B. If the absorption in B is the more important, the rate of production of electrons from A will have a peak at a level which is determined by the absorption coefficient of B. [75, 237]

If the ionizing radiation is composite,[119] and the atmosphere consists of more than one ionizable gas, the resulting production function, $q(h)$, is the sum of the functions for the separate ionizing processes. It can be shown that even in this case the peak rate of production (q_m) is proportional to cos χ, as for a single gas.

If the ionizing radiation is in the X-ray region of wavelengths, the absorption coefficient, A, depends only on the types of atom present and not on their association into molecules. Ionization is accompanied by secondary electrons and photons which can themselves ionize, and the final $q(h)$ function giving the height distribution of electron production depends on the absorbability of these secondaries. If they are easily absorbed, the resulting $q(h)$ function is similar to that for the primary X-rays, so that it is Chapman-like; if, however, the secondaries can travel appreciable distances before producing ionization, the resulting $q(h)$ function will be considerably wider than the Chapman function.[131]

9.2.2 The Loss of Electrons [31, 32, 33, 34, 35, 39, 177]

Electrons can leave a given volume either by moving outside it, or by being removed by recombination or attachment. In this section we shall discuss only the latter processes.

Let the number densities of electrons, of positive ions, and of atoms to which attachment can take place be denoted by $n(e)$, $n(A^+)$, $n(a)$, respectively. Then the rate at which electrons are lost by recombining with positive ions is given by

$$dn(e)/dt = -\alpha n(e) . n(A^+) \tag{9.9}$$

where α is the recombination coefficient. If there are few negative ions compared with electrons, we can write $n(e) \rightleftharpoons n(A^+)$, so that

$$dn(e)/dt = -\alpha(n(e))^2. \tag{9.10}$$

We shall call this the equation of recombination.

Since the effect of free charges on the propagation of radio waves is inversely proportional to their mass (see § 9.4.1) an electron becomes relatively ineffective when it has attached itself to an atom to form a heavy ion. The rate at which electrons are rendered ineffective by attachment is given by

$$dn(e)/dt = -b.n(e). n(a). \tag{9.11}$$

In most cases we shall consider $n(a)$ to be so great that it does not change appreciably when some of the atoms are converted to ions, so that (9.11) may be written

$$dn(e)/dt = -\beta n(e) \tag{9.12}$$

where β is a constant called the attachment coefficient. Equation (9.12) will be called the equation of attachment.

The equations of recombination and attachment, (9.10) and (9.12), may result from a series of processes involving more complicated molecular phenomena. Only a few of the more important possibilities will be discussed here. In the process of recombination or attachment two bodies combine to produce one, and it would be impossible to conserve both momentum and mechanical energy unless another body shares in the reaction, or there is a possibility of energy being stored in one or other of the bodies. If, as in a gas at very low pressure, no third body is available, recombination can occur if a photon is emitted to carry away the necessary energy. The recombination is then said to be "radiative," and α has a magnitude about 10^{-12} cm^3 sec^{-1}. If the air is sufficiently dense, the third body can be a neutral atom or molecule, and α is then proportional to the concentration of these neutral molecules. At the pressures with which we are concerned in the ionosphere the recombination coefficient of electrons by this "three-body" process is less than 10^{-12} cm^3 sec^{-1}.

Electrons can attach themselves only to certain atoms for which the energy relations are suitable. In the atmosphere attachment is possible to O and O_2 but not to N or N_2. Once a negative ion has been formed, various processes can detach the electron again, and the final ratio of electrons to negative ions will depend on the balance between the rates of attachment and detachment. Detachment may be produced by collision with another particle which can provide the necessary energy, such as an excited atom, or by the action of photons. Photo-detachment cannot, of course, occur at night. The balance between attachment and detachment results in a finite ratio between the number of negative ions and the number of electrons, usually denoted by λ. In the attachment process there is a certain amount of energy (the electron affinity of the atom or molecule) to be removed from the system, either by radiation or as a result of a three-body collision. Hence above some moderate pressure (possibly of the order of 1 mm Hg) it might be expected that λ would become pressure-dependent.

When negative ions are present, they may recombine with positive ions with a recombination coefficient α_i. This process may be considered as one of charge transfer from one ion to the other, and, since there are two particles present after the transfer, there are no problems of conserving momentum and energy in the process. It is, however, still necessary to absorb an energy equal to the difference between the ionization energy of the positive ion and the electron affinity of the negative ion. The two-body recombination coefficient of positive and negative ions is probably about 10^{-8} cm^3 sec^{-1}, but the energy excess is more easily taken up by a third body, and at pressures less than about 300 mm Hg the three-body recombination coefficient of heavy ions is represented approximately by $6.65 \times 10^{-9} (273/T)^{7/2} p$ cm^3 sec^{-1}, when p is measured in millimeters of mercury, so that the three-body recombination process which is pressure-dependent is comparable with the two-body rate when the pressure is about 1 to 5 mm Hg.

If electrons are produced at a rate q and are lost by attachment to neutral atoms to form ions, and if these ions are subsequently lost by ionic recombination with coefficient α_i, it may be shown that the continuity equation becomes

$$dn(e)/dt = \{q/(1 + \lambda)\} - (\alpha_e + \lambda\alpha_i)[n(e)]^2$$
$$= q_{\text{eff}} - \alpha_{\text{eff}}[n(e)]^2. \tag{9.13}$$

In the lower ionosphere the value of λ may lie between 1 and 10, and the process becomes important; moreover, at the lowest levels λ and α_i may both become pressure-dependent, so that α_{eff} may increase rapidly as the height is reduced.

It is next necessary to consider one of the more complicated processes which is thought to be of particular importance in the ionosphere.[33, 39] It is represented by the series of reaction expressions

$$
\begin{array}{lll}
\text{Production} & A + h\nu \rightarrow A^+ + e & \text{(a)} \\
\text{Loss} & \left\{ \begin{array}{ll} A^+ + XY \rightarrow XY^+ + A & \text{(b)} \\ XY^+ + e \rightarrow X' + Y' & \text{(c)} \end{array} \right. &
\end{array} \tag{9.14}
$$

where (a) represents the photoionization of an atom, A,

(b) represents a charge exchange between the positive ion of A and a molecule, XY,

(c) represents the recombination of an electron with the charged XY$^+$ molecule by a process which results in dissociating it into the atoms X and Y, the primes indicating that these atoms may be left excited.

The rates for processes (b) and (c) are given, in terms of reaction constants K_b and K_c, by the expressions

for (b): $$dn(A^+)/dt = - K_b n(A^+)n(XY) \tag{9.15}$$

for (c): $$dn(e)/dt = - K_c n(XY^+)n(e). \tag{9.16}$$

Suppose now that the atmosphere is electrically neutral, so that

$$n(A^+) + n(XY^+) = n(e) \tag{9.17}$$

and that the ionization is in equilibrium. Then, if electrons and positive ions are produced by incident radiation at the rate q per unit volume,

and $$q = K_b n(A^+)n(XY) \tag{9.18}$$

$$q = K_c n(XY^+)n(e) \tag{9.19}$$

25

from which it may be deduced that

$$q = \frac{K_b K_c n(XY) n^2(e)}{K_b n(XY) + K_c n(e)}. \tag{9.20}$$

If $K_b n(XY) \gg K_c n(e)$, this reduces to

$$q = K_c n^2(e) \tag{9.21}$$

which corresponds to the "recombination equation" (9.10) with $\alpha = K_c$. Since two bodies are involved in the reaction 9.14(c), both before and after it takes place, the energy and momentum conditions are fairly easily satisfied and the value of $K_c = \alpha$ can be comparatively large. Values as great as 10^{-8} cm^3 sec^{-1}, required for the E region, are quite possible.

If, next, $K_b n(XY) \ll K_c n(e)$, (9.20) reduces to

$$q = K_b n(XY) n(e) \tag{9.22}$$

which corresponds to the "attachment equation," (9.12), with the attachment coefficient, β, given by

$$\beta = K_b n(XY). \tag{9.23}$$

If $n(XY)$ decreases upward, so will the attachment coefficient.

If $n(XY)$ is comparatively great at small heights and small at great heights, then low down it will be appropriate to use the recombination equation, and higher up the attachment equation with β a function of height as given by (9.23). It will be suggested in § 9.8.6 that in the ionosphere A represents atomic oxygen and XY molecular oxygen, and that the change from behavior represented by the recombination equation to one represented by the attachment equation occurs in the neighborhood of 200 km. Above this level the effective attachment coefficient decreases upward in proportion to the decrease of the molecular oxygen.

By combining experimental and theoretical results, Mitra[313] has suggested that the loss processes in the ionosphere at noon over middle latitudes can be represented in terms of an effective recombination coefficient given by

$$\alpha_{\text{eff}}(\text{cm}^3 \text{ sec}^{-1}) = \begin{cases} 5 \times 10^{-21} n(O_2) + 3 \times 10^{-20} n(O) & \text{(a)} \\ + \dfrac{2 \times 10^{-19} n(O_2)}{2 \times 10^{-11} n(O_2) + 10^{-8} n(e)} & \text{(b)} \\ + \qquad\qquad 10^{-12} & \text{(c)} \end{cases} \tag{9.23a}$$

In this expression the term (a) corresponds to processes involving attachment to O and O_2, governed by expressions like (9.13); the term (b) corresponds to processes of the type described by expressions (9.14) and governed by equation (9.20); the term (c) represents radiative recombination.

9.2.3 *Layers in Equilibrium*

If there are no movements, the electron density, N, at a fixed height is determined by the equation

$$dN/dt = q - L \qquad (9.24)$$

where q is the rate of production and L is the rate of loss by recombination and attachment. There are many circumstances when $dN/dt \ll q$ or L, so that

$$q \fallingdotseq L. \qquad (9.25)$$

The electrons are then said to be in quasi-equilibrium. The equation is exact at a turning point in the function $N(t)$, such as often occurs near midday and in the early morning.

If, as often happens, the electron density is in quasi-equilibrium throughout the layer, then we may write, at each level,

$$q = \alpha N^2$$

or

$$q = \beta N$$

so that, for a simple layer in which α (or β) is independent of height, we have, by inserting q from (9.2) and (9.6),

$$N = \{(q_0/\alpha)\cos\chi\}^{1/2}\exp\{\tfrac{1}{2}[1 - z - \exp(-z)]\} \qquad (9.26)$$

or

$$N = (q_0/\beta)\cos\chi\exp[1 - z - \exp(-z)]. \qquad (9.27)$$

In each case the functions $N(z)$ and $q(z)$ have their peaks at the same height. We shall call the electron distribution described by (9.26) an equilibrium α-Chapman layer, and that described by (9.27) an equilibrium β-Chapman layer.[74] If N_m represents the peak electron density, then we have, in the two cases,

$$N_m = [(q_0/\alpha)\cos\chi]^{1/2} \qquad \text{for } \alpha\text{-Chapman} \qquad (9.28)$$

and

$$N_m = (q_0/\beta)\cos\chi \qquad \text{for } \beta\text{-Chapman.} \qquad (9.29)$$

If the loss coefficient (α or β) decreases upward, (9.26) and (9.27) show that the peak of N will be at a greater height than the peak of q.[22,76] The steeper the gradient of the loss coefficient, the higher will be the peak of N. If the loss is caused by recombination with α proportional to $\exp(-h/H_L)$, and the density of the ionizable gas proportional to $\exp(-h/H_i)$, so that H_L and H_i can be called the scale heights of the loss coefficient and of the gas, respectively, then it can be shown that the peak will be at an infinite height if $H_L < H_i$.* If $H_L > H_i$, it can be shown that N reaches its peak value, N_m, at a height h_m, where

$$h_m = h_m(q) - H_i \log(1 - H_i/H_L) \qquad (9.30) \dagger$$

and that

$$N_m \propto (\cos \chi)^{\frac{1}{2}(1 - H_i/H_L)} . \qquad (9.31)$$

Comparison of (9.31) and (9.8) shows that a gradient (γ) of the scale height of the ionizable gas affects the cos χ-variation of N_m in the same way as a gradient of the recombination coefficient, α.

An equilibrium layer in which the loss coefficient decreases upward with a gradient sufficient to produce a peak of electron density (N) at a height considerably above the peak of electron production (q) was first discussed by Bradbury. It is often called a "Bradbury layer." [59,195]

9.2.4 Time-Varying Layers

If the rate of production (q) varies with time, and if the electrons are lost by recombination, the electron density varies according to the expression

$$dN/dt = q - \alpha N^2. \qquad (9.32)$$

Although this expression is strictly applicable only to a fixed height, it can be applied without much error to the peak value (N_m) of the electron density.[22] It is then interesting to consider how the changes of N_m are related to the changes of q.

Suppose that while q is changing relatively slowly, with time, as given by $q(t)$, it is increased by an amount $\Delta q(t)$, which changes comparatively rapidly. Suppose, also, that N and $N + \Delta N$ represent the corresponding electron densities. Then

$$\frac{d(N + \Delta N)}{dt} = q(t) + \Delta q(t) - \alpha(N + \Delta N)^2 \qquad (9.33)$$

and

$$dN/dt = q(t) - \alpha N^2 \qquad (9.34)$$

so that, after substracting the equations and ignoring a term $(\Delta N)^2$ compared with $2N \Delta N$, we have

$$d(\Delta N)/dt = \Delta q(t) - 2\alpha N . \Delta N. \qquad (9.35)$$

---

* In practice, even in this case, there will be a peak at a finite height, because at great enough heights there is no gas to ionize. This possibility is not deducible from the simple form of Chapman's theory, which supposes that the gas available for absorbing is not diminished when some of it becomes ionized. A full discussion is complicated and involves the consideration of diffusion.

$\dagger$ It should be noted that, since $H_i/H_L < 1$ equation (9.30) implies that $h_m > h_m(q)$.

If, at any subsequent time, $\Delta q = 0$, this equation shows that the excess electron density would decay according to the expression

$$\Delta N = (\Delta N)_0 \exp(-2\alpha N t) \qquad (9.36)$$

as though with a time constant $1/2\alpha N$. This quantity has been called the "sluggishness of the ionosphere." Equation (9.35) shows that the excess electron density, ΔN, follows a small perturbation, $\Delta q(t)$, like a system with this time constant.[16]

The perturbation, $\Delta q(t)$, might be the result of a sudden ionosphere disturbance (S.I.D.) (see § 9.11.2), and it has often been supposed that the time delay between the maximum of q and the maximum of N is then equal to the time constant, and the corresponding value of α has been deduced.[192] This argument should be used with discrimination, since the interval between maxima depends on the form of the $\Delta q(t)$ variation and (9.35) applies only to perturbations in which $\Delta N/N$ is small.

It can be shown that the time constant, $1/2\alpha N$, also represents the time interval between the maximum value of q and the maximum value of N even when q is changing slowly and smoothly as through the day. Measurements of this time delay near midday have provided useful estimates of αN.[191]

If, during an eclipse of the sun, the intensity of the incident ionizing radiation varies proportionally to $f(t)$, then, in the absence of movements, the peak electron density (N_m) of an α-Chapman layer approximately obeys the equation

$$q_m f(t) \cos \chi = dN_m/dt + \alpha N_m{}^2. \qquad (9.37)$$

From this equation attempts have been made to determine from measured values of N_m and dN_m/dt both the value of α and the function $f(t)$. One method is to assume that $f(t) = 0$ when the visible eclipse is total and then to deduce α from (9.37), and for the rest of the time use this value of α to determine $f(t)$. It has usually been found that $f(t)$ does not vary in the same way as the optical obscuration function, and suggestions have been made that the ionizing radiation is not emitted uniformly from the visible disk of the sun.[184, 242]

9.2.5 *Vertical Movements of Electrons*

If the electrons move with a mean drift velocity, $\mathbf{v}$, then the continuity equation takes the form

$$dN/dt = q - L - \mathrm{div}\,(N\mathbf{v}) \qquad (9.38)$$

$$= q - L - N\,\mathrm{div}\,\mathbf{v} - \mathbf{v}.\mathrm{grad}\,N. \qquad (9.39)$$

There are usually good reasons for thinking that $\mathbf{v}$ and N change much more rapidly in the vertical than in the horizontal direction, so that $\mathrm{div}\,\mathbf{v} \doteqdot dw/dh$, where w is the upward component of $\mathbf{v}$, and grad $N \doteq dN/dh$, so that (9.38) and (9.39) become

$$dN/dt = q - L - d(Nw)/dh \qquad (9.40a)$$

$$= q - L - Ndw/dh - w\,dN/dh. \qquad (9.40b)$$

The vertical drift velocity could be caused by (1) changes of temperature, (2) diffusion, or (3) electromagnetic forces. The first two possibilities will be considered here, and the third will be discussed in the next section in a somewhat wider context.

9.2.5.1 *Changes of Temperature*[108]

If a gas is in equilibrium under the action of gravity, and if the temperature distribution changes, a given "cell" of the gas moves so as to remain at a height where the pressure is constant, as may be seen by remembering that the pressure is equal to the weight of the superincumbent gas. It then follows that, if the temperature is uniform above a height zero, and changes at the rate dT/dt, the vertical velocity (w) at a height h is given by

$$w = (h/T)\ dT/dt. \qquad (9.41)$$

If, instead, there is a linear gradient of temperature, and the gradient changes with time, the same expression is approximately correct if T is taken to be the temperature at the height considered.

9.2.5.2 *Diffusion*[93,101,175]

The electron—positive-ion plasma can diffuse through the neutral air according to laws which can be derived from those governing the diffusion of a minor constituent through a major constituent. If, in the latter case, F is the upwards force exerted on each molecule of the minor gas, which has mass m and collision frequency v, then the vertical drift velocity, v, of these molecules is given by

$$w = F/mv. \qquad (9.42)$$

If, now, the gases are at constant temperature T and are subject to the force of gravity, and if there is a vertical gradient of the partial pressure, p, of the minor constituent, the upward force, F, is given by

$$F = -\,(1/N)\,dp/dh - mg$$

$$= -\,(kT/N)\,dN/dh - mg. \qquad (9.43)$$

Combination of (9.42) and (9.43) gives

$$w = -(kT/mv)\left(\frac{1}{N}\frac{dN}{dh} + \frac{mg}{kT}\right). \qquad (9.44)$$

This expression shows that, at all levels, $w = 0$ if $(1/N)(dN/dh) = -mg/kT$, or $N = N_0 \exp(-hmg/kT)$, which is the usual equilibrium condition with scale height $H = kT/mg$. If there is not equilibrium, (9.44) shows that the vertical velocity may be written

$$w = -D\left(\frac{1}{N}\frac{dN}{dh} + \frac{1}{H}\right) \tag{9.45}$$

where $D = kT/mv$ is the diffusion coefficient.

The electrons in the ionosphere have a greater diffusion coefficient than the ions, but electrostatic forces between them prevent any appreciable space charge from being built up, and the plasma diffuses as a whole, with a diffusion coefficient, D_{12}, called the ambipolar diffusion coefficient. It can be shown that $D_{12} = 2D_i$, where D_i is the diffusion coefficient for the ions, and that in (9.45) H must have the value $2H_i$, where $H_i = kT/m_i g$, to allow for the fact that the mean molecular mass of the electron-ion mixture is approximately $\frac{1}{2}m_i$. Equation (9.45) then takes the form

$$w = -D_{12}\left(\frac{1}{N_i}\frac{dN_i}{dh} + \frac{1}{2H_i}\right). \tag{9.46}$$

The term $-d(Nw)/dh$ in (9.40a) then becomes

$$-\frac{d(Nw)}{dh} = \frac{dD_{12}}{dh}\left(\frac{dN}{dh} + \frac{N}{2H}\right) + D_{12}\left(\frac{d^2N}{dh^2} + \frac{1}{2H}\frac{dN}{dh}\right). \tag{9.47}$$

Now D_{12} is inversely proportional to v and hence to the number density, n, of the neutral gas. Moreover, the presence of the earth's magnetic field largely prevents diffusion across the lines of force, and it can be shown that when vertical gradients are considered $D_{12} \propto \sin^2 I$, where I is the inclination of the field. We may then write

$$D_{12} = (A/n)\sin^2 I \tag{9.48}$$

where A is a constant.

Under many conditions it may be supposed that the neutral gas has the same molecular weight as the ions, so that its scale height is H_i, and

$$n = n_0 \exp(-h/H_i) \tag{9.49}$$

Combination of (9.47), (9.48), and (9.49) then gives

$$-\frac{d(Nw)}{dh} = [(A/n)\sin^2 I]\left(\frac{d^2N}{dh^2} + \frac{3}{2H}\frac{dN}{dh} + \frac{N}{2H^2}\right). \tag{9.50}$$

We shall call the expression $-d(Nw)/dh$ the "movement term" in the continuity equation. It can be either positive or negative, depending on the signs and sizes of the derivatives dN/dh and d^2N/dh^2. For any given distribution of electron density, (9.50) may be written

$$-d(Nw)/dh = [(A/n)\sin^2 I]\phi(h/H). \tag{9.51}$$

For a distribution of N which has a parabolic form with half-thickness t, the movement term varies with height below the peak of the layer, as shown in Fig. 2. The different curves show $\phi(h/H)$ for different values of the ratio $t/H = a$. It will be seen that diffusion can introduce either a positive or a negative movement term into the continuity equation. In particular, it will

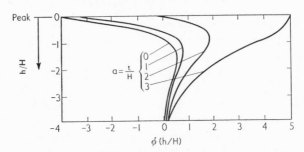

FIG. 2. The movement term, proportional to $\phi(h/H)$, at different normalized distances (h/H) below the peak of a parabolic layer of electrons with half-thickness t. The different curves correspond to different values of $a = t/H$. A positive value of ϕ is equivalent to production of electrons. The vertical scale should read h/H.

be noticed that, at the peak of a parabolic layer, diffusion will increase the electron density if $a > 2$ and decrease it if $a < 2$.[175, 217]

Some other effects of diffusion are considered in § 9.8.8.2.

9.3 The Ionosphere as a Dynamo and a Motor

9.3.1 *The Atmospheric Dynamo*[28, 99, 125]

The ionosphere contains equal numbers of positive ions and negative electrons embedded in a neutral gas. At some levels the neutral gas is moved by the gravitational forces of the sun and moon, and possibly also by forces of thermal origin. The charged particles share this motion, to some extent, and since they behave like a conductor moving through the earth's steady magnetic field a current is induced, as in a dynamo. It is convenient to give the name "atmospheric dynamo" to those parts of the ionosphere where this current is produced.

The current in the dynamo region produces changes in the magnetic field at the ground, from which it is possible to estimate the magnitude of the current. Its flow is accompanied by an electrostatic field, which, reaching the other parts of the ionosphere, causes currents to flow there, also. The earth's field, acting on these currents, then causes the electron-ion plasma at these distant places to move bodily. It is convenient to give the name "atmospheric motor" to this part of the ionosphere. It appears that, to a first approximation, the "dynamo" is situated in the E region, and the "motor" in the F region.

There is also an important "motor" effect in the dynamo region itself, since the currents there also flow in the earth's steady magnetic field. This might be said to be the result of forces analogous to the "armature reaction" forces in a commercial dynamo. It is responsible for important movements of the E layer and will be considered further in § 9.6.6.

9.3.2 *The Tensor Conductivities*[27,77,160]

Several attempts have been made to calculate in some detail the ionospheric currents and movements which would result from postulated tidal movements of the neutral air. Conversely, starting with the E-region currents as deduced from geomagnetic changes, attempts have been made to deduce the neutral air movements which would produce them, and the "motor" movements which they would produce in the F region. In these calculations it must be remembered that under the action of the earth's magnetic field the ionosphere is a nonisotropic conductor, with a tensor conductivity, $\mathbf{T}$, relating the current density, $\mathbf{j}$, and the electric field, $\mathbf{E}$, as given by the following expressions, in which the earth's field, B, is taken along the Z-axis.

$$\mathbf{j} = \mathbf{T} \cdot \mathbf{E}$$

with

$$\mathbf{T} = \begin{pmatrix} \sigma_1 & -\sigma_2 & 0 \\ \sigma_2 & \sigma_1 & 0 \\ 0 & 0 & \sigma_0 \end{pmatrix} \tag{9.52}$$

where

$$\sigma_0 = \left(\frac{n_e}{m_e \nu_e} + \frac{n_i}{m_i \nu_i} \right) e^2 \tag{9.53}$$

$$\sigma_1 = \left[\frac{n_e}{m_e \nu_e} \left(\frac{\nu_e^2}{\nu_e^2 + \omega_e^2} \right) + \frac{n_i}{m_i \nu_i} \left(\frac{\nu_i^2}{\nu_i^2 + \omega_i^2} \right) \right] e^2 \tag{9.54}$$

$$\sigma_2 = \left[\frac{n_e}{m_e \nu_e} \left(\frac{\omega_e \nu_e}{\nu_e^2 + \omega_e^2} \right) + \frac{n_i}{m_i \nu_i} \left(\frac{\omega_i \nu_i}{\nu_i^2 + \omega_i^2} \right) \right] e^2 \tag{9.55}$$

and n, m, and ν represent the number density, mass, and collision frequency of charged particles, $\omega = eB/m$, the angular gyro-frequency of the particle, and the subscript e or i indicates electrons or massive ions. The following points are important:

1. Along the direction of the imposed field (the Z-direction) the conductivity takes the value σ_0 which it would have if there were no field.

2. In directions (X or Y) perpendicular to the magnetic field an electric field, $\mathbf{E}$, produces a current density, $\mathbf{j}$ which is not along its own direction. The component along its own direction is given by a conductivity, σ_1. This is often called the "transverse" conductivity, because the field $\mathbf{E}$ is "transverse to" $\mathbf{B}$. The electronic and ionic components of σ_1 are each smaller than σ_0 by the factors $[\nu^2/(\nu^2 + \omega^2)]$ which vary with ν and hence with height.

3. When $\mathbf{E}$ is perpendicular to the imposed field it also produces a component of current perpendicular to itself, of magnitude determined by σ_2. This current is related to the phenomenon of the Hall effect; it is often called the Hall current, and σ_2 is called the Hall conductivity. The electronic and ionic components of σ_2 are less than σ_0 by the factors $[\omega\nu/(\nu^2 + \omega^2)]$, which are small in many parts of the ionosphere.

Complications arise because the ionosphere is inhomogeneous. To illustrate these let us suppose that it consists of two separate slab-like layers, the E and the F, each uniform throughout, and a region between in which the ionization is comparatively weak. Let us also suppose that the E later is moved by gravitational or thermal forces, so that it acts like the dynamo. Then if the tensor, $\mathbf{T}$, is used to calculate the current flowing, it will in general be found that there is a component perpendicular to the top and bottom boundaries of the layer. Since, however, in our simple picture no current can flow vertically, perpendicular to the boundaries, charges must appear on those boundaries, just sufficient to stop the flow. The electric field of these charges will also alter the components of currents in the horizontal direction. If the Z-axis is now taken upward, and the earth's magnetic field is in the ZX plane, making an angle, I, with OX, then it can be shown that the resulting horizontal current density is given by $\mathbf{j} = \mathbf{T}' \cdot \mathbf{E}$, where

$$\mathbf{T}' = \begin{pmatrix} \sigma_{xx} & \sigma_{xy} \\ -\sigma_{xy} & \sigma_{yy} \end{pmatrix} \tag{9.56}$$

and

$$\sigma_{xx} = \frac{\sigma_0 \sigma_1}{\sigma_0 \sin^2 I + \sigma_1 \cos^2 I} \tag{9.57}$$

$$\sigma_{yy} = \sigma_1 + \frac{\sigma_2^2 \cos^2 I}{\sigma_0 \sin^2 I + \sigma_1 \cos^2 I} \tag{9.58}$$

$$\sigma_{xy} = \frac{\sigma_0 \sigma_2 \sin I}{\sigma_0 \sin^2 I + \sigma_1 \cos^2 I} \tag{9.59}$$

$\mathbf{T}'$ may be called the layer conductivity, and it must be used in calculating the dynamo currents flowing.

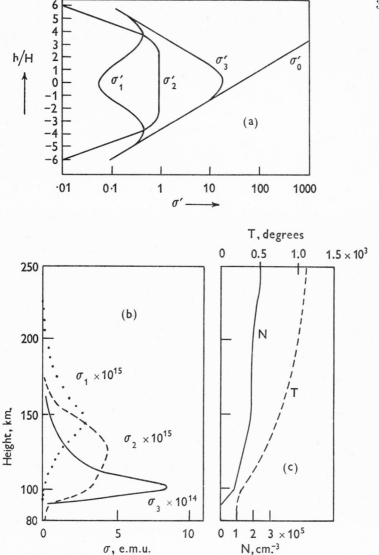

FIG. 3. (a) The conductivities σ_0', σ_1', σ'_2, and σ_3' per ion pair, given by equations (9.53, 9.54, 9.55, 9.61). The conductivities in emu are given by multiplying the magnitudes shown here by $1.6 \times 10^{-20}/F$ gauss. The atmosphere is supposed to have a constant scale height, H, and heights are expressed in terms of h/H measured from the level where $\nu_e \nu_i = \omega_e \omega_i$. It is further supposed that ν_e/ν_i is independent of height, and $\nu_i/\omega_i = 1500 \, \nu_e/\omega_e$. (b) The specific conductivities σ_1, σ_2, σ_3 as functions of height for an ionosphere in which the electron density (N) and the temperature (T) vary as shown at (c). It is supposed that $F = 0.49$ gauss. Note that the scale for σ_3 is smaller than that for σ_1 and σ_2 by a factor of 10. After S. Chapman, *Nuovo Cim.* **4** (*Suppl.*), 1385 (1956).

At the geomagnetic equator $I = 0$ and

$$\begin{aligned}
\sigma_{xx} &= \sigma_0 \\
\sigma_{yy} &= \sigma_1 + \sigma_2^2/\sigma_1 = \sigma_3 \\
\sigma_{xy} &= 0
\end{aligned} \tag{9.60}$$

where σ_3 is a new component of conductivity, defined by

$$\sigma_3 = \sigma_1 + \sigma_2^2/\sigma_1. \tag{9.61}$$

The magnitudes of σ_0, σ_1, σ_2, and σ_3 at different heights in certain model atmospheres are shown in Fig. 3. At (a) the atmosphere is supposed to have a constant scale height, H, so that $\nu = \nu_0 \exp(-h/H)$, and height is measured in terms of H as a unit, from a level where $\nu_e \nu_i = \omega_e \omega_i$. The conductivities, denoted by σ_0', σ_1', σ_2', and σ_3', refer to a single electron-ion pair. $\nu_e = \omega_e$ near $h/H = -4$, and $\nu_i = \omega_i$ near $h/H = +4$.

At (b) the conductivities σ_1, σ_2, and σ_3 are plotted as functions of height for a model atmosphere in which electron density, N, and temperature, T, are as shown at (c). This atmosphere is representative of what is thought to exist above White Sands, New Mexico, in the United States. It should be noted that the scale for σ_3 is smaller than that for σ_1 and σ_2 by a factor of 10.

Near the geomagnetic equator the conductivity σ_3 is the most important, and Fig. 3b shows that it is great within a comparatively narrow range of heights near 100 km. For this reason it is permissible, in a first approximation, to consider that the "dynamo" region, near the equator, consists of a bounded slab near these heights. Equations 9.57, 9.58, 9.59, and 9.60, together with Fig. 3b, also show that the conductivity (σ_3) near the equator is about ten times as great as that elsewhere, so that the current there is also greater. This enhanced current is also deducible from observations of geomagnetic variations; it has been called the "equatorial electrojet."

At places not near the equator, Fig. 3b, in conjunction with the appropriate equations, shows that the main contribution to the conductivity lies at heights between about 90 and 140 km, between which the dynamo region may be supposed to lie. When air velocities deduced from tidal theory are used, in conjunction with the conductivity, $\mathbf{T}'$, deduced from Fig. 3b and the equations, it is found that the calculated currents are of the same order as those deduced from geomagnetic data.

Even in a simple "slab" model of the dynamo region there are complications. The dynamo emf, given in terms of the air velocity, $\mathbf{v}$, and the earth's magnetic induction $\mathbf{B}$ by $\mathbf{v} \times \mathbf{B}$ varies over the surface of the earth. A full calculation must therefore take into account a horizontal distribution of space charge which is built up before the currents can flow. The electric field of this horizontally distributed space charge will modify the tensor conductivity in the same kind of way as the vertical distribution previously mentioned, and the problem becomes complicated. When allowance is made for the fact that the ionization density and the direction and magnitude of the earth's magnetic field also vary over the earth, the complexity is even greater.

9.3.3 The Atmospheric Motor[99,126,127,171,172,174]

The horizontal distribution of space charge produces an electric field which influences the F region. In the simple slab picture this field has to reach that region through the intervening weakly ionized region, where it may be supposed that the tensor conductivity is given by $\mathbf{T}$, and is therefore predominantly along the lines of magnetic force and has the large magnitude, σ_0. In the F layer, therefore, there is a horizontal emf, conducted up these lines of force from the horizontal space-charge in the E region. This emf then produces horizontal currents in the (supposed) slablike F layer, as determined by the horizontal layer conductivity, $\mathbf{T}'$. These currents, acted on by the magnetic field of the earth, experience forces, and the plasma moves bodily, constituting the "atmospheric motor." Movements of the F layer have been interpreted in this way.

It is obvious that the above description is oversimplified, and in particular that the division into slablike layers is invalid. Attempts have been made to perform the calculations for models which simulate the real ionosphere more exactly, but no clearly different conclusions have yet been reached. The results of these calculations are discussed in § 9.8.8.1.

9.4 Theory of Wave Propagation through the Ionosphere

9.4.1 The Penetration Frequency[7, 218]

The refractive index(μ) of a wave of angular frequency ω traveling through a plasma containing free charges is given by

$$\mu^2 = 1 - \frac{4\pi}{\epsilon_0 \omega^2} \sum_j \frac{N_j e_j^2}{m_j} \tag{9.62}$$

where N_j, e_j, and m_j represent the number density, charge, and mass of each type of charged particle. In the ionosphere the electrons, of small mass, are considerably more important for this purpose than the massive ions, and the refractive index may be written

$$\mu^2 = 1 - 4\pi N_e e_e^2 / \epsilon_0 m_e \omega^2 \tag{9.63}$$

where N_e, m_e, and e_e refer to electrons. It is particularly to be observed that the departure of μ from its free-space value of unity is inversely proportional to the square of the wave frequency.

If the ionosphere is horizontally stratified, with N increasing upward, a plane wave incident at an angle i will be refracted until it is traveling horizontally at a level where N is sufficiently great to reduce the refractive index to a value of $\mu = \sin i$, and after that it will return to the ground. If the wave is incident vertically, with $i = 0$, it will be returned from a level where $\mu = 0$, and therefore where

$$N = (\epsilon_0 m/4\pi e^2)\omega^2 = 1.24 \times 10^{-8} f^2 \qquad (9.64)$$

where f is the wave frequency. This frequency is also the "plasma resonance frequency" appropriate to a plasma of electron density N, so that a wave is reflected, at vertical incidence, from that level in the ionosphere where the wave frequency is equal to the plasma frequency.

If there is a layer of electrons having a plasma frequency, f_m, at the peak, frequencies less than f_m will be reflected, but greater frequencies will not. The frequency f_m is called the "critical" or "penetration" frequency of the layer. It is an easily determined quantity which has been much used in ionosphere research. If the layer is an equilibrium α-Chapman layer, then, from (9.64) and (9.28) we have

$$f_m = 9 \times 10^3 N_m^{1/2} = 9 \times 10^3 [(q_0/\alpha) \cos \chi]^{1/4}. \qquad (9.65)$$

The electrons in the ionosphere collide with heavy particles with an average frequency usually denoted by ν. These collisions result in the wave's being absorbed as it travels, and they also alter the refractive index. In general this alteration is slight, but it has the one important result that μ never reaches the value zero, so it might be thought that the statements made above, about reflection of the wave at vertical incidence, were incorrect. A fuller investigation of the problem shows, however, that, although μ does not reach zero, its gradient is great near the level where the wave frequency and the plasma frequency are equal. If a full wave theory is then used, it can be shown that reflection still occurs near this level.

9.4.2 *The $h'(f)$ Curves or Ionograms, and $N(h)$ Curves*

A simple method of exploring the ionosphere is to send upward a series of short wave trains on a radio-frequency which can be varied, and to record the time delay between emission and reception after reflection from the ionosphere. The time delay (t) is expressed as the "equivalent height" (h') from which the wave would have been reflected if it had traveled all the way with free space velocity, c, so that $2h' = ct$, and h' is recorded as a function of the frequency (f) in an $h'(f)$ curve, sometimes called an ionogram. Examples are shown in Fig. 4 and are described in the following paragraphs.

The permanent magnetic field of the earth renders the ionosphere birefringent, so that, in general, an incident wave is split into two characteristic waves, with different polarizations. These are called the Ordinary and the Extraordinary waves. Except under special conditions, to be considered later, they travel independently, and with their own speeds, so that each emitted pulse returns to the ground doubled. If the resolving time of the equipment is small enough, the two components are recorded separately, as shown by the continuous and dashed lines in Fig. 4a. A layer of electrons is penetrated by each of the two characteristic waves at a different frequency. For the Ordinary wave, this frequency is, under normal conditions, the peak plasma frequency of the layer, just as it would be if the earth's field were absent. In what follows we shall be concerned almost entirely with ionograms and critical frequencies for the Ordinary wave only, and, unless it is specifically mentioned, we shall ignore the presence of the Extraordinary wave.

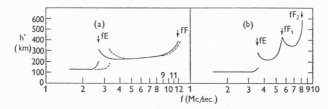

FIG. 4. Examples of "ionograms" or $h'(f)$ curves, in which the equivalent height (h') of reflection of a radio wave is plotted against the frequency (f). The dashed line refers to the Extraordinary wave and is shown only in (a).

The ionograms usually show at least two clearly defined penetration frequencies, denoted by fE and fF, and it was at one time thought that they corresponded to two clearly separated layers of electrons, called the E and F layers, with their peaks at heights of about 100 and 250 km. Later experiments in which the electron densities were measured by means of rockets have shown that any decrease of the electron density above the peak of the "E layer" is slight and comparatively unimportant (see Chapter 3). This conclusion has been re-enforced by deductions from the $h'(f)$ curves, described below.

Sometimes the $h'(f)$ curve for the F layer itself shows a second more or less well-defined critical frequency, as indicated in Fig. 4b. It is called $fF1$, and, when it occurs, the final penetration frequency of the F layer is called $fF2$. Rocket experiments, and electron distributions calculated from $h'(f)$ curves, show that $fF1$ usually corresponds only to a slight inflection in the curve of N plotted against h.[134, 234]

The present idea is that the electron distributions corresponding to the $h'(f)$ curves of Fig. 4 are as shown in Fig. 5, which gives the electron density, N, plotted against h. Curves of this kind are often called $N(h)$ curves, or electron profiles. They show that, contrary to the view held a few years ago, the electrons are not arranged in separate layers, E, $F1$, and $F2$, but in a thick layer with points of inflection at heights corresponding to fE and $fF1$ and a peak at a height corresponding to $fF2$.

The equivalent height (h') depends on the group velocity, and hence on the electron density, at all heights, and it is possible to deduce the $N(h)$ curve from the $h'(f)$ curve. The presence of the earth's magnetic field complicates these calculations but also makes it possible in principle to remove some uncertainties by using observations on both the Ordinary and the Extraordinary waves. The $N(h)$ curves shown in Fig. 5 were deduced by these methods. Several ionospheric observatories now publish their results in the form of tables showing the electron density, N, at different heights.[111, 135, 230, 250, 251, 252]

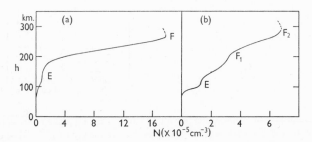

Fig. 5. Electron density (N) plotted against height (h) for the ionospheres which gave rise to the $h'(f)$ curves of Fig. 4.

Although, according to the present view, the frequencies fE and $fF1$ do not correspond to any clearly marked feature on the $N(h)$ curve, they represent well-marked characteristics of the observed $h'(f)$ curves, and it is found that they undergo regular changes with time of day, with season, and with epoch in the solar cycle. They have therefore been extensively observed and tabulated at a series of ionospheric observatories spread all over the world.

9.4.3 More Detailed Wave Theory[68]

When the gradient of electron density is such that important changes occur within a distance of one wavelength, it is unsatisfactory to use simple ray optics to discuss the reflection. Full-wave theory has been used to investigate the oblique reflection of waves from different model ionospheres in the presence of the earth's magnetic field. The calculations are complicated but have been possible with the help of digital computors.

In discussing propagation to a great distance it is best for some problems to consider "rays" reflected back and forth between the ionosphere and earth, whereas for others, particularly those concerned with long waves, it is more convenient to consider the propagation of "wave-guide modes" traveling in the space between the ionosphere and the ground. Both methods have been used: they must, of course, give the same result.

A full-wave treatment of the problem of a wave traveling through the anisotropic ionosphere indicates the conditions under which the two characteristic waves are propagated independently.[52,103] In particular it shows that, under certain conditions, their propagation is not independent, so that, for example, a purely Ordinary wave gives rise to some Extraordinary. This "coupling" is most intense when the collision frequency (ν) is related to the earth's magnetic induction (B) and the angle (θ) between it and the wave normal in such a way that

$$\nu = (\tfrac{1}{2} \sin^2 \theta / \cos \theta)(2\pi e B / m) \tag{9.66}$$

and if this value of ν is found at the level where the wave frequency and the plasma frequency are equal, the coupling can become really important: it can even produce a measurable reflected wave, called the "coupling echo." [52,68,86,103]

9.4.4 The "Whistler Mode" of Propagation[246,247,286,287]

Lightning flashes radiate intense electromagnetic waves on low frequencies, in the range, for example of 500 to 10,000 cps. When waves of these frequencies enter the ionosphere, the Ordinary component is guided by the earth's magnetic field so that its *ray* direction follows a line of force of that field. If, then, there are sufficient electrons at the outermost part of the line of force to continue the guidance, the waves will return to earth approximately at the magnetically conjugate point at its other end. The waves of the different frequencies which make up the spectrum of the original lightning discharge travel through the ionosphere with different speeds, so that the higher frequencies arrive first. If, then, the wave is received on a long aerial, amplified at an audio-frequency without any rectification, and applied to a loudspeaker, there is heard a characteristic whistle of descending pitch. This is called a "whistling atmospheric" or a "whistler," and the mode of propagation is called the "whistler mode." Man-made signals, radiated on low radio-frequencies from commercial senders, have been received after traveling by this mode.

The dispersion of the different frequencies in the whistler depends on the total path, on the distribution of the electron density, and on the variation of the magnetic field along the path.

A detailed study of the dispersion can, under some conditions, lead to deductions about the electron density at the outermost part of the line of

26

force. Since lines of force ending at different latitudes have penetrated
different distances into space, studies of this kind, made at different latitudes,
provide the possibility of exploring the electron density out to different
distances, which may be as great as three or four earth radii.

9.4.5 *Absorption*[8,18]

A uniform ionosphere would absorb a plane wave traveling vertically
through it so that the electric field would vary with height (h) like
$E = E_0 \exp(- \kappa h)$. A wave emitted with field E_0 from a point on the ground
and reflected normally from a height h_1 in a varying ionosphere will therefore
return to the ground with a field E given by

$$E = \left(\frac{E_0}{2h_1}\right) \exp\left(- 2 \int_0^{h_1} \kappa \, dh\right). \tag{9.67}$$

If it had traveled without absorption and had been reflected with reflection
coefficient, ρ, the returned field would have been

$$E = (E_0/2h_1) \, \rho$$

so that

$$- \log \rho = 2 \int_0^{h_1} \kappa \, dh. \tag{9.68}$$

The reflection coefficient, ρ, can be measured and provides useful information
about the absorption index, κ.

The magneto-ionic theory shows that

$$\kappa = \left(\frac{2\pi e^2}{\epsilon_0 mc}\right) \frac{1}{\mu} \frac{N \nu}{(\omega \pm \omega_H)^2 + \nu^2} \tag{9.69}$$

where ω_H is the angular gyrofrequency, and the two signs represent the
Ordinary $(+)$ and the Extraordinary $(-)$ waves. In many parts of the
ionosphere it can be assumed that $\nu^2 \ll (\omega \pm \omega_H)^2$, and, if the plasma
frequency is not too close to the wave frequency, $\mu \doteqdot 1$, so that, approximately

$$\kappa \propto N\nu/(\omega \pm \omega_H)^2$$

and

$$- \log \rho \propto \frac{1}{(\omega \pm \omega_H)^2} \int_0^{h_1} N\nu \, dh. \tag{9.70}$$

If observations of $\log \rho$ on different frequencies show it to be proportional to
$(\omega \pm \omega_H)^2$, it is therefore usually supposed that the approximations leading
to (9.70) are satisfied, and the magnitude of $\int_0^{h_1} N\nu \, dh$ can be deduced.

Absorption which obeys this frequency law is called "nondeviative" because it is supposed to occur at levels where $\mu \doteqdot 1$, so that, if incidence were oblique, the wave would not be deviated.

For frequencies greater than a few times the gyrofrequency (9.69) can be transformed to yield, approximately,

$$\kappa = \frac{\nu}{2c}\left(\frac{1}{\mu} - \mu\right) \tag{9.71}$$

so that

$$-\log \rho = \frac{1}{c}\int_0^{h_1} \nu\left(\frac{1}{\mu} - \mu\right) dh. \tag{9.72}$$

Under the conditions previously considered $1/\mu$ is approximately equal to the group refractive index, so that $\int dh/\mu = h'$, the "equivalent" or "group" height, and $\int \mu\, dh = h''$, the "optical" or "phase" height. If, therefore, ν were constant over the height range of the integration, we should have

$$-\log \rho = (\nu/c)(h' - h''). \tag{9.73}$$

This expression is particularly useful when μ differs appreciably from unity so that h' and h'' are not nearly equal.

It is, for example, sometimes possible to associate changes $\Delta h'$ and $\Delta h''$ of the measured group and phase heights with changes $\Delta \log \rho$, and to determine the part of the ionosphere in which these changes occur. It is then possible to use (9.73) to calculate ν in that part of the ionosphere. Since the condition that μ departs appreciably from unity is also the condition that, at oblique incidence, there would be appreciable deviation of the wave, the type of absorption envisaged here is often called "deviative absorption," in contradistinction to the "nondeviative" considered earlier.[6]

9.5 The Undisturbed D Region [260, 261, 285]

9.5.1 *Introduction*

In the exploration of the E and F regions of the ionosphere much use has been made of the fact that radio waves are reflected from well-determined heights, and that, as the wave frequency is altered, these reflections cease near well-marked "critical" or "penetration" frequencies. When an attempt is made to study the D region, however, this simple method is not widely applicable, partly because it is difficult to operate sweep-frequency equipment at the low frequencies required, and partly because there do not seem to be well-defined layers in the region. Deductions about the D region have therefore usually been made somewhat indirectly either by studying its effect on waves which have traversed it to be reflected in the layers above, or by studying waves returned from within it on a few isolated frequencies.

To pass from the observed facts to deductions about the distribution of electrons, the collision frequencies, and the rates of production and loss of electrons in the D region often involves much indirect argument. It is not too difficult to suggest a model which could explain some of the facts, but care must always be taken to ensure that no known facts are at variance with it.

Although several models of the D region have been suggested, it cannot yet be said that any one has been fully tested in this way. It will, however, be shown that some of the suggested models are roughly similar, so that perhaps a first-order picture of the D region is emerging.

9.5.2 *Experimental Methods for Investigating the D Region*

It is convenient to divide the experimental methods which have been used for investigating the D region into two groups which use, respectively, waves returned from above and from inside that region.

9.5.2.1 *Waves Which Have Traversed the D Region*

9.5.2.1.1 *Absorption.*[50a,189,257] When waves are reflected from above the D region, their amplitude is determined partly by their travel through the region and partly by what happens above. If experiments are made to find how the absorption varies with frequency, it is sometimes possible to isolate a part which corresponds to "nondeviative" absorption, to ascribe it to the D region, and to estimate the quantity $\int N \nu \, dh$ taken over the thickness of that region.[238]

9.5.2.1.2 *Polarization.*[289] Any wave incident on the ionosphere is resolved into two component characteristic waves, and if the wavelength is great, so that gradients of electron density are important, a full-wave theory is required to determine how each component travels and what is its polarization when it leaves the ionosphere. With a frequency of 150 kc/sec, for example, reflection is from the E region and the Extraordinary wave is strongly absorbed, so that the emerging wave might be expected to have a polarization corresponding to the Ordinary wave. Now although the angle between the magnetic meridian and the major axis of the polarization ellipse should, according to simple theory, lie within certain limits, it is frequently found in practice that it falls outside them. The phenomenon has been attributed to passage of the wave through the D region and has been used to make deductions about that region.

9.5.2.1.3 *Ionospheric Cross-Modulation.*[26,132] In an interesting experiment Fejer[100] has used the phenomenon of ionospheric cross-modulation to examine the D region. This phenomenon is noticeable when two waves of different frequencies traverse a part of the ionosphere simultaneously, or in rapid succession. The absorption of one of the waves "heats up" the ionospheric electrons through which it passes, so that their collision frequency is increased. If, then, the other wave passes through the same region before the electrons have had time to cool down again, the increased collision frequency results in its being absorbed more strongly. This modulation of the amplitude of the second wave by the presence of the first is the phenomenon of ionospheric cross-modulation.

Fejer transmitted two radio-wave pulses on different frequencies in succession, so that one on its upward journey passed the other on its downward journey at a height which was known and could be altered. He then studied the amount by which the amplitude of the one was decreased by the phenomenon of ionospheric cross-modulation from the other. He used, in succession, first the Ordinary wave and next the Extraordinary wave to "heat up" the electrons so that, knowing from theory how the absorption coefficients for these two waves varied, and varying the height at which the cross-modulation took place, he was able to deduce how both the electron density and the collision frequency varied with the height. The magnitude of the cross-modulation was small, and a long integration time was required to measure it. Although the results were only just significant, they provide some useful hints about the electrons in the D region.

9.5.2.2 *Waves Returned from within the D Region*

9.5.2.2.1 *Partial Reflections.*[90, 96, 105, 114, 116] When pulses of frequency greater than 0.5 Mc/sec are returned vertically from the ionosphere, they are usually reflected from above the D region. If, however, the power is very great, or the background noise is small, or special techniques are used to improve the signal-to-noise ratio, it is possible to detect very weak echoes, with reflection coefficients of 10^{-3} or 10^{-5}, from heights between about 70 and 90 km. These echoes are often, but not invariably, accompanied by much stronger echoes from greater heights.

The amplitude of these partially reflected waves is determined partly by the process of scattering responsible for their return and partly by their travel through the region below. A study of the different amplitudes of the Ordinary and the Extraordinary component waves has provided useful information about the integrated electron content below the reflection level.

In recent years much use has been made of waves scattered, at comparatively large angles of incidence, from irregularities in the D region, so as to provide a communication link over distances of about 1200 km. Although a formidable mass of observational data has been collected concerning this phenomenon, it does not seem that it can yet provide useful knowledge about the fundamental physics of the D region.[25]

It does appear, however, that the irregularities responsible for forward scattering of high-frequency waves are located near a rather definite

height—about 70 km by day and 90 km by night—and that they are
the same as those responsible for the weak return of waves at vertical
incidence.[115, 213]

A confusing feature of the partial reflections observed at vertical incidence is that some observers report a tendency for them to occur at a
series of separate and discrete heights, separated by about 5 km. It is
probably best, at present, to treat this observation with some reserve.

9.5.2.2.2 *Pulses on Lower Frequencies.* To study the vertical reflection of
pulses on frequencies less than 0.5 Mc/sec is difficult, first because it is
difficult to make an aerial which will radiate efficiently in the vertical
direction, second because of the difficulty of making and observing short
pulses at these frequencies,* and third because in the daytime the returned
pulses are very weak. Watts[258, 259] has been able to make sweep-frequency
records at night over a range of 50 to 500 kc/sec, and detailed studies have
been made on fixed frequencies near 75, 100, 150, and 300 kc/sec.[120, 284]
With pulses it is possible to study the group delay time, but only after considerable care has been taken to separate any overlapping pulses by some
differentiating system, and to identify the start of the pulse.

The fact that waves returned obliquely from the ionosphere are reflected
lower down renders it possible to investigate the D region by using comparatively high frequencies from distant transmitters. In this way pulses
emitted on 2 Mc/sec from the senders of the Loran radio navigational aid
have been used at a distance of several hundred kilometers. The observed
delays between the arrival of the ground and sky waves show that these
obliquely reflected waves are often reflected from the D region.[199]

9.5.2.2.3 *Phase and Amplitude Measurements on Lower Frequencies.*[58] Much
use has been made of commercial radio transmitters working on frequencies
below 150 kc/sec. These emit either continuous unmodulated waves (as in
the Decca navigational aid system) or Morse signals which are so long that
they can be treated as continuous. The phase of the downcoming wave from
this type of sender has been compared with the phase of the ground wave by
using suitable aerial systems. The way in which the phase varies with time
of day and year for different frequencies reflected more or less obliquely
has been studied in some detail.

Measurement of the phase of the downcoming wave cannot lead to a
determination of its height of reflection; it can show only how this height
changes with time. Some information about the actual height can be obtained by studying the changes on two frequencies simultaneously. A more
profitable method, however, is to study how the phase of the downcoming

---

* On a frequency of 150 kc/sec a pulse containing ten cycles of radio-frequency
corresponds to a distance of 20 km and has a frequency spectrum extending over a
band width 15 kc/sec.

wave changes as the distance from the sender is increased. The simple way to do this is to record the Hollingworth[128] interference pattern which is formed over the ground by the interference of the ground-wave and the downcoming wave. Many studies of these patterns have been made, and it is usual to describe the results in terms of a model in which it is supposed that the downcoming wave is reflected sharply from a horizontal surface at a fixed height. It must be very specially emphasized that this is merely a descriptive model and does *not* imply either that the wave was really reflected from that height or that the refractive index of the ionosphere at that height is what would be calculated on a simple theory. There has been danger of misunderstanding on this point.

Useful information has also been derived from observations of the night-time amplitude of the wave received from broadcasting stations on frequencies near 250 kc/sec.[152, 154]

9.5.2.2.4 *Atmospherics.*[55, 56,121, 229] Lightning flashes give rise to electromagnetic impulses, lasting about 100 μsec, and having a spectral distribution of power with a maximum at about 10 kc/sec. When the corresponding wave is received at a distance, it is called an atmospheric. Often the wave form of the atmospheric consists of a series of sharp impulses which are separately distinguishable and can be explained in terms of successive reflections from a height which can be determined. Some serious difficulties arise in the explanation, concerned particularly with the first one or two component impulses, but on the whole it seems that the deduced heights should provide useful information about the D region.

Instead of studying the wave-form of the atmospheric some workers have studied its spectrum, with the particular object of finding how it changes as the wave travels. Attempts have been made to discuss these changes in terms of a "wave guide" having the earth or sea as its lower boundary and the D region as its upper one.

In still another experimental arrangement, the integrated intensity of atmospherics received in a narrow range of frequencies is recorded as a function of the time of day and season. Attempts are then made to explain the results in terms of a set of transmitters all on the recorded frequency, but at different distances. Because of the wide range of distance it can usually be correctly assumed that any interference effects between ground and sky wave are smoothed out, so that the observed changes represent changes in the amplitude of the sky wave alone. Interesting results are obtained near sunrise and sunset.

9.5.2.2.5 *Ordinary and Extraordinary Waves Received from Rockets.*[235] Measurements of the relative amplitudes of the Ordinary and Extraordinary waves received at the ground from a rocket at different heights has led to some useful estimates of the electron distribution.

9.5.2.3 *Radiation from the D Region*[106,207]

An absorbing medium must also radiate, and it has proved possible, at a very quiet site, to measure the natural "thermal" radiation from the absorbing portions of the D region. By observing separately the Ordinary and the Extraordinary waves, useful deductions can be made, particularly about the changes during a sudden ionosphere disturbance (see § 9.11.2).

9.5.3 *Anomalous Winter Absorption*[18,46,89,211,269]

If the absorption of a wave reflected at midday from the E or F layer is measured in middle latitudes, and the 5 days of smallest absorption in each month are considered, it is found that the absorption varies in a smooth way with the sun's zenith distance. On most days, however, the absorption is considerably greater. Sometimes, particularly in summer, this increase can be ascribed to extra absorption resulting from penetration of the E layer, when the wave frequency is near the critical frequency for that layer. Often, however, in winter, days of increased absorption are observed when that explanation is impossible.

This "anomalous winter absorption" is found to occur over limited areas extending for distances of about 1000 kilometers. It has been shown that it represents an addition to the nondeviating part of the absorption and that it is related to the occurrence of unusually strong echoes from the D region. On days when the absorption is great the phase of waves of frequency 16 kc/sec, reflected from heights of 70 or 75 km, is such as to suggest that the height of reflection is lower than it is on the days when the absorption is small. There is, however, no difference in the amplitudes measured on this frequency on the two types of day.

All these phenomena suggest that, on some days in local winter in middle latitudes, there is increased ionization in the D region, in limited areas extending over distances of the order of 1000 kilometers. No corresponding anomalous absorption has been observed at low latitudes, where, of course, there is not much difference between winter and summer. At high latitudes violent increases of absorption associated with ionosphere storms are so common that it is doubtful whether any winter anomaly in absorption would be noticed even if it existed.

9.5.4 *The D Region and Solar Activity*

The profound disturbance of the D region during a S.I.D., or an ionosphere storm, will be discussed in § 9.11.3.2. In this section we shall mention those other changes in the ionization of the undisturbed D region which appear to be related to changes in the sun.

The effect of the D region on radio waves is most easily observed continuously in terms of the absorption of waves which penetrate it and are reflected from either the E or F region, under conditions when changes in absorption can be ascribed to changes in "nondeviative" absorption.

The logarithm of the reflection coefficient (ρ) is then proportional to $\int N\nu \, dh$ taken through the D region. Measurements[18] made at noon at Slough, England, on 4 Mc/sec from 1935 to 1953 show that $|\log \rho|$ increases with the sunspot number, R, and that the increase is more marked in summer than in winter. There is good numerical agreement with the expressions

Winter $|\log \rho| = 1.1(1 + 9.4 \times 10^{-3} R)$.

Summer $|\log \rho| = 1.4(1 + 13.2 \times 10^{-3} R)$.

Since $\int N\nu \, dh$ depends both on the magnitude of N and on its height distribution, it is not a simple matter to use these results to estimate how the ionizing radiation depends on R. It is interesting to note that the intensity of the radiation responsible for the peak of the E layer varies with R approximately like $(1 + 8 \times 10^{-3} R)$(see § 9.6.5).

It has been shown[150] that, even when there are no clearly marked S.I.D.'s or ionosphere storms, there is a 27-day periodicity in the nondeviative absorption of waves traversing the D region and hence, presumably, in the magnitude of $\int N\nu \, dh$.

9.5.5 *The Electron Content of the D Region*

9.5.5.1 *The Background Electron Distribution*

It has been shown how difficult it is to devise experiments which give direct evidence about the electron distribution in the D region. The best at present seems to be the experiment of Gardner and Pawsey,[105] who measured waves on the comparatively high frequency of 2 Mc/sec returned weakly by a process of partial reflection from inside the region, and the experiments of Fejer[100] on ionospheric cross modulation. The electron distributions deduced by these two methods are indicated by continuous lines in Fig. 6. Unfortunately, when measurements of electron density have been made with rockets the equipment has not been sensitive enough to measure concentrations less than about $2 \times 10^4 \, \text{cm}^{-3}$. The average results of the measurements which have been made are indicated in Fig. 6 by a continuous line.

The experimental results of Gardner and Pawsey and of Fejer refer to heights less than about 80 km; the rocket results refer to heights greater than about 90 km, and there are no experimental results between these levels.

Houston[130] has made two suggestions, indicated in Fig. 6, about how the curves should be joined up.

The large amount of experimental evidence obtained from the study of long and very long waves reflected from the D and lower E regions has proved difficult to interpret. Several attempts have been made by the workers at the Pennsylvania State University,[206] and the electron distribution deduced by Nertney[201] seems to have been the most successful. It is indicated by the dotted line in Fig. 6.

Attempts have been made to calculate, from a knowledge of the atmosphere and the solar ionizing radiation, what distribution of electron density would be expected. Houston[130] has carried those attempts further than most: his conclusions are shown at H(th) in Fig. 6. They are based on the supposition that the electrons in the D region arise mainly from the ionization of NO by

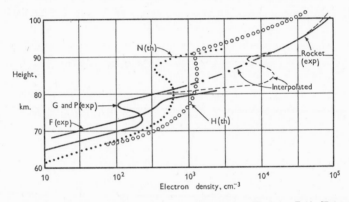

FIG. 6. Suggested electron distributions in the D region. F(exp)—J. A. Fejer (experimental), *J. Atmos. Terr. Phys.* **7**, 322 (1955); G and P (exp)—F. E. Gardner and J. L. Pawsey (experimental), *ibid.* **3**, 321 (1954); N(th)—R. J. Nertney (theory), *ibid.* **3**, 92 (1953); H(th)—R. E. Houston (theory), *ibid.* **12**, 225 (1958).

Lyman-α radiation. The theory is complicated and involves a subsidiary theory about how the NO is produced, and it assumes that the recombination coefficient is a known function of height (see § 9.5.6). In this theory, although it is NO which is ionized, it is O_2 which is mainly responsible for absorbing the Lyman-α radiation, so that this gas determines the height of the ionization peak which is near 85 km.[188]

The results shown in Fig. 6 are somewhat disappointing. The direct experimental results, indicated by the continuous lines, depend on very difficult experiments made on only a few occasions, and with no great accuracy. The distribution of Nertney, based on a much longer series of diverse experiments, appears to bear little relation to the continuous curve. His method was to suggest a model and then to calculate what would be the amplitude, phase, group delay, or polarization of a wave returned from it at vertical incidence. This is a difficult calculation involving a "full-wave" solution in an inhomogeneous nonisotropic medium. No model has yet been compared with the extensive experimental results available for oblique incidence.

The purely theoretical curve of Houston appears to agree better with Nertney's deductions than with those of the more direct experiments. It must, however, be remembered that it is based on several interlocking hypotheses, which it would presumably be possible to alter if experiment indicated clearly what the electron distribution really was.

It will be noticed that Nertney's distribution, based on a large amount of experimental information, indicates the presence of a peak of electrons in the D region at a height of about 80 km. The trough of electron density above this is necessary, in his theory, to avoid introducing too much absorption into the path of a wave reflected from higher up. In this connection it must be remembered that he was using Nicolet's figures for the collision frequency, which are probably too great at these heights. If the alternative values given in § 9.9 are used instead, it is probable that Nertney's curve would lie closer to Houston's theoretical one, and it might not indicate a peak of ionization. The possibility of the existence of a peak of electron density near 80 km is considered from the experimental side in the next section.

9.5.5.2 *The Irregularities Responsible for Scattering*

The reflections observed on frequencies greater than about 500 kc/sec from inside the D region are very weak. There have been some indications that they represent reflections from a level where the wave frequency equals the plasma frequency and that, as the frequency is changed, phenomena associated with the penetration of a layer are observed.[109] If this were substantiated, it would imply that there is a separate layer in the D region, and the consequences for the theory of that region would be important. The evidence for the existence of a separate layer is, however, not strong, and most workers consider the weak reflections to represent a partial return of the incident wave from irregularities in the ionization.

Some have suggested that there are gradients of electron density sufficiently sharp to produce the observed reflections, but it has been pointed out that these would rapidly be reduced, by diffusion, so far as to be ineffective. The most widely accepted view at present is that the partial reflections come from levels where, for some reason, the ionosphere is particularly irregular.

There has been much discussion about the nature, and the origin, of these irregularities. The evidence is reviewed in § 9.10, when the weaker irregularities which pervade the whole of the ionosphere are discussed.

9.5.6 *Recombination in the D Region*[39,186,191,193,194]

To deduce the recombination coefficient (α) in the D region it is necessary to know how the electron density (N) varies with time at each height, the rate at which electrons are produced at each height, and the magnitude of any vertical movements in the region.

In spite of the doubt about each of these items of knowledge, attempts have been made to deduce the value of α as a function of height and time. One of these attempts has been based on the diurnal asymmetry of some quantity, such as the absorption, phase, or polarization of an echo reflected from a higher level, which is believed to be determined by the electron density in the D region. The corresponding time lag is then equated to $1/2\alpha N$; N is supposed known from independent evidence, and α is deduced for the height taken as appropriate for the chosen value of N.

Another attempt involves the time lag between the maximum of a solar flare observed in visible light and the maximum of the S.I.D. which accompanies it. The S.I.D. has usually been measured in terms of the phenomena known as S.W.F., S.P.A., or S.E.A. (see § 9.11.2). The S.I.D. is then supposed to correspond to an increase in the electron density at some level which has to be decided by independent evidence, and α at this level is then deduced by equating the observed time delay to $1/2\alpha N$. In this method there are uncertainties about the level concerned, about the increase of N, and about the applicability of the expression for the time delay.

Attempts to measure α in the D region by observation of eclipses have not proved useful.

Attempts have been made to determine the recombination coefficient at night by measuring the changes of phase of waves returned from the D region on frequencies of 16 and 150 kc/sec. It is assumed that the height of reflection corresponds to a fixed value of the electron density and that the gradient dN/dh is known, so that, from observations of the rate of increase of reflection height (dh/dt), the quantity dN/dt can be determined from the equation

$$dN/dt = (dN/dh)(dh/dt). \tag{9.74}$$

In all these methods of calculation it is supposed that there are no vertical movements of importance.

It will be realized that any deduction about the recombination coefficient in the D region involves an interrelated series of deductive reasonings of some complexity, and it is not easy to assess how far all steps in the argument are valid. It would be useful if there were independent justification for some of them. On the assumption that all are acceptable, it has been deduced that the recombination coefficient varies with height as shown in Fig. 7. It is suggested that the height variation changes after sunset.

Attempts have also been made to calculate the recombination coefficient in the D region from molecular theory. It has been suggested that above 90 km the process is one of dissociative recombination, but that below 90 km it is influenced by reactions involving the mutual neutralization of ions, so that $\alpha_{\text{eff}} = \alpha_e + \lambda \alpha_i$, where λ is the ratio of ion density to electron density (see 9.23(a)). The change in α_{eff} from day to night, and during the night, is

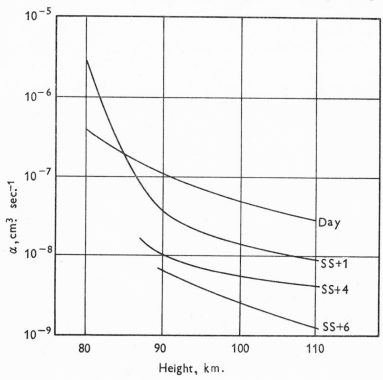

Fig. 7. The recombination coefficient, α, as a function of height by day, and 1, 4, and 6 hours after ground sunset, according to A. P. Mitra, *J. Atmos. Terr. Phys.* **10**, 140 (1957).

supposed to be the result of a change in λ, which is determined by a balance between the rate of production of ions by attachment and the rate of destruction by detachment, either by solar radiation or by collision.

It is probably wisest at present to be cautious about accepting either the experimental or the theoretical values of the recombination coefficient.

9.5.7 *Negative Ions in the D Region*[36, 37]

Before the full implications of the tensor conductivities in the ionosphere were realized, it was thought that the comparatively great conductivities required by the dynamo theory of geomagnetism might arise from the presence of comparatively numerous negative ions. Detailed theoretical estimates were therefore made of the quantity λ, which represents the ratio of the concentrations of negative ions and of electrons. It was concluded that during the day at 90 km height the magnitude of λ was probably about 0.05 and certainly less than 5, and at 75 km it was probably about 0.5 and certainly less than 50.

9.6 The Undisturbed E Layer[222, 280]

9.6.1 *Approximate Behavior*[7]

If an ionogram is examined somewhat superficially, it might be thought that because the penetrations of the E and $F2$ layers are the most clearly marked phenomena the corresponding critical frequencies fE and $fF2$ were simple quantities capable of straightforward interpretation. It will be shown in § 9.6.2, however, that the penetration of the E layer is, in reality, quite complicated, and in § 9.8.1 that, although the F penetration is unambiguously measurable, the explanation of its occurrence is far from clear. For a first understanding of the ionosphere these complications will, however, be ignored and an over-simplified preliminary account of the facts will be given.

The critical frequency (fE) of the E layer varies with the time of day, season, and epoch in the solar cycle, and with the position on the earth. At one epoch in the cycle it is approximately a unique function of the sun's zenith distance (χ), whether χ changes through the day, or the season, at one place, or by displacement over the earth at one time. The functional relation is approximately that of (9.75) (see § 9.4.1)

$$fE = 9 \times 10^3[(q_0/\alpha) \cos \chi]^{1/4} \sec^{-1} \qquad (9.75)$$

expected for an equilibrium α-Chapman layer. Measurements made during eclipses, first, suggest that the ionizing radiation travels in straight lines with the speed of light, and, second, confirm that the loss process is one of recombination with $\alpha \doteqdot 10^{-8}$ cm^3 sec^{-1}.

9.6.2 *Complications in the Penetration of the E Layer*[50, 222, 267]

Closer examination of ionograms shows that the penetration of the E layer is not a simple matter. There are usually several "critical" frequencies, near which the shape of the $h'(f)$ curve can take a diversity of shapes. An $h'(f)$ curve, showing no more than average complication near the E-layer penetration, is shown in Fig. 8a, and Fig. 8b shows the corresponding $N(h)$ curve. The well-marked "critical" frequencies in (a), indicated by arrows, correspond to almost imperceptible kinks in the $N(h)$ curve, where they are marked by corresponding arrows. It is clear that the shape of an $h'(f)$ curve much overemphasizes the shape of the subsidiary "layers" and that it is dangerous to make deductions about the shape of the layer simply from a superficial examination of the $h'(f)$ curve.

The precise form of the $h'(f)$ curve changes with time of day, season, solar cycle, and position on the earth, so that no summarizing description is possible. Usually, however, it is found that the "critical" frequencies observable at any one place in any one month can be divided into (1) those which are frequently observable and follow roughly the law $f \propto (\cos \chi)^{0.25}$, and (2) those which are observable intermittently and do not obey that law, even approximately.

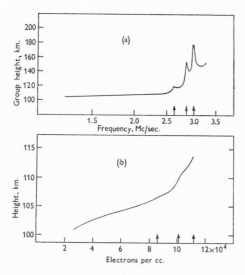

FIG. 8. (a) Typical $h'(f)$ curve for the E region. (b) The $N(h)$ curve calculated from it. Corresponding points are marked with arrows.

Although some of the frequencies listed in class (1) may not be observable continuously during any one day, it is usually possible, by comparing successive days, to identify them when they do appear, and to show that they vary fairly smoothly. It is usual to lay particular emphasis on one of these and to call it *the* critical frequency, fE, but when more than one critical frequency is observable and when the distinctness of one or the other changes from time to time it is not at all clear how one specific one should be followed through a single day. It is even less certain how one and the same critical frequency can be followed from season to season, or from place to place. It is probable that the values of fE tabulated by ionosphere observatories suffer, in many instances, from ambiguities arising from these complications.

Since, however, at the present time these tabulated values provide the most widely spread information about the E layer, they have been studied in detail by several workers.

9.6.3 *Tabulated Critical Frequencies*[3,4,183,305]

The tabulated critical frequencies have been examined to see how well they fit the expression

$$fE = (fE)_0 (\cos \chi)^n \qquad (9.76)$$

with $n = 0.25$, as they would if the E layer were an equilibrium α-Chapman layer. In this examination an attempt has been made to distinguish between changes of χ at one place during the day, and during the year, and at one time over the earth. Although during the day the layer is *not* in equilibrium, it can be shown[22] that the departures from equilibrium are likely to be small compared with other departures from the ideal α-Chapman layer, and they can be neglected for the present purpose.

When diurnal variations are considered they are found to fit (9.76) best with values of n somewhere between 0.30 and 0.36.[118,253] Different investigators find different results, and the behavior may be different in different places. There is, however, no doubt that n is greater than the value (0.25) required by the idealized theory, so that the effect of the diurnal variation of χ is greater than would be expected.

When annual variations of fE at midday are considered, it is found that, on the average, (9.76) fits the results fairly well if $n = 0.25$ as in the simple theory. It has, however, been shown that the value of n varies with latitude in an interesting way, which is discussed in § 9.6.6.

The variation over the earth can be usefully studied by selecting a fixed value of χ (which will correspond to different times at different places) and finding how the corresponding values of fE vary with latitude. It is then found that fE is greatest at the equator and decreases gradually toward the poles.

9.6.4 *The Shape and Height of the E Layer*[139,222]

There have not been many reliable measurements of the shape or height of the E layer. The only satisfactory method is to calculate the electron distribution—the $N(h)$ curve—from an accurate $h'(f)$ curve, making due allowance for the earth's magnetic field and for low-lying ionization with plasma frequency less than the lowest recorded frequency.* One set of

* This can be allowed for only by considering both the Ordinary and the Extraordinary echoes.

measurements made in S.E. England shows that, when subsidiary "ledges" are not well marked, then, down to where $N = 0.5N_m$ the shape of the layer and the way in which its height varies through the day are roughly what would be expected for an equilibrium α-Chapman layer formed in an atmosphere of scale height 8 km, with its peak at a level of 105 km for vertically incident ionizing radiation.

9.6.5 *Intensity of the Ionizing Radiation*[10,48, 50, 66,140,141, 220, 307]

Several attempts have been made to determine how the intensity of the ionizing radiation varies with the state of the sun. If this is represented by q_0, the peak rate of production of electrons for vertically incident radiation, then (9.75) shows that, if the simple laws were valid, q_0 should be proportional to $(fE)^4/\cos \chi$. This quantity has therefore sometimes been called the E-layer character figure. If attention is restricted to midday at one place, so that χ varies with the season, (9.75) is known to be approximately correct, and this character figure leads to useful conclusions. Although the results of different investigators are not very consistent, they appear to be represented approximately by the expression

$$q_0 = 180(1 + aR) \text{ cm}^{-3} \text{ sec}^{-1} \tag{9.77}$$

with a value of a between 7 and 9.5×10^{-3}.

At times when there is pronounced solar activity the character figure, measured in the way described, is found to fluctuate in sympathy with fluctuations in the numbers and sizes of spots, flocculi, and faculae on the solar disk, but the ionosphere fluctuations lag behind the solar variations by times of the order of 10 days.[3, 4]

An attempt has been made to separate the effects of the steady "background" radiation from those of the fluctuating radiation, and reasons have been given for supposing that the intensities of these two components vary differently with sunspot number R.[49] It has also been shown that the intensity of the total ionizing radiation varies periodically with a 27-day period.[48]

Day-to-day variations of the E-layer character figure are well correlated with variations in the intensity of the solar radio emission on a wavelength of 10 cm. This correlation appears to be greater than that between most other phenomena on the earth and on the sun.

9.6.6 *Detailed Diurnal Variations and Vertical Movements*

Because of the finite recombination time it would not be expected that the variations of fE would be symmetrical about midday, and from the departures from symmetry it should be possible to determine the recombination

27

coefficient. These departures are small, but when examined in detail they are found to differ from those required by simple theory. It has been shown, for example, that, at Slough, in summer, the curve of fE plotted against time has a subsidiary minimum near 1000 hours. This anomaly has been attributed to a vertical movement of the layer, associated with the maximum which is supposed to occur in the E-W Sq current system of the atmospheric dynamo at that time (see § 9.3.3).[20, 21]

This conclusion is comparatively new, and there is little doubt that it will be extended and possibly modified, as the result of more widespread and more frequent measurements made during the International Geophysical Year. There are other, less clear, indications that vertical movements associated with the Sq current system influence the behavior of the E layer. One of these is in the magnitude of n in (9.76) appropriate to a seasonal variation of χ at midday. This quantity is found to vary with latitude in such a way that it is roughly symmetrical about latitude $\pm 35°$. It is suggested that this symmetry results, in a rather complicated way, from a "tilting" of the Sq current loop about an E–W line through its center, which lies near these latitudes and moves with the seasons, so that a given place may be on different sides of it in summer and in winter.[47, 317]

Observation of the equivalent height of reflection on a fixed frequency over a period of 500 days has revealed a periodic vertical movement of the E layer with a period of half a lunar day and an excursion of about ± 1 km in the equivalent height. The maximum height was reached about an hour before lunar transit. Similar results have been obtained elsewhere, and there is some indication, not yet very clear, that the phase of the oscillation is opposite at latitudes greater and less than $35°$.[9, 156, 168, 293]

The interpretation of these lunar "tidal" motions is not clear. One explanation is that they correspond to the "tipping" of the L current ring responsible for the quiet day lunar magnetic variation. This would be expected to result in opposite phases north and south of the center, but it appears that they would be in a sense opposite to those observed.

9.6.7 *The E Layer at Night*[212, 258, 259]

There is little information about the nocturnal E layer because at night the critical frequency lies outside the working range of most ionosondes. The most extensive information comes from $h'(f)$ curves made at Boulder, Colorado, with an ionosonde working over a range of frequencies from 50 to 5000 kc/sec. The records show that at night the E layer critical frequency varies so much from hour to hour and from night to night that it is impossible to describe a regular behavior. This variability is probably evidence that at night the phenomenon of Es, to be discussed in § 9.6.8, is particularly noticeable. It is, however, important to notice that on some occasions the critical frequency of the E layer, at an equivalent height around 120 km, is as low as 0.3 Mc/sec, a result which implies that fE for the "normal" E layer decays to at least this value. If the recombination coefficient continues to have its daytime value (10^{-8} cm³ sec⁻¹) at night, then it would be expected that fE would decrease to about 0.5 Mc/sec after 10 hours of darkness, regardless of its precise magnitude at sunset.

One important fact which is clear from the Boulder records is that often when fE decreases below about 0.75 Mc/sec a higher echo is revealed, reflected from an equivalent height near 160 km. The detailed behavior of this "intermediate" echo is not yet clear. If, however, there is, as is now commonly supposed, no gap by day between the peak of the E layer and the bottom of the F layer, it is not surprising that, at night, when the E-layer critical frequency is small, the higher ionization, presumably with a smaller loss rate, is revealed. The fact that there is another peak or ledge, marked by another critical frequency, is perhaps a little unexpected.

9.6.8 *Sporadic E (Es Ionization)*[11, 240, 249, 300]

9.6.8.1 *Experimental Facts*

It was mentioned in § 9.6.2 that frequently one of the E-layer critical frequencies varies in an irregular way so that it is not a smooth function of the solar zenith angle, χ. Because of the general randomness of its behavior, this critical frequency has been said to refer to a "sporadic E layer," or Es ionization, and has been named fEs. As previously explained, the different critical frequencies of the E region present a complex and diverse range of phenomena, different at different places. It is therefore not surprising that a considerable effort has been devoted to classifying the different forms taken by fEs on ionograms. Although this classification is of value for ensuring that results from different observatories can be compared, it does not yet seem to have led to useful knowledge about the nature of the Es ionization.

Extensive studies have been made of the statistics of occurrence of Es ionization, usually by computing the percentage of time for which fEs is greater than some fixed threshold. Some of the results are shown in Fig. 9. Near the equator the occurrence of Es is a daytime phenomenon, and, as might be expected, there is little seasonal variation. In the auroral regions Es ionization occurs most frequently between 1800 and 0600 hours, i.e., during the night at the equinoxes, but again there is little seasonal variation.

The behavior in middle latitudes is markedly different. First, the magnitude of fEs is smaller; second, its variations are mainly seasonal, and the diurnal variation is less clearly marked. There is a maximum probability of occurrence,

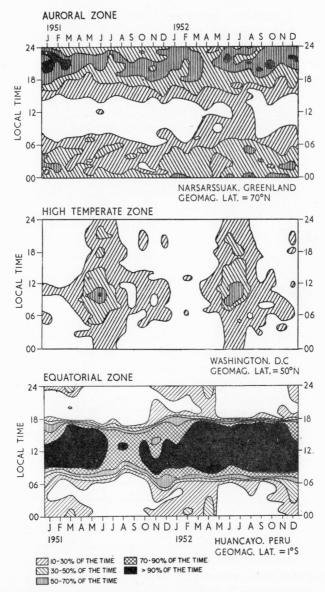

FIG. 9. The fraction of the total time for which *Es* echoes were observed on frequencies greater than 5 Mc/sec. From E. K. Smith, *Natl. Bur. Standards* (*U.S.*) *Circ.* **582** (1957).

in local summer, and a less clearly emphasized probability for *Es* to be found during the daytime. The seasonal variation is well seen in Fig. 10, which is based on results for five observatories situated between 30° and

43° N. In spite of the apparent trend in Fig. 10, no clear relation between the incidence of Es ionization and the epoch of the solar cycle has been established.

In the auroral zone there is some indication that Es ionization tends to be observed at the same time as auroral and magnetic disturbances. In middle latitudes there is a negative correlation, so that Es is less likely to be observed during periods of magnetic disturbance.

It has been suggested that Es can be produced by the action of certain kinds of thunderstorm.[190]

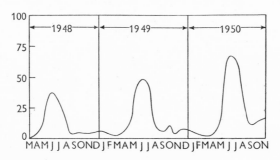

FIG. 10. The percentage of the time for which Es echoes were observed on frequencies greater than 5 Mc/sec at five observatories in the United States. From E. K. Smith, *Natl. Bur. Standards (U.S.) Circ.* **582** (1957).

It has previously been mentioned that much work has gone into the classification of Es into different "types," some of which are evidenced by traces at different equivalent heights on the $h'(f)$ curves. When, however, these $h'(f)$ curves are converted into electron-density profiles, the differences in height are seen to be much less significant. It therefore seems useful to consider the height most commonly measured at the majority of observatories. Unfortunately the measurements are not very good, but they are so numerous that averages probably have some significance. It is found that the average equivalent height is near 100 km and that it changes little with time of day or season or from the equator to the auroral zone.

One type of Es noticed fairly regularly in moderate latitudes is always partially transmitting at the higher frequencies and occurs at a height near 105 km. Its intensity has been correlated with the number of meteors incident on the atmosphere, and it has been suggested that it consists of an irregular stratum of ionization produced by them. It has been called "meteoric Es." [200]

The behavior of the Es ionization depends to some extent on lunar time. Near the equator, when it is observed by day, it is often seen to disappear suddenly at a fixed lunar hour. Elsewhere lunar "tidal" oscillations have been observed both in the equivalent height and in the mean value of fEs.[179, 180, 181, 239]

There are two peculiarities in the $h'(f)$ records of the most common form of Es ionization: first, the Es echo often occurs simultaneously with an F echo, over quite a wide range of frequencies, as though the Es layer were partially transparent; and, second, the Es trace on the record disappears without increasing in height as the "critical" frequency, fEs, is approached. There is no satisfactory explanation of these phenomena. A thin layer would allow simultaneous observations of Es and F echoes over a small range of frequencies and would produce little "group retardation" when it was penetrated, but it would have to be very thin indeed to explain the common observation that the two echoes can occur over a wide frequency range. A layer in which there were important small-scale irregularities in the horizontal direction might allow simultaneous observation of the two echoes over a wide range of frequencies, but, unless it were also very thin, it would produce measurable group retardation. Observations of the intensities of the two echoes as the frequency is varied near the "critical" value have been used to show that both "thin" and "irregular" layers do occur, and that the "thin" ones usually have a thickness of about 5 km.[62, 79] On one occasion[136] a rocket, equipped for measuring electron density, was observed to pass through a layer of thickness 1 km at a height of 101 km when simultaneous observations of the $h'(f)$ trace showed an Es echo (see also § 3.4).

The Es ionization occurs in patches which extend over distances of a few hundred kilometers, and, when observed at one place, it lasts generally for times of the order of 1 or 2 hours. What evidence there is goes to show that the appearance and disappearance of Es overhead is the result of growth and decay of the ionization rather than of the transfer of a patch from one place to another, but the evidence is not yet very satisfactory.[80,102,107,110, 255]

Inside the patch the Es ionization has an irregular horizontal structure. Methods of investigation like those described in § 9.10.2 show that, in the auroral regions, the irregularities are elongated in the E–W direction with an axis ratio of about 4, in middle latitudes there is no obvious elongation, and in equatorial regions the elongation is in the N–S direction with an axis ratio of about 10. The irregularities have sizes of about 200 meters along their smallest dimensions.

9.6.8.2 *Electron Distribution in Es*[104]

The first step in making deductions from the observations is to decide what distributions of electrons could produce the observed echoes. Since there are many types of echo, each with its own special characteristics, it would not be surprising if there were a corresponding number of electron distributions. The ones that have been suggested include:

Horizontally irregular distributions $\begin{cases} \Delta N/N \text{ small} \\ \Delta N/N \text{ large} \end{cases}$

Horizontally stratified distributions $\begin{cases} \text{thin layers} \\ \text{sharp gradients} \end{cases}$

Horizontally irregular distributions with $\Delta N/N$ large could be the cause of that type of Es for which there is a wide range of frequencies which give simultaneous reflections from F and from Es. The lowest frequency to give F echoes would then correspond to the smallest electron density, and the highest frequency on which E echoes were observed would correspond to the greatest electron density.

The only evidence that sharp gradients of electron density, as distinct from thin layers, might be responsible comes from the results of rocket soundings. It appears, however, that spurious sharp gradients might appear in the electron density profiles if the rocket traversed a region where there were marked inhomogeneities in the horizontal plane, so that this evidence is unreliable.[210]

There is little doubt that, on some occasions, Es reflections are produced by uniform horizontally stratified thin layers of electrons, but it is probable that these occasions represent only a small fraction of those on which Es is observed.

9.6.8.3 *The Ultimate Causes of Es*

If the types of electron distribution responsible for Es were known it would next be necessary to consider how they could be produced. They might result from (1) redistribution of existing electrons or (2) changes in the rates of production or loss of electrons.

There is possibly a little evidence that thin layers of electrons are sometimes produced by vertical redistribution, for it has been noticed that the shape of the remainder of the $N(h)$ curve, determined on one occasion by vertical sounding, and on another by a rocket experiment, changed when a thin layer was formed.

It seems that the only type of force which could reasonably be expected to redistribute electrons into a thin layer would be an electromagnetic one and would involve a loop of current which ought to be detectable by a magnetometer sent through the layer.

The recombination time (the "sluggishness" of Appleton, see § 9.2.4) in the E layer is known to be about 10 minutes, so that if a thin layer were to be kept in being for an hour (the average duration of an Es patch) the forces redistributing the electrons would have to continue for nearly the whole of that time.

A redistribution of electrons to produce irregularities in the horizontal plane could be the result of turbulence. It has to be remembered, however, that recent work[256] has shown that turbulence is insufficient to produce even the weaker irregularities in the normal E region by simple compression and dilation. A vertical gradient of electron density is first required so that turbulent whirls can move denser and less dense parts up and down to produce the irregularities required. Enhancement of these irregularities to produce an Es echo might result from an increased gradient, or increased turbulence, or both. If in, the irregular layer, $\Delta N/N$ were large, it could be produced only if there were a steep gradient for the turbulent whirls to work on. But a gradient of the necessary steepness would almost certainly be sufficient to produce an Es echo by itself.

The electron distributions responsible for Es echoes could be the result of modifications to the rates of production or loss of electrons. Direct increases of the production rate by incoming particles may well be the cause of the irregular ionization responsible for the "meteoric" Es layer and the auroral Es. It is less likely to be responsible for the equatorial Es because of the difficulty which incoming charged particles experience in reaching the equator. It is difficult to see how smooth thin layers, having the extent of Es patches, could be produced at any part of the earth by any ionizing agency.

Patches of increased ionization, either smooth or irregular, could be produced by modifications of the atmosphere in one or another of the following ways.

The presence of a minor atmospheric constituent, more easily ionizable by the sun's radiation, could be responsible for extra ionization during the day. A similar constituent which modified the recombination rate could be effective either by day or by night. It has been suggested that minor constituents of these kinds might collect near a height of 100 km by the diffusion of matter from meteor trails.[306]

Another mechanism by which extra electrons might be produced is through the transport upward of some atmospheric constituent which carried stored energy, ready to be released in the production of free electrons. The most likely constituent of this kind appears to be negative ions. The precise mechanism for detaching the electrons has not been suggested, and it is difficult to see why it should be most efficient near 100 km.

The fact that the equatorial zone of Es coincides approximately with the zone of the equatorial electrojet has suggested that the current in the electrojet might be directly responsible for the Es ionization. Another suggestion might be that the ions in the electrojet experience a force which carries them up to a level where the electrons are, for some reason, more easily detached.

None of these possibilities has been properly tested against experimental results, and it cannot yet be said that there is any accepted theory to account for Es ionization.

9.7 The Undisturbed $F1$ Layer (or Ledge)

9.7.1 *The Appearance of the $F1$ Ledge*

Although when $N(h)$ curves are examined the $F1$ layer seldom shows as more than a rather insignificant inflection, the corresponding critical frequency ($fF1$) observed on the $h'(f)$ record is much more clearly marked. It is found to vary in a remarkably regular way and is probably of fundamental significance for ionosphere theory.

The critical frequency, $fF1$, is never observed at night, and not always by day; it is most pronounced in summer and at the minimum of the solar cycle; in winter at the maximum of the cycle it is never observed. The height of the $F1$ ledge on the $N(h)$ curve lies in the neighborhood of 180 km.

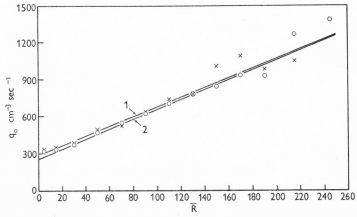

FIG. 11. The rate (q_0) of production of electrons at the level of the $F1$ ledge when the sun's radiation is incident vertically, plotted against the mean Zurich sunspot number, $\bar{R}$. The value of q_0 is calculated from (9.75), on the assumption that $\alpha = 5 \times 10^{-9}$ cm³ sec⁻¹. Crosses represent the average of 258 observations from Slough. Circles represent the average of 1218 observations for nine observatories spread over the world. The line labeled 1 corresponds to $q_0 = 280(1 + 0.014\bar{R})$, see ref. 217; and that labeled 2 corresponds to $q_0 = 250(1 + 0.016\bar{R})$, which fits the points a little better.

9.7.2 *Approximate Behavior of the Critical Frequency, $fF1$[217]*

To a first approximation the critical frequency, $fF1$ varies with the seasons, and over the earth, as though it were the critical frequency of an α-Chapman layer. The value of α has been estimated, from the results of observations made during eclipses, to be about 5×10^{-9} cm³ sec⁻¹. This estimate should be treated with some caution because there are difficulties in interpreting the eclipse results in detail.[297]

If it is supposed that $fF1$ corresponds to the peak of an α-Chapman layer, then, with its magnitude at the midday maximum known and with the value of α determined from eclipses, it is possible to use the expression (9.75) to deduce q_0, the rate at which electrons would be produced at the peak of the layer, if the ionizing radiation were incident vertically. The value of q_0 is

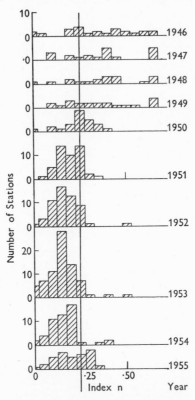

Fig. 12. If $fF1 \propto (\cos \chi)^n$ when measurements are made at midday and χ varies through the seasons, these histograms show how values of n calculated for several different observatories are distributed at different epochs of the solar cycle. In years near sunspot minimum n is *less* than the value (0.25) it would have if the $F1$ ledge behaved like the peak of an α-Chapman layer.

found to vary through the solar cycle as shown in Fig. 11, where it is plotted as a function of $\overline{R}$, the mean Zurich sunspot number. The equation of the straight line which fits the results best is

$$q_0 = 250(1 + 16 \times 10^{-3}\,\overline{R})\,\mathrm{cm}^{-3}\,\mathrm{sec}^{-1}. \qquad (9.78)$$

9.7.3 *Departures from Simple Behavior*[72]

If $fF1$ corresponded to the peak of an α-Chapman layer in quasi-equilibrium, it should be proportional to $(\cos \chi)^n$, with $n = 0.25$. It is found, in fact, that

n is appreciably different from 0.25 and varies from place to place and from season to season. Thus for Washington it is found that, for diurnal variations, $n = 0.18$ in summer and about 0.25 in winter. The values of n appropriate to *seasonal* variations of the midday magnitude of $fF1$ from a large number of observations are shown graphically in Fig. 12.[221]

Figure 12 shows that n appropriate to the seasons varies over the earth (see the spread of values among the different observations) and with the epoch in the solar cycle. The solar cycle change is also noticeable in the value of n for the diurnal variation. For the $F1$ ledge in years near sun-spot minimum $n < 0.25$, whereas for the E layer $n > 0.25$.

Although the height (h_mF1) of the $F1$ ledge is determined from the $h'(f)$ curves only after a complicated calculation in which there may be errors,* it nevertheless appears fairly certain that it does not vary like the height of the peak of an α-Chapman layer. It is found, for example, that although h_mF1 increases toward evening, as expected, it is greater in summer than in winter, and is greater at low than at middle latitudes, just the opposite of what would be expected.

These departures of the $F1$ ledge from simple behavior have not received much attention. They may be the result of gradients of the scale height, gradients of the recombination coefficient, or vertical movements. The present view seems to be that anomalies in the more clearly marked E and $F2$ layers must be explained first, and then it will probably be comparatively simple to explain the anomalies in the $F1$ ledge.

9.8 The Undisturbed $F2$ Layer[170, 173]

9.8.1 *Anomalous Critical Frequency, $fF2$*

When the $F2$ layer is investigated at different observatories at different times, its behavior is found to be very complicated and is difficult to summarize. Any summary will over-simplify the facts and will not mention some of the more striking peculiarities. Since, however, a mere catalog of all the phenomena which have been observed is neither readable nor useful, we shall here make an attempt to summarize the present knowledge, having given due warning that we have over-simplified the account.

It is usual, and useful, to describe the over-all behavior of the $F2$ layer by pointing out how it differs from that of a hypothetical Chapman layer. The differences will be called "anomalies": we shall first list the more striking anomalies in the parameter $fF2$.

---

* For example, it depends on the making of a proper estimate of the electron density in the base of the E layer.

9.8.1.1 *The Geographic Anomaly*[12, 17, 24, 157]

In Fig. 13b $fF2_2$ is plotted as a function of magnetic latitude for midday at the equinox. There is a minimum at the equator where, on a simple theory, there should be a maximum, since there the sun's radiation is incident

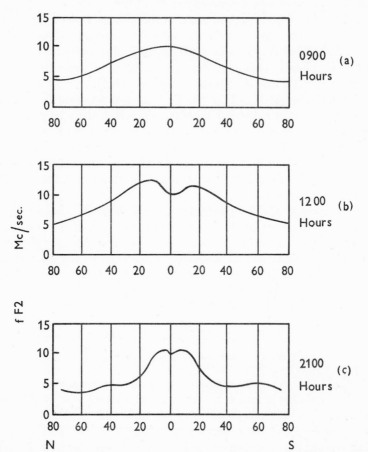

FIG. 13. $fF2$ as measured at different times of day at the equinox plotted as a function of magnetic latitude to illustrate the "geographic anomaly." After E. V. Appleton, *J. Atmos. Terr. Phys.* **5**, 348 (1954).

vertically. The points are less spread if magnetic latitude* is used instead of geographic. This fact gives a hint that movements of the $F2$ layer associated with the earth's permanent magnetic field are probably important in explaining this anomaly.

* Magnetic latitude is defined in such a way that lines of magnetic latitude are also lines of constant dip.

If $fF2$ is plotted in the same way at other times of day, the minimum at the magnetic equator is not so pronounced. At midnight, for example, the minimum is even replaced by a peak of anomalously great values of $fF2$ as shown in Fig. 13c.

9.8.1.2 *The Diurnal Anomaly*

When $fF2$ (or N_mF2) is studied as a function of the time of day, it is often found that it has a maximum value at a time far removed from midday; indeed there is frequently a subsidiary minimum near midday, often referred to as the "midday bite-out." At many places the maximum is reached in the late afternoon. An example is shown in Fig. 14.

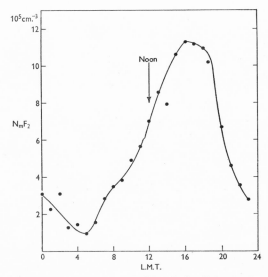

FIG. 14. The peak electron content (N_mF2) of the F layer above Maui, Hawaii, plotted against local mean time for the average of five international quiet days in June, 1954, to illustrate a marked example of the "diurnal anomaly."

9.8.1.3 *The December and Seasonal Anomalies*[29, 42, 44, 71, 166, 167, 233, 308]

If $fF2$ reached a maximum near midday, it would be interesting to see how it varied with the season. Since, however, it does not, the next best thing is to consider either its value at the diurnal maximum, or at a fixed time during the daylight hours. If either of these quantities is examined it is found that the deviations from a simple Chapman behavior can be expressed as two anomalies.

1. Over that part of the world between latitudes 50° N and 35° S $fF2$ measured at midday is too large in November, December, and January. We shall call this the "December anomaly."

2. At all places, and particularly near latitudes 50°, $fF2$ measured at midday is, in addition, too large in local winter. This we shall call the "seasonal anomaly."

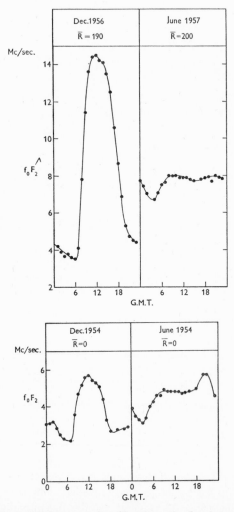

FIG. 15. Mean values of $fF2$ measured at Slough on the five international quiet days in June and December in years of small and great sunspot number ($\bar{R}$). The fact that the midday values are greater in December than in June (particularly for the greater sunspot number) illustrates the "December anomaly," which is superimposed on the "winter anomaly" at Slough. At midnight the "anomaly" is not observed.

In the northern hemisphere, where December is in winter, the two anomalies add, and the result is well exemplified in the ionosphere over Slough (latitude

54° N). Figure 15 shows the diurnal variation of $fF2$ observed at Slough for June and December in years of low and high sunspot number. It is noticeable that the ratio of the midday value in December to that in June is about 1.8 for high sunspot number and about 1.0 for low sunspot number, whereas if $fF2 \propto (\cos \chi)^{0.25}$ we should expect this ratio to be 0.725. The December and the seasonal anomalies are both most marked at the maximum of the solar cycle, a conclusion which is confirmed by results from other places.

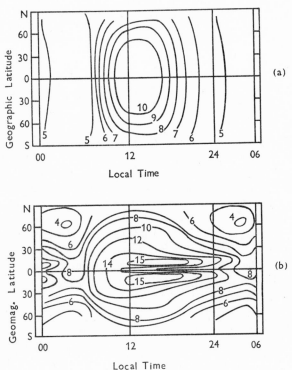

FIG. 16. Smoothed contour maps to show the distribution of $fF2$ over the world at the equinox. (a) Theoretical contours calculated for an α-Chapman layer. (b) Observed contours, plotted with respect to geomagnetic latitude. Note that the variation of $fF2$ along a line of fixed time in the afternoon shows the "geomagnetic anomaly" illustrated in Fig. 13. From D. F. Martyn, *Phys. Soc. Rept. Ionosphere Conf.* 260 (1955).

These two anomalies are not present when midnight values of $fF2$ are examined. This point is illustrated, for Slough, in Fig. 15.

9.8.1.4 *Other Anomalies*

One way of showing the "anomalous" behavior of the quantity $fF2$ is to compare the values observed all over the earth at a given time with what would be expected on a simple theory. In Fig. 16 a smoothed contour map of values observed at an equinox is compared with a corresponding theoretical map for an α-Chapman layer. It is especially noticeable that there are important differences near the equator, and particularly near sunrise and sunset.[172]

Allen[5] has studied the behavior of $fF2$ as measured at a series of observatories throughout a solar cycle and has compared it with the ideal "Chapman" behavior. He drew attention to a nocturnal anomaly, particularly noticeable near sunspot minimum, which is characterized in the winter hemisphere by an *increase* in $fF2$ during the night and in the summer hemisphere by an unexpectedly rapid decrease. Superimposed on this there is, at all epochs of the solar cycle, a short-lived anomalous decrease about an hour before ground sunrise, followed by a short-lived anomalous increase. He also noticed the "winter anomaly" but did not analyze it so fully as others have done.

9.8.2 *Electron Profiles* [$N(h)$ *Curves*][250, 251, 252]

The $N(h)$ curves for the $F2$ layer take a variety of shapes. Often they are roughly semi-parabolic, with a half-thickness of about 100 km; this shape is particularly common during the night. At other times, particularly near the equator, the $N(h)$ curve is nearly straight right up to the end. Sometimes there are one, or more, small inflections near the end, quite apart from any $F1$ inflection which may be present. These small inflections produce well-marked cusps on the $h'(f)$ curve, study of which has shown that their occurrence is sometimes associated with lunar time. The phenomenon has been referred to as the "equatorial lunar layer."[158,159]

It is possible, by integrating an $N(h)$ curve, to calculate the sub-peak electron content (n) in a column of unit cross section. When this is done it is found that, although the peak electron density often changes irregularly, from hour to hour, the sub-peak electron content changes smoothly. On these occasions it appears that there are irregular movements which alter the distribution of the electrons, but not their total number.*

It was at one time thought that the major anomalies in $fF2$ were not noticeable in n, and the suggestion was made that they were the result of "anomalous" distributions of a total number of electrons which did not vary anomalously. This suggestion now appears to be only partially correct; it is found that the major anomalies are noticeable in the sub-peak electron content (n), but to a smaller extent than in the peak electron density [proportional to $(fF2)^2$].[214]

---

* There is, however, some evidence[73] that irregular changes of the critical frequency $fF2$, occur simultaneously at widely separated places, as though caused by irregular changes in the ionizing radiation.

A study of $N(h)$ curves shows that the height (h_m) of the peak of the $F2$-layer behaves anomalously, particularly in its seasonal variation, being greater in summer than in winter. In some places, particularly, for example, at Huancayo, Peru, there are violent and unexpected changes during the day, of the type illustrated in Fig 17.

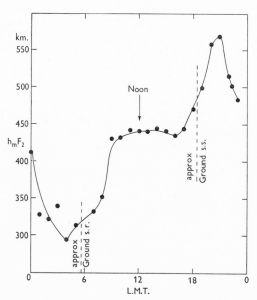

FIG. 17. The unexpected changes in the height $(h_m F2)$ of the peak of the $F2$ layer. This example shows the mean results of observations made at Huancayo on five international quiet days in December, 1958. Taken from S. A. Croom, A. R. Robbins, and J. O. Thomas, "Tables of Ionospheric Electron Density". Cavendish Laboratory, Cambridge.

9.8.3 *Solar Cycle Variations*[3,4,145,165]

The critical frequency, $F2$, of the $F2$ layer varies markedly with the solar cycle, being greatest at sunspot maximum. The world-wide results have been summarized by the expression $(fF2)^2 \propto (1 + 0.02\overline{R})$, where $\overline{R}$ is the mean Zurich sunspot number. In this expression it should be noticed that $(f)^2$ and not $(f)^4$ has a linear relation to $\overline{R}$. This conclusion, arrived at from a study of the observations, suggests that attachment rather than recombination may be the effective process of loss in the $F2$ region. In the polar regions the variation with the solar cycle is markedly different at different places, hours, and seasons.[232]

The dependence on the epoch in the solar cycle suggests that there might be relations with more detailed phenomena on the sun. Allen[3,4] has shown that day-to-day fluctuations of $fF2$ can be related to the number of flocculi

28

on the solar disk. It must not necessarily be supposed, however, that all fluctuations in $fF2$ are accounted for by corresponding changes in the sun; it has already been mentioned, in §9.8.2, that some are the result of expansion or contraction of the layer.

It has been shown that variations in $fF2$ at Huancayo show a 27-day recurrence tendency, and that this recurrence is in step with the corresponding one for sunspots.[30]

Many other anomalies in the $N(h)$ curve occur with some regularity, quite apart from those violent and irregular ones which are observable at times of ionosphere disturbance. But, until there is some reasonably complete theory to compare the observations with, there does not seem to be any point in extending the list further.

9.8.4 *Effects of Eclipses*[242, 297]

Although the critical frequency of the $F2$ layer has been studied frequently at times of solar eclipse, the results have been merely confusing. Sometimes there has been a marked decrease, occasionally a slight increase, and frequently variations which are no greater than those occurring from hour to hour, or from day to day, when there is no eclipse. Attempts to deduce the loss coefficient have sometimes given reasonable results, and sometimes most unreasonable ones.

These results are not surprising, for, if the loss coefficients suggested in §9.8.6 are correct, they would lead to time constants of the order of 3 hours at 300 km and 1 hour at 250 km. The electron content would not have time to follow an eclipse in which all the important change took place in a time of about one hour.

It has been suggested that those changes which have unmistakably been observed to accompany eclipses might have their origin in movements resulting from a change in the electrostatic polarization field of the dynamo region, itself produced by the effect of the eclipse on that region.[299]

There have occasionally been reports of eclipse phenomena occurring in the $F2$ layer at times considerably removed from the time of the optical eclipse, and it has been suggested that they might have been caused by the eclipse of a stream of corpuscular radiation emitted from the sun. Random variations in $fF2$ are, however, so frequent when there is no eclipse that these isolated observations cannot yet be considered statistically significant.

9.8.5 *Above the Peak of the F2 Layer*

The ionization above the peak of the $F2$ layer cannot be explored by the usual method of observing pulses reflected from the ionosphere. A start has been made in exploring it by other methods, as follows.

In one,[241] a measurement is made of the ionospheric refraction of waves incident on the earth from a radio star. In another[178, 263, 301, 304] the radiations emitted from an artificial satellite are studied, in particular by measuring their Doppler effect, and their angle of arrival, as modified by the ionosphere. The rotation of the plane of polarization of a wave as it travels through the anisotropic ionosphere, analogous to the magneto-optical Faraday effect, has been observed both for waves radiated from artificial satellites and for waves reflected from the moon.[1, 98] Radio waves of audible frequencies, radiated by lightning flashes and passing through the outer ionosphere by the "whistler" mode of propagation, described in § 9.4.4, have been investigated.[246, 247, 286, 287]

In another experiment[314] the power incoherently scattered from different heights when an intense beam of radio waves is directed vertically upwards, on a frequency which penetrates the F region, was measured. This power is proportional to the electron density at the scattering level, so that information is available concerning the electron density above the peak of the $F2$ layer.

None of these methods has yet given much detailed information. All lead to the belief that the electron density does not fall off very rapidly above the peak of the $F2$ layer; indeed, it has been estimated that it has fallen to only about 0.8 of its peak value at a height of 100 km. above the peak and to about 600 cm^{-3} (i.e., 10^{-3} of its peak value) at a distance of two earth radii (see also § 3.4).

9.8.6 *Outline Theory of the F Layer*[40, 172, 173, 216, 217, 272–276, 309, 310]

In recent years there have been many attempts to explain the observed behavior of the F layer, none of which has been very successful, and the position at present is confused. It does, however, seem that the fundamental reasons for the existence of the $F1$ and $F2$ layers, and for some aspects of their behavior, are becoming clear. In this section we shall give an account of a theory which seems at present most likely to be right, and which will probably be more completely developed in the next few years. Although it explains the existence of the $F2$ layer it cannot explain the major "anomalies": these will have to be accounted for in terms of other phenomena, some of which are discussed in the following section.

The most probable process of electron loss at heights greater than about 200 km is that discussed in § 9.2.2 in which an exchange of charge from an ion to a molecule is followed by dissociative recombination, under conditions where the exchange process determines the rate. The over-all result is as though electrons were lost by attachment, with the attachment coefficient decreasing upward with a gradient determined by the height distribution of the molecules. Measurements[217] at night have suggested that the equivalent attachment coefficient is given approximately by

$$\beta = 10^{-4} \exp\left(\frac{300 - h_{km}}{50}\right) \sec^{-1}$$

It is probable that the electrons in the F region are formed by the ionization of atomic oxygen, represented by A in the reaction expressions (9.14), and the molecule represented there by XY is probably an oxygen molecule, O_2.*

Above about 100 km, O_2 is dissociated by solar radiation to form O, and in a static atmosphere there would be no O_2 left; in the actual atmosphere, however, O_2 remaining lower down diffuses upward, so that at each level the number of O_2 molecules is determined by a balance between the rate of arrival by diffusion and the rate of destruction by dissociation.[204, 306] It has been suggested that the gradient of O_2, and hence of the effective attachment coefficient, β, would be the same as for O_2 in diffusive equilibrium, so that it could be described by a scale height $H_L = RT/M_2 g$, where M_2 is the molecular weight of O_2.

If the effective attachment coefficient decreases upward, it is probable that the $F2$ layer is formed considerably above the peak of q, the electron production function, so that the layer would be of the "Bradbury" type discussed in § 9.2.3. It is reasonable to suppose that the peak of q is at, or near, the level of the $F1$ ledge at 180 km. Consideration of possible values of the absorption coefficient of the ionizing radiation, which determines the height of this peak, suggests that the gas whose ionization is represented by q is probably atomic oxygen.[40] The appropriate scale height (H_i) of the ionizable gas would then be given by $H_i = RT/M_1 g$, where M_1 is the atomic weight of oxygen. It then appears that $H_L/H_i = M_1/M_2 = 0.5$, which is less than unity, so that, as explained in § 9.2.3, there would be no peak in the electron density in the $F2$ layer; it would continue to increase upward until it became comparable with the molecular density.

* Another process by which positive ions of atomic oxygen may disappear may be of importance in the F region; this may be described as an ion-atom interchange reaction of the type

$$N_2 + O^+ \rightarrow NO^+ + O$$

followed by

$$NO^+ + e \rightarrow N' + O'.$$

There is some evidence that the rates of reactions of this type are great at small energies.[38,122]

The greater concentration of N_2 at all heights makes it likely that this process will be predominant unless the rate coefficient is appreciably less than for the charge exchange process.

If the ion-atom interchange is the dominant process, however, it is difficult to understand why the effective loss process simulates an attachment process at heights as low as 200 km.

Two hypotheses might be suggested to explain the occurrence of the observed peak. In one it is supposed that, at some greater height, the gradient of β becomes less steep, so that $H_L/H_i > 1$, and a peak of electron density can be formed. At a sufficiently great height, for example, the magnitude of α resulting from the charge-exchange process would fall below the constant value appropriate to radiative recombination, with $\alpha = 10^{-12}$ cm^3 sec^{-1}. It seems, however, that the resulting peak would then be considerably higher than those observed.

Another explanation supposes[273-276] that diffusion is responsible for the production of the peak, at least at moderate latitudes, and the order of magnitude calculated for its effect seems reasonable. Detailed theories are at present being worked out to deal with the possibility. Where the geomagnetic field is horizontal, diffusion cannot readily produce vertical movements, and the electron peak would be expected to be much higher. It is perhaps significant in this connection that the peak of electron density is found to be much higher near the magnetic equator.

Present-day views can be summarized by stating that the $F1$ and $F2$ layers are probably produced in atomic oxygen, ionized by radiations having an absorption coefficient such that the peak of q is near 180 km. At this level the complicated loss process discussed in § 9.2.2 simulates recombination so that an $F1$ ledge is produced with $fF1$ agreeing, to a first order, with an α-Chapman theory. Above about 200 km, however, the proportion of O_2 is so small that electrons are lost by what is effectively an attachment process in which β varies with height. The gradient is, moreover, so steep that the electron density, N, increases continuously upward. The existence of a peak of N at heights near 250 or 300 km in moderate latitudes is explicable by diffusion, but it is still an open question whether the same explanation will suffice at the equator. These ideas can be elaborated to explain how the $F1$ region is noticeable more frequently in summer, at sunspot maximum, and during an eclipse.[216, 309]

Of course a theory of the kind mentioned above would lead to a well-behaved $F2$ region, not showing the anomalies listed in § 9.8.1. The fact that no simple theory has yet been found to give even a first-order explanation of the facts has led to the suggestion that electromagnetic forces might produce vertical movements which play an important part in determining the behavior of the layer.

9.8.7 *Evidence for Vertical Movements*[51,168, 291-294]

9.8.7.1 *Movements Deduced from Experimental Results*

From time to time so many different vertical movements have been suggested in explanation of one or another limited set of observations that the situation has become somewhat confused. It would be desirable, if it were possible, not to calculate from some theory what these movements might be but to demonstrate their existence in a direct way from the observations. If data were available to show how the electron density, $N(t)$, at a fixed height varied with the time, t, then the continuity equation

$$dN/dt = q(t) - \beta N - (d/dh)(Nw) \qquad (9.79)$$

could be applied to deduce the "movement term" $(d/dh)(Nw)$, if $q(t)$ and β were known. If, however, the movement is determined, even indirectly, by the influence of the sun, as it almost certainly is, the movement term has a period of one day, as do the other terms, and it is not possible to isolate it unless the form of $q(t)$ is known. It is the impossibility of this separation which makes it so difficult to suggest a reliable theory of the $F2$ layer.

There is, however, one possibility of demonstrating the presence of important movements and of determining their magnitude, and that is to search for movements controlled by the moon, with a period related to the lunar day. This search has been made, not with values of N at a given height, but with the magnitudes (N_m) of N at the peak of the layer, the height (h_p) of the peak, and $h'_{min} F2$, the minimum recorded virtual height on the $F2$ trace. The magnitude of h_p has been determined, not from detailed $N(h)$ curves deduced by the methods described in § 9.4.2 but by more approximate methods which involve the assumption that the $N(h)$ curve is parabolic, and which also neglect the effect of the earth's magnetic field, and the group retardation produced by electrons in lower regions. The symbol h_p is used to denote heights determined in this way, and h_m is reserved to denote heights deduced from $N(h)$ curves. When $h'_{min} F2$ is used, it is necessary to be very cautious, since this quantity is strongly influenced by group retardation in the underlying $F1$ region.

It has been found that there is a lunar "tidal" effect in all these quantities; for example at Ibadan, Nigeria, the amplitude of the tide in h_p is 7.7 km, and that in $fF2$ is 0.12 Mc/sec. Comparable values are obtained at Huancayo, but in more moderate latitudes the amplitudes are not so great. The phase relation between the tides in h_p and N_m appears to be different at different places. Not much use has yet been made of these lunar tidal results in formulating a theory of the $F2$ layer.[65, 70, 158, 159, 168, 292, 293]

The existence of the lunar tide, supposedly produced indirectly by the lunar tidal movements in the dynamo region lower down, suggests at once that there might be solar tidal motions produced in the same way. But, as remarked previously, it is difficult to separate movement terms with a period of one solar day. Even if they could be separated they would not necessarily be ascribable to electromagnetic forces originating in the dynamo region, because other types of movement, originating, for example, in diffusion, or temperature change, might also have a period of one solar day.

9.8.7.2 *Movements Suggested Empirically*[91,146,265,266]

There have been several attempts to explain anomalies in the F region by making some empirical assumptions about the nature of the vertical movement, the production term, q, and the loss coefficient, β, in (9.79), and comparing the calculated results with experimental ones. There are so many adjustable variables in a comparison of this kind that it is difficult to be sure that any conclusion is unique. In order to remove one of these, some workers have restricted their investigations to nighttime, when $q = 0$.

Up to the present most work of this kind has been concerned with the parameters N_m and h_p, and sometimes with h'_{min} (which is significant at night but not in the day when an $F1$ layer is present.[250]). When N_m is being considered, and if $q = 0$, as at night, it is the gradient dw/dh of the vertical velocity which is important, since $(d/dh)(Nw) = N(dw/dh) + (dN/dh)w$, and $dN/dh = 0$ at the peak of the layer.

The usual method of working has been to insert into the continuity equation values of the movement term based on an empirically assumed velocity, w, which varies sinusoidally with a period of 24 or 12 hours, and to find what its magnitude and phase must be to give best agreement with experimental results. When it has been necessary to consider a gradient of w, it has been inserted, empirically, sometimes in the amplitude, and sometimes in the phase.

In view of the diversity of assumptions which can be made about the other terms q and β,* and in view of the fact that different workers have investigated results from different places and different times, it is not surprising that no useful conclusions have yet emerged from this "empirical" approach.

9.8.8 *Theories of Movements*

A different approach has been to try to calculate, on some theoretical basis, what movements are expected, and then, by inserting them into the continuity equation, to determine the magnitudes of the other terms. We shall review the theories suggested for movements caused by (1) electromagnetic forces, (2) diffusion, and (3) temperature changes.

9.8.8.1 *Electromagnetic Forces*[99,126,127,142,143,161,162,171]

It was explained in § 9.3.3 how the electrostatic field, arising from that part of the lower ionosphere in which the atmospheric dynamo is situated,

---

* And in the earlier work α, when it was thought that recombination was the appropriate loss process in the $F2$ layer.

could act on the F layer to move it vertically. Attempts have been made to calculate this field from the assumed type of air movement in the dynamo region. In the calculations made up to the present, rather drastic simplifications have been made about the electron density in the dynamo region. The results of different workers agree in suggesting that there is an oscillating vertical velocity in the F region with amplitude about 10 m sec^{-1} over most of the earth, but the different calculations suggest different phases for it. The phase and amplitude of the oscillation near the equator may be very different from those over the rest of the world.

An alternative approach to the problem starts from the observed daily variations of geomagnetism. It is quite complicated and involves assumptions about the distribution of the tensor conductivity. Although it cannot yet be supposed that the results are final, this approach, also, suggests that vertical velocities of about 10 m sec^{-1} will occur in the F region.

At the magnetic equator there may be a vertical gradient of velocity, but in moderate latitudes, between about 10° and 60°, it is likely to be negligible, except, possibly, under disturbed conditions. Movements with electromagnetic origin would therefore be expected to alter the peak electron density at night only near the equator.* At other places theories of this kind are therefore best tested by applying them to $N(t)$ curves which show the variation of N at levels not too near the peak.

9.8.8.2 *Diffusion*

It was explained in § 9.2.5.2 that, when movements are caused by diffusion in a parabolic layer of electrons of semithickness t, the movement term in the continuity equation is given by $- d(Nw)/dh = [(A \sin^2 I)/n] \phi (h/H)$, where A is a constant derivable from theory, n is the number density of the neutral gas, I is the angle of the dip, h is the depth below the peak of the layer, and $\phi (h/H)$ is a function described graphically in Fig. 2. It is clear that the movements caused by diffusion are small near the magnetic equator (I small) and increase toward the poles.

It is interesting to compare the magnitudes of the "diffusion term," $d(Nw)/dh$, and the "attachment term," βN, in equation (9.40a) for places at moderate latitudes—for example, where $\sin^2 I = 0.5$. It is then found that the two terms are equal for an atmosphere with the characteristics listed below, which agree roughly with results from satellites at a height of 300 km.

$$A = 5 \times 10^{18} \text{ cm}^{-6} \text{ sec}^{-1} \qquad n = 2.5 \times 10^9 \text{ cm}^{-3}$$

$$H = 45 \text{ km} \qquad\qquad N = 4 \times 10^5 \text{ cm}^{-3}$$

$$\beta = 10^{-4} \text{ sec}^{-1} \text{ as suggested in ref. (217)}.$$

* If, however, diffusion is important near the peak of the layer, a *uniform* vertical velocity could alter the magnitude of N_m.

The diffusion term increases exponentially upward as n decreases, and it is believed that β decreases exponentially upward (see § 9.2.2), so that at heights greater than 300 km diffusion is more important than attachment, and at lower heights attachment is more important than diffusion. It is the overwhelming importance of diffusion at the greater heights that has led to the suggestion that it may be responsible for producing the electron peak.[272–276, 310]

When a layer of electrons is left to decay at night under conditions where the loss coefficient varies exponentially with height, diffusion affects it in an interesting way.[92, 93, 176, 273, 274] If the layer has the "α-Chapman" form it keeps that form, but at first it sinks, or rises, until its peak is at a level where β and n have the values β_1 and n_1, related by the expression

$$4\beta_1 n_1 H^2 = A \sin^2 I. \tag{9.80}$$

The time to reach this equilibrium level is of the order $1/(4\beta_1)$, and after it has been reached the whole layer decays, keeping the same shape, as if the attachment coefficient were β_1 at all levels. During this decay process the height of the peak remains constant. For the atmosphere considered above this height is about 300 km, and the time for it to be reached is of the order of 1 hour. It is convenient to call the uniformly decaying layer a "diffusion equilibrium layer." If the original layer has some other form, not necessarily α-Chapman, it will ultimately take up the form of the diffusion equilibrium layer.

9.8.8.3 *Temperature Changes*

From time to time it has been suggested that the anomalous behavior of the $F2$ layer could, in part, be explained by a change of temperature which could alter the electron density in two ways. First, it could alter the air density, and in consequence the rate (q) of production of electrons. The consequences of this are best studied by altering the magnitudes of the scale height, and hence z, in the expression (9.2) which gives q as a function of height. Second, a change of temperature would move the gas vertically up or down, and it would carry the electrons with it. The resulting vertical velocities have been discussed in § 9.2.5.1.

Although it was at one time thought that temperature changes might have a profound effect on the $F2$ layer, it has more recently been realized that movements due to other causes would also be quite important. The relative importance of all the different causes is yet to be settled.

9.9 The Collision Frequency of Electrons

The absorption of radio waves in an ionized medium depends on the frequency with which electrons effectively collide with heavy particles (see § 9.4.5) and may be used to give estimates of this frequency.

The average collision frequency depends on the density of heavy particles and on the velocity of the electrons, so that a knowledge of its magnitude would be useful in understanding the physical state of the upper atmosphere.

9.9.1 *Measurements of Effective Collision Frequency*

Attempts have been made to measure the effective collision frequency in the D and lower E regions by ionospheric cross modulation, using both continuous waves[236] and pulses,[100] and by measuring the difference in the absorption of Ordinary and Extraordinary waves in their passage through the region.[235]

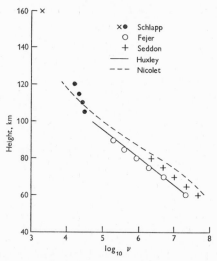

FIG. 18. Collision frequency (ν) of electrons plotted against height.

Near the peak of the E layer measurements have been made by the group-retardation method[6, 228] and by observing how the amplitudes of waves reflected from, and transmitted through, a thin layer vary with the radio frequency.[283] Measurements have been made in the neighbourhood of the $F1$ ledge by the group-retardation method.[6]

The results of the most reliable measurements are plotted in Fig. 18. All these measurements provide reasonable accuracy for the collision frequency but not always for the height at which that frequency is measured. The height may, indeed, be uncertain to about 10 km, and, since the scale height of the atmosphere in these regions is of the order 8 km, this inaccuracy corresponds to a change by a factor 3 in the value of the collision frequency.

In the $F2$ layer the results are less satisfactory.[23] Although several measurements of collision frequency have been reported, recent experiments seem to indicate that the variability of amplitude produced by "focusing" effects in the F region is so great as to render the results valueless. The most that can be said is that at a height of about 230 km the collision frequency is not greater than 3×10^3 sec^{-1}.

It is possible to deduce the collision frequency of electrons in air as a function of density and temperature by measuring, in the laboratory, the drift velocity of a cloud of electrons under the influence of a small electric field. These experiments have been carried out with electron energies down to 1.1 times thermal energy.[133] Since the composition of the air up to about 90 km is probably the same at that at the ground, it is possible to estimate the magnitude of ν up to these heights from the laboratory measurements. The resulting estimate is indicated by the continuous line in Fig. 18.

It will be seen that the magnitudes of the collision frequencies measured between heights of 60 and 95 km agree well with those inferred from the laboratory experiments. At higher altitudes the effective collision frequency does not seem to fall off as quickly as would be expected.

Nicolet[203, 311] calculated the collision frequencies at different heights, and his results are indicated by the dashed line in Fig. 18. They are three or four times as great as those suggested by the latest experiments and theories.

9.9.2 *Interpretation of the Measured Values*

Even if the effective collision frequencies were known at each level there would still be difficulties in relating them to other physical quantities. In the first place it must be realized that the effective collision frequency introduced in the magneto-ionic theory is not necessarily equal to the average collision frequency involved in the kinetic theory. The relation between these two quantities is not simple and will be discussed below.

In kinetic theory the average collision frequency depends on the velocity distribution of the electrons and on how the collision cross section of the heavy particles varies with the velocity of the electrons. If $n_e(v)dv$ is the number of electrons with velocities between v and $(v + dv)$, and $Q(v)$ is the collision cross section for velocity v, then the collision frequency, ν, is given by

$$n_e \nu = n_a \int n_e(v) \cdot Q(v) v \, dv. \qquad (9.81)$$

The dependence of the collision cross section, Q, on the electron velocity is not, in general, well known at low electron energies. Theoretical calculations of Q require a knowledge of the wave functions at large distances from the nucleus and are seldom reliable. In all the cases so far investigated the value of Q has a minimum at some low electron energy, as in the well-known Ramsauer effect, but the exact energy at which the minimum occurs is difficult to calculate, Experiments on the behavior of electron clouds in air at energies between $1/30$ ev and $1/3$ ev give a value

$$\nu = 8.7 \times 10^4\, p \text{ sec}^{-1} \; (p \text{ in dynes cm}^{-2}) \tag{9.82}$$

This formula has been used to calculate the values of ν shown at different levels in the D region in Fig. 18. This calculation involves some extrapolation of the formula to lower energies.

An important special case of electron collision with heavy particles is that of collision with ions, for which the force between the colliding particles varies as the inverse square of their separation. The situation is exactly similar to the scattering of α-particles by a heavy nucleus, and a calculation, well known in that connection, shows that the collision cross section is proportional to v^{-4}; hence the collision frequency varies as v^{-3}.

When the electrons have a distribution of velocities (as in the case of electrons in thermal equilibrium with the neutral gas), a detailed consideration of the effective damping term in the equation of motion of the electrons shows that the effective value of ν in the magneto-ionic theory is not equal to the average collision frequency, ν_G, of kinetic theory, and in the general case bears no simple relation to it. The relation between the two quantities has been evaluated for the simple case of a constant collision cross section, independent of velocity, with a Maxwellian distribution of velocities.[209] For this simple case, provided ω and $(\omega \pm \omega_H) \gg \nu_G$, then the effective collision frequency is given by

$$\nu = \tfrac{4}{3} \nu_G$$

If, however, ω and $(\omega \pm \omega_H) \ll \nu_G$,

$$\nu = (3\pi/8)\nu_G.$$

In an alternative treatment of collisions in the magneto-ionic theory, Huxley[318] has evaluated the damping effects, assuming that the mean free path of the electrons is constant (and hence that Q is constant), and in this case the effective collision frequency, ν_B, is equal to ν_G if ω and $(\omega \pm \omega_H) \gg \nu_G$, and if ω and $(\omega \pm \omega_H) \ll \nu_G$,

$$\nu_B = (\pi/4)\nu_G$$

9.9.3 *Comparison of Theory and Experiment*

It is useful to estimate the relative importance of collisions with neutral and with charged heavy particles in the various regions of the ionosphere. If we suppose for this purpose that the collisions with neutral particles are mainly with nitrogen molecules for which $Q(v) \propto v$, we may write

$$\nu = 4.4 \times 10^{-9}(T/300)n_n + 6.1 \times 10^{-3}(T/300)^{-\frac{3}{2}}n_i \tag{9.83}$$

where n_n is the number density of neutral molecules, and n_i is the number density of ions of either sign. There is evidence to show that in the E and F regions $n_i = n_e$. Then for the E region if we insert the values $T = 300°K$, $n_n = 10^{13}$ cm^{-3}, and $n_e = n_i = 10^5$ cm^{-3} into (9.83), it is seen that collisions with neutral particles are overwhelmingly important. Conditions in the F region probably correspond to $T = 1200°K$, $n_n = 3 \times 10^9$ cm^{-2}, and $n_e = n_i = 10^6$ cm^{-3}, so that (9.83) gives $\nu = 53 + 760$, and collisions with charged particles predominate.

The experimental values plotted in Fig. 18 agree quite well with those deduced from the laboratory experiments up to a height of about 90 km, above which the laboratory formula leads to a value of ν appreciably less than the experimental values. No satisfactory explanation of this discrepancy has yet been given, but it may be significant that it is in this region that atomic oxygen becomes an important constituent of the atmosphere.

9.10 Horizontal Irregularities and Movements [288, 296]

9.10.1 *Experimental Evidence* [63, 215, 198]

When either the E or F layer is explored by vertically reflected pulses at points on the ground separated by more than a few kilometers, it is often found that the shapes of the $h'(f)$ curves, or the shapes or amplitudes of the pulses returned on a fixed frequency, undergo some characteristic change noticeable at all the observing points, but occurring at different times at the different places. It is deduced that some corresponding irregularity, traveling horizontally in the ionosphere, is responsible, and it has been possible to calculate its velocity.

Even when the amplitude of the returned pulse does not undergo any clearly identifiable change, it is usually found to vary randomly in the process called "fading." A study of this fading at two or more places, of the order of one or two wavelengths apart, can be made to provide an outline description of the statistical nature of the irregular amplitude pattern over the ground. [60, 61] This pattern arises because the pulse is reflected from an irregular ionosphere, and diffraction theory has been applied to make deductions about the irregularities. Instead of using pulses emitted from senders on the ground and reflected from the ionosphere, it is also possible to use waves emitted from radio stars and transmitted through the ionosphere. [123]

Other evidence for ionospheric irregularities is provided by the phenomenon known as "forward scattering." In this a wave with a frequency (say 50 Mc/sec) sufficiently great to penetrate the ionosphere even at very oblique incidence is found to be returned, with appreciable amplitude, by a process of forward scattering, to points distant about 1200 km on the earth's surface. There is good evidence that this scattering occurs in the D and E regions at heights of about 80 or 90 km.[25, 213]

9.10.2 *Sizes of Irregularities*

It seems, at the present time, that a distinction should be made between large irregularities, occurring more or less in isolation, and smaller ones randomly distributed. The isolated ones travel considerable distances with little change. The largest, observed in the F region, have extent greater than 1000 km and have been observed to travel over distances at least as great as 3000 km.[196–198] Smaller isolated ones, observed in both the E and F regions, have sizes of 1 or 2 kilometers and have been observed to travel about 50 km without much change.[137, 268]

This kind of isolated irregularity, observable as kinks on the $h'(f)$ curve, distortions on the $h'(t)$ trace, or bursts of amplitude on the amplitude-time trace, can all be ascribed to distortions of the ionosphere analogous to distortions of a reflecting surface, and it seems probable that they correspond to a wave of distortion propagated through the ionosphere. Although several suggestions have been made about the nature of these waves, none seems entirely satisfactory.[124, 295]

The smaller irregularities, responsible for the irregular fading of returned pulses, appear to be randomly distributed in size, in the D, E, and F regions, in such a way that the distribution of excess electron density can be described in terms of a spatial spectrum in which all spatial periods occur, at least down to a size of about 200 meters.[60, 61]

Those random irregularities which produce fading of the radiation from radio stars are situated at heights greater than about 250 km and occur only at night. They are larger and are on the whole elongated along the direction of the earth's magnetic field. They are best described by saying that their autocorrelation function falls to 0.5 in a distance of about 1 km across the field and about 5 km along it. There are fairly clear indications that irregularities are more pronounced in auroral and equatorial regions.[82, 84, 85, 123, 147, 243] These conclusions are supported by the results of measurements made on the radiation from an artificial satellite as it moves past the irregularities.[144]

9.10.3 *Irregular Movements*[60, 61]

The fading of the radio echoes shows that the irregularities are in motion, and simultaneous observations at two or more places have been used to show that the motion is in part irregular and in part represents an average horizontal drift. The random velocities have magnitudes in the range 5 to

50 m sec^{-1}. It is surprising that these random movements seem to be present at all heights. No proper theory has yet been suggested to account for them.

The smaller-scale random irregularities in the E region could be produced either by turbulence or by the ionizing action of meteors. There has been much discussion of the rival theories, particularly as explanations of the irregularities which are responsible for forward scatter of high-frequency waves. It seems clear that both mechanisms must be active, with their relative importance changing from time to time, but the details are not yet known.[53, 54]

The observed irregularities of electron density are too intense to be produced simply by the turbulent changes of air density.[256] If they are indeed produced by turbulence, it must be through its mixing action on a gradient of ionization, and they would be most marked where the gradient was steepest. It has been suggested that scattering from irregularities concentrated near fixed levels might indicate comparative steep gradients of electron density at these heights.

It does not seem likely that irregularities in the F region could be caused by turbulence. An interesting suggestion[82, 83, 315] has been made that the larger irregularities, responsible for the "scintillations" of radio stars, could be produced by an irregular electrostatic field resulting from the irregularities in the E layer, but the detailed implications of the suggestion have not yet been worked out. Other hypotheses about these irregularities, which occur only at night, suppose that they are caused by streams of particles entering the earth's atmosphere, or evaporating from it, along the lines of force.[223]

9.10.4 *Regular Horizontal Movements or Drifts*[63, 185]

In a discussion of the regular horizontal movements a distinction must be made between the movements of the large isolated wavelike disturbances and those revealed by a study of the smaller-scale structure. Munro[198] has made a detailed study of the larger ones, in the F region, over Australia, during the period April, 1948, to March, 1957. He found that traveling disturbances of the isolated type were observable, on the average, about six times during any one day, but hardly ever at night. In the winter the movement was predominantly towards the NE and in the summer to the SE, with average velocities of about 120 m sec^{-1}. During an average winter day the direction changed from about 60° E of N to about 20° E of N as time advanced from 0800 to 1600 hours.

We turn now to consider the smaller, random irregularities. It is found that their horizontal velocities vary with time, more or less rapidly, much as the velocity of a wind would at the surface of the earth. If, however, the results for several successive days are compared, it is usually found that the average velocity can be determined with a statistical significance sufficient to indicate variations with periods related to the day and the year.

Regular horizontal movements in the E region have also been studied by observing radio echoes from ionized meteor trails[94,112,113,164] (see § 11.7). Both kinds of observation agree in showing that, in general, there is a "prevailing" drift on which are imposed components which vary with the season and with the time of day. In England the seasonal component is toward the west in winter and the east in summer. There is also a component which remains roughly constant in magnitude but rotates twice in a day in a clockwise direction. Measurements in the southern hemisphere reveal a much smaller "prevailing" component, a seasonal E–W component which is toward the west in winter and the east in summer, as in the northern hemisphere, and a component which rotates twice in a day in an anticlockwise direction. There is also a component in the E–W direction which oscillates with a period of one day. Other aspects of the world-wide picture will emerge from the work of the IGY.

The rotating component of the drift velocity is found to have different "phases" at different heights, so that the time at which it is directed toward the north increases with height by 0.2 hour per kilometer, within the range of heights between 85 and 110 km. The magnitude of this rotating component also increases upward with a gradient of about 3 m sec^{-1} km^{-1}. More detailed analysis reveals variations in the rotating component throughout the year, and in particular some which occur rather suddenly within a week or two near the start of November.[112,113,138]

Regular movements in the F region are predominantly in the E–W direction. The velocity is of the order 80 m sec^{-1} and is predominantly toward the east by day and the west by night. Over England the variation is not even approximately sinusoidal but corresponds to a rather sudden reversal near sunrise and sunset.

Regular drift velocities of the electrons in the ionosphere could be caused either by a movement of the surrounding gas or by the presence of a superimposed electric field. In either case the motion is considerably complicated by the presence of the earth's magnetic field.[81,171,264] In considering the details it must be remembered that the radio observations are concerned with the movements of irregularities embedded in a background plasma. If the neutral air moves for any reason, it cannot in general be concluded that the plasma will move with it, nor that the irregularities will move with it, or with the plasma. If, on the other hand, an electric field is applied the plasma will move, but will not necessarily carry the neutral air with it, and the irregularities may move in a direction different from that of the plasma. The details of these complicated motions depend on the ratios of the collision frequencies to the gyrofrequencies of the electrons and the ions. In the D and lower E regions the plasma and the ionospheric irregularities can be moved relatively more easily by air movements than by electric fields, and at these levels it is probable that the radio observations provide information about the air movements. In the F region, however, the situation is reversed, and it is relatively easier to move the electrons by means of an electric field. It is also probable, but not certain, that the irregularities will move with the plasma. It is therefore thought, at present, that the observed horizontal drifts in this region represent movements of the plasma caused by electric fields. It is not likely that the moving plasma carries the neutral air with it.

On the supposition, then, that the radio observations reveal the movement of the air in the D and lower E regions it is interesting to enquire how the semidiurnal rotating component of this movement compares with that expected from the dynamo theory of geomagnetism. There are two ways of deducing this velocity. In one the oscillations of the atmosphere under the driving force of solar gravitation and heating are calculated from fluid dynamical theory. In the other the daily variations of geomagnetism are used to give a measure of the currents in the "dynamo region" of the atmosphere, the conductivity under the action of the earth's magnetic field is calculated from a knowledge of the ionosphere, and the movements responsible for inducing the currents are deduced.[142, 143, 161, 162]

The agreement between the dynamical theory and the observations appears to be satisfactory, although the model atmosphere used in the dynamical calculations does not correspond very closely to what is now believed to be correct. Some phenomena, such as the sudden change in November, seem inexplicable on the dynamical theory.

Calculations based on the observed changes of the geomagnetic field suggest that the drift should have a predominantly diurnal variation. Since this result is in conflict with the observations, it must be supposed that the dynamo theory is not yet sufficiently well understood.

The observed movements in the F region are thought to be the result of electric fields produced in the dynamo region, and in middle latitudes they are roughly what would be expected from dynamo theory.[142, 143, 161, 162, 171, 174] Theory leads us to expect that the direction of the movement would be in the opposite sense near the equator, and experimental results confirm this expectation.[205]

The regular drift velocities in the F region increase when the K index of magnetic disturbance increases, presumably because of an increase in the electric field which has its source in the dynamo region. Only the greatest magnetic disturbances are accompanied by a measurable increase of the velocities in the E region. These facts have not yet been adequately explained.

29

9.10.5 *Spread-F Echoes*[64, 82-84, 302]

It is often found that the echo returned from the F region has a much longer duration than the incident pulse: it is then described as a spread-F echo. There is evidence that the spread of the echo is caused by scattering in depth rather than by scattering from irregularities at distances considerably removed from the vertical reflection point.

The incidence of spread-F echoes is closely associated with the occurrence of "scintillations" in the radiation from radio stars. Both occur more frequently by night, and near the equator.[147, 270] In higher latitudes (e.g., 60°) the irregularities causing spread-F echoes seem to occur in patches which lie roughly along lines of magnetic latitude.

Martyn[170] has suggested that irregularities of ionization on the underside of a layer are automatically enhanced if the layer moves upwards. He considers that these enhanced irregularities are responsible for spread-F echoes and points out that observation shows them to be related in the expected way to movements of the F layer.

9.11 Disturbances and Storms in the Ionosphere

9.11.1 *Two Types of Disturbance* (see also § 12.9.2)

Two different types of abnormal ionospheric behavior can be clearly distinguished, both associated with abnormal occurrences on the sun. It is simplest to describe them in terms of present-day theory, in the following way. When a solar flare is observed, in Hα light, to occur suddenly on the sun, it is often accompanied by an increase in ultraviolet and X-radiations which produce, at the same time, a sudden increase of ionization in the ionosphere.[95] This increase is sudden, its effects are most noticeable in the D region, the recovery to normal usually takes about 20 to 90 minutes, and the phenomenon is noticed only in the sunlit hemisphere. It constitutes what is usually called a sudden ionosphere disturbance, or S.I.D. The larger disturbances of this kind are sometimes accompanied by a relatively small, and short-lived, disturbance of the geomagnetic field, called a "crochet," which corresponds approximately to an enhancement of the ionospheric currents flowing at the time of the disturbance.

It is further supposed that, at the time when the flare occurs, a stream of rapidly moving charged particles often leaves the sun and travels outward with a speed which brings them to the distance of the earth in a time of 24 to 36 hours. If the earth intercepts the stream, the ionosphere is disturbed, by a complicated process discussed more fully in § 9.11.4. This disturbance takes a form quite different from that of an S.I.D. It is most easily noticed in the F region, it can last several hours or even days, it is observable on the light and dark sides of the earth equally, and it is frequently accompanied by auroras and severe disturbances of the geomagnetic field known as magnetic storms. It is called an ionosphere storm.

The two types of disturbance will be discussed separately.

9.11.2 *Sudden Ionosphere Disturbances (S.I.D.)*[87] (see also § 4.5)

An S.I.D. is most easily detected through its effect on the D region, partly because that effect is usually large, and partly because it is noticeable on continuous records made on a single frequency. It is more difficult to decide how far the E and F layers are modified, partly because the effects on radio waves are smaller, and partly because information about these layers is available mainly from ionospheric observatories where records are made at intervals (of one, or occasionally one-quarter, hour) which are too long for observation of an event which starts suddenly and lasts only 30 to 90 minutes. In spite of these limitiations, however, it seems that the most intense, and possibly all, S.I.D.'s are accompanied by an increase in fE.[43, 248] There is less evidence about what happens to the F layer, but at least on two occasions very large, and unusual, S.I.D.'s * are known to have accompanied an increase in fF.[88, 184a]

The remaining phenomena occurring during an S.I.D. can be ascribed to an increase of ionization in the D and lower E regions, below the peak of the E layer. In describing them it is convenient to distinguish between those observed with waves which have traversed this part of the ionosphere and those which have been reflected inside it.

9.11.2.1 *Waves Traversing the D and Lower E Regions*

1. A decrease of strength of radio waves arriving from cosmic sources. This has been called a sudden cosmic noise absorption (S.C.N.A.).

2. A decrease of strength of short radio waves reflected either vertically or obliquely from the E or F layers. This has been called a short-wave fadeout (S.W.F.).

3. A change of phase of waves reflected nearly at vertical incidence from the E or F layer.

4. A change of group path of waves reflected nearly at vertical incidence from the E or F layer.

9.11.2.2 *Waves Reflected in the D and Lower E Regions*[58]

5. A *decrease* in the strength of waves of frequencies below 300 kc/sec reflected at *near vertical* incidence.

6. An *increase* in the strength of the waves of the same frequencies reflected at *oblique* incidence.

* Those of February 23, 1956 (see § 9.11.5) and of November 19, 1949.

7. An increase in the strength of very-low-frequency atmospherics, particularly marked near a frequency of 22 kc/sec. This has been called a sudden enhancement of atmospherics (S.E.A.).[69]

8. A decrease in the phase lag of waves of frequency less than 300 kc/sec. This has been called a sudden phase anomaly (S.P.A.).[57]

9. An increase in the strength of waves of frequency about 50 Mc/sec, received by forward scatter from the D region.[25]

10. Appearance of weak reflections from levels near 60 km when waves of frequency near 1 Mc/sec are incident at vertical incidence.[117]

11. Change in the intensity of thermal radio-frequency radiation from the ionosphere.[106]

All these phenomena indicate that there is a considerable increase in the electron content of the D or lower E region during an S.I.D., but it is a difficult matter to decide how it is distributed in height.

At the present time it seems that most of the phenomena observed during an S.I.D. can be explained by supposing that extra electrons are produced at all levels from below 60 km to above the peak of the E region. Those in the D region, below 80 km, play some part in producing all the phenomena listed above; those in the E region, above 80 km, also play a part in those numbered 3 and 4 and in altering the peak electron density of the E layer. There is evidence that the ratio of the numbers of electrons produced in the two regions varies from one S.I.D. to another, as it would if the responsible radiation were composite with a spectral distribution which was different on different occasions. Until several phenomena providing evidence about the electron densities at different levels have been observed simultaneously during a series of S.I.D.'s, it cannot be said that their effects are understood in detail.

9.11.3 *Ionosphere Storms*

The occurrence of ionosphere storms is noticeable in both the F and the D regions. The F-region phenomena are better known and will be described first.

9.11.3.1 *The F Region*[15,19,45,169,290]

Over most of the earth the most obvious effect of an ionosphere storm is a decrease of the critical frequency, $fF2$, and since this is a parameter tabulated by ionospheric observatories its changes have been widely studied. Although the normal storm is most clearly marked by a decrease of $fF2$, there are occasions when a storm is accompanied by an increase, and it has become common to refer to the increase as the "positive phase" and the decrease as the "negative phase." It has been shown that in middle latitudes the negative phase is the most pronounced but it is usually preceded by a short positive phase; that the positive phase becomes more important at lower latitudes; and that near the geomagnetic equator the positive phase is the more pronounced.

If the $h'(f)$ curve is examined at times of ionosphere storm it is clear that the decrease of $fF2$ characteristic of the negative phase is accompanied by a marked change in the form of the curve, as seen in Fig. 19, which shows the

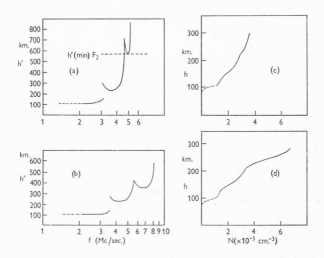

FIG. 19. The $h'(f)$ and corresponding $N(h)$ curves for a quiet and a disturbed day at Slough. (a and c) A disturbed day, July 25, 1950 (1200 hours). (b and d) A quiet day, July 20, 1950 (1200 hours).

records for a normal day and a day of storm in middle latitudes. The most striking phenomenon, in addition to the decrease of $fF2$, is the increase of h' at a given frequency, and it has been customary to specify the magnitude of the increase by measuring the minimum equivalent height of the $F2$ layer, a quantity denoted by $h'_{min}F2$. If, however, $N(h)$ curves are deduced from the $h'(f)$ curves, it becomes clear that, although the height of the $F2$ layer does, in fact, increase during a storm, the increase is much smaller than the increase in h', and in particular than the increase of $h'_{min}F2$, which is chiefly determined by group retardation in the $F1$ layer. All results based on measurements of $h'_{min}F2$ should therefore be treated with caution.

Ionosphere storms are nearly always associated with magnetic storms, and it is of importance to know the details of that association.[155] Some magnetic storms show a "sudden commencement" (usually denoted S.C.) observed all over the world at the same time; but the main and obvious ionospheric effects are not apparent until the "main phase" of the magnetic storm occurs. There is some evidence to show that the S.C. is, in fact, accompanied by a comparatively small change in $fF2$, but, possibly because routine tabulations of $fF2$ are made only once an hour, this evidence is not as good as it might be. If it were well established that the S.C. is accompanied by a change in the F region, the evidence would be in conflict with theories of the S.C. which attribute it entirely to the formation of a "ring current" at a distance of several earth radii.

When the "main phase" of the magnetic storm is observed, it usually corresponds to changes in the $F2$ region, but it seems that, when a storm starts at night, it is necessary to wait until the following day before its full effect is noticed in the ionosphere records.

The details of the effects of ionosphere storms on the F region have been found to be different at different epochs of the sunspot cycle.

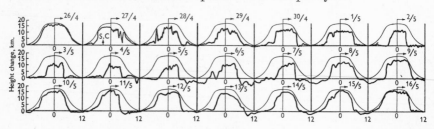

FIG. 20. Variations in the "phase height" of waves of frequency 16 kc/sec observed at Cambridge on the dates shown in 1956. The thin line indicates the mean diurnal variation of phase for all the days of the month. A magnetic storm started with a "sudden commencement" at the time marked SC on 26/4. From 0300 on 27/4 to about 1200 on 28/4 the phase was violently disturbed. During the nights from 30/4 to 9/5 the shape of the curve is unusual; after that it regains its normal shape slowly. This is the "storm after-effect."

9.11.3.2 *The D Region*

The occurrence of an ionosphere storm is very clearly marked in the auroral zone by a decrease in the strength of waves reflected from the ionosphere, and this is often so great that high-frequency signals disappear completely and the phenomenon is called a "polar blackout." These blackouts are more pronounced by day than by night. They correspond to a large increase in the electron content of the D region.[148, 234, 245] (see § 12·9·1)

Although in temperate latitudes the decreased amplitude associated with polar blackouts is not observed, there are other clear signs that the D region is disturbed. These are most obvious in records of the phase and amplitude of low-frequency and very-low-frequency waves (< 300 kc/sec) reflected either at vertical or oblique incidence.[58, 151] The "main phase" of a magnetic storm is frequently accompanied by a rapid variation of the amplitude of low-frequency waves (30 to 300 kc/sec) and of the phase of very-low-frequency waves (< 30 kc/sec). These irregularities cease when the "main phase" is over, but, if the storm is an intense one, there may be an "after-effect" starting about a day later and lasting possibly several days. It is noticed as an unusual diurnal phase variation on the very low frequencies. An example is shown in Fig. 20, in which it will be seen how, before and after the storm, the diurnal variation of phase is smooth and regular, during the main phase there are rapid irregularities superimposed on it, and during the "after-effect" it has a different shape and is smaller in magnitude. This D-region after-effect seems to correspond to the "recovery phase" of large magnetic storms, but it has not been noticed that it has any counterpart in phenomena in the F region.

9.11.3.3 *The E and F1 Layers*[224, 281, 282]

There appears to be some evidence that the critical frequency fE is often depressed by about 10 % during ionosphere storms, but it is not so well documented as it might be. There is somewhat better evidence that $fF1$ is depressed.[149]

9.11.4 *Theories of Ionosphere Storms*

Although there is not yet any satisfactory theory of ionosphere storms, there seems to be little doubt that they are the result, primarily, of an injection of ionizing particles near the auroral zone. The most recent theory[78] suggests that incoming protons produce the visible aurora, while very energetic electrons (100 kev) ionize the D region down to about 80 km and produce secondary X-rays which continue the ionization down to about 40 km. It is this ionization which causes the polar blackout. The resulting ionization is more intense by day than by night because, during the day, the disappearance of electrons by attachment is countered by the process of photo-detachment. Increase of ionization by the incident protons above 95 km would increase the conductivity in the dynamo region in such a way as to produce the intense currents which are required near the auroral zone to explain the magnetic storm.

Although little attempt has yet been made to explain the other phenomena observed during magnetic storms, it seems possible that an explanation may ultimately be found along the following lines.[169, 225, 226, 227]

The F-region phenomena are probably the result of large vertical movements of the electrons resulting from the electrostatic fields which accompany the storm currents in the dynamo region. The D-region phenomena accompanying the main phase in moderate latitudes are possibly produced indirectly by the comparatively weak extra storm currents which flow there. The after-effects in the D region are observed so long after the main phase is over that it is tempting to suggest that they are the result of some special chemical constitu-ent formed in the auroral zone during the main phase, and drifting away from that zone to produce the after-effect with a long time delay determined by a chemical time constant. All this is, however, pure speculation at present.

9.11.5 The Disturbance of February 23, 1956[2, 41, 97, 129, 153, 303]

Before leaving this account of ionospheric disturbances mention should be made of the unusual solar event of February 23, 1956. On this occasion an intense solar flare was accompanied, on the sunlit side of the earth, by all the usual phenomena of an S.I.D. in an enhanced form. A few minutes later a great increase of cosmic-ray intensity was observed all over the earth, and, on the night side, it was accompanied by marked disturbances in the D region. Any possible disturbances of a similar kind on the sunlit side of the earth were masked by the effects of the S.I.D. An intense ionosphere storm, of the ordinary kind, followed 48 hours later.

The remarkable feature on this occasion was the intense disturbance occurring in the D region on the dark side of the earth, coincident with the sudden increase in the intensity of cosmic rays. This nocturnal disturbance was more severe at higher latitudes and does not seem to have been noticed at latitudes less than 30°. It was characterized by major changes in the absorption, particularly on the low frequencies, and by changes in the phase of low-frequency waves. The absorption remained abnormally great through much of the following day, the total duration of this period of abnormal absorption being greater at higher latitudes. Phenomena occurring at sunrise, in particular the phase changes of low-frequency waves, were unusual, as though the atmospheric composition had been altered by the disturbance.

Observations of the intensity of cosmic radio noise at high latitudes have recently shown[316] that abnormal increases of absorption can be of two types. One occurs at night, varies rapidly, and is correlated with auroras. The other occurs by day, varies less rapidly and can occur for several days in succession. It has been suggested that the abnormal absorption observed on February 23, 1956 was an unusually intense manifestation of the second type.

No satisfactory theory has yet been proposed to explain these phenomena.

References

1. G. J. Aitchison and K. Weekes, "Some deductions of Ionospheric information from the observation of emissions from Satellite 1957α2 I. The Theory of the analysis. II (with J. H. Thomson) Experimental procedure and results," J. Atmos. Terr. Phys. 14, 236, 244 (1959).
2. A. H. Allen, D. D. Crombie, and W. A. Penton, "Long path V.L.F.-Frequency variations associated with the solar flare of 23/2/56," J. Atmos. Terr. Phys. 10, 110 (1957).

3. C. W. Allen, "Variation of the sun's ultra violet radiation as revealed by ionospheric and geomagnetic observations," *J. Geophys. Res.* **51**, 1 (1946).

4. C. W. Allen, "Critical frequencies, sun spots and the sun's ultra violet radiation," *J. Geophys. Res.* **53**, 433 (1948).

5. C. W. Allen, "World wide variations in the $F2$ region," *J. Atmos. Terr. Phys.* **4**, 53 (1954).

6. E. V. Appleton, "A method of measuring the collisional frequency of electrons in the ionosphere," *Nature* **135**, 618 (1935).

7. E. V. Appleton, "Radio exploration of the upper atmospheric ionization," *Repts. Progr. in Phys.* **2**, 129 (1936).

8. E. V. Appleton, "Regularities and irregularities in the ionosphere," *Proc. Roy. Soc.* A**162**, 451 (1937).

9. E. V. Appleton and K. Weekes, "On lunar tides in the upper atmosphere," *Proc. Roy. Soc.* A**171**, 171 (1939).

10. E. V. Appleton and R. Naismith, "The variation of solar ultra violet radiation during the sun spot cycle," *Phil. Mag.* **27**, 144 (1939).

11. E. V. Appleton and R. Naismith, "Normal and abnormal region-E ionization," *Proc. Phys. Soc.* **52**, 402 (1940).

12. E. V. Appleton, "Geomagnetic control of $F2$-layer ionization," *Science* **106**, 17 (1947).

13. E. V. Appleton and W. J. G. Beynon, "Lunar tidal oscillations in the ionosphere," *Nature* **162**, 486 (1948).

14. E. V. Appleton and W. J. G. Beynon, "Lunar oscillations in the D layer of the ionosphere," *Nature* **164**, 308 (1949).

15. E. V. Appleton and W. R. Piggott, "The morphology of storms in the $F2$ layer of the ionosphere," *J. Atmos. Terr. Phys.* **2**, 236 (1952).

16. E. V. Appleton, "A note on the 'sluggishness' of the ionosphere," *J. Atmos. Terr. Phys.* **3**, 282 (1953).

17. E. V. Appleton, "The anomalous equatorial belt in the $F2$-layer," *J. Atmos. Terr. Phys.* **5**, 348 (1954).

18. E. V. Appleton and W. R. Piggott, "Ionospheric absorption measurements during a sun spot cycle," *J. Atmos. Terr. Phys.* **5**, 141 (1954).

19. E. V. Appleton and W. R. Piggott, "Storm phenomena and the solar cycle variations in the $F2$ layer," *Phys. Soc. Rept. Ionosphere Conf.* 219 (1955).

20. E. V. Appleton, A. J. Lyon, and A. G. Pritchard, "The detection of the Sq. current system in ionospheric radio sounding," *J. Atmos. Terr. Phys.* **7**, 292 (1955).

21. E. V. Appleton, A. J. Lyon, and A. G. Turnbull, "Distortion of the E layer of the ionosphere by electrical currents flowing in it," *Nature* **176**, 897 (1955).

22. E. V. Appleton and A. J. Lyon, "Studies of the E layer of the ionosphere. I. Some relevant theoretical relationships," *J. Atmos. Terr. Phys.* **10**, 1 (1957).

23. E. Argence and K. Rawer, "Sur la détermination du nombre de chocs relatif à la region $F2$ de l'ionosphere," *Nuovo Cim.* **4** (*Suppl.*), 1511 (1956).

24. D. K. Bailey, "The geomagnetic nature of the $F2$-layer longitude effect," *J. Geophys. Res.* **53**, 35 (1948).

25. D. K. Bailey, R. Bateman, and R. C. Kirby, "Radio transmission at V.H.F. by scattering and other processes in the lower ionosphere," *Proc. IRE.* **43**, 1181 (1955).

26. V. A. Bailey, and D. F. Martyn, "The influence of electric waves on the ionosphere," *Phil. Mag.* **18**, 369 (1934).

27. W. G. Baker and D. F. Martyn, "Electric currents in the ionosphere. I. The conductivity," *Phil. Trans. Roy. Soc.* **246**, 281 (1953).

28. W. G. Baker, "Electric currents in the ionosphere. II. The atmospheric dynamo," *Phil. Trans. Roy. Soc.* A**246**, 295 (1953); see also ref. 171.

29. J. Bannon and F. Wood, "Cause and effect in region $F2$ of the ionosphere," *J. Geophys. Res.* **51**, 89 (1946).

30. J. Bartels, "27-day variations in $F2$ layer critical frequencies at Huancayo," *J. Atmos. Terr. Phys.* **1**, 2 (1951).

31. D. R. Bates, R. A. Buckingham, H. S. W. Massey, and J. J. Unwin, "Dissociation. recombination and attachment processes in the upper atmosphere," *Proc. Roy, Soc.* A**170**, 322 (1939).

32. D. R. Bates and H. S. W. Massey, "The basic reactions in the upper atmosphere I", *Proc. Roy. Soc.* A**187**, 261 (1946).

33. D. R. Bates and H. S. W. Massey, "The basic reactions in the upper atmosphere II. The theory of recombination in the ionized layers," *Proc. Roy. Soc.* A**192**, 1 (1947).

34. D. R. Bates and M. R. C. McDowell, "Recombination in the ionosphere during an eclipse," *J. Atmos. Terr. Phys.* **10**, 96 (1957).

35. D. R. Bates and M. J. Seaton, "Theoretical considerations regarding the formation of the ionized layers," *Proc. Phys. Soc.* **63**, 129 (1950).

36. D. R. Bates and H. S. W. Massey, "The negative ion concentration in the lower ionosphere," *J. Atmos. Terr. Phys.* **2**, 1 (1952).

37. D. R. Bates and H. S. W. Massey, "On negative ions of molecular oxygen in the D layer," *J. Atmos. Terr. Phys.* **2**, 253 (1952).

38. D. R. Bates, "Charge transfer and ion-interchange collisions," *Proc. Phys. Soc.* **68**, 344 (1955).

39. D. R. Bates, "Recombination in the ionosphere," *J. Atmos. Terr. Phys.* (*Eclipse Suppl.*) **6**, 191 (1956).

40. D. R. Bates, "Formation of the ionized layers," *J. Atmos. Terr. Phys.* (*Eclipse Suppl.*) **6**, 184 (1956).

41. J. S. Belrose, M. H. Devenport, and K. Weekes, "Some unusual radio observations made on 23/2/56," *J. Atmos. Terr. Phys.* **8**, 281 (1956).

42. L. V. Berkner, H. W. Wells, and S. L. Seaton, "Characteristics of the upper region of the ionosphere," *J. Geophys. Res.* **41**, 173 (1936).

43. L. V. Berkner and H. W. Wells, "Further studies of radio fade-outs," *J. Geophys. Res.* **42**, 301 (1937).

44. L. V. Berkner and H. W. Wells, "Non-seasonal change of $F2$-region ion density," *J. Geophys. Res.* **43**, 15 (1938).

45. L. V. Berkner, H. W. Wells, and S. L. Seaton, "Ionospheric effects associated with magnetic disturbances," *J. Geophys. Res.* **44**, 283 (1939).

46. W. J. G. Beynon and K. Davies, "Simultaneous ionospheric absorption measurements at widely separated stations," *J. Atmos. Terr. Phys.* **5**, 273 (1954).

47. W. J. G. Beynon and G. M. Brown, "Region E and the Sq. current system," *Nature* **177**, 583 (1956).

48. W. J. G. Beynon and G. M. Brown, "Ionospheric indices of solar activity," *J. Atmos. Terr. Phys.* **11**, 128 (1957).

49. G. M. Brown, "Geophysical discussion," *Observatory* **77**, 94 (1957).

50. K. Bibl, "L'ionisation de la couche-E, sa mesure et sa relation avec les éruptions solaires," *Ann. Géophys.* **7**, 208 (1951).

50a. K. Bibl and K. Rawer, "Les contributions des régions D et E dans les mesures de l'absorption ionosphérique," *J. Atmos. Terr. Phys.* **2**, 51 (1952).

51. K. Bibl, "Phénomènes dynamiques dans les couches ionosphériques," *C. R. Acad. Sci.* (*Paris*) **235**, 734 (1952).

52. H. G. Booker, "Oblique propagation of electro-magnetic waves in a slowly-varying non-isotropic medium," *Proc. Roy. Soc.* **A155**, 235 (1936).

53. H. G. Booker, "Radio star scintillations, auroral radar echoes, and other phenomena," *J. Atmos. Terr. Phys.* (*Polar Atmosphere Suppl.*) **2**, 52 (1957).

54. H. G. Booker, "Concerning ionospheric turbulence at the meteoric level," *J. Geophys. Res.* **63**, 97 (1958).

55. P. W. A. Bowe, "The waveforms of atmospherics and the propagation of very-low-frequency radio waves," *Phil. Mag.* **42**, 121 (1951).

56. P. W. A. Bowe, "A study of individual radio atmospherics received simultaneously at two places," *Phil. Mag.* **44**, 833 (1953).

57. R. N. Bracewell and T. W. Straker, "The study of solar flares by means of very long radio waves," *Monthly Not. Roy. Astron. Soc.* **109**, 28 (1949).

58. R. N. Bracewell, K. G. Budden, J. A. Ratcliffe, T. W. Straker, and K. Weekes, "The ionospheric propagation of low- and very-low-frequency radio waves over distances less than 1000 km," *Proc. IEE* **98** (3), 221 (1951).

59. N. E. Bradbury, "Ionization, negative ion formation, and recombination in the ionosphere," *Terr. Mag.* **43**, 55 (1938).

60. B. H. Briggs and G. J. Phillips, "A study of the horizontal irregularities of the ionosphere," *Proc. Phys. Soc.* **63**, 907 (1950).

61. B. H. Briggs, G. J. Phillips, and D. H. Shinn, "The analysis of observations on spaced receivers of the fading of radio signals," *Proc. Phys. Soc.* **63**, 106 (1950).

62. B. H. Briggs, "An investigation of certain properties of the ionosphere by means of a rapid frequency-change experiment," *Proc. Phys. Soc.* **64**, 255 (1951).

63. B. H. Briggs and M. Spencer, "Horizontal movements in the ionosphere," *Repts. Progr. in Phys.* **17**, 245 (1954).

64. B. H. Briggs, "A study of the ionospheric irregularities which cause spread-F echoes and scintillations of radio stars," *J. Atmos. Terr. Phys.* **12**, 34 (1958).

65. R. A. Brown, "Lunar variations of the $F2$ layer at Ibadan," *J. Atmos. Terr. Phys.* **9**, 144 (1956).

66. E. T. Bryam, T. A. Chubb, and M. Friedman, "The contribution of solar X-rays to E-layer ionization," *Phys. Rev.* **92**, 1066 (1953).

67. K. G. Budden, "The theory of the limiting polarization of radio waves reflected from the ionosphere," *Proc. Roy. Soc.* **A215**, 215 (1952).

68. K. G. Budden, "The mathematics of wave-propagation through the ionosphere," *Phys. Soc. Rept. Ionosphere Conf.* 276 (1955).

69. R. Bureau, "Les renforcements de la propagation des ondes longues en coincidence avec les évonouissements des ondes courtes: leur observation par l'enregistrement des parasites atmosphériques," *J. Phys. Radium* **10**, 260 (1939).

70. O. Burkard, "Gezeiten in der oberen Ionosphäre," *J. Geophys. Res.* **53**, 273 (1948).

71. O. Burkard, "Die halbjährige Periode der $F2$-Schicht-Ionisation," *Arch. Meteorol. Geophys. Bioklimatol.* **4**, 391 (1951).

72. O. Burkard, "Die tages-und jahreszeitlichen Variation der $F1$-Ionisation. Ein Deutungs-versuch," *J. Atmos. Terr. Phys.* **8**, 83 (1956).

73. O. Burkard, "Simultaneous variations of $F2$ layer ionization at two places," *Öst. Z. Tel. Telephon. Furn u. Fern.* **5**, 57 (1955).

74. S. Chapman, "The absorption and dissociative or ionizing effect of monochromatic radiation in an atmosphere on a rotating earth. Part I. Part II. Grazing incidence," *Proc. Phys. Soc.* **43**, 26, 484 (1931).

75. S. Chapman, "The atmospheric height distribution of band-absorbed solar radiation," *Proc. Phys. Soc.* **51**, 93 (1939).

76. S. Chapman, "A monochromatically ionized layer in a non-uniformly recombinant atmosphere: with applications to the D and E ionospheric regions," *Proc. Phys. Soc.* **67**, 717 (1954).

77. S. Chapman, "The electrical conductivity of the ionosphere: a review," *Nuovo Cim.* **4**, (*Suppl.*) 1385 (1956).

78. S. Chapman and C. G. Little, "The non-deviature absorption of high-frequency radio waves in auroral latitudes," *J. Atmos. Terr. Phys.* **10**, 20 (1957).

79. B. Chatterjee, "Nature and origin of sporadic E regions as observed at different hours," *J. Atmos. Terr. Phys.* **3**, 229 (1953).

80. C. Clark and A. M. Peterson, "Motion of sporadic-E patches determined from high-frequency backscatter records," *Nature* **178**, 486 (1956).

81. P. C. Clemmow, M. A. Johnson, and K. Weekes, "A note on the motion of a cylindrical irregularity in an ionized medium," *Phys. Soc. Rept. Ionosphere Conf.* 136 (1955).

82. M. Dagg, "The origin of the ionospheric irregularities responsible for radio-star scintillations and spread F—I. Review of existing theories," *J. Atmos. Terr. Phys.* **4**, 133 (1957).

83. M. Dagg, "The origin of the ionospheric irregularities responsible for radio-star scintillations and spread F. II. Turbulent motion in the dynamo region," *J. Atmos, Terr. Phys.* **11**, 139 (1957).

84. M. Dagg, "Diurnal variations of radio-star scintillations, spread F and geomagnetic activity," *J. Atmos. Terr. Phys.* **10**, 204 (1957).

85. M. Dagg, "The correlation of radio-star scintillation phenomena with geomagnetic disturbance and the mechanism of motion of the ionospheric irregularities in the F region," *J. Atmos. Terr. Phys.* **10**, 194 (1957).

86. N. Davids and R. W. Parkinson, "Wave solutions for critical and near-critical coupling conditions in the ionosphere," *J. Atmos. Terr. Phys.* **7**, 173 (1955).

87. J. H. Dellinger, "Sudden ionospheric disturbances," *J. Geophys. Res.* **42**, 49 (1937).

88. W. Dieminger *et al.*, "Solare und terrestrische Beobachtungen wärend des Mögel-Dellinger Effektes (SID) am 19/11/49," *J. Atmos. Terr. Phys.* **1**, 37 (1950).

89. W. Dieminger, " Über die Ursache der excessiven Absorption in der Ionosphäre an Wintertagen," *J. Atmos. Terr. Phys.* **2**, 340 (1952).

90. W. Dieminger, "Short-wave echoes from the lower ionosphere," *Phys. Soc. Rept. Ionosphere Conf.* 53 (1955).

91. R. A. Duncan, "Lunar variations in the ionosphere," *Austral. J. Phys.* **9**, 112 (1956).

92. R. A. Duncan, "The behaviour of a Chapman layer in the night $F2$ region of the ionosphere, under the influence of gravity, diffusion, and attachment," *Austral. J. Phys.* **9**, 436 (1956).

93. J. W. Dungey, "The effect of ambipolar diffusion in the night-time F layer," *J. Atmos. Terr. Phys.* **9**, 90 (1956).

94. W. G. Elford and D. S. Robertson, "Measurement of winds in the upper atmosphere by means of drifting meteor trails II," *J. Atmos. Terr. Phys.* **4**, 271 (1954).

95. M. A. Ellison, "The Hα radiation from solar flares in relation to SEAs on frequencies near 27 kc/sec," *J. Atmos. Terr. Phys.* **4**, 226 (1954).

96. C. D. Ellyett, "Echoes at D-heights with special reference to the Pacific islands," *J. Geophys. Res.* **52**, 1 (1947).

97. A. Emhert and K. Revello, "Solare Ultrastrahlung und ionosphärische D-Schicht am 23/2/56," *Z. Geophys.* **23**, 113 (1957).

98. J. V. Evans, "The electron content of the ionosphere," *J. Atmos. Terr. Phys.* **11**, 259 (1957).

99. J. A. Fejer, "Semidiurnal currents and electron drifts in the ionosphere," *J. Atmos. Terr. Phys.* **4**, 184 (1953); Erratum, *J. Atmos. Terr. Phys.* **5**, 103 (1953).

100. J. A. Fejer, "The interaction of pulsed radio waves in the ionosphere," *J. Atmos. Terr. Phys.* **7**, 322 (1955).

101. V. C. A. Ferraro, "On diffusion in the ionosphere," *J. Geophys. Res.* **51**, 427 (1946).

102. O. P. Ferrell, "Upper-atmospheric circulation as indicated by drifting and dissipation of intense sporadic-E clouds," *Proc. IRE* **36**, 879 (1948).

103. K. Försterling, "Uber die Ausbreitung elektromognetischen Wellen in einem magnetisierten Medium bei senkrechter Inzidenz," *Hochfrequenztech. u. Elek. Akus.* **59**, 10 (1942).

104. R. Gallet, "Sur la nature de la couche E sporadique et la turbulence de la haute atmosphere," *C. R. Acad. Sci. (Paris)* **233**, 1649 (1951).

105. F. F. Gardner and J. L. Pawsey, "Study of the ionospheric D-region using partial reflections," *J. Atmos. Terr. Phys.* **3**, 321 (1953).

106. F. F. Gardner, "Ionospheric thermal radiation at radio frequencies. II. Further observations," *J. Atmos. Terr. Phys.* **5**, 298 (1954).

107. V. B. Gerard, "Correlation of sporadic E over short distances," *New Zealand J. Sci. Tech.* **30**, 27 (1949).

108. N. C. Gerson, "A critical survey of ionospheric temperatures," *Repts. Progr. in Phys.* **14**, 316 (1951).

109. S. Gnanalingam and K. Weekes, "D-region echoes observed with a radio wave of frequency 1.4 Mc/sec," *Phys. Soc. Rept. Ionosphere Conf.* 63 (1955).

110. G. L. Goodwin, "The movements of sporadic-E layer clouds," *J. Atmos. Terr. Phys.* **11**, 177 (1957).

111. G. Grawert and H. Lassen, "Die Auswertung von Ionosphären-Beobachtungen," *Z. angaw. Phys.* **6**, 136 (1954).

112. J. S. Greenhow, "Systematic wind measurements at altitudes of 80–100 km using radio echoes from meteor trails," *Phil. Mag.* **45**, 471 (1954).

113. J. S. Greenhow and E. L. Neufeld, "The height variation of upper atmospheric winds," *Phil. Mag.* **1**, 1157 (1956).

114. J. B. Gregory, "Ionospheric reflections from heights below the E-region," *Austral. J. Phys.* **9**, 324 (1956).

115. J. B. Gregory, "The relation of forward scattering of V.H.F. radio waves to partial reflection of M.F. waves at vertical incidence," *J. Geophys. Res.* **62**, 383 (1957).

116. J. B. Gregory, "The mesopause region of the ionosphere," *Nature* **181**, 753 (1958).

117. J. B. Gregory, "Medium-frequency observations of the lower ionosphere during sudden disturbances," *J. Geophys. Res.* **63**, 273 (1958).

118. E. Harnischmacher, "L'influence solaire sur la couche E normale de l'ionosphere," *C. R. Acad. Sci. (Prais)* **230**, 1301 (1950).

119. R. J. Havens, H. Friedman, and E. O. Hulbert, "The ionospheric $F2$ region," *Phys. Soc. Rept. Ionosphere Conf.* 237 (1955).

120. R. A. Helliwell, A. J. Mallinckrodt, and F. W. Kruse, "Fine structure of the lower ionosphere," *J. Geophys. Res.* **56**, 53 (1951).

121. F. Hepburn, "Wave-guide interpretation of atmospheric waveforms," *J. Atmos. Terr. Phys.* **10**, 121 (1957).

122. M. Herzberg, "Atomic nitrogen production by ion-atom interchange reactions in the upper atmosphere," *J. Geophys. Res.* **63**, 856 (1958).

123. A. Hewish, "The diffraction of galactic radio waves as a method of investigating the irregular structure of the ionosphere," *Proc. Roy. Soc.* A**214**, 494 (1952).

124. C. O. Hines, "Electron resonance in ionospheric waves," *J. Atmos. Terr. Phys.* **9**, 56 (1956).

125. M. Hirono, "A theory of diurnal magnetic variations in equatorial regions and conductivity of the ionospheric E region," *J. Geomag. Geoelec.* **5**, 22 (1953).

126. M. Hirono and H. Maeda, "Geomagnetic distortion of the $F2$ region on the magnetic equator," *J. Geophys. Res.* **60**, 241 (1955).

127. M. Hirono and T. Kitamura, "A dynamo theory of the ionosphere," *J. Geomag. Geoelec.* **8**, 9 (1956).

128. J. Hollingworth, "The propagation of radio waves," *J. Inst. Elec. Eng.* **64**, 578 (1926).

129. R. E. Houston, W. J. Ross, and E. R. Schmerling, "Some effects of intense solar activity on radio propagation," *J. Atmos. Terr. Phys.* **10**, 136 (1957).

130. R. E. Houston, "The effect of certain solar radiations on the lower ionosphere," *J. Atmos. Terr. Phys.* **12**, 225 (1958).

131. F. Hoyle and D. R. Bates, "The production of the E layer," *J. Geophys. Res.* **53**, 51 (1948).

132. L. G. H. Huxley and J. A. Ratcliffe, "A survey of ionospheric cross-modulation," *Proc. IEE* **96** (3), 433 (1949).

133. L. G. H. Huxley, R. W. Crompton, and D. J. Sutton, "Experimental studies of the motions of slow electrons in air with applications to the ionosphere," *Proc. Roy. Soc.* **218**, 507 (1953).

134. J. E. Jackson, "Measurements in the E layer with the Navy Viking rocket," *J. Geophys. Res.* **59**, 377 (1954).

135. J. E. Jackson, "A new method for obtaining electron-density profiles from $P'(f)$ records," *J. Geophys. Res.* **61**, 107 (1956).

136. J. E. Jackson and J. C. Seddon, "Ionosphere electron-density measurements with the navy aerobee-hi rocket," *J. Geophys. Res.* **63**, 197 (1958).

137. I. L. Jones, B. Landmark, and C. S. G. K. Setty, "Movements of ionospheric irregularities observed simultaneously by different methods," *J. Atmos. Terr. Phys.* **10**, 296 (1957).

138. I. L. Jones, "The height variation of drift in the E region," *J. Atmos. Terr. Phys.* **12**, 68 (1958).

139. R. E. Jones, "The development of an E region model consistent with long-wave phase path measurements," *J. Atmos. Terr. Phys.* **6**, 1 (1955).

140. H. K. Kallmann, W. B. White, and H. E. Newell, "Physical properties of the atmosphere from 90 to 300 km," *J. Geophys. Res.* **61**, 518 (1956); **62**, 168 (1957).

141. H. K. Kallman, "Electron distribution in a new model of the ionosphere," *J. Atmos. Terr. Phys.* (Polar Atmosphere *Suppl.*) **2**, 82 (1957).

142. S. Kato, "Horizontal wind systems in the ionospheric E region deduced from the dynamo theory of the geomagnetic Sq variation. Part II rotating earth," *J. Geomag. Geoelec.* **8**, 24 (1956).

143. S. Kato, "Horizontal wind systems in the ionospheric E region deduced from the dynamo theory of the geomagnetic Sq variation. Part IV (see Maeda for parts I and III)," *J. Geomag. Geoelec.* **9**, 107 (1957).

144. G. S. Kent, "High frequency fading observed on the 40 Mc/s wave radiated from artificial satellite 1957d," *J. Atmos. Terr. Phys.* **16**, 10 (1959).

145. K. O. Kiepenhauer, "On the relation between ionosphere, sunspots and solar corona," *Monthly Not. Roy. Astron. Soc.* **106**, 515 (1946).

146. C. B. Kirkpatrick, "The influence of vertical ionic drift on a 'Chapman region',"
     Austral. J. Sci. Res. **1**, 423 (1948).

147. J. R. Koster, "Radio star scintillations at an equatorial station," *J. Atmos. Terr.
     Phys.* **12**, 100 (1958).

148. B. Landmark, "Echoes from the lower ionosphere during Polar blackouts," *J.
     Atmos. Terr. Phys.* **12**, 79 (1958).

149. G. Lange-Hesse, "Einfluss der erdmagnetischen Unruhe auf die Durchschnitts
     abweichungen der Fl-Schicht-Tagesgrenz frequenzen," *J. Atmos. Terr. Phys.* **11**,
     293 (1957).

150. G. Lange-Hesse, "27 tägige Variation in der *D* Schicht. Absorption der Ionosphäre
     über Singapore und Slough," *J. Atmos. Terr. Phys.* **3**, 153 (1953).

151. E. A. Lauter and K. Sprenger, "Nächtliche Ionisatsstörungen der teifen Iono-
     sphäre," *Z. Meteorol.* **6**, 161 (1952).

152. E. A. Lauter, "Variatonen der *D*-Schicht dämpfung auf 245 kHz," *Z. Meteorol.*
     7, 321 (1953).

153. E. A. Lauter, G. Bartels, K. Sprenger, and G. Skeib, "Der Intensitätsanstieg der
     Kosmischen Strahlung am 23.2.1956 und gleichzeitige Effekte in der tiefen Iono-
     sphäre," *Z. Meteorol.* **10**, 129 (1956).

154. E. A. Lauter, "Der atmosphärische Storspiegel im Längst-Wellenbereich und
     seine tages-und jahreszeitlichen Variationen," *Z. Meteorol.* **10**, 110 (1956).

155. R. P. W. Lewis and D. H. McIntosh, "Geomagnetic and ionospheric relationships,"
     J. Atmos. Terr. Phys. **4**, 44 (1953).

156. C. A. Littlewood and J. H. Chapman, "A measurement at Ottawa of the change
     in height with lunar time of the *E* region of the ionosphere," *Canad. J. Phys.*
     33, 11 (1955).

157. H. L. Lung, "Seasonal variations of world-wide *F*2 ionization for noon and
     midnight hours," *J. Geophys. Res.* **54**, 177 (1949).

158. A. G. McNish and T. N. Gautier, "Theory of lunar effects and midday decrease
     in *F*2 ion-density at Huoncuyo," *J. Geophys. Res.* **54**, 181 (1949).

159. A. G. McNish and T. N. Gautier, "Lunar ionospheric variations at low-latitude
     stations," *J. Geophys. Res.* **54**, 303 (1949).

160. H. Maeda, "The vertical distribution of electrical conductivity in the upper
     atmosphere," *J. Geomag. Geoelec.* **5**, 94 (1953).

161. H. Maeda, "Horizontal wind systems in the ionospheric *E* region deduced from
     the dynamo theory of the geomagnetic Sq variation Pt I. Non-rotating earth,"
     J. Geomag. Geoelec. **7**, 121 (1955).

162. H. Maeda, "Horizontal wind systems in the ionospheric *E* region deduced from
     the dynamo theory of the geomagnetic Sq variation. Part III," *J. Geomag. Geoelec.*
     9, 86 (1957). (For Parts II and IV see Kato.)

163. H. Maeda, "Wind systems for the geomagnetic S_d field," *J. Geomag. Geoelec.* **9**,
     119 (1957).

164. L. A. Manning, O. D. Villard, and A. M. Peterson, "Meteoric echo study of upper
     atmosphere winds," *Proc. IRE* **38**, 877 (1950).

165. F. Mariani, "Sulle correlazioni fra densità elettronica ionosferica e attività solare."
     Ann. Geofis. **10**, 71 (1958).

166. F. Mariani, "Variazioni stagionali e non stagionali della densità elettronica iono-
     sferica," *Ann. Geofis.* **10**, 167 (1958).

167. F. Mariani, "The electron density in the *F*2 layer and its correlation with solar
     activity," *J. Atmos. Terr. Phys.* **10**, 239 (1957).

168. D. F. Martyn, "Tidal phenomena in the ionosphere," *U.R.S.I.* Spec. Rept.

169. D. F. Martyn, "The morphology of the ionospheric variations associated with magnetic disturbance. I. Variations at moderately low latitudes," *Proc. Roy. Soc.* A**218**, 1 (1953).

170. D. F. Martyn, "The normal F-region of the ionosphere," *Proc. IRE* **47**, 147 (1959).

171. D. F. Martyn, "Electric currents in the ionosphere. III. Ionization drift due to winds and electric fields," *Phil Trans. Roy. Soc.* A**246**, 306 (1953); see also refs. 27 and 28.

172. D. F. Martyn, "Geomagnetic anomalies of the F2 region and their interpretation," *Phys. Soc. Rept. Ionosphere Conf.* 260 (1955).

173. D. F. Martyn, "A survey of present knowledge of the F2 region," *Phys. Soc. Rept. Ionosphere Conf.* 212 (1955).

174. D. F. Martyn, "Interpretation of observed F2 'winds' as ionization drifts associated with the magnetic variations," *Phys. Soc. Rept. Ionosphere Conf.* 163 (1955).

175. D. F. Martyn, "Theory of height and ionization density changes at the maximum of a Chapman-like layer, taking account of ion production, decay, diffusion, and tidal effect," *Phys. Soc. Rept. Ionosphere Conf.* 254 (1955).

176. D. F. Martyn, "Processes controlling ionization distribution in the F2 region of the ionosphere," *Austral. J. Phys.* **9**, 161 (1956).

177. H. S. W. Massey, "Recombination of gaseous ions," *Advances in Physics* **1**, 395 (1952).

178. H. S. W. Massey and R. L. F. Boyd, "Scientific observations of the artificial earth satellites and their analysis," *Nature*, **181**, 78 (1958).

179. S. Matsushita, "Intense Es near the magnetic equator," *J. Geomag. Geoelec.* **3**, 44 (1951).

180. S. Matsushita, "Semi-diurnal lunar variations in the sporadic E," *J. Geomag. Geoelec.* **4**, 39 (1952).

181. S. Matsushita, "Lunar effect on the equatorial Es," *J. Atmos. Terr. Phys.* **10**, 163 (1957).

182. A. Maxwell and M. Dagg, "A radio astronomical investigation of drift movements in the upper atmosphere," *Phil. Mag.* **45**, 551 (1954).

183. D. H. Menzel, J. G. Wolbach, and H. Glazer, "The E-layer of the ionosphere: statistical analysis," *Solar Eclipses and the Ionosphere*, p. 282, Pergamon, London, 1956.

184. C. M. Minnis, "The interpretation of changes in the E and F1 layers during solar eclipses," *J. Atmos. Terr. Phys.* **12**, 272 (1958).

184a. C. M. Minnis and G. H. Bazzard, "Solar flare effect in the F2-layer of the ionosphere," *Nature* **181**, 690 (1958).

185. S. N. Mitra, "A radio method of measuring winds in the ionosphere," *Proc. IEE* **96**, (3), 441 (1949).

186. A. P. Mitra, "Effects of the variations of recombination coefficient and scale height on the structures of the ionized regions," *Indian J. Phys.* **26**, 79 (1952).

187. S. K. Mitra, " The Upper Atmosphere," The Asiatic Society, Calcutta, India, 1952.

188. A. P. Mitra, "A tentative model of the equilibrium height distribution of nitric oxide in the high atmosphere and the resulting D-layer," *J. Atmos. Terr. Phys.* **5**, 28 (1954).

189. A. P. Mitra and C. A. Shain, "The measurement of ionospheric absorption using observations of 18.3 Mc/sec cosmic radio noise," *J. Atmos. Terr. Phys.* **4**, 204 (1954).

190. S. K. Mitra and M. R. Kundu, "Thunderstorms and sporadic E ionization of the ionosphere," *Nature* **174**, 798 (1954).

191. A. P. Mitra and R. E. Jones, "Recombination in the lower ionosphere," *J. Geophys. Res.* **59**, 391 (1954).

192. A. P. Mitra and R. E. Jones, "Determination of the location of the ionospheric current system responsible for geomagnetic effects of solar flares," *J. Atmos. Terr. Phys.* **4**, 141 (1954).

193. A. P. Mitra, "Night time ionization in the lower ionosphere. I. Recombination processes," *J. Atmos. Terr. Phys.* **10**, 140 (1957).

194. A. P. Mitra, "Night time ionization in the lower ionosphere. II. Distribution of electrons and positive and negative ions," *J. Atmos. Terr. Phys.* **10**, 153 (1957).

195. F. L. Mohler, "Recombination and electron attachment in the F layers of the ionosphere," *J. Res. Natl. Bur. Standards* **25**, 507 (1940).

196. G. H. Munro, "Travelling disturbances in the ionosphere," *Proc. Roy. Soc.* A**202**, 208 (1950).

196a. G. H. Munro, "Reflections from irregularities in the ionosphere," *Proc. Roy. Soc.* A**219**, 447 (1953).

197. G. H. Munro, "Travelling disturbances in the ionosphere: changes in diurnal variation," *Nature* **180**, 1252 (1957).

198. G. H. Munro, "Travelling ionospheric disturbances in the F region," *Austral. J. Phys.* **11**, 91 (1958).

199. R. Naismith and E. M. Bramley, "Time-delay measurements on radio transmissions," *Wireless Eng.* **28**, 271 (1951).

200. R. Naismith, "Some properties of the meteoric E-layer used in radio wave propagation," *Nuovo Cim.* **4** (*Suppl.*), 1413 (1956).

201. R. J. Nertney, "The lower E and D region of the ionosphere as deduced from long radio wave measurements," *J. Atmos. Terr. Phys.* **3**, 92 (1953).

202. M. Nicolet, "Effects of atmospheric scale height gradient on the variation of ionization and short wave absorption," *J. Atmos. Terr. Phys.* **1**, 141 (1951).

203. M. Nicolet, "The collision frequency of electrons in the ionosphere," *J. Atmos. Terr. Phys.* **3**, 200 (1953).

204. M. Nicolet and P. Mange, "The dissociation of oxygen in the high atmosphere," *J. Geophys. Res.* **59**, 15 (1954).

205. B. W. Osborne, "Horizontal movements of ionization in the equatorial F-region," *J. Atmos. Terr. Phys.* **6**, 117 (1955).

206. R. W. Parkinson, "The night time lower ionosphere as deduced from a theoretical and experimental investigation of coupling phenomena at 150 kc/s.," *J. Atmos. Terr. Phys.* **7**, 203 (1955).

207. J. L. Pawsey, L. L. McCreedy, and F. F. Gardner, "Ionsopheric thermal radiation at radio frequencies," *J. Atmos. Terr. Phys.* **1**, 261 (1951).

208. W. Pfister, "Effect of the D-ionospheric layer on very low frequency waves," *J. Geophys. Res.* **54**, 315 (1949).

209. W. Pfister, "Studies of the refractive index in the ionosphere: the effect of the collision frequency and of ions," *Phys. Soc. Rept. Ionosphere Conf.* 394 (1955).

210. W. Pfister and J. C. Ulwick, "The analysis of rocket experiments in terms of electron-density distributions," *J. Geophys. Res.* **63**, 315 (1958).

211. W. R. Piggott, "On the variation of ionospheric absorption at different stations," *J. Atmos. Terr. Phys.* **7**, 244 (1955).

212. W. R. Piggott, "The measurement of normal E-layer critical frequencies at night," *J. Atmos. Terr. Phys.* **7**, 341 (1955).

213. V. C. Pineo, "Oblique incidence measurements of the heights at which ionospheric scattering of V.H.F. radio waves occurs," *J. Geophys. Res.* **61**, 165 (1956).

214. J. A. Ratcliffe, "Some regularities in the F2 region of the ionosphere," *J. Geophys. Res.* **56**, 487 (1951).

215. J. A. Ratcliffe, "Some aspects of diffraction theory and their application to the ionosphere," *Repts. Progr. in Phys.* **19**, 188 (1956).

216. J. A. Ratcliffe, "The formation of the ionospheric layers F1 and F2," *J. Atmos. Terr. Phys.* **8**, 260 (1956).

217. J. A. Ratcliffe, E. R. Schmerling, C. S. G. K. Setty, and J. O. Thomas, "The rates of production and loss of electrons in the F-region of the ionosphere," *Phil. Trans. Roy. Soc.* A**248**, 621 (1956).

218. J. A. Ratcliffe, "The Magneto Ionic Theory," Cambridge University Press, 1959.

219. K. Rawer, "The Ionosphere," Frederick Ungar Publishing Co., New York, 1957.

220. K. Rawer and E. Argence, "Region E formation," *Ann. Géophys.* **9**, 1 (1953).

221. A. R. Robbins, private communication.

222. B. J. Robinson, "Experimental investigations of the ionospheric E layer," *Repts. Progr. in Phys.* **22**, 241 (1959).

223. M. Ryle and A. Hewish, "The effects of the terrestrial ionosphere on the radio waves from discrete sources in the Galaxy," *Monthly Not. Roy. Astron. Soc.* **110**, 381 (1950).

224. T. Sato, "Disturbances in the F1 and E regions of the ionosphere associated with geomagnetic storms," *J. Geomag. Geoelec.* **9**, 57 (1957).

225. T. Sato, "Disturbances in the ionospheric F2 region associated with geomagnetic storms. I. Equatorial Zone," *J. Geomag. Geoelec.* **8**, 129 (1956).

226. T. Sato, "Disturbances in the ionospheric F2 region associated with geomagnetic storms. III. Auroral latitudes," *J. Geomag. Geoelec.* **9**, 94 (1957).

227. T. Sato, "Disturbances in the ionospheric F2 region associated with geomagnetic storms. II. Middle latitudes," *J. Geomag. Geoelec.* **9**, 1 (1957).

228. D. M. Schlapp, "Collision frequency in the E-region of the Ionosphere," *J. Atmos. Terr. Phys.* **16**, 340 (1959).

229. B. F. J. Schonland, J. S. Elder, and J. W. van Wyk, "Reflection of atmospherisc from the ionosphere," *Nature*, **143**, 893 (1939).

230. E. R. Schmerling and J. O. Thomas, "The distribution of electrons in the undisturbed F2 layer of the ionosphere," *Phil. Trans. Roy. Soc.* A**248**, 609 (1956).

231. E. R. Schmerling, "An easily applied method for the reduction of $h'(f)$ records to $N(h)$ profiles, including the effects of the earth's magnetic field," *J. Atmos. Terr. Phys.* **12**, 8 (1958).

232. J. C. W. Scott, "The distribution of F2 region ionization at high latitudes," *J. Atmos. Terr. Phys.* **3**, 289 (1953).

233. S. L. Seaton and L. V. Berkner, "Non-seasonal behaviour of the F-region," *J. Geophys. Res.* **44**, 313 (1939).

234. J. C. Seddon, A. D. Pickar, and J. E. Jackson, "Continuous electron density measurements up to 200 km," *J. Geophys. Res.* **59**, 513 (1954).

235. J. C. Seddon, "Differential absorption in the D and lower E regions," *J. Geophys. Res.* **63**, 209 (1958).

236. I. J. Shaw, "Some further investigations of ionospheric cross-modulation," *Proc. Phys Soc.* **64**, 1 (1951).

237. T. Shimazaki, "A theoretical study of the dynamical structure of the ionosphere," *J. Radio Res. Lab.* **6**, 107 (1959).

238. N. J. Skinner and R. W. Wright, "Equatorial ionospheric absorption," *J. Atmos. Terr. Phys.* **9**, 103 (1956).

239. N. J. Skinner and R. W. Wright, "The effect of the equatorial electrojet on the ionospheric Es and F2 layers," *Proc. Phys. Soc.* **70**, 833 (1957).

240. E. K. Smith, "World wide occurrence of sporadic E," *Natl. Bur. Standards (U.S.) Circ.* **582** (1957).

241. F. G. Smith, "Ionospheric refraction of 81.5 Mc/s radio waves from radio stars," *J. Atmos. Terr. Phys.* **2**, 350 (1952).

242. "Solar Eclipses and the Ionosphere," Pergamon, London, 1956.

243. M. Spencer, "The shape of irregularities in the upper ionosphere," *Proc. Phys. Soc.* B**68**, 493 (1955).

244. Standards on wave-propagation. Definition of terms, 1950. *Proc. IRE* **38**, 1264 (1950).

245. W. Stoffregen, "Radio reflections on low frequencies from 75–90 km height during intense auroral activity," *J. Atmos. Terr. Phys.* **13**, 167 (1958).

246. L. R. O. Storey, "An investigation of whistling atmospherics," *Phil. Trans. Roy. Soc.* A**246**, 113 (1953).

247. L. R. O. Storey, "A method for interpreting the dispersion curves of whistlers," *Canad. J. Phys.* **35**, 1107 (1957).

248. J. Taubenheim, "The influence of solar flares on the ionospheric E layer," *J. Atmos. Terr. Phys.* **11**, 14 (1957).

249. J. A. Thomas and A. C. Svenson, "Lunar tide in sporadic E at Brisbane," *Austral. J. Phys.* **8**, 554 (1955).

250. J. O. Thomas and A. R. Robbins, "The electron distribution in the ionosphere over Slough. II. Disturbed days," *J. Atmos. Terr. Phys.* **13**, 131 (1958).

251. J. O. Thomas, J. Haselgrove, and A. R. Robbins, "The electron distribution in the ionosphere over Slough. I. Quiet days," *J. Atmos. Terr. Phys.* **12**, 46 (1958).

252. J. O. Thomas, "The distribution of electrons in the ionosphere," *Proc. IRE* **47**, 162 (1959).

253. K. W. Tremellen and J. W. Cox, "Influence of wave propagation on planning of short-wave communication," *Proc. IEE* **94** (3A), 200 (1947).

254. J. A. Thomas and F. Hibberd, "Satellite Doppler measurements and the ionosphere," *J. Atmos. Terr. Phys.* **13**, 376 (1959).

255. O. D. Villard, A. M. Peterson, and L. A. Manning, "A method for studying sporadic-E clouds at a distance," *Proc. IRE* **40**, 992 (1952).

256. F. Villars and V. F. Weisskopf, "On the scattering of radio waves by turbulent fluctuations of the atmosphere," *Proc. IRE* **43**, 1232 (1955).

257. J. W. Warwick and H. Zirin, "Diurnal absorption in the D region." *J. Atmos. Terr. Phys.* **11**, 187 (1957).

258. J. M. Watts and J. N. Brown, "Some results of sweep-frequency investigation in the low-frequency band," *J. Geophys. Res.* **59**, 71 (1954).

259. J. M. Watts, "Complete night of vertical incidence ionosphere soundings covering frequency range from 50 kc/s to 25 Mc/s," *J. Geophys. Res.* **62**, 484 (1957).

260. A. H. Waynick, "The lowest ionosphere," *Phys. Soc. Rept. Ionosphere Conf.* 1 (1955).

261. A. H. Waynick, "The present state of knowledge concerning the lower ionosphere," *Proc. IRE* **45**, 741 (1957).

262. K. Weekes, "The physical state of the upper atmosphere," *Quart. J. Meteorol. Soc.* **80**, 2 (1954).

263. K. Weekes, "On the interpretation of the Doppler effect from senders in an artificial satellite," *J. Atmos. Terr. Phys.* **12**, 335 (1958).

264. K. Weekes, "The drift of an ionized layer in the presence of the geomagnetic field," *J. Atmos. Terr. Phys. (Polar Atmosphere Suppl.)* **2**, 12 (1957).

265. A. A. Weiss, "Solar ionosphere tides in the $F2$ region," *J. Atmos. Terr. Phys.* **3**, 30 (1953).

266. A. A. Weiss, "Solar tides in the $F2$ region from the study of night-time critical frequencies," *J. Atmos. Terr. Phys.* **4**, 175 (1954).

267. H. A. Whale, "Fine structure of the ionosphere region E," *J. Atmos. Terr. Phys.* **1**, 323 (1951).

268. J. D. Whitehead, "The focussing of short radio waves reflected from the ionosphere," *J. Atmos. Terr. Phys.* **9**, 269 (1956).

269. J. D. Whitehead, "The absorption of short radio waves in the ionosphere," *J. Atmos. Terr. Phys.* **10**, 12 (1957).

270. R. W. Wright, J. R. Koster, and N. J. Skinner, "Spread F echoes and radio-star scintillation," *J. Atmos. Terr. Phys.* **8**, 240 (1956).

271. D. G. Yerg, "Ionospheric wind systems and electron concentrations of the F layer," *J. Meteorol.* **8**, 244 (1951).

272. T. Yonezawa, "A consideration of the electron disappearance in the $F2$ layer of the ionosphere," *J. Rad. Res. Labs. Japan* **1**, 1, 63 (1954).

273. T. Yonezawa, "On the influence of electron-ion diffusion on the electron density and height of the nocturnal $F2$ layer (supplement)," *J. Rad. Res. Japan* **2**, 281 (1955).

274. T. Yonezawa, "On the influence of electron-ion diffusion on the electron density and height of the nocturnal $F2$ layer," *J. Rad. Res. Lab. Japan* **2**, 125 (1955).

275. T. Yonezawa, "A new theory of formation of the $F2$ layer," *J. Rad. Res. Lab. Japan* **3**, 1 (1956).

276. Do.   II. The effect of the vertical movement of electrons and ions on the electron density distribution," *J. Rad. Res. Lab. Japan* **4**, 1 (1957).

280. E. V. Appleton, "The normal E region of the ionosphere," *Proc. IRE* **47**, 155 (1959).

281. E. V. Appleton, R. Naismith, and L. J. Ingram, "Radio observations during the polar year 1932–33," *Phil. Trans. Roy. Soc.* **236**, 191 (1937).

282. L. V. Berkner and S. L. Seaton, "Ionospheric changes associated with the magnetic storm of March 24, 1940," *Terr. Mag.* **45**, 393 (1940).

283. B. H. Briggs, "The determination of the collision frequency of electrons in the ionosphere from observations of the reflection coefficient of the abnormal E layer," *J. Atmos. Terr. Phys.* **1**, 345 (1951).

284. N. Davids and R. Lindquist, "Theoretical and experimental investigation of the group heights of reflection of 150 kc/s radio waves vertically incident on the ionosphere," *Trans. IRE* PGAP **3** (1952).

285. J. J. Gibbons and A. H. Waynick, "The normal D region of the ionosphere," *Proc. IRE* **47**, 160 (1959).

286. R. A. Helliwell and E. Gehrels, "Observations of magneto-ionic duct propagation using man-made signals of very low frequency," *Proc. IRE* **46**, 785 (1958).

287. R. A. Helliwell and M. G. Morgan, "Atmospheric whistlers," *Proc. IRE* **47**, 200 (1959).

288. C. O. Hines, "Motions in the ionosphere," *Proc. IRE* **47**, 177 (1959).

289. J. M. Kelso, H. J. Nearhoof, R. J. Nertney, and A. H. Waynick, "The polarization of vertically incident long radio waves," *Ann. Géophys.* **7**, 215 (1951).

290. K. I. Maeda and T. Sato, "The F region during magnetic storms," *Proc. IRE* **47**, 232 (1959).

291. D. F. Martyn, "Atmospheric tides in the ionosphere. I. Solar tides in the $F2$ region," *Proc. Roy. Soc.* A**189**, 241 (1947).

292. D. F. Martyn, "Atmospheric tides in the ionosphere. II. Lunar tidal variations in the F region near the magnetic equator," *Proc. Roy. Soc.* A**190**, 273 (1947).

293. D. F. Martyn, "Atmospheric tides in the ionosphere. III. Lunar tidal variations at Canberra," *Proc. Roy. Soc.* A**194**, 429 (1948).

294. D. F. Martyn, "Atmospheric tides in the ionosphere. IV. Studies of the solar tide and the location of the regions producing the diurnal magnetic variations," *Proc. Roy. Soc.* A**194**, 445 (1948).

295. D. F. Martyn, "Cellular atmospheric waves in the ionosphere and troposphere," *Proc. Roy. Soc.* A**201**, 216 (1950).

296. J. A. Ratcliffe, "A survey of existing knowledge of irregularities and horizontal movements in the ionosphere," *Phys. Soc. Rept. Ionosphere Conf.* 88 (1955).

297. J. A. Ratcliffe, "A survey of solar eclipses and the ionosphere," *Solar Eclipses and the Ionosphere*, p. 1, Pergamon, London, 1956.

298. R. Silberstein, "The origin of the current nomenclature for the ionospheric layers," *J. Atmos. Terr. Phys.* **13**, 382 (1959).

299. J. O. Thomas and A. R. Robbins, "Movements in the $F2$ layer of the ionosphere during some solar eclipses," *Solar Eclipses and the Ionosphere*, p. 94, Pergamon, London, 1956.

300. J. A. Thomas and E. K. Smith, "A survey of the present knowledge of sporadic-E ionization," *J. Atmos. Terr. Phys.* **13**, 295 (1959).

301. Y. L. Al'pert, E. F. Chudesenko, and B. S. Shapiro, "Results of research on the outer region of the ionosphere from observations of the radio signals of Sputnik I," *Uspekhi Fiz. Nauk* **65**, 2 (1958).

302. G. Reber, "World-wide spread F," *J. Geophys. Res.* **61**, 157 (1956).

303. D. K. Bailey, "Abnormal ionization in the lower ionosphere associated with cosmic-ray flux enhancements," *Proc. IRE* **47**, 255 (1959).

304. W. W. Berning, "Earth satellite observations of the ionosphere," *Proc. IRE* **47**, 280 (1959).

305. D. H. Menzel, "The E-layer of the ionosphere. Physical theory," *Solar Eclipses and the Ionosphere*, p. 279, Pergamon, London, 1956.

306. P. Mange, "The theory of molecular diffusion in the atmosphere," *J. Geophys. Res.* **62**, 279 (1957).

307. C. M. Minnis and G. H. Bazzard, "Some indices of solar activity based on ionospheric and radio noise measurements," *J. Atmos. Terr. Phys.* **14**, 213 (1959).

308. T. Yonezawa and Y. Arima, "On the seasonal and non-seasonal annual variations and the semi-annual variation in the noon and midnight electron densities in the $F2$ layer in middle latitudes," *J. Rad. Res. Lab. Japan*, **6**, 293 (1959).

309. T. Yonezawa, H. Takahashi, and Y. Arima, "A theoretical consideration of the electron and ion density distributions in the lower portion of the F region," *J. Rad. Res. Lab. Japan* **6**, 21 (1959).

310. T. Yonezawa, "On the influence of electron-ion diffusion exerted upon the formation of the $F2$ layer," *J. Rad. Res. Lab. Japan* **5**, 165 (1958).

311. M. Nicolet, "Collision frequency of electrons in the terrestrial ionosphere," *Phys. of Fluids* **2**, 95 (1959).

312. M. V. Wilkes, "A table of Chapman's grazing incidence integral $Ch(x, \chi)$," *Proc. Phys. Soc.* B**67**, 314 (1954).

313. A. P. Mitra, "Time and height variations in the daytime processes in the Ionosphere. Part I. A noontime model of the ionosphere loss coefficient from 60 to 600 km over middle latitudes," *J. Geophys Res.* **64**, 733 (1959).

314. K. L. Bowles, "Observation of vertical-incidence scatter from the ionosphere at 41 Mc/sec," *Phys. Rev. Letters* **1** (1959).

315. D. T. Farley, "A theory of electrostatic fields in a horizontally stratified ionosphere subject to a vertical magnetic field," *J. Geophys. Res.* **64**, 1225 (1959).
316. G. C. Reid and C. Collins, "Observations of abnormal VHF radio wave absorption at medium and high latitudes," *J. Atmos. Terr. Phys.* **14**, 63 (1959).
317. W. J. G. Beynon and G. M. Brown, "Geomagnetic distortion of region *E*," *J. Atmos. Terr. Phys.* **14**, 138 (1959).
318. L. G. H. Huxley, "A general formula for the conductory of a gas containing free electrons" *Proc. Phys. Soc.* **64**B, 844 (1951).

Chapter 10

The Upper Atmosphere and Geomagnetism

E. H. Vestine

10.1 Solar Daily Variation, S_q 471
   10.1.1 Introduction 471
   10.1.2 Geographical and Seasonal Features 472
   10.1.3 Day-to-Day Variability of E-Region Winds 488
   10.1.4 The Equatorial Electrojet 489
   10.1.5 Additional Features of S_q 490
10.2 Lunar Daily Magnetic Variation 490
   10.2.1 General Features 490
   10.2.2 Harmonic Components of L 490
   10.2.3 Early Derivations of L 491
   10.2.4 Equatorial Values of L 491
   10.2.5 Spherical Harmonic Analysis of the L Field 493
   10.2.6 Location of Regions Producing Lunar Daily Magnetic Variation ... 494
   10.2.7 Dynamo Theory of L 494
10.3 Magnetic Storms 495
   10.3.1 General Features 495
   10.3.2 Average World-Wide Features 496
   10.3.3 Current Systems 498
   10.3.4 Peculiar Magnetic Storms 503
   10.3.5 Solar Streams 504
10.4 Minor Magnetic Disturbances 506
   10.4.1 Auroral Zone Electrojets 506
   10.4.2 Irregular Magnetic Disturbances 507
10.5 Magnetic Pulsations 508
10.6 Geomagnetism in Relation to Other Geophysical Phenomena 509
   References 511

10.1 Solar Daily Variation, S_q

10.1.1 *Introduction*

The solar daily variation is one of the transient geomagnetic changes closely related to solar events, as well as to a number of other phenomena of the upper atmosphere. The variation is believed to be caused by electric current systems flowing in the lower ionosphere. These current systems are believed to arise from fluctuating ionospheric winds, which blow the ionized air across the lines of force of the geomagnetic field thereby generating electric fields to drive the electric currents. Hence the observed solar daily variation on any particular day reflects effects of the solar influences operating to produce ionization and the strength of upper air winds, though the latter are also in part a contribution of the atmospheric tides.

At any instant the magnetic variation shows a regular world-wide pattern of changes in magnetic field tending to be larger on the sunlit hemisphere, and greatest in amplitude about an hour in advance of solar noon. It hence occurs daily in the continuous records of the field made at several score of magnetic observatories distributed at various points over the earth's surface. At these observatories the magnetic components or elements recorded continuously, as magnetograms, are normally the horizontal intensity, H, the (eastward) magnetic declination, D, measured as an angle (or equivalent intensity) from true north, and the (downward) vertical component, Z.[1]

Figure 1 shows magnetograms for Watheroo, Australia, for the days February 13 and 17, 1933, according to 120° east meridian mean time. The solar daily magnetic variation is the main feature of these records and is usually the dominant feature on the magnetograms of stations in low and middle latitudes. It is apparent also that the variations on the two days resemble one another, though the correspondence is not perfect.

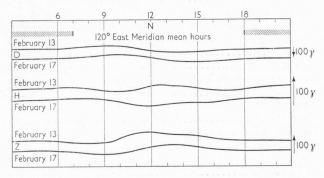

FIG. 1. Magnetic records, Watheroo Magnetic Observatory, February 13 and 17, 1933.

On most days of any month other magnetic fluctuations comprising regular and irregular pulses in field, and varying in intensity from day to day, are found superposed upon magnetograms of this type; these disturbances have quite interesting relationships to other natural phenomena and will be studied later. For the present, records such as those of Fig. 1 will be considered, especially those derived from averages for the five least disturbed days, or magnetically quiet days of the month, which are selected internationally.

10.1.2 Geographical and Seasonal Features

10.1.2.1 Averages for International Quiet Days

Figure 2 shows the solar daily variation at a number of stations in various latitudes and longitudes, averaged for the winter season over a sunspot cycle, deduced in a study by the Carnegie Institution of Washington.[2] The values in the field are averaged for the five international quiet days. The north and east components (X' and Y') are tangential to the earth and directed towards geomagnetic north and east, respectively, the pole of reference being the

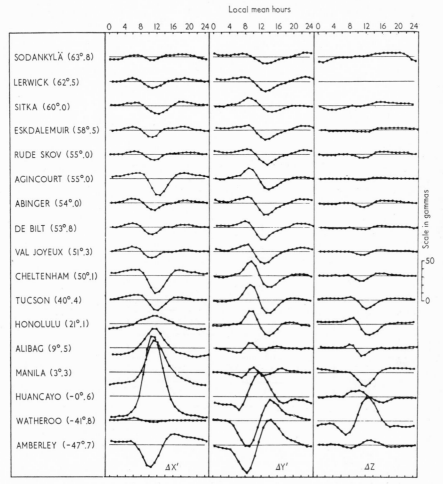

FIG. 2. Solar daily magnetic variation on quiet days (S_q), various stations, geomagnetic components, winter, 1922–1933 (geomagnetic latitudes indicated in parentheses).

geomagnetic north pole taken to be at geographic latitude $\phi = 78.5°$ north, and longitude $\lambda = 291.0°$ east. The stations indicated are Sodankylä ($\phi = 67.4°$ N, $\lambda = 26.6°$ E), Lerwick (60.1°, 358.8°), Sitka (57.0°, 224.7°), Eskdalemuir (55.3°, 356.8°), Rude Skov (55.8°, 12.4°), Agincourt (43.8°, 280.7°), Abinger (51.2°, 359.6°), De Bilt (52.1°, 5.2°), Val Joyeux (48.8°, 2.0°),

Cheltenham (38.7°, 283.2°), Tucson (32.2°, 249.2°), Honolulu (21.3°, 201.9°), Alibag (18.6°, 72.9°), Manila (14.6°, 121.2°), Huancayo (− 12.0°, 284.7°), Watheroo (− 30.3°, 115.9°), and Amberley (− 43.5°, 172.7°).

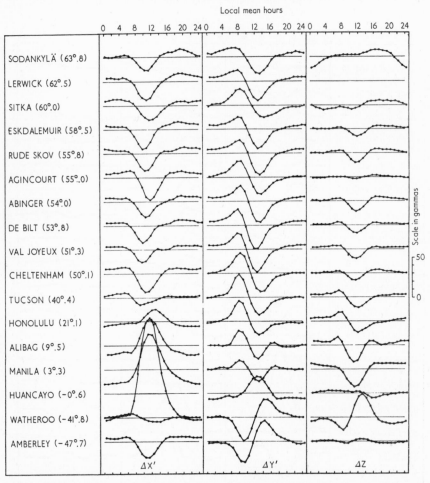

FIG. 3. Solar daily magnetic variation on quiet days (S_q), various stations, geomagnetic components, equinox, 1922–1933 (geomagnetic latitudes indicated in parentheses).

The north component (X') is a maximum about an hour before local noon near the magnetic equator (defined as the globe-encircling line along which the vertical component of the earth's main magnetic field is zero). This is clearly shown by Huancayo. The north component reverses in sign near latitudes $\phi = \pm 30°$ as shown by Tucson ($\phi = 32.2°$) in the northern hemisphere, and Watheroo at $\phi = − 30.3°$ in the southern hemisphere. The geomagnetic east component (Y') has a morning maximum and an evening minimum in the northern hemisphere, the reverse being true in the southern hemisphere. The vertical component shows a minimum near noon in middle

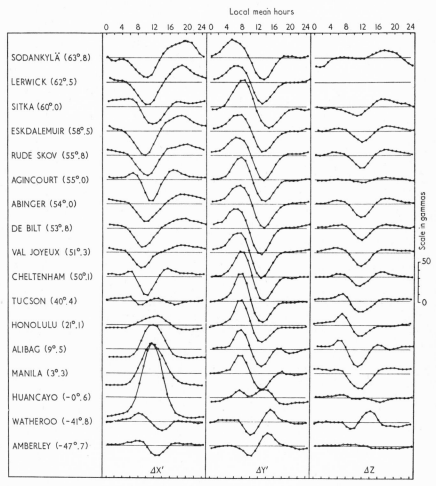

Fig. 4. Solar daily magnetic variation on quiet days (S_q), various stations, geomagnetic components, summer, 1922–1933 (geomagnetic latitudes indicated in parentheses).

latitudes, is small near the equator, and is a maximum just before noon in middle latitudes of the southern hemisphere.

The results for Fig. 2 may be compared with those of Fig. 3 giving corresponding values averaged for the spring months of March and April, and for the autumn months of September and October. The results are intended to indicate, though not precisely, the solar daily variation for the time of equinox when the sun is overhead at the geographic equator. A principal feature noted is that the amplitude of S_q in middle latitudes is about the same in the northern and southern hemispheres. Comparison with corresponding results for summer shown in Fig. 4 indicates that in the northern hemisphere

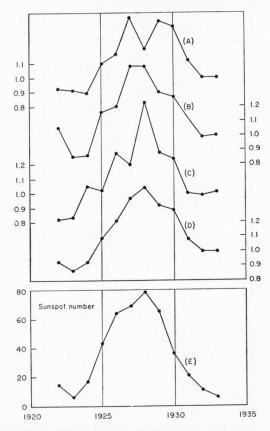

FIG. 5. Yearly means of daily range of horizontal intensity (H) at Manila, quiet days, expressed as ratio to that for 1932–1933; (A) winter, (B) equinox, (C) summer, and (D) year; also (E) mean sunspot numbers.

field changes in middle latitudes are somewhat augmented, whereas the opposite effect is noted for the southern hemisphere.

The data of Figs. 2, 3, and 4 were averaged for the five international quiet days per month, for each season, and for the twelve years 1922-1933. The seasonal averages themselves also varied with sunspot number and are indicated in amplitude as a ratio, year by year, to the amplitude for the Second International Polar Year, 1932–1933, in Fig. 5. It would appear that the correlation between the average amplitude of S_q and the average sunspot number R, is likely to be very good. In fact it will later be verified by using a more precise concept of the daily range, due to Bartels,[5] that the correlation is very good indeed, establishing the reality of a close link between solar phenomena measured by average sunspot number and the amplitude of the solar daily magnetic variation.

10.1.2.2 *Fourier and Spherical Harmonic Representations of* S_q

A number of theoretical studies of S_q have been made involving mathematical representations of the data. One of these will be considered here. In an important paper Chapman[3] derived and analysed data for S_q for the sunspot-maximum year 1905 and the sunspot-minimum year 1902. In this work he used north $(X -)$ and east $(Y -)$ components referred to the geographic rather than the geomagnetic north pole used for Figs. 2 to 4. He represented his results for S_q at each station in terms of Fourier coefficients and spherical harmonics, as Schuster[4] had done previously, and used more extensive data.

A method of representing such data in terms of spherical harmonics has been described elsewhere,[1, 3] and only a brief summary will be indicated here. A convenient procedure is to begin by making a Fourier analysis of S_q in each of the components X, Y, and Z at each station, using either the bihourly or hourly mean departures from the daily mean of magnetograms derived from scaling of records for the various magnetic observatories. Thus

$$S_q = \sum(a_n \cos nt + b_n \sin nt)$$
$$= \sum s_n \sin (nt + \alpha_n) \tag{10.1}$$

where terms up to and including the integer $n = 4$ are usually determined with useful accuracy. The average noncyclic change given by the difference 24 hours minus 0 hour is removed from the data in each component separately.

Except for very feeble electric currents of atmospheric electricity the measurements in X, Y, and Z are in free space, so that they are derivable from a scalar potential, V, using

$$X = \frac{\partial V}{a \, \partial \theta}, \; Y = -\frac{\partial V}{a \sin \theta \, \partial \phi}, \; Z = \frac{\partial V}{\partial r} \tag{10.2}$$

where there are used spherical co-ordinates r, θ increasing to the south, and ϕ increasing to the east.

The potential V, a function of the time, may be written $V = V^e + V^i$, where

$$V^e = a \sum_{s=1}^{\infty} \left(\frac{r}{a}\right)^s T_s^e, \; V^i = a \sum_{s=1}^{\infty} \left(\frac{a}{r}\right)^{s+1} T_s^i \tag{10.3}$$

where V^e and V^i are the parts of the potential V, respectively, of origin external and internal to the earth; also

$$T_s = \sum_{m=0}^{s} (g_s^m \cos m\phi + h_s^m \sin m\phi) P_s^m(\theta) \qquad (10.4)$$

and $P_s^m(\theta)$ is the associated Legendre function of degree s and order m. Since

$$g_s^m = g_s^{me} + g_s^{mi}, \quad h_s^m = h_s^{me} + h_s^{mi} \qquad (10.5)$$

at the surface $r = a$:

$$X = \sum_{s=1}^{\infty} \sum_{m=0}^{s} (g_s^m \cos m\phi + h_s^m \sin m\phi)[dP_s^m(\theta)/d\theta] \qquad (10.6)$$

$$Y = \sum_{s=1}^{\infty} \sum_{m=0}^{s} m (g_s^m \sin m\phi - h_s^m \cos m\phi)[P_s^m(\theta)/\sin\theta] \qquad (10.7)$$

$$Z = \sum_{s=1}^{\infty} \sum_{m=0}^{s} (g_s^{mz} \cos m\phi + h_s^{mz} \sin m\phi) P_s^m(\theta) \qquad (10.8)$$

where

$$g_s^{mz} = sg_s^{me} - (s+1)g_s^{mi}, \quad h_s^{mz} = sh_s^{me} - (s+1)h_s^{mi} \qquad (10.9)$$

The values of a_n, b_n are obtained separately for X (or Y) or both, and for Z, using the Fourier analyses of the magnetic data at each station.

In the case of the solar daily magnetic variation it may be convenient to identify time, t, with the east longitude. Thus the Fourier representations in X, Y, and Z at a station may be written at $r = a$ as

$$X = \sum_{m=1}^{\infty} \left[\left(\sum_{n=m}^{\infty} a_n^m X_n^m \right) \cos mt + \sum_{n=m}^{\infty} b_n^m X_n^m \sin mt \right] \qquad (10.10)$$

$$Y = \sum_{m=1}^{\infty} \left[\left(\sum_{n=m}^{\infty} - b_n^m Y_n^m \right) \cos mt + \sum_{n=m}^{\infty} a_n^m Y_n^m \sin mt \right] \qquad (10.11)$$

$$Z = \sum_{m=1}^{\infty} \left[\left(\sum_{n=m}^{\infty} \mathrm{a}_n^m P_n^m \right) \cos mt + \sum_{n=m}^{\infty} \mathrm{b}_n^m P_n^m \sin mt \right] \qquad (10.12)$$

where

$$a_n^m = n(e_{n,a}^m + i_{n,a}^m), \quad b_n^m = n(e_{n,b}^m + i_{n,b}^m) \qquad (10.13)$$

$$\mathrm{a}_n^m = ne_{n,a}^m - (n+1)i_{n,a}^m, \quad \mathrm{b}_n^m = ne_{n,b}^m - (n+1)i_{n,b}^m \qquad (10.14)$$

$$X_n^m(\theta) = \frac{1}{n} \frac{\partial P_n^m}{\partial \theta}, \quad Y_n^m(\theta) = \frac{m}{n \sin\theta} P_n^m \qquad (10.15)$$

The spherical harmonic functions X_n^m, Y_n^m, and P_n^m have been tabulated by Schmidt for various colatitudes, θ, for various values of m and n.[1] Since the Fourier coefficients for $\cos mt$ and $\sin mt$ in equations (10.10), (10.11), and (10.12) are known from the data at each station, the spherical harmonic coefficients a_n^m, b_n^m, a_n^m, and b_n^m can be found by solving sets of simultaneous linear equations in the number of unknowns up to a required degree n, $m \leqslant n$.

The functions X_n^m, Y_n^m, and P_n^m are the same as the functions X_{nm}, Y_{nm}, P_{nm} multiplied by $[2(n-m)!/(n+m)!]^{1/2}$, $m \leqslant n$, $m \neq 0$, and hence are actually expressible in terms of the simple functions $c = \cos\theta$, $s = \sin\theta$ in Table I. If $m = 0$, $P_n^m(\theta) = P_{nm}(\theta)$, etc., also

$$P_{nm}(\theta) = \sin^m\theta[d^m P_n(\cos\theta)/d(\cos\theta)^m].$$

TABLE I

Values of $X_{n,m}$, $Y_{n,m}$ and $P_{n,m}$

$X_{11} = c$	$Y_{11} = 1$	$P_{11} = s$
$X_{21} = \dfrac{3}{2}(2c^2 - 1)$	$Y_{21} = \dfrac{3}{2}c$	$P_{21} = 3sc$
$X_{31} = \dfrac{1}{2}c(15c^2 - 11)$	$Y_{31} = \dfrac{1}{2}(5c^2 - 1)$	$P_{31} = \dfrac{3}{2}s(5c^2 - 1)$
$X_{22} = 3sc$	$Y_{22} = 3s$	$P_{22} = 3s^2$
$X_{32} = 5s(3c^2 - 1)$	$Y_{32} = 10sc$	$P_{32} = 15s^2c$
$X_{42} = \dfrac{15}{2}sc(7c^2 - 4)$	$Y_{42} = \dfrac{15}{4}s(7c^2 - 1)$	$P_{42} = \dfrac{15}{2}s^2(7c^2 - 1)$
$X_{33} = 15s^2c$	$Y_{33} = 15s^2$	$P_{33} = 15s^3$
$X_{43} = \dfrac{105}{4}s^2(4c^2 - 1)$	$Y_{43} = \dfrac{314}{4}s^2c$	$P_{43} = 105s^3c$
$X_{53} = \dfrac{63}{2}s^2c(15c^2 - 7)$	$Y_{53} = \dfrac{63}{2}s^2(9c^2 - 1)$	$P_{53} = \dfrac{105}{2}s^3(9c^2 - 1)$
$X_{44} = 105s^3c$	$Y_{44} = 105s^3$	$P_{44} = 105s^4$
$X_{54} = 189s^3(5c^2 - 1)$	$Y_{54} = 756s^3c$	$P_{54} = 945s^4c$
$X_{64} = \dfrac{315}{2}s^3c(33c^2 - 13)$	$Y_{64} = 315s^3(11c^2 - 1)$	$P_{64} = \dfrac{945}{2}s^4(11c^2 - 1)$

10.1.2.3 Calculation of Current Systems for Flow in Concentric Spherical Shell within the Atmosphere

It has been noted that the solar daily magnetic variation (S_q) can be represented by spherical harmonic functions, and that the coefficients of the terms can be separated into parts of origin internal and external to the earth. It was also clear that available data on S_q did not provide a very good world-wide coverage, since stations yielding data have distributions dictated mainly by geography or by political divisions of the terrestrial globe. For this reason some details in the overhead current systems causing S_q can scarcely be represented, especially with respect to changes in these current systems with longitude, though data such as those for the International Geophysical Year of 1957–1958 will provide a better world-wide representation of S_q than has been available heretofore.

The external field of S_q at ground level can be represented by a thin spherical current sheet in a region of good electric conductivity such as the E region.[1] Then if J is the amount of electricity crossing a line, AP, on the sheet in unit time, from left to right as seen by an observer looking along AP from outside the spherical surface, J (in electromagnetic units) is called the current function at P, if referred to a fixed point, A. In fact the contribution of J_n to J due to each harmonic term V_n^e in the surface potential will be (in amperes)

$$J_n = -\frac{10}{4\pi}\frac{2n+1}{n+1}\left(\frac{r}{a}\right)^n V_n \tag{10.16}$$

where r is the radius of the spherical current sheet overhead, and a is the radius of the earth, $r > a$, and $J = \sum J_n$. Conversely,

$$V_n = -\frac{4\pi}{10}\frac{n+1}{2n+1}J_n\left(\frac{a}{r}\right)^n \tag{10.17}$$

Figures 6 and 7, drawn by Bartels from Chapman's analysis of S_q, illustrate the overhead electric current systems for sunspot minimum, for equinox and for northern summer, respectively. A total of 10,000 amp flows between successive current lines. The main features include an anticlockwise current circulation in the northern hemisphere, with a central focus about an hour in advance of noon. In the southern hemisphere the current circulation above the sunlit part of the earth is clockwise. In northern summer the northern daytime circulation is considerably more intense than the circulation in the southern hemisphere. In the same way, current functions may be derived for other variations to be discussed later, such as the lunar daily magnetic variation and various aspects of magnetic disturbance or storms. In the case of the latter, however, too many terms of the form of (10.16) are ordinarily required to make the formal summation of these terms practical in actual applications.

The current systems of Figs. 6 and 7 are drawn for data averaged around parallels of latitude and therefore depict the part of S_q depending mainly on local time or, in other words, a part independent of the longitude. The current systems also vary in average intensity with sunspot cycle, as can be seen in an examination of corresponding coefficients for sunspot maximum listed in Table II p. 482. There are also changes in current intensity from one day to the next, sometimes by a factor as much as 2 in amplitude.[5,6] The current systems also fail to express the considerable augmentation in overhead currents in a narrow belt along the magnetic equator (see the data for Huancayo, Peru, in Fig. 2). According to Chapman,[7] an electrojet overhead at the magnetic equator (where the magnetic dip is zero), and there directed from west to east, affords a convenient physical indication of the correction to Figs. 6 and 7 required at the magnetic equator. As will be seen later, the electrojet is of considerable theoretical interest, since any theory of the

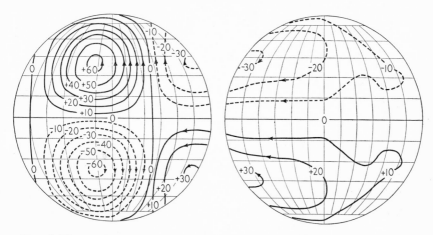

FIG. 6. The overhead electric current systems corresponding to S_q over the sunlit hemisphere (left) and the night hemisphere (right), sunspot minimum, at equinox. From Chapman and Bartels, "Geomagnetism," Vols. 1 and 2, Oxford Univ. Press, New York, 1949.

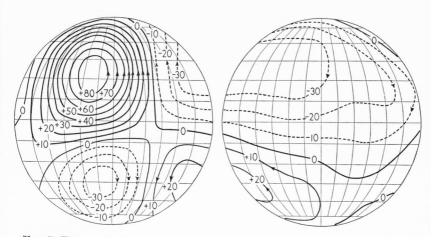

FIG. 7. The overhead electric current systems corresponding to S_q over the sunlit hemisphere (left) and the night hemisphere (right), sunspot minimum, in northern summer. From Chapman and Bartels, "Geomagnetism" Vols. 1 and 2, Oxford Univ. Press, New York, 1949.

origin of S_q must also include an explanation of this equatorial singular feature.

31

10.1.2.4 *Dynamo Theory of S_q* (see also § 9.3).

Stewart[8] in 1882 proposed that convective currents established by the sun's heating influence in the upper regions of the atmosphere are to be regarded as conductors moving across lines of magnetic force and are thus the vehicle of electric currents which act on a measuring magnetometer.

TABLE II

Coefficients of Spherical Harmonic Terms for the S Field (after Chapman)

(Unit of force 1 γ)

| n | m | 1905, sunspot maximum | | | | 1902, sunspot minimum | | | |
| | | From Y | | From Z | | From Y | | From Z | |
		a_n^m	b_n^m	a_n^m	b_n^m	a_n^m	b_n^m	a_n^m	b_n^m
		Mean equinox							
2	1	+ 18.7	− 9.0	+ 7.1	− 2.4	+ 11.8	− 8.7	+ 5.9	− 0.7
3	2	− 16.7	+ 8.6	− 6.6	+ 0.1	− 11.8	+ 8.3	− 4.2	+ 0.2
4	3	+ 9.0	− 8.0	+ 4.4	− 1.5	+ 6.2	− 7.4	+ 3.6	− 1.5
5	4	− 2.6	+ 4.3	− 1.7	+ 0.9	− 1.7	+ 3.3	− 1.6	+ 1.1
		Mean solstice = $\frac{1}{2}(N + S)$ solstice							
2	1	+ 18.0	− 7.6	+ 6.4	− 2.1	+ 10.7	− 7.6	+ 5.4	− 1.2
3	2	− 14.8	+ 7.2	− 5.6	− 0.4	− 10.7	+ 6.7	− 4.5	+ 0.5
4	3	+ 6.8	− 5.8	+ 3.6	− 1.5	+ 4.8	− 4.8	+ 2.3	− 1.2
5	4	− 1.8	+ 1.9	− 0.8	+ 0.4	− 0.8	+ 1.5	− 0.6	+ 0.6
		$\frac{1}{2}(N - S)$ solstice							
1	1	+ 4.2	− 2.1	+ 0.4	+ 0.1	+ 4.0	− 1.7	+ 1.0	0.0
3	1	+ 7.8	+ 3.3	+ 3.4	+ 0.6	+ 5.9	+ 1.7	+ 1.9	+ 0.9
2	2	− 2.7	+ 5.4	− 0.5	+ 0.9	− 1.9	+ 3.7	− 1.2	+ 0.9
4	2	− 3.2	+ 1.9	− 1.9	− 0.5	− 4.2	+ 2.0	− 1.1	− 0.5
3	3	− 1.0	− 4.0	+ 0.1	− 0.1	− 0.1	− 3.6	+ 0.1	− 0.1
5	3	− 1.8	+ 0.6	+ 0.3	+ 0.7	− 0.8	+ 0.3	+ 0.2	+ 0.5
4	4	+ 2.7	− 0.4	+ 0.7	+ 0.5	+ 1.6	− 0.6	+ 0.4	+ 0.6
6	4	+ 2.6	− 5.7	− 1.2	− 3.8	+ 1.1.	− 5.8	− 1.2	− 5.0

Thus, in this dynamo theory the earth is the magnet, the moving air the armature, and the convective conducting ionosphere the windings. Later Schuster[4] and Chapman[3] developed this concept quantitatively, showing that the external part of the S_q field was indeed larger than the internal part and hence compatible with Schuster's view that the source of S_q lay within the ionosphere. Schuster suggested that the required electric conductivity of the upper atmosphere must be produced by ultraviolet radiation. He also considered tidal action as the cause of the upper air winds. These ideas were later extended in considerable detail in 1919 by Chapman, who made the spherical harmonic analysis referred to above, and then proceeded to attempt an explanation of these data in terms of the dynamo theory. Chapman took the velocity potential of the tidal circulation to be proportional to the spherical harmonic term $P_2^2(\cos \theta)$, and took the electric conductivity, σ, to be given by

$$\sigma = (1 + \tfrac{3}{2} \cos \chi)^2 \qquad (10.18)$$

where χ is the sun's zenith angle. In fact

$$\cos \chi = \sin \delta \cos \theta + \cos \delta \sin \theta \cos t$$

where δ is the sun's declination, θ the colatitude, and t the local time expressed in angular measure. He then developed a suitable dynamo theory for both the solar and lunar daily variation. He did not, however, take into account the dependence of σ on the geomagnetic field, although Chapman and Cowling[9] later discussed this matter in some detail. The need for taking into account the influence of the geomagnetic field on the electric conductivity was indicated by Pedersen[10] in 1927, and the ionosphere itself postulated by Kennelly and Heaviside was discovered experimentally by Appleton and Barnett[11] and by Breit and Tuve.[12] Cowling[13] in 1932 indicated that electric polarization might reduce the retarding influence of the geomagnetic field upon electric current conduction, and his findings were applied to the dynamo theory of the solar daily variation by a number of workers about twenty years later.[14-18] In recent years there has also emerged a considerable wealth of new information on upper air winds, summarized by Briggs and Spencer[19] and others especially for radio methods, and by Whipple[20] and others using precise photographs of meteor trains. Also of note were useful meteorological studies, based on early information, by Kellogg and Schilling[21] and later by Pant.[22] As a result it is now known that winds with velocities of the order of 100 m/sec are commonplace within the E region, although the causes of the main systematic winds are as yet somewhat uncertain. It is not yet clear whether the dynamo theory should assume winds which are mainly of tidal origin, or whether the winds are mainly generated by solar heating within the atmosphere. In this connection the early work of Schuster has been extended by Taylor,[23] Pekeris,[24] Wilkes,[25] and Sen and White[26] in connection with tidal oscillations. The role of atmospheric heating in producing winds of suitable type for the explanation of S_q has been studied by Chapman and Bartels,[1] Wulf,[27] and others, but much remains to be done in this connection.

The region of S_q currents of principal interest has been identified directly by means of a rocket-borne magnetometer by Singer et al.,[28] who located the magnetic field changes identified by them with S_q at a height of 95 km to

120 km. Rocket results by Van Allen and his colleagues at State University of Iowa during the International Geophysical Year are also under study and may indicate that there is appreciable electric current flowing in the lower F region as well. Consequently, the site of current flow is apparently becoming established, though all aspects of the air flow and electric conductivity are not yet fully understood. Recent rocket and ionospheric studies have also provided much useful information on the ion density as a function of height in the upper atmosphere.[29]

In the case of the electric conductivity the problem is that for a slightly ionized gas comprising the ionosphere, the basic theory being that of Cowling.[13] Several workers have applied this theory to the ionosphere. An electric field, E, within the partially ionized ionosphere will produce relative motion of the ions and electrons, and, since a circuit is ordinarily available, an electric current flow results.

If the component of the vector electric field $\mathbf{E}$ along the magnetic field $\mathbf{H}$ is taken to be E_0, positive ions will move along the field in the direction of E_0, spiraling meanwhile about the field with an angular frequency $\omega_i = He/m_i$, where e is the electronic charge and m_i is the mass of the ion. An electron will move in the opposite direction, spiraling with frequency $\omega_e = He/m_e$. The ions and electrons will also undergo collisions with heavy particles with frequencies ν_i and ν_e, respectively. These collisions serve to disorganize and slow down the orderly progression of ions and electrons along the line of magnetic force.

A component E_1 of $\mathbf{E}$ acting across the magnetic field will drive an electric current more readily across the field when the collisional frequency is about the same as the spiraling frequency, so that the spiraling tendency is disorganized. As Cowling has shown, suitable electric polarization of the gas can also minimize wasted motion, from an efficiency standpoint, in a direction perpendicular to both $\mathbf{E}$ and $\mathbf{H}$.

According to Baker and Martyn [14] a more detailed description of the simple theory of electric current flow in an ionized gas is as follows. If there are N electrons and ions per unit volume, with $m_{e,i}$ their respective masses, $\nu_{e,i}$ their respective frequencies of collision, and $\mathbf{H}$ a uniform magnetic field, the electric conductivity along $\mathbf{H}$ may be written

$$\sigma_0 = Ne^2 \left(\frac{1}{m_e \nu_e} + \frac{1}{m_i \nu_i} \right) = A(\tan \alpha_e + \tan \alpha_i)$$

where $\tan \alpha_{e,i} = \omega_{e,i}/\nu_{e,i}$ and $A = Ne/H$

The electric conductivity transverse to $\mathbf{H}$ is

$$\sigma_1 = Ne^2 \left[\frac{\nu_e}{m_e(\omega_e^2 + \nu_e^2)} + \frac{\nu_i}{m_i(\omega_i^2 + \nu_i^2)} \right] = A \sin(\alpha_e + \alpha_i) \cos(\alpha_e - \alpha_i)$$

There will ordinarily also be a Hall current flowing in the direction $-\mathbf{E} \wedge \mathbf{H}$ when as usual the electrons are more mobile than the ions. The Hall conductivity is

$$\sigma_2 = Ne^2 \left[\frac{\omega_e}{m_e(\omega_e^2 + \nu_e^2)} - \frac{\omega_i}{m_i(\omega_i^2 + \nu_i^2)} \right] = A \sin(\alpha_e + \alpha_i) \sin(\alpha_e - \alpha_i)$$

or the current $\mathbf{J}$ may be written

$$\mathbf{J} = \sigma_0 \mathbf{E}_0 + \sigma_1 \mathbf{E}_1 + \sigma_2 (\mathbf{H} \wedge \mathbf{E})/H$$

If u and v are the southward ($x-$) and eastward ($y-$) components of the air velocity within the (thin) ionosphere

$$E_x = vH_z, \quad E_y = -uH_z$$
$$J_x = \partial R/a \sin \theta \partial \phi, \quad J_y = -\partial R/a \, \partial \theta$$

where R is the current function. When charges flow, an electrostatic potential, S, builds up so that electric current closure results, whence from Ohm's law

$$\frac{\partial R}{a \sin \theta \, \partial \phi} = \sigma_1 \left(vH_z - \frac{\partial S}{a \, \partial \theta} \right) - \sigma_2 \left(uH_z + \frac{\partial S}{a \sin \theta \, \partial \phi} \right)$$

$$\frac{\partial R}{a \, \partial \theta} = \sigma_1 \left(uH_z + \frac{\partial S}{a \sin \theta \, \partial \phi} \right) + \sigma_2 \left(vH_z - \frac{\partial S}{a \, \partial \theta} \right)$$

With S eliminated, there results the differential equation for R:

$$\frac{\partial^2 R}{\partial \theta^2} + \cot \theta \frac{\partial R}{\partial \theta} + \frac{1}{\sin^2 \theta} \frac{\partial^2 R}{\partial \phi^2} = \frac{a(\sigma_1 + \sigma_2^2/\sigma_1)}{\sin \theta} \frac{\partial (uH_z \sin \theta)}{\partial \theta} + \frac{\partial (vH_z)}{\partial \phi}$$

the same as Chapman's results obtained in 1919, except that the value $\sigma_0 = \sigma_1 + \sigma_2^2/\sigma_1$ replaces the value of electric conductivity in the isotropic case. Baker and Martyn[14] estimate the integrated values of σ_1, σ_2, and σ_0 throughout the height of the ionosphere to be, in emu. cm . . . units,

$$\int \sigma_1 \, dh = 6.4 \times 10^{-9}, \quad \int \sigma_2 \, dh = 1.36 \times 10^{-8}, \quad \int \sigma_0 \, dh = 1.64 \times 10^{-7}$$

Results in quite good agreement were obtained by Hirono,[15] Maeda,[16] and Fejer,[17] and there seems reason for believing that the electric conductivity of the ionosphere is adequate for the dynamo theory to suffice for the explanation of S_q. The current flow is mainly near and within the E region, as the electric conductivity across the magnetic field in the F region is relatively small.

In the same publication Baker suggests that suitable tidal air velocities are derivable from a velocity potential $\psi = k \sin^2 \theta \sin 2\phi$, where k is the amplitude, θ the colatitude, and $\phi = t + \lambda + \alpha$, where t is the Greenwich time, λ the longitude, and α a phase constant.

Maeda[30] has recently derived upper air winds by estimating the electric conductivity of the ionosphere from the radio data, and assuming the dynamo theory to be correct.

It thus appears that the dynamo theory is reasonably well established as the cause of S_q, or the principal cause of S_q. It is known from ionospheric studies such as those of Appleton and Weekes[31] that tidal movements can be detected in the E region. Moreover, measurements such as those of Whipple[20] on meteors and of Briggs and Spencer[19] and others show that winds of reasonable magnitude also exist. Winds are of course also expected as a consequence of solar heating of the upper atmosphere, and at the present time it is not definitely known whether the E region winds arise mainly from solar heating or from tidal action.

Another theory due to Chapman[1] is the drift current theory, and, though it has been criticized by Cowling[9] and others, it may be that it contributes a part of the S_q field. According to this theory, when the mean free paths of ions and electrons are sufficiently long as they move within the geomagnetic and gravitational fields, they will drift perpendicular to the force mg and H. The velocity to east is then $v = (mg/eH) \sin \theta$, where θ is the magnetic colatitude at the height under consideration in the atmosphere, and g is the acceleration of gravity. Since for the terrestrial dipole

$$H = H_0(1 + 3 \cos^2 \theta)^{1/2}/R_e,$$

where H_0 is the equatorial value of field, and R_e is the radial distance from the earth's centre measured in earth radii, the current density will be $j = Nev = Nmg \sin \theta/\{H_0(1 + 3 \cos^2 \theta)\}$ emu. At the equator the drift of positive ions to the east is therefore about 10 cm/sec, and if $N = 10^6$ cm^{-3}, $j \sim 2 \times 10^{-13}$ emu. At high levels, particles moving along lines of force of the magnetic field due to centrifugal force effects and gravity acquire a lateral drift, which for positive charges, is to the west.[1] There also will be an effect due to the gradient with height in the magnetic field tending to lead to drift motions.

The drift current theory is often criticized, since the supposed falling ions would usually be supported by hydrostatic pressure. In equilibrium there should therefore be negligible effects due to gravity. If there is absence of equilibrium, effects are possible, but, since downward motion of ions in one region is likely to be accompanied by upward motion in others, little current due to gravity seems possible. On the other hand, owing to centrifugal (outward) force a feeble westward-directed current may be possible.

A study of winds was made by Maeda,[30] who deduced horizontal wind systems for the E region, using the dynamo theory of S_q. In this study, using approximate values of the electric conductivity of the ionosphere, the wind system of Fig. 8 was deduced; it agrees fairly well with a result due to Kato.[31a] It was suggested that the semidiurnal term was of tidal origin, about fifty times as great in amplitude as at ground level and nearly the same in phase; the diurnal term was assumed to be due to solar heating. The corresponding electrostatic field is shown in Fig. 9, which differs from the older study of McNish.[1] The electric fields calculated were assumed to be operative also

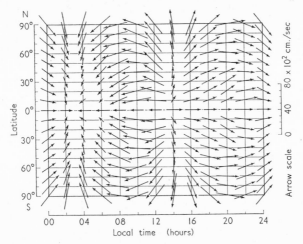

FIG. 8. Distribution of the total wind velocity. From Maeda, *J. Geomag. Geoelect.* **7,** 121 (1955).

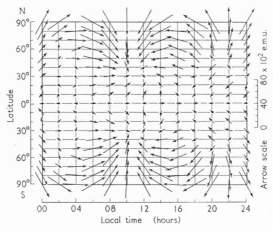

FIG. 9. Distribution of the total electric field. From Maeda, *J. Geomag. Geoelect.* **7,** 121 (1955).

in the F region where, if diffusion terms are neglected, a vertical drift of the ionosphere, W, is estimated to be given by[15]

$$W = (E_y/F) \cos I$$

where E_y is the eastward electric intensity, F the total magnetic intensity, and I the magnetic dip. In colatitudes about 50° to 90° he found vertical drift motions reaching upward velocities of the order of 10 to 20 m/sec during the hours 6 to 12 local time, the effect extending also into the early afternoon in equatorial regions.

Attempts have also been made to study effects on the wind systems due to the earth's rotation. It seems likely that these various exploratory studies will be extended to monthly and seasonal distributions in upper air winds, making use also of radio, rocket, and other data on upper air winds based on broader coverage geographically afforded by observations of the International Geophysical Year.

10.1.3 Day-to-Day Variability of E-Region Winds

Hasegawa and Tamur[32] studied day-to-day changes in the world-wide pattern of the S_q field at ground level and discovered that sometimes marked shifts in pattern, extending over thousands of miles, appeared from one day to the next. They found that centers of current circulation in the overhead current systems might be displaced as much as 15° of latitude from one day to the next. Hasegawa was able to trace the motion around the earth of overhead current centers in the northern and southern hemispheres and found that these centers fluctuated by many degrees of latitude in their positions on successive days. He was unable to connect these substantial changes in current system pattern with solar activity. This work provided insight respecting the statistical results of Chapman and Stagg,[33] who examined the day-to-day variability of S_q at a number of stations distributed over the earth.

Vestine[34] found that day-to-day changes in F region critical frequency were closely related, on an average, to day-to-day changes in the noon values of S_q at the magnetic equator. He attributed this correspondence to day-to-day differences in the dynamo electrostatic field generated by winds near or within the E region, in accord with ideas of Baker and Martyn[14] and Hirono.[15] This eastward-directed electric field, **E**, at the equator would tend to raise the electrons and ions in the direction **E** $\wedge$ **H**. He also suggested that an increase in the generating wind speed from sunspot minimum to sunspot maximum in the E region might contribute significant changes in the variation of ion density with height during the sunspot cycle.

Forbush[35] approached the problem of the variability in E region winds in another way by measuring the amplitude of sudden pulses (crochets) in magnetic field caused by solar flares occurring at different times of the sunspot cycle. The crochet was interpreted as being an effect due to the increase in electric conductivity associated with the increase in ionizing radiation from the solar flare, the electric driving force which produced S_q before the flare being supposed also to drive an increased current surge during the flare. An increase in crochet size was on an average found to occur on days of larger S_q. He considered that this was most simply explained by supposing that an increase in wind speed caused larger values of S_q. Changes in wind speed as great as 50 % from one day to the next appeared commonplace on this basis. In this connection it can be recalled also that changes in S_q by a factor of 2 in amplitude from one day to the next may be best explained as due to changes in wind speed, possibly on a nearly global scale.

10.1.4 The Equatorial Electrojet

In Figs. 2 to 4 it can be seen that the averaged results for the observatory Huancayo, on the magnetic equator, have a horizontal component greater than that at the other low-latitude stations, such as Honolulu. This anomalous feature appears at points elsewhere along the magnatic equator, for instance at Koror in the Western Pacific, as determined by Knapp of the U.S. Coast and Geodetic Survey (private communication). It was ascribed by McNish[1] to locally concentrated electric currents flowing from west to east above the magnetic equator. Later the term electrojet was suggested for this system by Chapman, who discussed its magnetic field pattern at ground level. The field pattern is being measured as a part of the program of the International Geophysical Year by Forbush of the Carnegie Institution of Washington, by Giesecke of the Geophysical Institute of Huancayo, using a series of recording stations on the ground, and also by Van Allen and his associates by using a magnetometer aboard a rocket.

According to Baker and Martyn[14] the equatorial electrojet is due to enhanced electric conductivity within a narrow belt a few degrees of latitude wide along the magnetic equator. This arises because a Hall current attempts to flow in a direction perpendicular to the eastward-flowing current along the equator, and to the magnetic field. According to Baker and Martyn, this vertical current gives rise to a vertical electric polarization which is able to stop the vertical flow of current at the magnetic equator, so that the electric conductivity rises to a value about equal to that applicable if the geomagnetic field were absent. The physical basis for this effect was noted by Cowling in 1932, but he did not note its applicability to the equatorial ionosphere. An electrostatic field arising from winds in higher latitudes thus drives a stronger current within the belt of high electric conductivity at the magnetic equator. The motions of the F region referred to by Baker and Martyn[14] and by Hirono[15] are such that they are in good accord with this idea, though the features of middle latitude winds giving rise to the equatorial electric field are unknown. Thus the electrojet appears to be expected as a consequence of the dynamo theory of S_q and the modern theory of the electric conductivity of the ionosphere.

10.1.5 *Additional Features of S_q*

A number of aspects of S_q as yet but little studied are the effects dependent on longitude. The presence of effects dependent on noncoincidence of the magnetic and geographic axes was discussed many years ago by Schuster.[4] Data of the Second International Polar Year, 1932–1933, for summer were analysed by Benkova,[35a] who estimated world-wide electric current systems of S_q at 0 hour, 6 hours, 12 hours, and 18 hours universal time. Additional important studies by Japanese workers have also been undertaken, including considerable study of the polar part of S_q. These valuable studies have shown the need for an extensive network of stations such as will be forthcoming when present IGY data become available for 1957–1958. There is also need for extension of studies such as those of Vacquier,[35b] who found remarkable differences in the values of S_q at stations only a few hundred miles apart. It also appears that many of the meteorological aspects relating to zonal flow and the actual generation of upper air winds discussed by various workers such as Wulf[27] and Sen and White[26] require further study. The theory of tidal oscillations in relation to S_q as developed especially by Taylor,[23] Pekeris,[24] and Wilkes[25] is of course of considerable importance to the student who is interested in the generation of upper air winds responsible for S_q. At present it does not appear to be clear whether solar heating or tidal air flow is the more important in the generation of S_q.

10.2 Lunar Daily Magnetic Variation

10.2.1 *General Features*

The lunar daily magnetic variation is governed by lunar time, as opposed to solar time, and is denoted by L. It undergoes change in form with each day of the lunar month measured from one new moon to the next. It is too small in amplitude to be seen by inspection on magnetograms, except at stations along the magnetic equator. It can be derived from averages for the same lunar day of many lunar months. This is usually done by using mean hourly values of scaled magnetograms.

The lunar daily magnetic variation, apart from seasonal changes, is periodic monthly but not daily because it changes form from one day to the next.

10.2.2 *Harmonic Components of L*

Although hourly mean departures from a suitable mean in each geomagnetic force component can be used to describe the course of L throughout a lunar month, say, it may also be represented as the sum of harmonic terms derived from these departures. For L these terms may be donated L_n, with $n = 1, 2, \ldots$ Owing to their convergence in nature it is usually sufficient to consider terms up to and including $n = 4$. Then, if L is expressed in terms of lunar time, t, in hours,

$$L = \sum L_n$$

where $n = 1, 2, 3,$ and 4. Also

$$L_n = l_n \sin (n't + \lambda_n)$$

where n' differs slightly from n except when $n = 2$ because the periods are not necessarily integral submultiples of the lunar day.

The harmonic terms are sometimes represented by means of a harmonic dial.[1] Such a dial has an origin, O, where for given n the cosine term has the upward axis Oa and the sine term the Ob axis to the right. In this way L_n can be plotted as a vector of length l_n and making the angle λ_n with Ob. The terminal point may be plotted for successive days or by months throughout the year and may result in either a closed or open curve.

Each lunar day at a station begins at the lower local transit of the moon or at lunar midnight. The lunar day equals about 24 hours, 50 minutes, 28 seconds of mean solar time. In arranging data on magnetic variations listed according to mean solar time it is of course necessary to take account of the fact that the lunar day ordinarily begins during and not at the beginning of a solar hour of time.

10.2.3 Early Derivations of L

Historically, following the detection of L by Kreil in 1850, it was found that, if hourly values for solar hours were averaged and then arranged to give averages approximately for the lunar day, the result was always the same in general type for all components and all stations. The variation is a simple semidiurnal wave.

If the data are regrouped and averaged separately for days of each phase of the moon, a result such as that in Fig. 10 is found. It will be noticed also that when the station is sunlit (indicated by heavier lines in the figure) the amplitude of L is greater; the average for the month appears as a simple semidiurnal curve.

10.2.4 Equatorial Values of L

Bartels[1] showed that there is an abnormally large amplitude of L at Huancayo at the magnetic equator. Thus an equatorial electrojet for L occurs there near and at solar noon. This affects the noon departure from midnight values which accordingly reflect, in addition to the much larger values of S_q, the influence of the lunar daily magnetic variation in L. Bartels

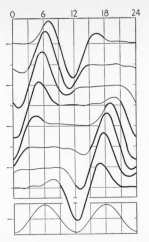

FIG. 10. The lunar daily variation of west declination at Batavia for 8 phases and for the over-all mean. The abscissa represents lunar time starting with new moon. Vertical scale unit = 4 gammas. From Chapman and Bartels, "Geomagnetism", Vols. 1 and 2, Oxford Univ. Press, New York, 1949.

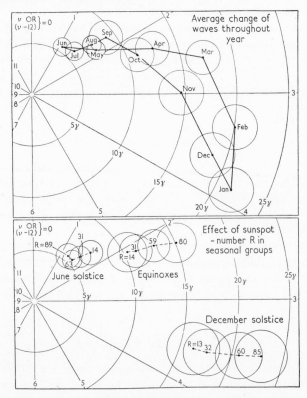

FIG. 11. Harmonic dials, lunar semimonthly sine waves in daily ranges, A, of horizontal intensity at Huancayo (1922–1939); averages with probable error circles. From Bartels and Johnston, *Trans. Amer. Geophys. Union*, Pt. 2, p. 280 (1940).

and Johnston[36] studied the range, A, defined by subtracting horizontal force values from 0 to 5 hours from those for 9 to 14 hours, 75° west meridian time, in terms of lunar effects. This averaged lunar effect is illustrated in Fig. 11, when taken for semimonthly sine waves. The upper figure shows a pronounced seasonal change, the amplitude being largest in January and least in June. The lower figure shows how the amplitude varies with sunspot number. Except in summer the amplitude is a little greater when the sunspot number, R, is greater.

10.2.5 Spherical Harmonic Analysis of the L Field

Chapman[1,3] analysed L for the five stations Pavlovsk ($\phi = 59.7°N$, $\lambda = 30.5°$ E), Pola (44.9°, 13.8°), Zikawei (31.2°, 121.4°), Manila (14.6°,

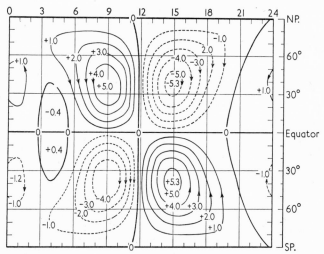

FIG. 12. The overhead electric current system for the lunar daily magnetic variation, L, new moon equinoxes, 1000-amp flow between successive current lines. Meridians numbered according to lunar hours. From Chapman and Bartel, "Geomagnetism", Vols. 1 and 2, Oxford Univ. Press, New York, 1949.

121.2°), and Batavia ($-$ 6.2°, 106.8°). He used the three elements declination (D), horizontal intensity (H), and vertical intensity (Z), deleting the most disturbed days and using the magnetically quiet years 1897–1903 (except for another series of such years at Batavia). The amplitudes of spherical harmonic terms estimated ranged from about 1 gamma to much smaller values. Chapman also separated these coefficients into the external and interval parts of the field and derived electric current systems for L in the same way as for S_q.[1] The electric currents responsible for L have intensities on the sunlit side of the earth, usually roughly one-tenth those for S_q, with two foci in the northern hemisphere instead of one as in the case of S_q. Those for equinox and the summer solstice are shown in Figs. 12 and 13.

10.2.6 Location of Regions Producing Lunar Daily Magnetic Variation

It was clear from Chapman's early studies that the sites of the electric current systems responsible for S_q and for L could scarcely be the same because they did not show sufficiently similar changes with season and with magnetic activity and solar phenomena. The most noteworthy discrepancy is that sunspots and L show only a very slight interrelationship. These

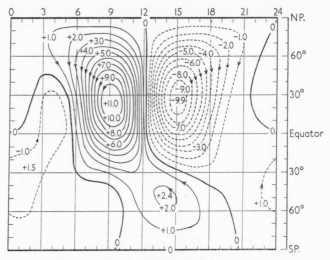

FIG. 13. Same as Fig. 12, new moon, June solstice. From Chapman and Bartel "Geomagnetism", Vols. 1 and 2, Oxford Univ. Press, New York, 1949.

questions have been studied by Martyn[37] by comparing daytime current circuits for S_q and L in winter and summer and crochets expected for S_q and for L. Studies of this kind have been helpful in indicating that, though the level of flow for S_q and L differs somewhat, the principal flows nevertheless appear to take place within the D and E regions.

10.2.7 Dynamo Theory of L

At present there exists no rival to the dynamo theory of L developed by Chapman in 1919. In the case of L the lunar tidal motion is mainly semi-diurnal, and the period is therefore well determined even if the amplitude is not. Actually, in spite of the simplicity of airflow theory for L as compared with S, a phase discrepancy of 180° was found by Chapman between predicted and required winds. According to Weekes, this phase discrepancy in the airflow for L is what would be expected on oscillation theory. In this connection studies of lunar atmospheric tides in the ionosphere seem of particular interest.

The dynamo theory of the variation L is obviously of considerable theoretical interest because, unlike the case of S_q, there is the possibility of separating effects due to solar heating from those due to tidal action, especially since it will soon be possible to locate the heights of each of the current layers responsible for S_q and L using rocket techniques.

10.3 Magnetic Storms

10.3.1 General Features

Magnetic disturbance (here, following Chapman, to be designated D) embraces transient geomagnetic changes of considerable variety both in form and in level of intensity.[1] It is the part of the transient changes in the geomagnetic field remaining after S_q and L are removed. Besides the diurnal variation on quiet days, S_q, there is also a disturbance daily variation, S_D, a part of D, and usually greater the greater the value of D and vice versa.

A day with large magnetic activity or field changes, D, is referred to as a time of magnetic storm. Magnetic storms are often events which begin suddenly the world over at about the same time. The time of beginning is referred to as the world-wide instant from which storm time for the storm in question is reckoned. Since there is a part of S_D depending more or less closely on local time and a part of D depending on storm time, as well as considerable characteristic changes with latitude in storm-field pattern, the over-all effect of a magnetic storm is one of considerable apparent complexity.

It is also convenient to note that at times D may consist of highly local changes as in the polar regions. In other instances, to be considered in greater detail later, there may be mentioned magnetic bays lasting from about one to several hours, named because in middle latitudes they are often convexities or concavities in the magnetogram, simulating the shape of marine bays. Large bays may be easily traced as a world-wide manifestation. At other times the effect may be small and difficult to trace to much distance beyond the polar caps where they tend to appear simultaneously in both the arctic and antarctic regions. There will also be considered later additional manifestations of disturbance of quite special kind known as pulsations; these are often regular or periodic in time, they may be world-wide in incidence, or they may appear localized in one area or another.

From the foregoing descriptive outline it is clear that the phenomenon of magnetic disturbance as it appears over the surface is complex and usually accessible to description only with the aid of a considerable number of stations. This is one reason why the observations of the International Geophysical Year 1957–1958 are potentially so valuable in the study of storms, since two hundred stations or more will record the natural changes in the geomagnetic field the world over. The very rapid magnetic surveys aloft using earth satellites will also prove of great value because the magnetometers carried provide very rapid world-wide coverage in three-dimensional space and time.

10.3.2 *Average World-Wide Features*

It has been indicated that the field of magnetic storms varies with the geographical position of a station. The field also varies in a complicated way with time. Also, except for features like sudden commencements, there may be conspicuous differences among the storms which appear at a station.

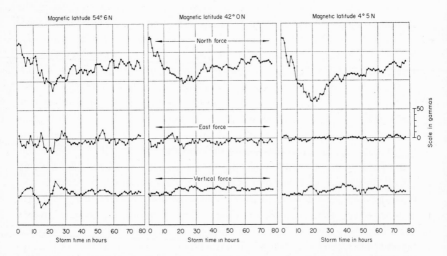

FIG. 14. Averaged storm-time magnetic disturbance—changes in different latitudes.

At any particular station when averages of a number of storms are taken (for instance according to hour), characteristic systematic changes are noted. These effects depend both on storm time reckoned from the sudden commencement of a storm and also on the local time.

Figure 14 shows the result of averaging eleven storms for various stations of the Second International Polar Year, 1932–1933, when the first hour of storms were the same at all stations. It will be seen that for a few hours after the sudden commencement the geomagnetic north force, $\Delta X'$, is positive and followed by a decrease reaching a minimum about 20 hours later. The departures in the geomagnetic east component, $\Delta Y'$, are small, especially at the equator. Departures for the vertical component tend to be opposite in sign to those in $\Delta X'$ and are somewhat smaller.[2]

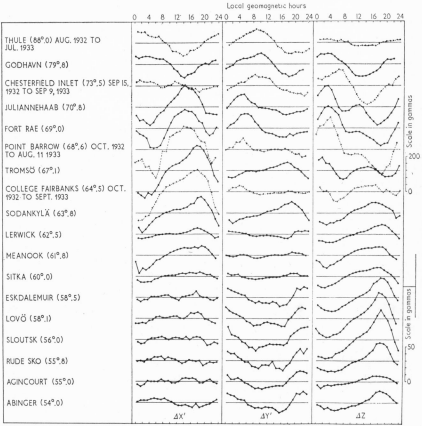

FIG. 15A. Average daily variation, disturbed minus quiet days (S_D), geomagnetic components, 12 months, 1932–1933. Geomagnetic latitudes indicated in parentheses. Geomagnetic hour angles are referred to geomagnetic north pole ($\phi = 78 \cdot 5° N$, $\lambda = 291 \cdot 0° E$).

Figures 15A and 15B give the daily variation of disturbance averaged for the storms of Fig. 14 and a number of additional disturbances of the same year 1932–1933.[2] A marked latitude effect in these values is in evidence. The changes are largest at arctic stations where departures from the average for quiet days show morning and evening maxima. A reversal in phase for the vertical component can be noted between Fort Rae in northern Canada and Sodankyla in Finland.

32

10.3.3 *Current Systems*

The magnetic field changes measured over the earth's surface at a time of magnetic storm are of course due to electric current systems. From potential analysis it is established that about six-tenths of the observed horizontal

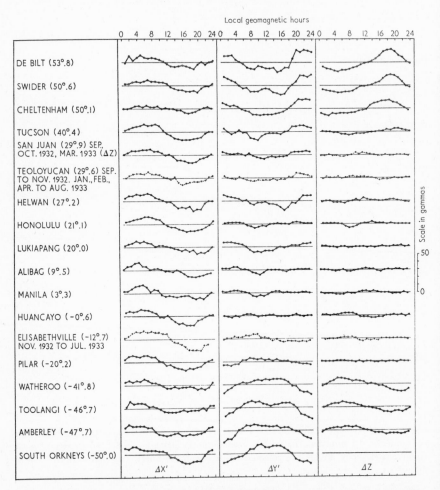

FIG. 15B. Average daily variation, disturbed minus quiet days (S_D), geomagnetic components, 12 months, 1932–1933. Geomagnetic latitudes indicated in parentheses.

force is due to electric current systems flowing above the earth's surface.[1,38,39] It is naturally inferred that the remainder of the field arises from electric current systems flowing within the earth, which are induced by the time variations of the external systems.[39a]

As in the case of S_q and L the equivalent current flow in a concentric spherical shell above the earth can be deduced by the methods of spherical harmonic analysis. Actually, a large number of terms would be required to fit the complicated polar magnetic fields, so that the method is not very useful in practice. Moreover, since it is not known whether or not some of the current flow takes place beyond the atmosphere, the problem is indeterminate. Nevertheless, electric current systems estimated for a thin spherical shell in the ionosphere provide a convenient means of representing the instantaneous field pattern of magnetic storms it is assumed to produce.

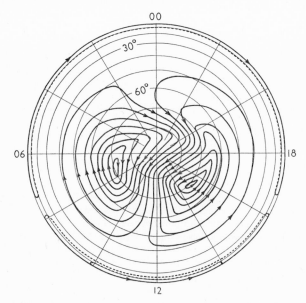

Fig. 16. Electric current system for $S_{\overline{D}}$ part of sudden commencement field, 10,000-amp flow between adjacent current lines. From Jacobs and Obayashi, *Geofis. pura e appl.* **37**, 21 (1956).

This current flow per unit width of sheet can be estimated by approximate devices combining results for various model current systems. It also turns out when this is done that there must indeed be polar electric currents flowing near or within the E region of the ionosphere.

The sudden commencements of storms have been studied by many workers. Newton[40] showed that the sudden commencements of the more intense magnetic storms often occurred about a day after the central meridian passage of active sunspots on the sun. Other statistical studies by Ferraro et al.[41] showed that their hourly frequency at stations in low and middle latitudes was about the same, though a weak maximum near 13 hours local time might be in evidence. On the other hand some preliminary movements to the sudden commencements showed a definite local time effect. In addition, Sugiura,[42] Yumura,[43] Oguti,[44] Forbush and Vestine,[45] and Kato[46] studied

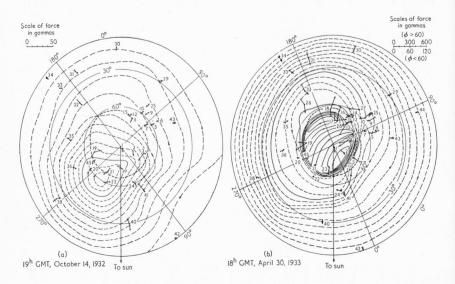

(a)   (b)
19^h GMT, October 14, 1932   To sun   18^h GMT, April 30, 1933   To sun

FIG. 17. Mean hourly disturbance vectors and corresponding electric current systems for height of 150 km for maximum of initial phase of magnetic storms, viewed from above geomagnetic north pole. (100,000-amp flow between successive full-drawn current lines; 10,000 amp flow between broken lines; average auroral zone shown dotted.) A total of 45 magnetic stations were used, which are indicated by numbers with a rough indication of the force at each. Height of the current-systems assumed was 150 km, and cannot be inferred uniquely since the same resultant field at ground level can be produced by a current-system flowing as a spherical current-sheet at some outer level of height, or by hydromagnetic waves propagated downward (in about one minute, say) from the area of contact between outer reaches of the geomagnetic field and solar streams impinging in the manner suggested by Chapman and Ferraro[1]. Note also that in an individual storm an equatorial electrojet such as that in Figure 16 could not be defined by the data, and may or may not have been present; note also that Figures 17(a) and (b) represent the sum of the so-called S_D- and D_{st}- parts. Before direct comparison can be made between the current-systems of Figures 16 and 17, the D_{st}-part obtained by averaging the current around parallels of latitude would have to be removed from the current flows indicated in each of Fig. 17(a) and (b) to get the S_D-part. Vertical downflow of current along lines of force into auroral regions on the afternoon side, with outflow on the night side (as suggested by Birkeland[51] and Alfvén[55]), is assumed to be zero.

the local time effects in sudden commencements observed at and near the magnetic equator. They ascribed these effects to concentrations of current flowing low in the ionosphere along the magnetic equator, as an electrojet.

Figure 16 shows an atmospheric current system derived by Jacobs and Obayashi[47] for sudden commencements, assuming flow in a concentric spherical shell within the ionosphere, which is compatible in general form to a polar pattern of current flow derived by Nagata and Abe.[48] Later studies by Sugiura and Vestine (as yet unpublished) suggest that much of the current flow arises from electric fields associated with the separation of incoming charges penetrating the ionosphere in auroral regions. These electric fields also sometimes appear to transport electrified particles in the F region.

Figure 17 illustrates possible hypothetical current systems for the initial phase of storms (the first half-hour or so of a storm when the horizontal force is often above normal in value). A total of 100,000 amps flows between successive full-drawn current lines. In the storm of April 30, 1933, effects are evident near the auroral zone, which may or may not be a part of the storm; in the storm of October 14 a simple pattern of current flow from west to east is in evidence over much of the earth.[2]

Figure 18, for the main phase of the magnetic storm averaged for 16 hours GMT and 18 hours GMT of May 1, 1933, indicates the appearance of polar electrojets especially at the auroral zone on the morning side of the earth. The current flow in lower latitudes, unlike that during the initial phase, is mainly from east to west. By averaging the current flow along parallels of latitude and subtracting the values from those derived in Fig. 18 for 16 hours GMT, an analysis into a storm-time part (D_{st}) and disturbance daily variation part (S_D) is achieved (Fig. 19). Similar current systems, though for an earth with the geomagnetic and geographic axes coincident, were earlier derived by Chapman,[39] using averages for forty moderate magnetic storms. It may be noted that the current system of Fig. 18 need be only partly atmospheric, and it was intimated by Birkeland and others that a ring current might encircle the earth in the equatorial plane at a distance of a few earth radii.

Fukushima[49] has shown that current systems such as those for 16 hours GMT of May 1 are even simpler if drawn for a particular instant of time of the storm. When this is done the flow pattern shown for the dawn area of the auroral regions in Fig. 20 becomes more easily defined as a simple electrojet directed from east to west. A smaller jet of current near the opposite side of the auroral zone is directed from west to east; the current arrows are vector linear currents thought of as producing the horizontal magnetic field at a station on the ground directly beneath its center. Both electrojets are presumably occasioned by electric charge separation at the auroral zone creating an electric field driving electric currents in adjacent regions of suitable electric conductivity, or transporting ionospheric charge in regions where differential flow of ions and electrons is difficult. The charge separation may arise from incoming charges in which penetration is different for the positive ions and electrons with secondary effects due to X-rays extending to lower levels. Indeed, it may be possible also that differential penetration of charges, suitably maintained, can give rise to the storm-time current

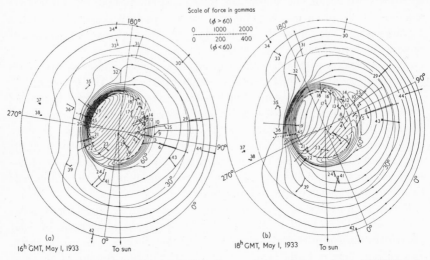

FIG. 18. Same as Fig. 17 averaged for 16 hours GMT and for 18 hours GMT, May 1, 1933, but for the main phases of the storms.

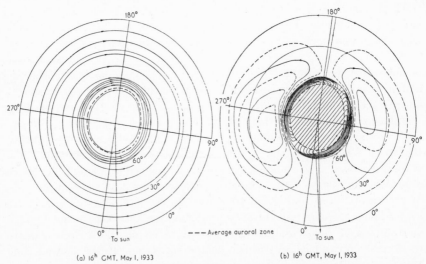

FIG. 19. *a* and *b*, partial current systems, D_{st} and S_D, respectively, main phase of storm (100,000-amp flow between successive, full-drawn current lines).

systems, D_{st}, of Fig. 19, though it is difficult to see how the required electric field in low latitudes directed radially inward could be maintained. For this reason many prefer to think that D_{st} is best regarded as a ring current flowing very high in the atmosphere or even at a distance of several earth radii.

In low latitudes and in equatorial regions it seems likely also that a considerable part of the current may flow at very high levels of the atmosphere, even though it is clear that the polar electrojets must operate low within the ionosphere in polar and auroral regions.

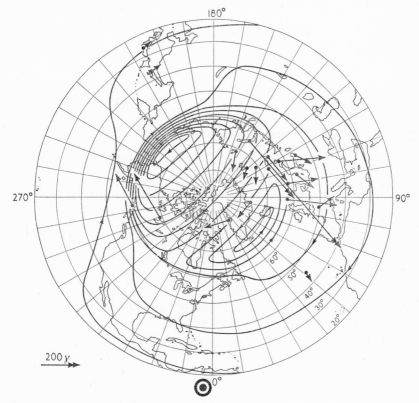

FIG. 20. Disturbance field at 16 hours 50 minutes on May 1, 1933, represented by a combination of current system and current lines.

10.3.4 *Peculiar Magnetic Storms*

Because magnetic storms are such complicated natural phenomena there has been a tendency to discuss them in their simplest forms, or the averages of many storms may be used. This is, of course, a natural first approach in studying a complex phenomenon, but it should be borne in mind that there are occasional peculiar storms of quite unorthodox character. A very common disturbance of the S_D type is the occurrence of isolated polar electrojets without any evidence of a D_{st} field; in fact this is the commonest of the minor storm forms. There are also found on occasion, though only with great rarity, effects suggesting a storm of D_{st} type without evidence of S_D. Finally, as Chapman[1] noted, very great magnetic storms may run through their phases of sudden commencement, initial phase, and main phase in the course of only a few hours instead of days, as is the more usual case.

10.3.5 *Solar Streams*

Of various theories of magnetic storms which have been considered the one most developed as to numerical detail is that of Chapman and Ferraro.[1] This was based on Lindemann's idea that streams or clouds of neutral ionized gas were emitted by active regions or flares on the sun, and traveled to the earth where they then interacted with the geomagnetic field to give magnetic effects identified as a magnetic storm at the earth. As the sun rotated, the solar material, propelled nearly radially outward into space, assumed a curved form like a stream of water from a hose rotated by the gardener. This stream, many times the earth in cross section, was thought to overtake the earth usually on its afternoon side, part of the material in the stream forming a broad encircling ring in the equatorial plane at a distance of a few earth radii. Actually their theory, as developed quantitatively, covered only the first hour or so of storm, the initial phase. But they suggested, as also did others commenting on this theory, that there would be leakage of charge from the current ring along the lines of force into auroral regions. In auroral regions the incoming charges added to the electric conductivity and facilitated or produced the flow of electric current there.

In this theory the interplanetary region was regarded as entirely empty. Chapman[50] has suggested that the solar atmosphere extends throughout the solar system, and that the earth's outermost atmosphere of ionized or neutral atomic hydrogen may have a radius of half the distance to the moon. At the present time, therefore, the theory needs reworking, with these additional likely features taken into account, but many features relating to the geometry of solar streams and of their interaction with the outer part of the geomagnetic field may require but little modification.

Various details of solar clouds and streams remain to be considered. For instance, clouds of solar material propelled away from the active regions near or within sunspots will carry with them a part of the solar or sunspot magnetic field. These magnetic fields will decay only very slowly with time when the blobs of gas are of large size, as they may often be. It also seems likely that there will be streaming of both rapid and slower particles within the cloud, so that many of the magnetic field lines will be aligned parallel to the direction of relative motion of electrically conducting cloud constituents. Blobs of gas may penetrate the geomagnetic field to different levels, depending on the cloud density. In fact, parts of these clouds may introduce or inject particles into the geomagnetic field. Within the geomagnetic field, as Birkeland[51] first showed, by projecting electrons into the field of a small magnetized terrella, a variety of phenomena may occur. Thus, a ring current may arise, revealing distribution of charged particles along magnetic field lines and drifting around the earth. Motions of charges have been extensively studied by Störmer,[1,52] who showed that charges may in fact move between the northern and southern hemispheres, meanwhile spiraling about the lines of force. It is not unlikely that such charges arriving suddenly in the polar regions may cause sudden field changes, such as those of sudden commencements, due to the differential penetration of positive and negative charges in auroral regions, giving rise to electric fields simulating electric doublets there. This may explain the oscillatory changes during a sudden commencement, if a blob of ions moves along the lines of force and returns upward, possibly more than once in the geomagnetic field. In this connection the results of the United States' IGY earth satellite, Explorer III, are of interest, since such a region of spiraling high-energy particles was encountered high above the equatorial plane.[53] In higher latitudes a similar result was noted at lower levels by the Soviet Sputnik III. It is therefore possible that the trapped orbits found by Bennett[54] in terrella experiments are verified as existing in nature with flow of charge also as a current perpendicular to the geomagnetic field. In fact such currents have been estimated by Alfvén,[55,56] and some interesting estimates of the electric current magnitudes have been made by Singer.[57] In connection with studies of energetic particles encountered by IGY satellites, similar estimates have also been reported by Vernov[58] for Störmer-type motions of electric charge and eastward drift of electrons. The charges penetrating to low levels in the polar regions are associated also with production of X-rays, and there will also be produced electric current systems engendered by the atmospheric winds moving the electrically conducting air in the polar regions.

The effective role of dynamo action in producing magnetic disturbance in the polar regions has been considered by a number of workers[49,59-61] but with as yet uncertain conclusions and with some of the possibilities mentioned today rendered unpromising. One attractive possibility is that sudden commencements are, in some instances at least, occasioned by a local electrojet in the polar regions set up by groups or clouds of electric charges penetrating into the E region and below, setting up local electrojets, sometimes of pulsating character.[62] There are also contributions giving rise to the auroral zone electrojets of magnetic bays and storms, to be discussed below, which must ensure that magnetic disturbance is mainly an atmospheric phenomenon. The discovery of high-energy particles in the aurora by Van Allen[53] and others using rockets and satellites, probably indicates that substantial electric currents must flow in a ring current encircling the earth at levels closer to the earth in the polar regions, and extending out to several earth radii above the equator. The natural inference is that, as in the Chapman-Ferraro theory, solar streams may impinge on the earth possibly as clouds of particles in which more energetic particles are imprisoned by magnetic fields while en route. On penetration of the geomagnetic field, to different levels in different storms, the required leakage of charge into the polar regions may ensue to assist in the production of magnetic bays and the disturbance daily variation, perhaps with the help of dynamo action. A part of the stream might remain as an encircling current ring broadly distributed both in latitude and in height. The electric fields which penetrate to adjacent regions of lower electric conductivity will there produce motions of the electric charges present, as in the case of aurora and the ionosphere. It seems likely that electric fields generated and produced in auroral regions will cause, as Baker and Martyn[14] have suggested, drifts of ionospheric charge and of auroral rays. The electric fields generated by winds should also accelerate electrons of interest in connection with aurora. There may also need to be consideration of compressions and expansions of the atmosphere and its magnetic field, as suggested by Chapman in 1919, an idea also discussed recently by students of hydromagnetism. The prospects for ascertaining additional new descriptive facts soon are of course facilitated by extensive rocket and satellite programs.

10.4 Minor Magnetic Disturbances

10.4.1 Auroral Zone Electrojets

Figure 21 shows an electric current system deduced from the average of the maximum field departure during a number of magnetic disturbances known as bays. The current is supposed to flow at a height of 150 km as a spherical current sheet. It is evident that a westward-directed electrojet appears to flow in the early morning and an easterly directed electrojet in the afternoon. The current circuits are completed in low latitudes and across the polar cap. Since the magnetic intensifications (or diminutions) in field, known as bays, last from about one to several hours, these electrojets persist for a considerable time. They may be caused by electric charge escaping during the night hours from the ring current, when conditions become favorable. Since they ordinarily tend to appear several nights in succession, their recurrence tendency seems likely to be produced by terrestrial conditions.

It has also been noted that electric current-flow patterns are engendered during large solar flares. An especially noteworthy instance was that of the great solar flare of February 23, 1956, which was accompanied by a marked increase in cosmic rays at the ground.

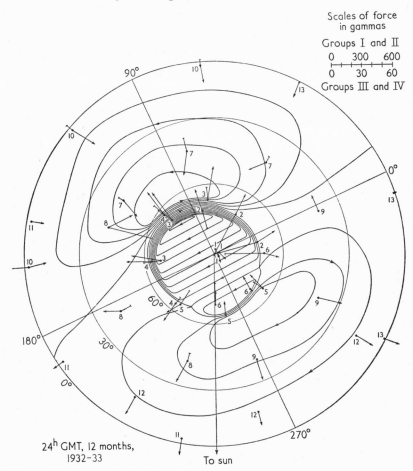

Horizontal force →. Vertical force ⊣ (vertical component positive when drawn outward from geomagnetic north pole) (50,000 amp flow between successive current lines).

Groups I and II		Stations	Groups III and IV	
1 Thule	4 Dickson	7 Erbo	10 Mogadiscio	
2 Juliannehaab	5 College-Fairbanks	8 Watheroo	11 Antipolo	
3 Tromsö	6 Fort Rae	9 Tucson	12 Apia	13 Huancayo

FIG. 21. Electric current system of geomagnetic bays.

10.4.2 Irregular Magnetic Disturbances

When hourly ranges in magnetic field components are averaged, it is found that they vary in magnitude as though they were produced by overhead currents such as shown in Fig. 21. In addition it was found by Stagg[63] and others that the changes in the western hemisphere tend to be greatest near local midnight. In the arctic regions of the U.S.S.R., Nikolsky[64] has found that there are additional (observational) features suggesting a dependence of disturbance not only on local time but also on universal time in the case of the night maximum in disturbance. The cause of the time dependence of irregular disturbance is not understood.

10.5 Magnetic Pulsations

In addition to magnetic bays there are other interesting features of disturbances known as pulsations. Pulsations of regular character in the geomagnetic field, of a period of a minute or so, were recorded photographically at Kew Observatory as early as 1859. Workers such as Van Bemmelen and Eschenhagen[1] conducted extensive studies of records during the first quarter of the present century. Examples of a class of so-called giant micropulsations of sinusoidal form are shown in Fig. 22.

Pulsations of a period of a minute or so are more often noted by night, especially near or somewhat after midnight. The same appears to be the case for pulsations of shorter period. In addition, Troitskaia[65] has suggested that there are also pulsations which seem to occur near the time of local midnight at the geomagnetic north pole and hence show a universal time effect.

High-frequency pulsations have also been measured by a number of workers such as Holzer and Deal.[66] According to Holzer, electromagnetic signals detected in the measured range 25 to 130 cps are atmospherics caused by thunderstorm activity. A summary of the frequency and sizes of pulsations in Japan has been given by Tereda[67] and more recently by Kato and Akasofu.[68] Additional information on a world-wide scale for the Second International Polar Year has been given by Vestine,[2] including statistics on the frequency of fluctuations of various sizes and time durations in different geographic locations.

During the International Geophysical Year pulsations are also being measured as induced electric potentials in the surface of the ground at earth current stations, especially in the U.S.S.R. This can be done with relatively simple apparatus even when rapidly changing amplitudes in the pulsations in the geomagnetic field are only of the order of 10^{-6} to 10^{-7} cgs unit.

It is found also that many longer-period magnetic changes enduring for many minutes to an hour or so may have a background of higher-frequency oscillations superposed, the frequency ranging from a cycle or so to several tens of cycles per second. Examples of longer pulsations of this type are noted at the magnetic equator superimposed on S_q, in great magnetic storms, and even in the case of magnetic bays and sudden commencements.

Efforts to explain micropulsations usually invoke supposed oscillatory motions in the upper atmosphere or the actual propagation of hydromagnetic waves through the ionosphere, and thence as an ordinary electromagnetic signal down to the surface of the ground.[68,69]

10.6 Geomagnetism in Relation to Other Geophysical Phenomena

In the foregoing sections it has been possible to describe some features of geomagnetism rather closely linked to other phenomena such as solar effects of both wave and corpuscular radiation. It was also clear that ionospheric

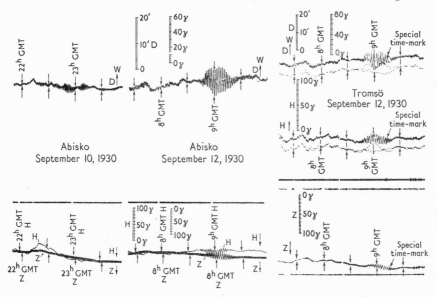

FIG. 22. Micropulsations recorded at Abisko, Sweden, and at Tromsö, Norway. From B. Rolf, *Terr. Mag.*, **36**, 9 (1921).

winds must produce measurable contributions to the geomagnetic field now becoming well understood for magnetically quiet days but not at all understood for magnetically disturbed days. Mention has also been made of the pronounced geomagnetic effects in auroral regions, especially within the northern and southern auroral zones. Since these auroral zones may be linked together by lines of the geomagnetic field, it is of interest to take a series of points around the northern auroral zone and note by integration of the field lines the southern terminus of the respective points at heights of the aurora. Figure 23 shows results of such a calculation of the shape and size of the southern auroral zone, based on points along the northern average auroral zone as given by Vestine *et al.*[2] The southern auroral zone deduced by numerical integration of the combined dipole and quadripole terms of the earth's field is indicated and compared with the average auroral zone previously deduced from actual auroral and geomagnetic observations in the Antarctic by Vestine and Snyder.[2] It is clear that rather good agreement (to a degree of latitude or so) is indicated between the calculated southern auroral zone and that derived from the data directly, though the calculated auroral zone appears to be actually somewhat smaller in size than that derived from the data. This feature also appeared in the theoretical derivations of the shapes of the northern and southern auroral zones by Quenby and Webber,[70] who applied the simple Störmer theory of allowed regions for

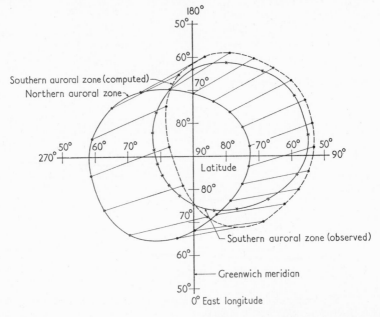

FIG. 23. Average northern and southern auroral zones estimated from data, and also southern zone estimated on the basis of linkage of auroral zones by geomagnetic field lines.

incoming auroral particles to an earth with a geomagnetic field including quadripole terms. Their theoretical calculations were also applied to explain the asymmetry in cosmic-ray intensity with longitude found by Simpson[71] near the geomagnetic equator where previously a discrepancy of about 45° in longitude was found between surface values of the surface geomagnetic field and the maximum and minimum in cosmic ray intensity. It would also be of interest to apply their method to polar asymmetries in cosmic rays noted by Rose, Neher, and Korff.

At the present time new data obtained aboard rockets and satellites will serve to define the actual spatial distribution of electric currents that flow above the earth and cause magnetic storms. There are, hence, exciting prospects of clarifying many of the obscure features of the storm field by the preferred method of direct measurement.[72,73]

References

1. S. Chapman and J. Bartels, "Geomagnetism," Vols. 1 and 2, Oxford Univ. Press, New York, 1949.
2. E. H. Vestine, L. Laporte, I. Lange, and W. E. Scott, *Carnegie Inst. Wash. Publ.* No. **580** (1947).
3. S. Chapman, *Phil. Trans. Roy. Soc.* A**218**, 1 (1919).
4. A. Schuster, *Phil. Trans. Roy. Soc.* A**180**, 467 (1889); A**208**, 163 (1908).
5. J. Bartels, *Terr. Mag.* **51**, 181 (1946).
6. E. H. Vestine, L. Laporte, I. Lange, C. Cooper, and W. C. Hendrix, *Carnegie Inst. Wash. Publ.* No. **578** (1947).
7. S. Chapman, *Arch. Meteorol. Geophys. u. Bioklimatol. Ser.* A4, 368 (1951).
8. B. Stewart, *in* "Encyclopedia Britannica," 9th ed., 36 pp. (1882).
9. S. Chapman and T. G. Cowling, "Mathematical Theory of Non-uniform Gases," 2nd ed., Cambridge Univ. Press, London, 1952.
10. P. O. Pedersen, "Propagation of Radio Waves, etc.," Danmarks Naturvidenskabelige Samfund., A. Nr. 15 a/b, 244 pp., Copenhagen, 1927.
11. A. V. Appleton and M. A. F. Barnett, *Proc. Roy. Soc.* A**109**, 621 (1925).
12. G. Breit and M. A. Tuve, *Phys. Rev.* **28**, 554 (1926).
13. T. G. Cowling, *Monthly Not. Roy. Astron. Soc.* **93**, 90 (1932).
14. W. G. Baker and D. F. Martyn, *Phil. Trans. Roy. Soc.* A**246**, 281 (1953).
15. M. Hirono, *J. Geomag. Geoelect.* **2**, 1 (1950); **4**, 7 (1952); **5**, 22 (1953).
16. K. Maeda, *J. Geomag. Geoelect.* **3**, 77 (1951).
17. J. A. Fejer, *J. Atmos. Terr. Phys.* **4**, 184 (1953); **5**, 103 (1954).
18. S. Chapman, *Nuovo Cime.* [10] **4**, No. 4, Suppl., p. 1385 (1956).
19. B. H. Briggs and M. Spencer, *Repts. Progr. in Phys.* **17**, 245 (1954).
20. F. L. Whipple, *Proc. Natl. Acad. Sci.* **40**, 966 (1954).
21. W. W. Kellogg and G. F. Schilling, *J. Meteorol.* **8**, 222 (1951).
22. P. S. Pant, *J. Geophys. Res.* **61**, 459 (1956).
23. G. I. Taylor, *Proc. Roy. Soc.* A**156**, 318 (1936).
24. C. L. Pekeris, *Proc. Roy. Soc.* A**158**, 650 (1937).
25. M. V. Wilkes, "Oscillations of the Earth's Atmosphere," Cambridge Univ. Press, London, 1949.
26. H. K. Sen and M. L. White, *J. Geophys. Res.* **60**, 483 (1955); M. L. White, *ibid.* **62**, 329 (1957).
27. O. R. Wulf, *J. Geophys. Res.* **61**, 489 (1956).
28. S. F. Singer, E. Maple, and W. A. Bowen, Jr., *J. Geophys. Res.* **56**, 265 (1951).
29. H. K. Kallmann, Properties of the atmosphere between 90 and 300 km, "Vistas in Astronautics," Pergamon, London, 1958.
30. H. Maeda, *J. Geomag. Geoelect.* **7**, 121 (1955).
31. E. V. Appleton and K. Weekes, *Proc. Roy. Soc.* A**171**, 171 (1939).
31a. S. Kato, *J. Geomag. Geoelect.* **8**, 24 (1956).
32. M. Hasegawa and Y. Tamur, *Proc. Imp. Acad.* (*Tokyo*) **13**, 311 (1937); **14**, 4 (1938).
33. S. Chapman and J. M. Stagg, *Proc. Roy. Soc.* A**123**, 27 (1929); **130**, 668 (1931).
34. E. H. Vestine, *Trans. Amer. Geophys. Union* **39**, 213 (1958).
35. S. E. Forbush, *J. Geophys. Res.* **61**, 93 (1956).
35a. N. P. Benkova, *Terr. Mag.* **45**, 425 (1940).

35b. V. Vacquier, *Terr. Mag.* **42**, 17 (1937).

36. J. Bartels and H. F. Johnston, *Trans. Amer. Geophys. Union* Pt. 2, p. 273 (1940).

37. D. F. Martyn, *Proc. Roy. Soc.* A**190**, 273 (1947).

38. S. Chapman, *Abhandl. Akad. Wiss. Göttingen, Math. Physik. Kl. Sonderheft* No. 3 (1959).

39. S. Chapman, *Terr. Mag.* **40**, 349 (1935).

39a. N. P. Benkova, Ministry of Agriculture and State Deliveries, U.S.S.R., State Publishing House for Hydrology and Meteorology, Leningrad, 1953.

40. H. W. Newton, *Monthly Not. Roy. Astron. Soc. Geophys. Suppl.* **5**, 159 (1948).

41. V. C. A. Ferraro, W. C. Parkinson, and H. W. Unthank, *J. Geophys. Res.* **56**, 177 (1915).

42. M. Sugiura, *J. Geophys. Res.* **58**, 558 (1953); Ph.D. Thesis, University of Alaska, College (1955), includes extensive new data on storms.

43. T. Yumura, *Mem. Kakioka Mag. Observ.* **7**, 27 (1954).

44. T. Oguti, *Rept. Ionosphere Res. Japan* **10**, 81 (1956).

45. S. E. Forbush and E. H. Vestine, *J. Geophys. Res.* **60**, 299 (1955).

46. Y. Kato, *Sci. Repts. Tôhkou Univ. Fifth Ser.* **4**, 5 (1952).

47. J. A. Jacobs and T. Obayashi, *Geofis, pura e appl.* **34**, 21 (1956).

48. T. Nagata and S. Abe, *Rept. Ionosphere Res. Japan*, **9**, 39 (1955).

49. N. Fukushima, *J. Fac. Sci. Univ. Tokyo* 8, Section II, 293 (1953).

50. S. Chapman, *Smithsonian Contrib. Astrophys.* **2**, 1 (1957).

51. Kr. Birkeland, "Norwegian Aurora Polaris Expedition, 1902–1903," Vol. 1, Part 1, pp. 39–315; Part 2, pp. 319–551, H. Aschehoug and Co., Christiania, 1908 and 1913.

52. C. Störmer, *Arch. Sci. Phys. et Nat.* **24**, 1, (1907).

53. J. A. Van Allen, G. H. Ludwig, E. C. Ray, and C. E. McIlwain, *IGY Satellite Rept. Ser.* No. **3**; *Proc. Natl. Acad. Sci.* **44**, 73 (1958).

54. W. H. Bennett, *Astron. J.* **127**, 731 (1958).

55. H. Alfvén, "Cosmical Electrodynamics," Oxford Univ. Press, New York, 1950.

56. H. Alfvén, *Tellus* **7**, 50 (1955).

57. S. F. Singer, *Trans. Amer. Geophys. Union* **38**, 175 (1957).

58. S. N. Vernov, Science Club Lecture, Fifth Reunion of the IGY, Moscow, August, 1958.

59. S. Chapman, *Proc. Roy. Soc.* A**115**, 242 (1927).

60. O. R. Wulf, *Terr. Mag.* **50**, 185 (1945); **50**, 259 (1945).

61. E. H. Vestine, *J. Geophys. Res.* **59**, 93 (1954).

62. Y. Kato and T. Saito, *Science Repts., Tohoku Univ. Ser. V* **9**, 44 (1958).

63. J. M. Stagg, *Proc. Roy. Soc.* A**149**, 298 (1935).

64. A. P. Nikolsky, *Terr. Mag.* **52**, 147 (1947); *Dokl. Akad. Nauk, SSSR* **115**, 84 (1957).

65. V. N. Troitskaia, *Dokl. Akad. Nauk SSSR* **93**, 261 (1953).

66. R. E. Holzer and O. E. Deal, *Nature* **177**, 536 (1956).

67. T. Tereda, *J. Coll. Sci. Imper. Univ. Tokyo* **37**, 1 (1917).

68. Y. Kato and S. Akasofu, *Sci. Repts. Tohoku Univ. Fifth Ser.* **7**, 103 (1956); **8**, 157 (1957).

69. J. W. Dungey, "Electrodynamics of the Outer Atmosphere, The Physics of the Ionosphere," pp. 229–236, Physical Society, London, 1955.

70. J. J. Quenby and W. R. Webber, Symposium on Cosmic Rays, Fifth Reunion of the IGY, Moscow, August, 1958.

71. J. A. Simpson, *Proc. Natl. Acad. Sci.* **43**, 42 (1957).

72. J. A. Van Allen, ed., "Scientific Uses of Earth Satellites," Univ. Michigan Press, Ann Arbor, 1956.

73. N. V. Pushkov and S. Sh. Dolginov, *Uspekhi Fiz. Nauk* **63**, 645 (1957).

Chapter 11

The Upper Atmosphere and Meteors

J. S. Greenhow and A. C. B. Lovell

11.1 Introduction.. 513
11.2 Techniques of Measurement.. 514
11.3 Evaporation of Meteors in the Upper Atmosphere...................... 515
11.4 Scattering of Radio Waves from Meteor Trails........................ 518
11.5 Total Meteor Influx.. 520
    11.5.1 Diurnal and Seasonal Variation of Sporadic Meteors............... 520
    11.5.2 Meteor Showers... 522
    11.5.3 Mass Distribution.. 522
    11.5.4 The Over-all Meteor Influx...................................... 524
    11.5.5 Total Meteor Contribution to the Ionization in the E Region........ 526
11.6 Determination of Scale Heights and Densities......................... 528
    11.6.1 Meteor Heights... 528
    11.6.2 Radio Echo Methods.. 529
    11.6.3 Photographic Methods... 533
    11.6.4 Results.. 534
11.7 Winds in the Upper Atmosphere: Determination by Meteor Techniques.... 536
    11.7.1 Visual and Photographic Observations........................... 536
    11.7.2 Radio Echo Results.. 537
11.8 Recombination and Diffusion of Ionization in Meteor Trails............. 544
    11.8.1 Diffusion.. 545
    11.8.2 Recombination... 545
    11.8.3 Attachment.. 546
    References... 548

11.1 Introduction

The common shooting stars which are frequently seen with the naked eye represent the evaporation of very small pieces of stone or iron in a region extending from about 80 to 120 km above the earth's surface. The numbers increase rapidly with diminishing brightness, and at the limit of naked-eye visibility under good sky conditions the mass of the individual meteor particle is about 10^{-3} gm. Although there are about 10^8 impacts per day over the entire atmosphere at this magnitude limit, the number seen by any individual observer is normally only a few per hour. Occasionally these numbers increase considerably when the earth moves through a concentration of debris often associated with cometary orbits.

Radio echo studies of the ionization produced by the evaporation of the meteors show that the number entering the atmosphere continues to increase below the limit of normal visibility. Contemporary high-sensitivity radio equipments are probably sensitive to at least ten magnitudes below the visible limit where the number of impacts per day on the atmosphere is of the order of 10^{15}. When the mass range of about 10^{-10} gm is reached, the particles are stopped before evaporation is complete and fall to the earth as fine micrometeoritic dust. The investigation of these micrometeorites by earth satellites is an important part of extraterrestrial studies. Although the investigations are in an early stage, it seems likely that the earth collects many millions of tons of dust per annum in this way.

The origin of these meteor particles is a subject of much importance in astronomy, but a discussion of these aspects lies outside the scope of this chapter. It should be mentioned, however, that nothing in the contemporary measurements supports the old belief that any meteors come from interstellar space. The evidence is that all meteors are moving in closed orbits in the solar system, and their velocity of entry into the atmosphere is confined within the range 10 km sec^{-1} to 72 km sec.^{-1} The shower meteors, which occur in groups moving in closely similar orbits, have clear associations with comets. It is likely that the sporadic meteors, which represent the bulk of the meteoric impact, were similarly associated in the past but have suffered perturbations which in the course of time have given their orbits a more random distribution. These astronomical aspects have been covered in another published work.[1] Here we are more concerned with the interaction of meteors with the upper atmosphere, particularly with the information which may be obtained about wind conditions, densities, diffusion, and the processes which govern the evaporation.

11.2 Techniques of Measurement

When a meteor enters the atmosphere the major part of its kinetic energy is probably dissipated as heat. No methods have yet been suggested for measuring the heat production, however, and the only methods at present available for the study of meteors are by the observation of either the luminous or the ionized trail. Much of the pioneer work on meteors was done purely by visual observation at night under clear sky conditions. Important results were obtained as regards the astronomy of meteors, but the contribution of this type of visual observation to the geophysical aspects has been small compared with the recent photographic and radio echo studies.

Whipple at Harvard has been primarily responsible for the development of the precision photographic methods now in use. The meteor trail is photographed simultaneously from two cameras over a base line of about 40 km, so that its trajectory can be determined. The velocity and deceleration are determined by occulting the lens with a shutter rotating at about 1800

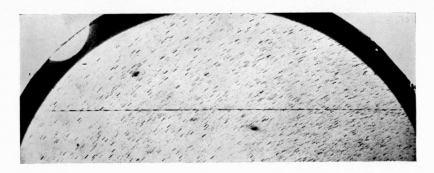

Fig. 1. A Geminid meteor photographed with the Schmidt camera at Jodrell Bank on December 14, 1957. The rotating shutter made twenty-two breaks per second in the trail. The effective aperture of the camera was $f = 0.78$, and the field of view was 56°. Radio echo data were obtained simultaneously from the ionized trail.

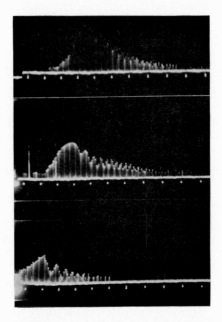

Fig. 2. The radio echo from a meteor trail recorded simultaneously at three stations triangularly situated at spacings of 4 km. The vertical deflection is proportional to echo amplitude, and successive echo pulses separated by 1.66 m.sec can be resolved on the horizontal axis. The small-amplitude fluctuations are the Fresnel diffraction patterns from which the velocity of the meteor can be determined. The time separation of the three patterns enables the orbit of the meteor to be calculated. The range is measured on a separate display.

[*To face page* 515

rpm so that the photographed trail is segmented. A typical photograph is shown in Fig. 1. The attainment of sufficient sensitivity and field of view for an adequate photographic rate is a major problem. For example, the conventional cameras used in the earlier Harvard program could only photograph meteors with magnitudes brighter than zero, and the average yield was about one meteor per hundred hours of exposure. Since 1950, however, the photographic techniques have been revolutionized by the development of Super Schmidt meteor cameras. The ones used in New Mexico for the Harvard program have a field of view of 55° with a focal ratio of 0.65. The limiting magnitude is + 3 or + 4, and the yield of photographed meteors is some fifty or one hundred times as good as that obtained with the conventional cameras.

The radio echo technique for the study of meteors has been largely developed since 1945. The basis of the method consists in the transmission of pulses of radio waves through a suitable aerial system. The radio frequency is chosen to be well above the critical frequency of the ionosphere, and frequencies in the region 30 to 80 Mc sec^{-1} are commonly used. The radio wave is scattered from the ionized meteor trail, and the returned signal is received as a transient echo which may either be viewed on a cathode-ray tube display or recorded photographically. A typical record from a single meteor is shown in Fig. 2. This apparatus uses three receiving stations, triangularly spaced at 4 km, and the Fresnel zone patterns as the meteor passes through each aerial beam are recorded on a single film. The velocity of the meteor is determined from the amplitude-time variations of the zone pattern, and the displacement in time of the three patterns enables the trail to be positioned in space. Thus complete orbital data can be determined for individual meteors, and in the apparatus developed by Davies and Gill[2] at Jodrell Bank between two hundred and three hundred such orbits could be determined in a 24-hour period. Some other developments of this radio echo technique for particular purposes will be mentioned later. Compared with the photographic techniques the radio echo method has the advantage of greater sensitivity—for example, it is readily possible to observe meteors down to magnitude + 10 or fainter—and observations can be made under any sky conditions. It does not, however, possess the precision of the photographic techniques for studies of individual meteors.

A more detailed account of the visual, photographic, and radio echo methods of observation have been given by Lovell.[1]

11.3 Evaporation of Meteors in the Upper Atmosphere

A meteor on the limit of naked-eye visibility with a visual magnitude of + 5 probably has a mass of 10^{-3} or 10^{-4} gm and a radius of about 10^{-2} cm.

Bright fireballs of magnitude — 3 probably have masses of about 1 gm. The mean free paths of the atmospheric atoms in the height range of 80 to 110 km in which these meteors evaporate are therefore large compared with the size of the meteor. Consequently the evaporation process may be considered to result from the impact of single air atoms on the meteor, which enters the atmosphere at velocities from 10 km sec^{-1} to 72 km sec^{-1}. The original investigators considered that a compression cap would be formed in front of the meteor, but it now seems certain that, except for very big meteors which appear as bright fireballs or which reach the earth as meteorites, this view is untenable.

The modern theory of the evaporation process has been summarized by Whipple[3] and Herlofson[4] and has been developed in considerable detail in the series of papers on The Physical Theory of Meteors from Harvard by Whipple and his collaborators.[5-12] Qualitatively, the process is that the surface of the meteor is bombarded by single air molecules a great proportion of which are trapped in the meteor and give up their kinetic energy as heat. This process brings the meteor to the temperature of evaporation, and atoms distil off the meteor with thermal velocities relative to the meteor surface. The binding energies of the meteor atoms will be a few electron volts only; hence the heat supplied by each trapped molecule will be sufficient to evaporate a great number of atoms, and the retardation is small during the evaporation process. The evaporated meteor atoms move into the surrounding atmosphere with the velocity of the meteor and are slowed down by collision with the air molecules. The energy of these evaporated atoms will be determined by the meteor velocity and will vary from about 10^2 to 10^3 ev. In the collisions with the air molecules this kinetic energy is converted into heat, light, and ionization.

Quantitatively the basic evaporation equations are obtained by writing down the conditions for the conservation of momentum, and the equation for the heat transfer between the impacting molecules and the latent heat carried away by the evaporated atoms. The rate of evaporation of meteor atoms, n, at any point is given by

$$n = \frac{1}{\mu} \frac{dm}{dt} \qquad (11.1)$$

and if p is the atmospheric pressure at this point it can be shown that

$$n = \frac{mv \cos \chi}{\mu H} \frac{p}{p_{max}} \left(1 - \frac{1}{3} \frac{p}{p_{max}} \right)^2 \qquad (11.2)$$

where m and v are the initial mass and velocity of the meteor before it enters the atmosphere at zenith angle χ, μ is the mass of an individual meteor atom, and H is the atmospheric scale height; p_{max} is the atmospheric pressure at the point of maximum evaporation and is given by

$$p_{max} = \frac{2lg}{\Lambda v^2 A} \cdot m^{1/3} \cos \chi \qquad (11.3)$$

where l is the latent heat of evaporation of the meteor, g is the gravitational acceleration, and A is a shape factor defined by $A = \mathscr{A}m^{-2/3}$, where $\mathscr{A}$ is the cross-sectional area normal to the line of flight. Λ is the heat transfer coefficient. In the case where all impinging air molecules are trapped in the lattice, $\Lambda = 1$. The actual value of Λ probably lies between 0.7 and 1.

If β is the probability that a single evaporated meteor atom produces a free electron in collision with the air molecules, then the line density of electrons produced by the meteor is, from (11.1),

$$\alpha = \frac{\beta}{\mu v} \cdot \frac{dm}{dt} \qquad (11.4)$$

and from (11.2) and (11.3) at the point of maximum evaporation

$$\alpha_{max} = \frac{\beta n_{max}}{v} = \frac{4}{9} \frac{\beta}{\mu H} m \cos \chi \qquad (11.5)$$

and at any point along the track

$$\alpha = \frac{\beta m \cos \chi}{\mu H} \cdot \frac{p}{p_{max}} \left(1 - \frac{1}{3} \frac{p}{p_{max}}\right)^2 . \qquad (11.6)$$

The energy emitted as light may be obtained by assuming that the luminosity is proportional to the kinetic energy of the mass lost. If τ is the luminous efficiency, the intensity, I, of the visual radiation from the meteor is then given by

$$I = \tfrac{1}{2}\tau v^2(dm/dt) \qquad (11.7)$$

with forms corresponding to (11.5) and (11.6) in terms of p and p_{max}.

The general shape of the light and ionization curve predicted by the above theory is shown in Fig. 3. Considering the simplifying assumptions made, the experimental curves show reasonable general agreement. There is much uncertainty over the values of the ionizing efficiency, β, and the luminous efficiency, τ; neither is the extent of the dependence of β and τ on the velocity yet agreed. By comparison of visual luminosity data and radio echo measurements of α, Greenhow and Hawkins[13] suggested that values of $\beta \sim 0.2$ and of $\tau \sim 10^{-3}$ gave satisfactory agreement with the observations for a velocity of 60 km sec^{-1}. More recently Millman and McKinley[14] have discussed the radio echo and visual data from over three thousand observations. Experimental work now in progress involving simultaneous photographic and radio echo studies of individual meteors should give more accurate information about β and τ and their dependence on velocity. Apart from the work on meteor ionization such results would be of considerable interest because of the difficulties of studying the transition probabilities in the collision of heavy atoms in the 100 to 1000 ev region in the laboratory.

The basic theory set out above will not apply to the extremes of meteor sizes. Meteors with masses of more than 1 gm are rather rare. They appear as brilliant fireballs and if large enough penetrate the entire atmosphere before evaporation is complete. In such cases the fundamental assumption that the free path is large compared with the meteor becomes invalid, and a compression cap probably forms in front of the meteor. The appropriate theories are not well developed and will not be considered here. At the other extreme there exist large numbers of meteors with radii of 10^{-3} cm or less

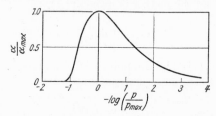

Fig. 3. The shape of the ionization curve produced by a meteor as it penetrates the atmosphere: α is the electron line density at atmospheric pressure, p, and α_{max} is the maximum electron density produced at the height where the pressure is p_{max}.

which have a ratio of surface area to mass large enough to ensure that the energy of interaction with the atmosphere is radiated away so rapidly that evaporation does not occur. These so-called micrometeorites are stopped before appreciable ablation occurs and eventually fall slowly through the atmosphere to reach the earth as very fine dust. The study of these micro-meteorites is in an early stage. They have been investigated from the theoretical aspect by Whipple[15] and will not be considered further here.

11.4 Scattering of Radio Waves from Meteor Trails

The straightforward calculation of the amount of energy scattered back to a radio receiver from an ionized meteor trail was first carried out by Lovell and Clegg[16] in the following way. It was assumed that the density in the trail containing α electrons per centimeter of path was at all times below the critical value for the wavelength in question, and that the electrons scattered independently and coherently. For a cluster of N electrons scattering under these conditions, it can be shown that the amount of power scattered back to the receiver will be given by

$$w = \frac{8}{3}\pi\left(\frac{e^2}{mc^2}\right)^2 N^2 \frac{PG^2\lambda^2}{16\pi^3 R^4} \tag{11.8}$$

where e and m are the electronic charge and mass, c is the velocity of light, P is the peak power of the transmitter, λ is the radio wavelength, R is the range of the meteor trail, and G is the power gain over a half-wave dipole of the transmitting and receiving aerials. For convenience the transmitting and receiving aerials are assumed to have the same power gain, G. It is also convenient to express the gain in terms of a half-wave dipole which itself has a gain of 1.64 over an isotropic radiator. It was assumed that the diameter of the ionized trail was small compared with λ, and the number of electrons, N, which would be effective in the scattering process was calculated by applying optical diffraction theory. In terms of α it can be shown, by using Fresnel's integral, that

$$N = \alpha \sqrt{\frac{\lambda R}{2}} \tag{11.9}$$

and hence (11.8) reduces to

$$w = \frac{\alpha^2 P G^2 \lambda^3}{12 \pi^2 R^3} \left(\frac{e^2}{mc^2} \right)^2. \tag{11.10}$$

The parameters P, G, and λ are known for any particular equipment, and the received power, w, can be measured from the amplitude of the radio echo. The range, R, is also measured for each individual meteor, and hence the line density, α, can be determined. It is important to note that the reflection is specular and that the value of α determined in this way relates to an arbitrary point on the ionization curve of Fig. 3.

More comprehensive scattering theories were subsequently developed by Herlofson,[17] by Kaiser and Closs,[18] and by Eshelman.[19] It has been shown that the assumptions made in developing (11.10) were valid only when the line density, α, was less than about 10^{12} electrons cm^{-1}, and that for higher densities the trail could be treated as a metallic cylinder in which case (11.10) becomes

$$w = \frac{\alpha^{1/2} P G^2 \lambda^3}{40 \pi^3 R^3} \left(\frac{e^2}{mc^2} \right)^{1/2}. \tag{11.11}$$

It is, in fact, now known that this is the condition for all trails in the visual magnitude range, and that (11.10) applies only for meteors fainter than about $+ 6$ magnitude. Plasma resonance effects may also occur in trails with $\alpha < 10^{12}$ electrons cm^{-1} when the electric vector is transverse to the ionized column. Experimental work has now fully justified the predictions of the above theories (for example, Greenhow[20]), including the occurrence of the plasma resonance effects.[21]

The main contribution to the reflection will come from the few Fresnel zones in the vicinity of the specular reflection point. As the meteor crosses this point the formation of the ionized column through the successive zones gives the amplitude-time pattern illustrated in Fig. 2, which enables the velocity of the meteor to be determined. Subsequently the trail will diffuse (§ 11.8), and the decay of echo amplitude is often superimposed on the same pattern.

It is important to note that when $\alpha < 10^{12}$ electrons cm^{-1}, the signal amplitude $V(\propto \sqrt{w})$, is directly related to α, but for $\alpha > 10^{12}$ electrons cm^{-1} the signal amplitude varies only as $\alpha^{1/4}$ and therefore provides only a very insensitive measure of this quantity. In these cases it is customary to use the duration, T_L, which varies directly as α [equation (11.22)], in measurements of the line density.

11.5 Total Meteor Influx

11.5.1 *Diurnal and Seasonal Variation of Sporadic Meteors*

Before the advent of the radio echo studies of the meteor influx it was believed that the sporadic meteor distribution was uniform so that for an earth at rest the number of meteors visible at any point would be constant. But the earth's orbital motion leads to an apparent concentration of radiants around the apex of the earth's way, so that the observed meteor rate should show a diurnal variation with a maximum at 06 hours local time and a seasonal variation with a maximum in the autumn months (that is, in the northern hemisphere). The subject has been discussed in detail by Lovell.[1] The radio echo results have given the true 24-hour variation without the gaps in the visual observations occasioned by daylight. These contemporary results show that the old belief in the uniform distribution of sporadic meteors is incorrect, and that during the summer daytime in the northern hemisphere the curve of variation is dominated to a remarkable extent by a concentration of shower and sporadic meteors not previously observable because of daylight. The mean diurnal rate curve, averaged over all days of the year, is shown in Fig. 4. This shows the concentration towards the apex at 06 hours as predicted by the theory of uniform distribution, but in addition there are equal concentrations toward the helion and antihelion points. From these data it is possible to derive the true distribution in longitude of orbital directions of sporadic meteors in space by correcting for the earth's motion.[22] The individual daily hourly rate curves show considerable departures from the maximum at 06 hours local time as demanded by the uniform distribution theory. For example, Fig. 5 shows the variation in time of the daily maximum in hourly rate throughout the year. In this analysis the effect of the major meteor showers has been excluded; the inclusion of the summer daytime showers would increase still further the variation of time of maximum shown in Fig. 5.

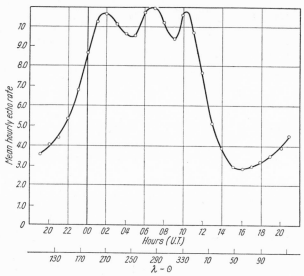

FIG. 4. The mean diurnal variation of the sporadic meteor rates, observed on a radio echo equipment. The abscissae show time in hours (U.T.) and in (longitude λ — sun's longitude $\odot$).

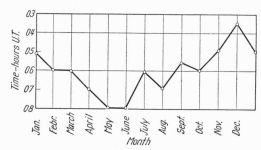

FIG. 5. Variation in time of the daily maximum in the sporadic meteor rate throughout the year as observed on a radio echo apparatus.

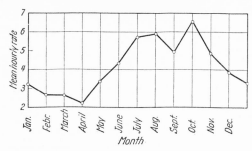

FIG. 6. The seasonal variation of sporadic meteor activity as recorded on a radio echo apparatus.

The seasonal variation, again excluding the major showers, is shown in Fig. 6. This reveals that in the northern hemisphere the seasonal maximum occurs in the summer months and not during the autumn.

11.5.2 *Meteor Showers*

The occurrence of the major meteor showers gives high meteor rates for short periods of time, and although they supply the most prominent visual phenomena their contribution to the total annual meteor influx is small compared with the sporadic contribution. The visual, photographic and radio echo data available at present on the major showers have been described by Lovell[1] together with a discussion of their origin. For the purpose of this chapter the data are summarized in Table I, which gives the date of maximum and duration of each shower together with an indication of the hourly rate at maximum (for convenience this is taken as the rate seen by a single observer under clear sky conditions).

TABLE I

The Major Meteor Showers

Shower	Date of maximum	Approximate hourly rate	Comments
Quadrantids	Jan. 3–4	50–100	
Lyrids	April 21	5–10	
η-Aquarids	May 4–6	15	
o-Cetids	May 14–23	10	Daytime shower
Arietids	May 29–June 18	70	Daytime shower
ζ-Perseids	June 1–16	40	Daytime shower
β-Taurids	June 26–July 5	20	Daytime shower
δ-Aquarids	July 28	30	
Perseids	Aug. 5–14	50	
Giacobinids	Oct. 10	Occasionally very great —see Davies and Lovell[23]	
Orionids	Oct. 20–23	15	
Taurids	Nov. 3–10	10	
Leonids	Nov. 16–17	10	Has produced great displays in the past
Geminids	Dec. 12–13	50–100	
Ursids	Dec. 22	10	

11.5.3 *Mass Distribution*

The mass distribution of the shower and sporadic meteors can be determined by visual and radio echo observations. In the visual observations the basic observational data consist of a count of the number of meteors which appear in different magnitude groups. It was found that the change in number, dN, with magnitude, M, could be expressed in the form

$$dN \propto x^M dM. \tag{11.12}$$

Extensive visual and telescopic counts indicated that for sporadic meteors $x = 2.5$ over a magnitude range of -2 to $+9$. Since the magnitude, M, is proportional to the logarithm of the light intensity which depends directly on the meteor mass, m, (11.12) becomes

$$dN \propto \frac{dm}{m^s} \tag{11.13}$$

for the mass frequency distribution. The relation between x and s is given by (11.12) and (11.13). Thus for $x = 2.5$, $s = 2.0$, that is, the mass distribution follows an inverse square law; and the total mass of meteoric material in each magnitude is roughly constant.

Various methods for the determination of the mass distribution using the radio echo technique have been developed,[24] and these agree with the visual observations in assigning a value of $s = 2.0$ for the sporadic mass distribution in the magnitude range 0 to $+10$. Our knowledge of the mass distribution in the showers depends almost entirely on the radio methods, apart from some visual and photographic work on bright Perseid, Leonid, and Giacobinid meteors.[1] The existing data on these mass distributions are summarized in Table II taken from Browne et al.[24]

TABLE II

The Mass Distribution [Value of Exponent (s) in Equation (11.13)] for Shower Meteors

(Columns 1 to 4 are from the radio echo data. Column 5 is from the visual data)

Shower	Magnitude range, M				
	$+7$	$+7 > M > +5$	$+3$	$+2 > M > 0$	$M < +3$
Quadrantids	—	1.78	—	1.8	2.5
Perseids	1.38	1.59	2.0	2.0	2.1
Arietids	—	2.7	—	1.8	—
ζ-Perseids	—	—	—	2.2	—
Geminids	1.45	1.62	2.24	2.3	2.3

It is apparent that, compared with the sporadic meteors, the value of s varies with magnitude and that with the exception of the daytime Arietids the showers appear to be deficient in faint meteors. Moreover, for the Quadrantids, Perseids, and Geminids the greater part of the meteoric mass appears to be concentrated in the magnitude range $+ 2$ to $+ 5$, whereas in the case of the Arietids (and probably the ζ-Perseids) the main mass is contributed by meteors fainter than magnitude $+ 7$. Cosmologically these variations are probably connected with the age of the showers. From the geophysical aspect it is important to note that the estimates of the mass of meteors entering the atmosphere depend critically on the values of s, especially with regard to the relative influence of the shower meteors and sporadic background on the upper atmospheric and ionospheric phenomena.

11.5.4 The Over-all Meteor Influx

A full discussion of the total meteor influx into the atmosphere has been given by Lovell.[1] In the case of sporadic meteors in the magnitude range from about 0 to $+ 9$ there are fairly good visual and radio echo data on the frequency and mass distributions. The conclusion is that down to this magnitude limit there are approximately 10^9 meteors incident on the whole earth's atmosphere per day. The distribution is such that each magnitude contains about the same mass of approximately 20 kg per day over the whole earth's surface. Hence in this range of ten magnitudes there are believed to be about 200 kg of meteors entering the entire atmosphere per day. Beyond these limits there is less certainty. For meteors brighter than magnitude 0, there is reasonable visual and photographic evidence that the same mass distribution applies to magnitude $- 3$. There is very little evidence of the distribution between $- 3$ and $- 10$, after which the meteors probably fall as meteorites. About 550 kg is believed to reach the earth in this way per day.

At the other extreme the experimental evidence is incomplete for meteors fainter than $+ 10$ or $+ 11$, and at present one can only assume that the same distribution continues until magnitudes between $+ 20$ or $+ 30$, at which limit the particles will be dispersed by radiation pressure from the sun before entering the atmosphere. At particle masses of 10^{-9} to 10^{-10} gm (corresponding to magnitudes of $+ 19$ or $+ 20$) it seems likely that new processes occur and that the ratio of surface area to mass is such that the particle is stopped by the atmosphere before complete evaporation occurs. These are the micrometeorites which form an important part of contemporary studies with earth satellites. At present the rates of influx of these particles as determined by the Sputniks and Explorer satellites differ by many orders of magnitudes, and until these discrepancies are clarified it is only possible to estimate the influx by extrapolating the number distribution which is found for larger meteors.

On this basis the evidence on the mass and space distribution of the sporadic meteors assembled by Lovell is summarized in Table III. In calculating the space distribution it has been assumed as an approximation that the meteors are moving at the parabolic velocity limit. Excluding meteorites, these figures indicate that there is probably between 700 and 800 kg of sporadic meteors entering the whole earth's atmosphere per day. The total energy brought into the atmosphere is approximately 10^{19} ergs per day, and the space density is in the region of 10^{-24} to 10^{-25} gm cm^{-3}.

TABLE III

The Daily Influx of Sporadic Meteors over the Entire Earth's Surface

Meteor magnitudes		Mass range of individual particles	Number per day	Mass per day (kg)	Number per cubic centimeter	Density (gm/cc)
Extra-polation	-10 to -8	500 to 100 gm	~ 300	~ 60	4×10^{-28}	7.5×10^{-26}
	-7 to -6	100 to 10 gm	~ 2500	~ 40	3×10^{-27}	5.0
	-5 to -4	10 to 1 gm	$\sim 1.8 \times 10^4$	~ 40	2×10^{-26}	5.0
	-3 to -1	1 gm to 100 mg	$\sim 4 \times 10^5$	~ 60	5×10^{-25}	7.5
Obser-vational data	0 to $+1$	100 to 10 mg	10^6	40	1.5×10^{-24}	5.0
	2 to 4	10 to 1 mg	3.6×10^7	60	4.5×10^{-23}	7.5
	5 to 6	1 to 0.1 mg	1.9×10^8	40	2.4×10^{-22}	5.0
	7 to 9	0.1 to 0.10 mg	3.3×10^9	60	4.1×10^{-21}	7.5
	10 to 12	0.01 to 0.001 mg	6.5×10^{10}	60	8.1×10^{-20}	7.5
Extra-polation	13 to 20	10^{-3} to 10^{-7} mg	$\sim 10^{14}$	160	$\sim 10^{-16}$	~ 20
	21 to 30	10^{-7} to 10^{-11} mg	$\sim 10^{18}$	160	$\sim 10^{-12}$	~ 20

In the case of the major showers the calculations are rather less certain, even in the 0 to $+10$ magnitude range, since many uncertainties remain in the mass distribution. Even so, useful data can be obtained by assuming as an approximation, that the mass distributions are the same as for the sporadics. The data in Table IV are summarized from the information given by Lovell,[1] for the magnitude range of Table III, and taking into account the number of days for which the showers are active.

TABLE IV

Meteoric Mass per Year Entering the Entire Atmosphere from the Major Meteor Showers

	Sporadic meteors (as in Table III)	Daytime Arietids and ζ-perseids	Daytime β-taurids	Quad-rantids	Perseids	Geminids	Other showers
Number of days of activity	365	16	11	2	9	6	23
Total mass per year (kg)	485×10^3	41.5×10^3	5.1×10^3	13.3×10^3	11.9×10^3	28.7×10^3	29.9×10^3

Although the major showers are the spectacular occurrences in meteor phenomena, they bring a total mass into the atmosphere per annum which is only about one-third or one-quarter of that brought in by the sporadic meteors. In addition to the showers of regular occurrence listed in Table IV, the occasional great meteoric storms such as those of the Giacobinids of October, 1946, or of the Leonids in 1799, 1833, and 1866, bring very great additional meteoric material into the atmosphere. For example, although the Giacobinid shower of October 10, 1946, lasted only a few hours, Lovell[1] has estimated that the meteor influx amounted to about 70,000 kg, a figure comparable with the total mass of all recurrent showers for a whole year. The total mass and densities in the orbits of these shower meteors have also been estimated.[1] Although not of immediate concern to this geophysical discussion, it is interesting to mention that the calculated total mass of meteoric material in the orbits of the major showers is about 10^{12} kg and the density is in the region of 10^{-23} to 10^{-24} gm cm^{-3}.

11.5.5 *The Total Meteor Contribution to the Ionization in the E Region*

From time to time there has been considerable dicussion about the contribution of meteors to the ionization in the E region. Some of the earlier workers, notably Skellett[25] and Pierce,[26] assumed that the major part of the energy of the meteor was spent in ionization, and they concluded that ionization due to meteors made a prominent contribution to the normal level of ionization in the E region. In a brief review of the subject in 1950, Lovell[27] assumed values of 0.01 for the ionization probability and estimated the rate of ion production to be about $q = 3 \times 10^{-5}$ electron cm^{-3} sec^{-1} for sporadic meteors, rising to 10^{-3} electrons cm^{-3} sec^{-1} during major showers and to 10^{-1} cm^{-3} sec^{-1} during meteoric storms like the 1946 Giacobinid shower. If the recombination coefficient is that appropriate to the E region ($\bar{\alpha} = 10^{-8}$ cm^3 sec^{-1}), these would give equilibrium electron concentrations [$N = (q/\bar{\alpha})^{\frac{1}{2}}$] of about 17 electrons cm^{-3} for sporadics, rising to 300 electrons cm^{-3} during major showers and to about 3×10^3 electrons cm^{-3} during the 1946 Giacobinid shower. These figures have to be compared with the average values of E-region ionization, amounting to the order of 10^5 electrons cm^{-3} during a midsummer day to 10^4 electrons cm^{-3} at night. Thus the contribution of meteors to E-region ionization is small, although at night intense showers might have an appreciable influence. In this connection it is of interest that Pierce[26] observed a reflection layer which persisted for several hours on a frequency of 3.5 Mc sec^{-1} during the 1946 Giacobinid shower.

The question has also been investigated by Kaiser,[28] who has deduced the ionization contribution from the radio echo measurements of the electron line densities without introducing the rather uncertain factor of the ionizing efficiency, β. He finds that sporadic meteors should produce 2.3×10^{-4} electrons cm^{-3} sec^{-1} independent of height (at least over the range of heights for which the sporadic meteors obey the mass law with $s = 2$). This is ten times as great as the rate deduced in the earlier calculations by Lovell but is compatible with the revised value for the ionization efficiency of ~ 0.1 compared with the value of 0.01 assumed in his calculations. The question of the significance of this in the E-region ionization depends on the value to be assumed for the recombination coefficient, $\bar{\alpha}$. If the normal E-region value of 10^{-8} applies, then the equilibrium electron density is about 150 electrons cm^{-3}. On the other hand, the recombination rate in the meteor trails is not greater than about 10^{-11} or 10^{-12} cm^3 sec^{-1} (see § 11.8.2.), and if this value applies then the equilibrium electron density would be about 10^4 electrons cm^{-3}.

Kaiser speculates on the nature of the ionospheric layer set up by this sporadic meteor influx. The condition that the production of electrons is continuous over a large volume is that a meteor must pass through the distribution of ionization from a previous meteor before it is significantly reduced below its initial value. Kaiser shows that on this basis the ionization should be continuous from about 130 km to 115 km, but below this height the individual trails will not join up to form a continuum and the ionization will be patchy. The normal value of the nighttime E-region electron density is 10^4 electrons cm^{-3}. The density of the continuum produced by the sporadic meteors is greater than 10^2 electrons cm^{-3}. If the recombination coefficient is much less than the E-region value of 10^{-8} cm^3 sec^{-1}, then it is possible that sporadic meteors could be a significant factor in the maintenance of the nocturnal E region.

Kaiser also studied the effects of the shower meteors, taking into account the recent evidence about the mass distribution. In the case of the intense daytime streams, the equilibrium electron density is unlikely to exceed 10^4 electrons cm^{-3}, even if the most favorable values of $\bar{\alpha}$ are assumed. This is not significant compared with the normal summer daytime E-region ionization. For the major nighttime showers such as the Perseids and Geminids, the conclusion is that the equilibrium electron density is comparable to that produced by the sporadic meteor ionization at 100 km for the Perseids and at 93 km for the Geminids. The probability that meteoric storms produce a temporary reflecting layer has already been mentioned.

The above discussion refers to the contributions which meteor ionization might make to the normal E-region ionization. With regard to the abnormalities in the E-region, there is little doubt that at least some forms of sporadic E are associated with meteor activity. The existing evidence about this was assembled by Lovell[29] in 1948; and since that time there has been no significant clarification of a very complex problem.

11.6 Determination of Scale Heights and Densities

11.6.1 *Meteor Heights*

Equation (11.3) predicts that the height at which a meteor produces its maximum light and ionization should depend on the atmospheric pressure and meteor velocity. As the velocity increases, more energy is supplied in

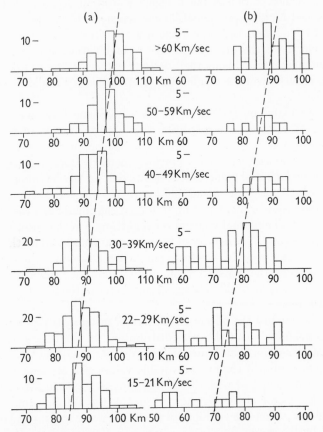

Fig. 7. Height distributions for different meteor velocity groups as determined (a) by the radio echo technique and (b) photographically. Ordinates are relative numbers; abscissae are the heights in kilometers.

collisions with individual air molecules which strike the surface of the meteor. This results in a greater rate of evaporation, causing a fast meteor to burn away after intercepting a smaller air mass than a low-velocity one. Initial mass and zenith angle also influence the height at which the ionized and luminous trails are formed. More massive meteors penetrate to lower heights, whereas those travelling almost horizontally will intercept a given air mass at a greater height than meteors entering the atmosphere vertically.

The difficulties in the visual measurements of heights and velocities have resulted in a widely different interpretation of the observations. From an analysis of the British meteor data Porter[30] concludes that the heights of appearance and disappearance are determined mostly by the elongation from the apex and magnitude, quantities directly related to velocity and mass. Measurements can now be made by photographic and radar techniques, enabling the form of the evaporation equations to be tested. The photographic observations refer to visual meteors brighter than absolute magnitude $+3$, and radio methods extend the measurements down to about $+10M$. Some results of the radio echo height-velocity determinations, carried out at Jodrell Bank,[31] are shown in Fig. 7. The highest velocity sporadic meteors moving at 60 to 70 km sec^{-1} ionize at a mean height of 100 km, whereas those with the minimum possible velocity of 11 km sec^{-1} ionize at only 85 km. Shower meteors behave in a similar way to sporadics, and the mean height of Perseids of $6M$ to $8M$ is 100 km ($V = 60$ km sec^{-1}), whereas the Geminid mean height ($V = 36$ km sec^{-1}) is only 92 km.

The effect of meteor mass can be seen by comparing the radio echo height-velocity distributions with those of bright photographic meteors recorded by Whipple and Jacchia[32] (Fig. 7b). The photographic results all refer to meteors brighter than zero magnitude, and the radar measurements to meteors fainter than $+6M$. The heights of the bright meteors are systematically 10 km below the heights of faint meteors with the same velocity.

Most of the observed heights lie between 60 and 110 km. Below 60 km all but the largest, slowest moving fireballs have burned away. Above 110 km the density of air molecules is insufficient to cause appreciable evaporation. Over this range of heights radio echo and photographic observations of meteors enable upper atmospheric densities and temperatures to be determined.

11.6.2 *Radio Echo Methods*

The radio echo technique first used at Jodrell Bank for the measurement of meteor heights has been described by Clegg and Davidson.[33] In this method the elevation of the reflecting region is given from the ratio in signal amplitudes received by two aerials with different vertical polar diagrams. A measurement of range with a pulsed transmitter then determines the height. This technique has been developed by Greenhow and Hall[31] and enables the heights and velocities of approximately 500 meteors to be determined each day. An example of the records obtained is shown in Fig. 8. Echo characteristics are displayed on four cathode-ray tubes. Range is given

34

by the range-amplitude display on tube A, where 10-km and 50-km markers enable an accuracy of 1 km to be achieved. Slow time bases of 0.5-second and 0.1-second duration are displayed on tubes B and C. These time bases are triggered by a meteor echo when its amplitude rises above a predetermined level. On C individual echo pulses separated by 1.6 msec are resolved, and the diffraction fluctuations described in § 11.4 can be seen. Together with the range, these fluctuations enable the meteor velocity to be determined. The majority of meteor echoes at a wavelength of 8.2 m have durations between 0.1 and 0.5 second. The very slow time base on tube B enables the amplitude variations throughout the lifetimes of these echoes to be investigated. The outputs of receivers connected to the two aerials used for elevation measurements are applied to the vertical and horizontal deflection plates of tube D. When a meteor echo of variable amplitude appears, a line of pulses is displayed on D. The slope of this line is equal to the ratio in echo amplitudes and determines the elevation of the reflecting point on the trail.

The theory of the distribution of meteor heights observed on a radio echo equipment has been given by Kaiser.[34] This theory relates velocity, v, and the maximum linear electron density, α_{max}, along a meteor trail, to the atmospheric pressure, p_{max}, at the point of maximum rate of evaporation, where

$$p_{max} = \text{const.} \frac{\cos^{2/3}\chi}{v^2} (\alpha_{max}H)^{1/3}. \tag{11.14}$$

The constant in this equation includes quantities depending on the constitution and shape of the meteor (§ 11.3) and on the probability of ionization.

In the experimental measurement of height the radar reflecting point does not necessarily lie at the point of maximum ionization, α_{max}. If meteors of a given mass distribution and velocity are observed, a distribution of heights is obtained the width of which is closely related to the length of the ionization curve shown in Fig 3. The most probable height, $\bar{h}$, corresponds to the point of maximum ionization. Equation (11.2) and Fig. 3 show that the vertical scale of the ionization curve depends on the scale height, H. If H is small, the ionization curve will contract to give a narrow height distribution. An increase in scale height will result in a lengthening of the ionization curve, giving a broader height distribution. Thus if the distribution of meteor masses is known, H can be determined from the widths of height distributions for homogeneous velocity groups. An experimental investigation has been made by Evans,[35] and the results for the variation of H with altitude are given in Fig. 9. The full line in this diagram is the profile adopted by the Rocket Panel,[36] and it is seen that the two sets of results are in good agreement.

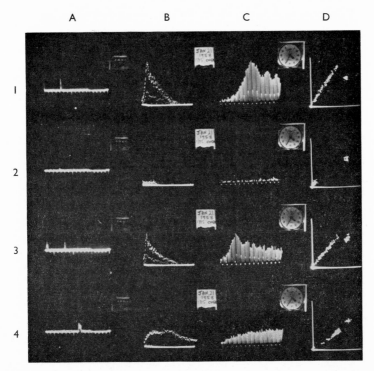

FIG. 8. Four successive records of radio echoes from meteor trails obtained in the radio echo technique for upper atmosphere density measurements. In *A* the meteor echo is shown on a range amplitude display, *B* and *C* show the echo decay time and Fresnel diffraction pattern, and *D* determines the elevation of the reflecting point.

[*To face page* 530

The scale height having been determined, equation (11.14) can be used to give a series of values of p at different heights, by observing meteors of different velocity groups. The relationship between v and $\bar{h}$ for sporadic meteors is shown in Fig. 10. For an isothermal atmosphere, log pressure is proportional to height, and equation (11.14) predicts that the slope of the height-log v curve should be 2 (when height is measured in units of H). As H varies very little between heights of 85 and 100 km, the individual points in Fig. 10 should lie on a line of this slope. This is approximately true for meteors with velocities greater than 30 km sec^{-1}, but at lower velocities

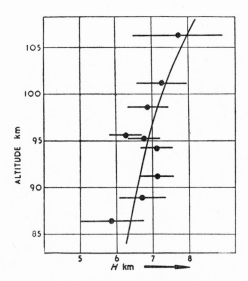

FIG. 9. The variation of scale height, H, with altitude as determined by the radio echo measurements on sporadic meteors. The full line is the variation determined by the rocket experiments.

there are serious departures from theory, and the slope of the line leads to an expression of the form $p \propto v^{-0.7}$ for equation (11.3). This indicates that slow meteors of about $+ 6M$ to $+ 8M$ do not ionize in the manner predicted by simple theory. Evidence that the ionization curves of such meteors are much shorter than expected is given by the measurements of Greenhow and Neufeld,[37] in which echoes are obtained from two points along a meteor trail by using spaced receiving stations. This behavior has been explained by a process of fragmentation, observed photographically in faint visual trails by Jacchia.[38] Instead of behaving as a single body, faint meteors appear to break up into a number of smaller particles, causing the meteoric material to vaporize over a shorter path length at a greater height. For this reason only meteors with velocities greater than 30 km sec^{-1} can be used in pressure and density determinations. These results are given in Fig. 12, p. 535, where they are compared with other measurements.

A second and more direct method of measuring atmospheric densities and temperatures, using radio echoes from meteor trails, is to observe the variation of echo duration with height. The rate of decay of echo amplitude at a given wavelength depends only on the molecular diffusion coefficient, D (§ 11.8.1), and D is simply related to atmospheric particle density and

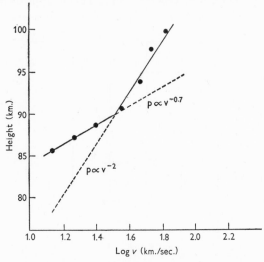

FIG. 10. The relation between the heights of occurrence of sporadic meteors, and meteor velocity, V, for the radio echo apparatus used in atmospheric density measurements.

temperature by kinetic theory. Kaiser[28] has considered the effect of electrostatic forces between the positive ions and electrons in a meteor trail, and derives the following expression for D:

$$D = \frac{8}{3}\lambda_i \left(\frac{2\,k\theta}{\pi\mu}\right)^{1/2} \tag{11.15}$$

where θ is the absolute temperature, k is Boltzmann's constant, and μ is the average mass of a meteor atom; λ_i, the mean free path of a positive ion, is given by

$$\lambda_i = \frac{0.9}{\pi n_a \sigma_i^2} \tag{11.16}$$

where σ_i is the collision diameter for a meteor ion and air molecule. If m is the mass of an air molecule, then the atmospheric density, ρ, is given by

$$\rho = \frac{3.5m}{\pi D \sigma_i^2}\left(\frac{k\theta}{\pi\mu}\right)^{1/2}. \tag{11.17}$$

This expression does not depend on meteor velocity, mass, luminous and ionizing efficiencies, or any of the constants introduced into the evaporation theory. The chief uncertainty in equation (11.17) is σ_i. This is accurately known for molecules of a neutral gas but is likely to be different for positive ions colliding with neutral molecules. Measurements of the collision cross sections for some metallic ions and air molecules have been made by Ramsauer and Beeck,[39] and these show that σ_i is approximately 9×10^{-8} cm. The variation of diffusion coefficient with height for a 7-day period in January, 1958, is shown in Fig. 11. The gradient of this curve at any point leads to a determination of the scale height, giving the temperature from $H = k\theta/mg$. Substitution for θ in equation (11.17) then determines the density. Measurements of diffusion coefficient versus height thus enable

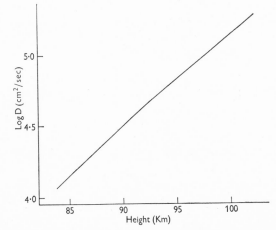

Fig. 11. The diffusion coefficient, D, measured from 85 to 100 km height in the radio echo meteor investigation.

density and temperature profiles to be derived between heights of 85 and 100 km. The density profile corresponding to these measurements of D is given in Fig. 12 and compared with other results in § 11.6.4.

11.6.3 Photographic Methods

The use of spaced cameras permits the trajectory of a meteor to be determined with considerable accuracy. The variation of light intensity along the trail can be obtained by photometric comparison with trailed star images, and the velocity is given by chopping the photographic trail with a rotating shutter. These photographic techniques have been developed at Harvard and used extensively by Whipple and Jacchia[32] for the measurements of upper atmospheric densities. Similar observations have also been carried out by workers in Czechoslovakia.[40]

The basic equation used in the determination of air density by this method is the drag equation

$$\rho = K m^{1/3} v^{-2} (dv/dt). \qquad (11.18)$$

This equation is derived from the theory of meteor evaporation (§ 11.3). Here K is a constant depending on the shape of the meteor, including a dimensionless drag coefficient, γ, which measures the efficiency of the momentum transfer. If the air molecules trapped in the surface of a meteor escape with zero relative velocity, then $\gamma = 1$.

The velocity, v, and acceleration, dv/dt, are determined from the breaks in the trail produced by the rotating shutter, and an expression for m at any instant is obtained from equation (11.7). It is assumed that the luminous efficiency, τ, is proportional to v, so that $\tau = \tau_0 v$. Integration of (11.7) gives

$$m = \frac{2}{\tau_0} \int_0^\infty \frac{I}{v^2} \cdot dt. \qquad (11.19)$$

Here I is the visual intensity of the meteor at any point, obtained by applying a color correction of $+ 1.8$ to the photographic magnitude determined photometrically. A large color correction arises because most of the meteor light is in the ultraviolet at wavelengths below 4000 A. This light is not seen by a visual observer but is recorded with the blue-sensitive emulsions used in meteor photography. Uncertainties arise in the photographic determination of ρ, largely from errors in the measured retardation, which range from 0.01 to 10 times its actual value, and in the determination of m. The constant, K, may be evaluated theoretically, or by comparison with atmospheric densities measured by other methods.

11.6.4 *Results*

The radar measurements of meteor heights and velocities lead to a determination of atmospheric pressure. For comparison the pressures have been converted to densities, with $p = \rho H g$. The resulting density profile is shown by the curve J_1 in Fig. 12. Similarly the mean curve of diffusion coefficient versus height has been converted to one of density by using equation (11.17) and the measured temperatures (curve J_2). The curves J_1 and J_2 refer to a latitude of 53° N; R is the density profile determined from high-altitude rocket flights at New Mexico (latitude 32° N).

Photographic observations have been carried out at New Mexico and Massachusetts (latitude 42° N). Differences were found between the two sets of observations, and these were first attributed to a large latitude variation.

In order to investigate this effect the New Mexico data were compared with the rocket profile by Jacchia,[32] in order to determine an empirical function which would reduce the computed meteor densities as closely as possible to the rocket measurements. The New Mexico meteor measurements therefore coincide with the curve R. When Massachusetts observations are reduced by using the same constants as for the New Mexico data, they are in good agreement up to 75 km. Above this height the Massachusetts densities are systematically greater (curve M, Fig. 12). The original Massachusetts meteor

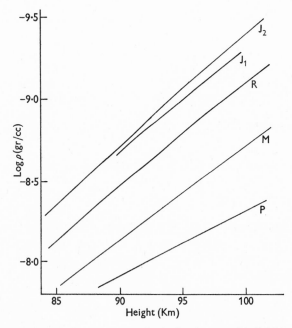

FIG. 12. The variation of upper atmospheric density, ρ, with height as determined by various techniques: R, rocket and photographic meteor data latitude $32°$ N; J_1 and J_2, Jodrell Bank radio echo results latitude $53°$ N; M, photographic meteor data latitude $42°$ N; P, photographic meteor data from Czechoslovakia latitude $50°$ N.

data showed an appreciable seasonal effect, but the Harvard workers interpret this result with some caution, since these meteors have a bad distribution with respect to season, velocity, and height. Curve P is given by Link[40] from photographic work near Prague at latitude $50°$. It can be seen that there is a considerable deviation between the measurements by different methods at different places. Part of this difference may be due to latitude, seasonal, or diurnal effects (since photographic observations refer to nighttime only). Because of the high rate of data available by the radio echo technique, which can be used at all times of day, this method is particularly suitable for the study of diurnal and seasonal variations. The observations for January, 1958, which include more than three thousand meteors, have been divided into a number of intervals to show any diurnal effects. Some profiles for different times of day are given in Fig. 13a, and these show large variations in density at a given height. In Fig. 13b the diurnal variation of atmospheric density at a height of 95 km, expressed as a percentage change of the mean density is given. These measurements, which are the means of 7 days' observations, show that the density undergoes a peak-to-peak diurnal

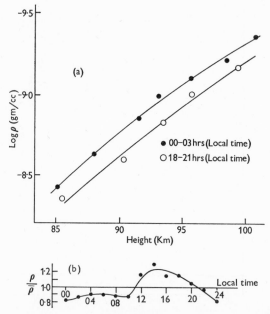

Fig. 13. (a) Examples of the atmospheric density profiles obtained with the radio echo technique, showing the diurnal variation. (b) The diurnal variation in atmospheric density at a height of 95 km, expressed as a fraction of the mean density $\bar{\rho}$.

variation of 1.5 to 1 at this height. Irregular day-to-day variations of the same order are also present, and on individual days the density can vary by as much as 2 to 1 at a fixed level.

11.7 Winds in the Upper Atmosphere: Determination by Meteor Techniques

11.7.1 Visual and Photographic Observations

Some of the first measurements of upper atmospheric winds were made by visual observations of the movements of the trails left by very bright meteors. These trails may persist for half an hour or more, and in this time they can drift many kilometers. In addition they frequently undergo large-scale distortion, showing the presence of a high degree of turbulence.

Olivier[41] has made an extensive study of such trails which lasted for more than one minute. He divided the observations into three groups—nighttime, twilight, and daytime—with corresponding mean heights of 92, 61, and 36 km. The mean wind velocities of the three groups increased from 48 m sec^{-1} by day to 56 m sec^{-1} at night. The frequency of the night wind vectors over America, determined by Olivier, are shown in Fig. 14. Similar measurements have been presented by Fedynsky[42] in the U.S.S.R., although these results include some very high velocities of up to 3000 m sec^{-1}, and the average velocity of 110 m sec^{-1} is also higher.

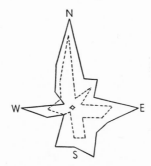

Fig. 14. The frequency of night wind vectors over America, as determined by Olivier from the movements of visual meteor trails. ——— before midnight ; — — — — after midnight.

Much more precise measurements have been made photographically by Liller and Whipple,[43] using the Super Schmidt meteor cameras in New Mexico. In these experiments the camera is moved through successive small angles at intervals of about one second after the appearance of a very bright meteor. In this way images of the trail are displaced on the photographic plate, and accurate measurements of its movements can be made. Liller and Whipple describe the results for five trails photographed between August, 1950, and May, 1952. One good example of their results, which shows the variation of wind velocity with height between 82 and 113 km, is shown in Fig. 15. The effect of turbulent winds on the meteor trail is very pronounced, and wind gradients of up to 50 m sec^{-1} km^{-1} are found with an eddy size of about 7 km. The mean wind speed for the five trails was 38 m sec^{-1}, although the irregular winds were as high as 100 m sec^{-1}.

11.7.2 Radio Echo Results

The chief disadvantage of visual and photographic observations is that persistent meteor trails occur infrequently, and systematic measurements of the wind cannot be made. With radio echo techniques a large number of meteors can be detected each hour, and diurnal and seasonal variations of the wind can be investigated in considerable detail.

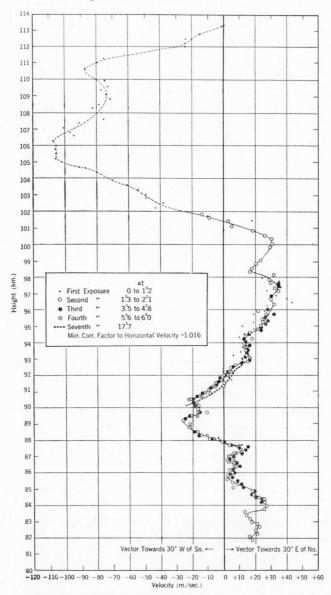

FIG 15. The variation of wind velocity with height as determined by Liller and Whipple from a meteor trail photographed over New Mexico on March 20, 1953.

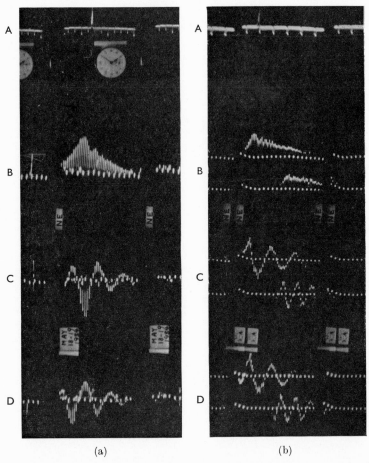

Fig. 16. (a) Record of a radio echo from a meteor trail obtained in upper atmospheric wind measurements: A is a range-amplitude display, B shows the Fresnel diffraction pattern and echo duration, C and D the phase changes caused by drift of the ionized trail. (b) Record of meteor radio echoes obtained from two points along the same trail, used in measurements of upper atmospheric turbulence: C and D enable the wind velocity to be measured simultaneously at two positions separated by a few kilometers.

[*To face page* 539

As soon as radio echo techniques began to be used extensively for the study of meteors, it was observed that in the case of echoes lasting more than a second or so deep fluctuations in the amplitude were nearly always present. It was found that many of these long-duration echoes showed a change of range with time. Many of the workers in this field suggested that winds at heights of 80 to 100 km might be an important factor in explaining these phenomena. At Jodrell Bank in 1949–1950 Greenhow[44] studied the fluctuations at two wavelengths and concluded that they were due to irregular winds in the upper atmosphere, which caused the initially linear trail to break up into a number of reflecting centers. Relative movements of the centers produce variations in phase of the scattered signals, giving rise to amplitude fluctuations at the ground. Ellyett[45] also explained the various types of range drift in terms of movement of the ionized columns under the influence of these high-altitude winds.

The development of a radio echo technique designed to measure upper atmospheric winds using C.W. methods was first made at Stanford by Manning et al.[46] During the period 3 to 6 A.M. (local time) on a number of occasions during the summer months, they found that the predominant wind direction was towards azimuths between northeast and north with speeds of approximately 30 m sec^{-1}. In Australia Elford and Robertson[47] developed a similar technique and obtained about fifty usable echoes daily. From the integration of about a month's continuous observations, these workers were able to determine periodic and prevailing wind components.

A technique for increasing the data rate to a level suitable for the measurement of hour-by-hour wind variations has been developed by Greenhow.[48] In this method a coherent pulse system is used, enabling changes in phase of the radio echo, as the meteor trails drift in range, to be measured. Over three thousand usable echoes are recorded daily, and it is possible to determine the mean wind vector at a height of 90 to 95 km in about 20 minutes of observation. A sample of the film record obtained is shown in Fig. 16a. Four cathode-ray tubes are photographed simultaneously for each meteor echo which triggers the recording mechanism; A gives the range of the echo on a conventional range-amplitude display, and B shows the variation in amplitude during the first 0.3 second of its lifetime (successive pulses separated by 6.6 msec can be resolved). From the rate of decay of amplitude the height of the reflecting region can be determined (§ 11.8.1). C measures the variation in phase of the echo. One fluctuation cycle corresponds to a change in phase of 2π, caused by a drift of the trail by $\lambda/2$, in this case approximately 4 m. D is similar to C, but the phase of the oscillation leads or lags C by $\pi/2$, so defining the sense of the drift (toward or away from the observer). Radial wind components are measured in this way, and in

order to determine the complete wind vector a beamed aerial is pointed
alternately in two directions at right angles.

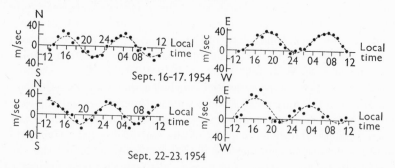

FIG. 17. The diurnal variation of the north-south and east-west wind components as
determined by the radio echo technique. These results refer to a mean height of approximately 92 km.

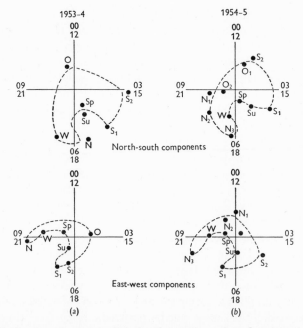

FIG. 18. Twelve-hour harmonic dials for the north-south and east-west components
of the semidiurnal periodic wind at a height of 92 km, as determined by the radio echo
technique: W—winter; Sp—spring; Su—summer; S—September; O—October;
N—November.

An example of the results obtained is given in Fig. 17 for two days in
September, 1954. North-south and east-west components of the wind are

plotted at hourly intervals. The most noticeable feature of the results is a regular semidiurnal variation in the wind. On any day this periodic component can be represented by a vector of amplitude 10 to 40 m sec^{-1} which rotates in a clockwise direction. At a height of 92 km the phase of this semidiurnal wind component is such that the wind vector is directed toward north at about 0600 and 1800 hours local time throughout most of the year. Between September and November, however, the phase changes progressively through about 360°, and comparison of the results shown in Fig. 17 shows that much of this change can take place in a few days. The seasonal variations in amplitude and phase are shown by the harmonic dials in Fig. 18. Each

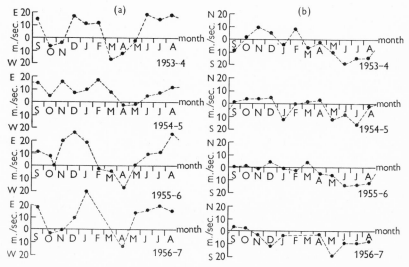

FIG. 19. The variation of the prevailing component of the wind throughout the year as deduced from the radio echo meteor observations. (a) The east-west component; (b) The north-south component. The results refer to a mean height of 92 km.

point in this diagram gives the amplitude of the wind vector, and the times at which its direction is toward north and east.

In addition to the periodic component Fig. 17 shows a steady wind of about 20 m sec^{-1} toward east. This prevailing wind appears as a displacement of the mean wind throughout the 24 hours above the line of zero velocity; it also shows large seasonal variations. The measurements for four successive years are compared in Fig. 19. Winds of approximately 15 m sec^{-1} toward east are found in summer and winter, and toward west in spring and autumn. There is also a large component toward south in the summer months.

These results refer to a mean height between 90 and 94 km. In later work Greenhow and Neufeld[49] have investigated how the wind velocity varies with height over the range 85 to 100 km. Marked changes in phase and amplitude of the semidiurnal component are found in this region. In winter the amplitude increases with height from 10 m sec^{-1} at 85 km to 40 m sec^{-1} at 100 km; the summer gradient is very much smaller. The phase of the wind vector shows a similar variation. In winter the time at which the vector is directed toward north becomes earlier at increasing heights by about one

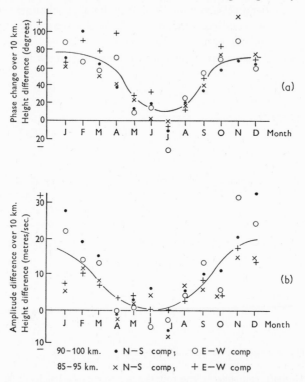

Fig. 20. (a) The difference in phase of the semidiurnal wind component as measured by the radio echo meteor technique at two heights separated by 10 km. A phase lead at greater heights is plotted as a positive number. (b) the difference in amplitude of the semidiurnal wind component as measured at two heights differing by 10 km.

hour every 6 km, whereas during summer the variation is quite small. These height variations of amplitude and phase are illustrated in Fig. 20.

The prevailing wind also varies with height, positive and negative wind gradients of about 0.5 m sec^{-1} km^{-1} occurring at different times of the year. The variations in the north-south and east-west components for 1954 are shown in Fig. 21. It is interesting to note that in this year the east-west component at 100 km blows toward west during both spring and autumn, but at 85 km it remains toward east during the autumn.

The cause of the large semidiurnal component is believed to be the result of thermal and tidal effects of the sun, increased by resonance in the high atmosphere. The observed variations in amplitude and phase of this periodic component are compatible with the predictions of this theory.

In the above experiments the wind has been determined at hourly intervals by averaging together more than one hundred drift velocities from individual meteor trails. If hourly histograms of these drifts are examined, a very large spread in the velocity is found. Even at times when the mean wind speed is zero, the individual trails show drift speeds as high as 40 m sec^{-1}, giving root-mean-square velocities of this order. This spread is due to intense turbulence, and by an extension of the coherent pulse technique Greenhow and Neufeld[50] have made a detailed study of the turbulent wind shears and

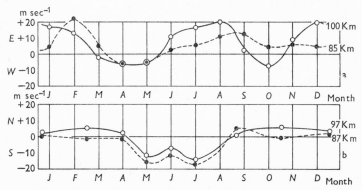

FIG. 21. The change in the prevailing wind with height throughout the year as determined by the radio echo meteor technique. (a) The east-west component at 85 and 100 km. (b) The north-south component at 87 and 97 km.

eddy sizes. Because of the specular reflecting properties of a meteor trail, the radio echoes at two spaced receiving stations are obtained from different parts of the trail. The distance apart of the reflecting regions can be varied, enabling the wind velocity to be measured at the same time at two points of variable separation in space. A section of the two-receiver film record is illustrated in Fig. 16b, p. 539. A radio link is used to bring the signal from a remote station to the home station for recording purposes, and the two signals are displayed together on split-beam oscilloscopes. The traces serve the same purposes as in Fig. 16a, the upper and lower traces giving the wind speed at two points along the meteor trail. The difference in time for a phase change of 2π in this echo pair is quite marked, showing the existence of a large change in wind velocity over a difference of a few kilometers. The difference in height between the reflecting points can be varied, and turbulent wind shears determined for various height separations. The distribution of wind shears measured between two points spaced by only 0.4 km are shown in Fig. 22. The median value is approximately 10 m sec^{-1} km^{-1}, although values as high as 140 m sec^{-1} km^{-1} are occasionally observed. These figures are an order of magnitude greater than the uniform wind gradients, and the intensity of the turbulence appears to be independent of both the gradient and velocity of the mean wind.

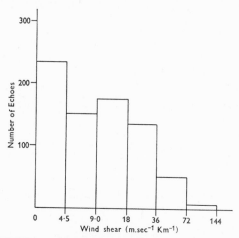

Fig. 22. The distribution of turbulent wind shears at heights of 90 to 100 km, as determined by the radio echo meteor technique.

By determining the falloff in correlation between the turbulent wind velocity at two points in space, as their separation is increased, the size of the large eddies can be deduced. The large-scale turbulence is found to be distinctly anisotropic with a vertical depth of approximately 7 km and a horizontal scale of over 100 km. The lifetimes of these large eddies are between 1 and 2 hours. In the region 80 to 100 km the atmospheric temperature increases with height. This is an inherently stable condition, and considerations of Richardson's criterion show that turbulence should be highly damped. The existence of such intense irregular winds is therefore contrary to present theories of turbulence, although from the anisotropy which exists it appears that the turbulent velocities are largely restricted to the horizontal plane, the vertical movements being largely damped.

11.8 Recombination and Diffusion of Ionization in Meteor Trails

Immediately a meteor trail is formed, the ionization begins to diffuse radially at a rate determined by the diffusion coefficient, D. Electrons are also lost by recombination and attachment processes. Which of these processes is the primary factor in determining the duration of an echo depends on the initial linear electron density in the trail and on its height of formation.

11.8.1 *Diffusion*

In the case of subvisual meteors with $\alpha < 10^{12}$ electrons cm^{-1}, Herlofson[4] has shown that the effect of diffusion alone is to give an exponential decay of echo amplitude of the form

$$A = A_0 \exp\left(- 16\pi^2 Dt/\lambda^2\right) \tag{11.20}$$

where A_0 is the initial amplitude, and A is the amplitude after a time t. The decay time, T_S, to $1/e$ of A_0 is

$$T_S = \lambda^2/16\pi^2 D. \tag{11.21}$$

The wavelength dependence of T_S has been investigated by Greenhow[20] by making observations simultaneously at wavelengths of 4 m and 8 m. A λ^2 variation was found showing that diffusion is the predominant factor in determining echo duration for these low-electron-density trails. Measurements of the variation of diffusion coefficient with height by Greenhow and Neufeld[51] and by Weiss[52] show that in the meteor region D increases from approximately 10^4 cm^2 sec^{-1} at 80 km to 10^5 cm^2 sec^{-1} at 100 km. A simple ambipolar theory of the diffusion of meteor ions has been given by Kaiser.[28] This relates the diffusion coefficient to the ionic mean free path and upper atmospheric density and temperature. The theoretical values of D are in good agreement with those observed experimentally.

When $\alpha > 10^{12}$ electrons cm^{-1}, the echo amplitude is no longer expected to decay exponentially. Instead the echo duration, T_L, is given by the time taken for the axial electron density to fall below the critical electron density at the wavelength employed. In this case, as α increases, T_L should also increase, where T_L is given by

$$T_L = \frac{\alpha\lambda^2}{4\pi^2 D}\left(\frac{e^2}{mc^2}\right). \tag{11.22}$$

For $\alpha = 10^{16}$ electrons cm^{-1} and $D = 10^4$ cm^2 sec^{-1}, average values for a bright meteor at a height 80 km, T_L becomes almost 3 hours at wavelengths of 8 to 10 m. Such echo durations are not observed, and it is clear that at some time greater than the decay times of short duration echoes (usually less than 0.5 second) processes other than diffusion become effective in removing electrons.

11.8.2 *Recombination*

If diffusion is neglected, the rate of decrease of electron density due to recombination alone is given in terms of the recombination coefficient $\bar{\alpha}$ by

$$dn_e/dt = - \bar{\alpha}n_e^2 \tag{11.23}$$

where n_e is the initial electron density in the trail. Integration of this expression gives

$$\frac{1}{n_e} = \bar{\alpha}t + \frac{1}{n_{ei}} \qquad (11.24)$$

where n_{ei} is the initial electron density in the trail. The radio echo will disappear when n_e falls below the critical electron density, n_c, so that echo duration, T_R, is given by

$$T_R = \frac{(1/n_c) - (1/n_{ei})}{\bar{\alpha}}. \qquad (11.25)$$

For a dense trail with an initial radius of a few mean free paths $n_{ei} \gg n_c$, so that

$$T_R = 1/\bar{\alpha}n_c. \qquad (11.26)$$

The effect of recombination was first considered by Lovell,[27] who took the observed E-region recombination coefficient of 10^{-8} cm³ sec⁻¹. At a wavelength of 8 m equation (11.26) shows that this would limit the duration of all echoes, no matter how large the initial electron density, to about 10 seconds. As echoes of several minutes' duration are observed, it is clear that the E-region recombination coefficient cannot be applied to meteor trails. The problem has been discussed further by Greenhow[20] and by Kaiser and Greenhow.[53] The high value of $\bar{\alpha}$ in the E-region is now thought to be due essentially to the loss of electrons by dissociative recombination. In this process an ionized air molecule recombines with an electron, at the same time dissociating to give two neutral air atoms. In the case of meteor trails, however, the bulk of the positive ions are those of meteor atoms such as Ca^+, Fe^+, Mg^+, and Si^+. These ions cannot dissociate, and recombination with electrons can take place only with the emission of a photon. Radiative recombination has the much smaller coefficient of 10^{-12} cm³ sec⁻¹ and would permit echo durations of up to 10^5 seconds.[54] Although electrons would eventually be lost by this mechanism, other processes must be present which limit echo duration to the observed maximum of 5 to 10 minutes.

11.8.3 *Attachment*

A free electron may become attached to a neutral oxygen molecule to give a negative ion O_2^-. Such an electron is then no longer available for the scattering of radio waves. The rate of decrease of electron density due to attachment is given by the equation

$$dn_e/dt = -\bar{\beta}n_0 n_e \qquad (11.27)$$

where $\bar{\beta}$ is the attachment coefficient, and n_0 is the density of oxygen molecules per cubic centimeter. Integration of this expression gives

$$t = (\log n_{ei} - \log n_e)/\bar{\beta}n_0 \qquad (11.28)$$

and with n_e equated to n_c, equation (11.28) gives for the echo duration, T_A, under the influence of attachment alone

$$T_A = (\log n_{ei} - \log n_e)/\bar{\beta}n_0 \qquad (11.29)$$

or

$$T_A \sim (\log n_{ei})/\bar{\beta}n_0 \qquad (11.30)$$

where n_{ei} is the initial electron density in the trail. This expression for T_A is independent of wavelength, and echoes whose durations have been limited by attachment will be characterized by a departure from the λ^2 law of echo durations for diffusion alone. Such departures are found to occur for echoes with durations greater than about 10 seconds at a height of 95 km.[20] With both diffusion and recombination the longest enduring echo would be received from near the point of maximum electron density in a meteor trail. The attachment time constant, $1/\bar{\beta}n_0$, on the other hand, depends on height. For example, a meteor of magnitude -2 producing 10^{16} electrons cm^{-1} at a height of 80 km would give an echo lasting 10^4 seconds under the influence of diffusion alone. Loss of electrons by attachment would, however, limit the duration to only a few seconds. At greater heights, even though the diffusion is more rapid and α is less, because of the reduction in $1/\bar{\beta}n_0$ an echo duration of a minute or so could be observed.

Combined photographic and radar observations made with the Super Schmidt meteor cameras and radar equipment at Jodrell Bank have enabled these effects to be investigated. The variation of linear electron density along a meteor trail can be determined from the photographic light curve, and the height of each part of the trail can be determined accurately. With the variation of diffusion coefficient with height known, the theoretical echo duration from all points of the trail for various values of attachment coefficient can be calculated. Observation of the part of the trail from which the longest duration echo is observed then determines the attachment coefficient and $\bar{\beta}$ is found to be 5×10^{-15} cm^3 sec^{-1}. This value is approximately fifty times as great as that expected for molecular oxygen.[55] Echo duration thus becomes a compromise between diffusion and attachment. At greater heights D increases rapidly, reducing echo duration, whereas at lower heights the density of oxygen molecules increases and electrons are lost more rapidly by attachment. The result of these two effects is to cause the final heights of long-duration meteor echoes to be near 95 km with a limiting duration of a few hundred seconds, irrespective or the actual height or electron density at the point of maximum brightness.

References

1. A. C. B. Lovell, "Meteor Astronomy," Oxford, 1954.
2. J. G. Davies and J. C. Gill, *Monthly Not. Roy. Astron. Soc.* **116**, 105 (1956).
3. F. L. Whipple, *Rev. Mod. Phys.* **15**, 246 (1943).
4. N. Herlofson, *Repts. Prog. in Phys.* **11**, 444 (1948).
5. M. A. Cook, H. Eyring, and R. N. Thomas, *Astrophys. J.* **113**, 475 (1951).
6. F. L. Whipple and R. N. Thomas, *Astrophys. J.* **114**, 448 (1951).
7. R. N. Thomas, *Astrophys. J.* **116**, 203 (1952).
8. R. N. Thomas and W. C. White, *Astrophys. J.* **118**, 555 (1953).
9. H. J. Smith, *Astrophys. J.* **119**, 438 (1954).
10. A. F. Cook, *Astrophys. J.* **120**, 572 (1954).
11. F. L. Whipple, *Astrophys. J.* **121**, 241 (1955).
12. L. G. Jacchia, *Astrophys. J.* **121**, 521 (1955).
13. J. S. Greenhow and G. S. Hawkins, *Nature* **170**, 335 (1952).
14. P. M. Millman and D. W. R. McKinley, *Canad. J. Phys.* **34**, 50 (1956).
15. F. L. Whipple, *Proc. Natl. Acad. Sci.* **36**, 687 (1950); **37**, 19 (1951).
16. A. C. B. Lovell and J. A. Clegg, *Proc. Phys. Soc.* **60**, 491 (1948).
17. N. Herlofson, *Ark. Fysik* **3**, 247 (1951).
18. T. R. Kaiser and R. L. Closs, *Phil. Mag.* **43**, 1 (1952).
19. V. R. Eshelman, *Stanford Electronics Res. Lab. Tech. Rept.* No. **49** (1952).
20. J. S. Greenhow, *Proc. Phys. Soc.* B**65**, 169 (1952).
21. I. C. Browne and E. R. Billam, *Proc. Phys. Soc.* B**69**, 98 (1956).
22. G. S. Hawkins, *Monthly Not. Roy. Astron. Soc.* **116**, 92 (1956).
23. J. G. Davies and A. C. B. Lovell, *Monthly Not. Roy. Astron. Soc.* **115**, 23 (1955).
24. I. C. Browne, K. Bullough, S. Evans, and T. R. Kaiser, *Proc. Phys. Soc.* B**69**, 83 (1956).
25. A. M. Skellett, *Proc. IRE* **23**, 132 (1935).
26. J. A. Pierce, *Phys. Rev.* **71**, 88 (1947).
27. A. C. B. Lovell, *Sci. Progr.* **38**, 22 (1950).
28. T. R. Kaiser, *Phil. Mag. Suppl.* **2**, 495 (1953); *J. Atmos. Terr. Phys. Suppl.* **2**, 119 (1955).
29. A. C. B. Lovell, *Repts. Progr. in Phys.* **11**, 415 (1948).
30. J. G. Porter, *Monthly Not. Roy. Astron. Soc.* **103**, 134 (1943); **104**, 257 (1944).
31. Unpublished observations.
32. See, for example, L. G. Jacchia, *Harvard Coll. Observ. Tech. Rept.* No. **10** (1952).
33. J. A. Clegg and I. A. Davidson, *Phil. Mag.* **41**, 77 (1950).
34. T. R. Kaiser, *Monthly Not. Roy. Astron. Soc.* **114**, 39 (1954); **114**, 52 (1954).
35. S. Evans, *Monthly Not. Roy. Astron. Soc.* **114**, 63 (1954).
36. Rocket Panel, *Phys. Rev.* **88**, 1027 (1952).
37. J. S. Greenhow and E. L. Neufeld, *Monthly Not. Roy. Astron. Soc.* **117**, 359 (1957).
38. L. G. Jacchia, *Astrophys. J.* **121**, 521 (1955).
39. C. Ramsauer and O. Beeck, *Ann. Physik* **87**, 1 (1928).
40. See, for example, Z. Ceplecha, *Bull. Astron. Czech.* **4**, 55 (1953); F. Link, *ibid.* **4** 168 (1953).
41. C. P. Olivier, *Proc. Amer. Phil. Soc.* **85**, 93 (1942); **91**, 315 (1948).
42. V. V. Fedynsky, *Astron. J. Soviet Union* **21**, 291 (1944).
43. W. Liller and F. L. Whipple, "Rocket exploration of the upper atmosphere," *J. Atmos. Terr. Phys.* **112** *Spec. Suppl.* (1954).
44. J. S. Greenhow, *Phil. Mag.* **41**, 682 (1950).

45. C. D. Ellyett, *Phil. Mag.* **41**, 694 (1950).
46. L. A. Manning, O. G. Villard, and A. M. Peterson, *Proc. IRE* **38**, 877 (1950).
47. W. G. Elford and D. S. Robertson, *J. Atmos. Terr. Phys.* **4**, 271 (1953).
48. J. S. Greenhow, *Phil. Mag.* **45**, 471 (1954).
49. J. S. Greenhow and E. L. Neufeld, *Phil. Mag.* **1**, 1157 (1956).
50. J. S. Greenhow and E. L. Neufeld, *Proc. Phys. Soc.* **74**, 1(1959).
51. J. S. Greenhow and E. L. Neufeld, *J. Atmos. Terr. Phys.* **6**, 133 (1955).
52. A. A. Weiss, *Austral. J. Res.* **8**, 279 (1955).
53. T. R. Kaiser and J. S. Greenhow, *Proc. Phys. Soc.* B**66**, 150 (1953).
54. D. R. Bates, R. A. Buckingham, H. S. W. Massey, and J. J. Unwin, *Proc. Roy. Soc.* A**170**, 322 (1939).
55. D. R. Bates and H. S. W. Massey, *Phil. Trans.* A**239** (1943).

Chapter 12

Advances during the International Geophysical Year, 1957/1958

The International Geophysical Year (IGY) ran from July 1957 to December 1958. This chapter records some of the advances made during that time and appropriate references are included. The sections in this chapter are numbered to correspond to the numbers of the chapters in the rest of the book: they have been written by the authors of those chapters.

12.1 The Van Allen Radiation Belts That Surround the Earth................ 551
12.3 The Upper Atmosphere Studied by Rockets and Satellites................ 555
12.4 The Sun's Ionizing Radiations... 556
12.8 Radar Studies of the Aurora.. 558
12.9 The Ionosphere... 558
12.11 The Upper Atmosphere and Meteors 561

12.1 The Van Allen Radiation Belts that Surround the Earth

Among the most remarkable and interesting results that have come from the IGY enterprise is the discovery in 1958 that the earth is surrounded by two great "radiation" belts. It stems from cosmic ray studies by instruments carried by artificial earth satellites, and later by "moon" rockets.

The first inkling came from the U.S. satellites Explorers I and III, launched in 1958, on January 31 and March 26. Their successor Explorer IV, launched on July 26, definitely established the existence of a radiation region, and more fully explored it. It suggested that the region included not one belt only, but two. This was confirmed by the first two U.S. moon rockets, Pioneer I and III, launched on October 11 and December 6. Meanwhile the radiation region had been detected and investigated also by U.S.S.R. satellites—followed later by moon rockets, beginning on January 2, 1959.

The leader in the U.S. discoveries was J. A. Van Allen, of the State University of Iowa. He has given a detailed account of the course of the research, and of the part taken in it by his colleagues.[1] The leader in the U.S.S.R. was S. N. Vernov. With his colleagues he presented a joint paper on the region at the Moscow IGY Assembly (July/August 1959). They have published later papers on the subject[2] in English, in the periodical *Planetary and Space Science* (Pergamon Press).

The general nature of the radiation region is illustrated by Fig. 1, due to Van Allen.[3] It shows a section of the region by a half-plane bounded by the geomagnetic axis. The most intense parts of the cross sections of the

551

belts are shaded, and elsewhere are lines of equal radiation intensity. The inner belt has maximum intensity at about 2,000 miles above the ground, in low latitudes. For the outer belt the height of maximum is about 10,000 miles. Beyond this distance the intensity falls away, to reach the normal cosmic ray level at about 40,000 miles. For both belts the form is determined by the geomagnetic field. In particular, the outer belt descends to much lower heights in high latitudes. The figure shows how the track of Pioneer III traversed two different parts of the region during its outward and return flights.

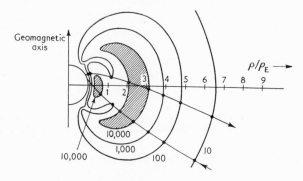

Fig. 1. Idealized distribution of radiation around the earth. Numbers against the contours represent the true counting rates of the Geiger counters carried in Explorer IV and Pioneer III. The two "van Allen Belts" are shown shaded. The outward and inward tracks of Pioneer III are indicated.

In the name "radiation" belt or region, "radiation" refers to charged particles of high energy. They include electrons and protons, but it is not yet known whether there are also other kinds of nuclei, like those of helium (alpha particles). The devices used to measure their number and energy can detect only those whose energy exceeds certain limits—usually expressed in kiloelectron volts (kev) or in millions of electron volts (Mev). The limit for electrons has so far been about 40 kev, and for protons a few Mev. The energy "spectrum" is still under investigation, but the number and flux of particles increases considerably towards lower energies (for electrons) of the order of 25 kev; electrons with energies over 5 Mev are however detected in small amount. The energy of the protons in the inner belt ranges up to several hundred Mev. The maximum energy flux is of order 10^{15} ev. cm^{-2} sec^{-1} ster^{-1}. Owing to the high speeds of the particles the estimate implies an extremely low number density.

The motion of the charged particles is complicated. They spiral to and fro across the equator, along the lines of geomagnetic force, between high latitudes where their travel along the lines of force is slowed to zero and reversed. But some have there a different fate. They collide with particles of the normal atmosphere. Some of the "radiation" particles after these collisions travel further downward, and become merged in the atmosphere and lost to the belt. Irregularities and fluctuations of the geomagnetic field help to bring the particles down to levels where this loss can occur. They may also unite with an atmospheric particle of opposite sign; becoming neutral, they cease to be influenced by the magnetic field, and again are lost to the belt. Thus there is a slow loss, and the belts are maintained only because there is continual replenishment—doubtless not at a uniform rate. The over-all strength of the radiation belts changes from time to time, particularly as regards the outer belt, for which already an immense mass of data has been collected.

Besides the spiral motion to and fro along the lines of force, the particles drift round the earth, in orbits whose form was first given by Størmer. The electrons drift eastward, the positive particles westward, in such a way that a westward electric current is associated with the belts. This modifies the magnetic field at the earth's surface, but only to a degree that has escaped certain detection on the basis of the surface magnetic surveys hitherto made. During magnetic storms, however, the current in the outer belt seems likely to be enhanced, contributing materially to the field disturbance observed at the earth's surface.

Entirely different origins are ascribed to the two belts. Cosmic rays (far more energetic than the particles of the belts) traverse our atmosphere down to levels depending on the magnetic latitude; some even penetrate well below ground. Some shatter nuclei of atoms of the atmosphere; the resulting debris includes neutrons, whose motion is unaffected by the magnetic field. Some of them fly far upward, but they are unstable, and after a short time they change into proton-electron pairs, in which the proton has by far the most of the energy. These charged particles are under the control of the magnetic field, which "traps" them and keeps them in the belt. This is supposed to be the cause of the inner belt, whose level and intensity depend on the speed and number and decay time of the neutrons. As cosmic rays are more numerous at sunspot minimum than at sunspot maximum, this would imply that during the decline of the IGY sunspot cycle, the inner belt will increase in intensity.

The outer belt has already been found to change quite considerably in intensity and extent in the course of weeks and months. It is thought to be produced and maintained by streams of gas ejected from the sun, from time to time, with speeds of order 1000 km sec^{-1}. The gas is neutral but ionized, consisting mainly of protons and electrons. Many of the most intense streams can be associated with bright solar "flares." Usually the source of the weaker streams cannot be detected. The energy of a proton travelling at 1000 km sec^{-1} is only about 5 kev; for an electron of the same speed it is only a few ev. If protons and electrons with the energies observed in the radiation belt travel with such streams of solar gas, it should seem that they must be confined therein by a magnetic field carried by the stream.

The emission of solar streams is very variable. During the IGY it was at an unusually high rate. The general intensity of the radiation belt may be expected to decline as sunspot minimum approaches. How solar particles of high energy become trapped in the belt is not clear. The onset of new streams may cause considerable disturbance of the belt, as well as adding to it. Its history is probably closely connected with geomagnetic disturbances and great auroral displays.

In 1958 several U.S. nuclear bombs were exploded high in the atmosphere, over the Pacific and South Atlantic oceans. The result was a considerable temporary addition to the radiation region, soon spreading all round the earth. The course of the changes added much to our understanding of the belts. A report on the "Argus" (South Atlantic) experiment has been issued by the U.S. Academy of Sciences.

The radiation region is of great interest and concern in connection with future human space travel, because the particles constitute a danger to life. For the outer belt the harm possible is similar to that suffered by the pioneers in the medical use of X-rays. The inner belt is still more dangerous, because of its highly penetrating protons. As the radiation region is least intense over the polar regions, these may offer the best escape routes. Energetic particles in solar streams may offer further hazards in interplanetary space.

Despite the great extent of the belts, and the high energy of the individual particles, the total mass of the "radiation" material is very small. It may amount only to a few pounds!

The "radiation" particles form a kind of alien population within the normal atmosphere of the earth, like some rare microbes within the human body. They are the product of violent actions, by cosmic rays deep in our atmosphere or in the sun. They have their own peculiar motions, under the influence of the geomagnetic field—to which the great majority of the normal particles of the atmosphere are almost completely insensitive.

The radiation belts are situated far above the earth's surface, in regions that not so long ago were thought of as effectively empty. But if the atmosphere has the enormous extension suggested in Chapter 1, the belts are to be considered as relatively near, low-level structures embedded in our atmosphere.

Satellite and high-rocket data concerning the belts are rapidly being accumulated. Already there is a large amount of material to be studied and interpreted. Progress in this field of knowledge is likely to be speedy, and should soon greatly enlighten us on many now obscure problems of cosmic rays, solar streams, geomagnetic storms and the aurora.

References

1. J. A. Van Allen, *Sci. American* **200** (1959).
2. S. N. Vernov, A. E. Chudakov, P. V. Vakulov and Yu. I. Logachev, *Soviet Phys. Doklady* 338 (1959).
3. J. A. Van Allen, *Nature* **183**, 433 (1959).

12.3 The Upper Atmosphere Studied by Rockets and Satellites

It has been noted that fluctuations in atmospheric drag on the satellites Vanguard I and Sputnik II were directly correlated with fluctuations in the 10 cm radiation from the sun.

Additional measurements of the radiation belt have been made in satellites and space probes. It now appears that the belt consists of at least two separate zones. The particles in the belt carry energies from approximately 20 kev to several million electron volts or more. It has been determined that the particles occur in appreciable quantities above 300 km in northern latitudes and above 1000 km over the equator. Their maximum density is about 1 particle per cm³. The inner zone shows its maximum intensity at an altitude of 4000 km, while the maximum of the outer zone occurs at an altitude of 16,000 km. The outer zone extends out into space to a distance of about 55,000 km. The extent of the outer zone, however, has been shown to vary markedly with activity in the sun. Thus, on a space probe flight which followed a 5-day period of solar activity the radiation of the outer zone extended thousands of kilometers beyond where it had been observed in a previous space probe flight.

The greater portion of the particles in the radiation belt is probably electrons, the remainder being protons. The more energetic particles in the inner belt have actually been identified as protons in a rocket flight to an altitude of 1230 km. In this flight protons of energies up to 700 Mev were observed. The total proton flux in the range from 0 to 700 Mev, omnidirectional, was measured as 1300 protons per square centimeter per second at the 1200 km level. The total radiation level at that altitude in space was estimated as one roentgen. It now appears quite certain that particles from the outer zone of the radiation belt are the immediate cause of the earth's aurora. It is also thought that these energetic particles coming into the auroral regions provide the energy that accounts for higher upper air temperatures in the northern latitudes.

The data presently at hand on the radiation belt indicate that exposure levels to crews in future manned space should be in the range from 2 to 5 per person in the case of a rocket flying directly through the belt to outer space. Such a radiation level is well below the lethal dosage for humans, and it may be further reduced by appropriate shielding. The radiation belt particles may, however, not be the greatest hazard to be found by the crews of future apace crafts. For, it should be noted that recent balloon flights by Winckler and his co-workers detected heavy fluxes of 100 million volt protons at low altitudes, occurring at the time of a major solar flare.

In regard to the earth's magnetic field, observations made by the U.S.S.R. on Mechta, or Lunik I, showed a large dip in the earth's magnetic field in the region of the radiation belt. Such a dip may indicate the existence of a coherent current flow, such as the so-called Chapman-Størmer current ring.

Micrometeor data continued to be collected by satellites and space probes. In general, the results seem to be consistent with the earlier observations. The Soviet results appear to have been brought in consonance with the U.S. measurements.

12.4 The Sun's Ionizing Radiations

12.4.1 *The Solar Helium 304 A Emission Line*

New data on the intensity of the solar He 304 A emission line and its absorption by the upper atmosphere were obtained by H. Hinteregger (U.S. Air Force Cambridge Research Center) on March 12, 1959. The rocket-borne spectrograph used a 2-meter radius concave grating mounted for grazing incidence at an angle of about 86 deg. Intensities were measured by a photo-multiplier tube, having an extended cathode surface almost totally insensitive to wavelengths longer than 1500 A, but highly efficient at shorter wavelengths. The portion of the Rowland circle normally covered by photographic film was instead scanned by an exit slit cut in a continuous steel belt. The belt was driven along the Rowland circle so that the spectrum was scanned repeatedly from 1300 to 250 A. Radiation emerging at any slit position in this wavelength range was received on the cathode of the multiplier tube and counting rates were telemetered to the ground.

From 140 km to the peak altitude of 210 km, seventeen wavelength scans were recorded. Each scan clearly showed the He 304 A line so that it was possible to plot the intensity versus altitude. No other spectrum line of comparable importance was detected below 1000 A. The rocket was flown in the morning with the sun at 58 deg. from the zenith. The maximum rate of absorption occurred at 180 to 185 km and the intensity was estimated to be 0.28 erg cm^{-2} sec^{-1} extrapolated to the top of the atmosphere.

12.4.2 *High Energy X-Ray Quanta Emitted during Solar Flares*

From July 14 to September 1, 1959, T. A. Chubb, R. W. Kreplin, D. McNutt, and H. Friedman of the U.S. Naval Research Laboratory conducted a new series of rocket measurements of X-ray emission during solar flares.

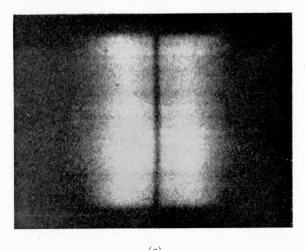

(a)

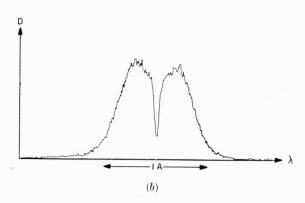

(b)

Fig. 2. The photograph is a reproduction of a spectrogram of Lyman-α obtained at a height of 200 km with a resolution of about 0.03 A (J. D. Purcell and R. Tousey, U.S. Naval Research Laboratory). The stigmatic image reproduces the distribution of intensity across a diameter of the sun parallel to the slit of the spectrograph. Non-uniformity in the Lyman-α intensity across the disk is responsible for the density variations visible on the spectrogram. (b) The microphotometer trace shows the variation of photographic density with wavelength. Some of the apparent width of the core is due to limited instrumental resolution. Future experiments will be performed with an echelle spectrograph capable of providing an order of magnitude better resolution.

[Facing page 557

Nike-Asp rockets were instrumented with a variety of X-ray detectors, including proportional and scintillation counters for the 2–20 and 20–200 kev ranges. In the early phases of large flares, X-rays with energies as high as 90 kev were detected. In each of three large flares observed, the emission was not in the nature of a brief burst but persisted for the full 6 min that the rockets remained above the height of 45 km to which the hardest X-rays penetrated.

During a class 3 flare, the total flux from 30–90 kev (0.41–0.14 A) was about 10^{-5} erg cm^{-2} sec^{-1}. The flux per unit energy range decreased by about a factor of 2 for every 15-kev increase in energy. It appears that the spectral distribution can best be approximated by a collection of thermal sources. This implies the existence of local temperatures of the order of 100 million ° C in the solar atmosphere.

Averaging the few available measurements of X-rays from the sun during flares in the range of class 2 to 3, the fluxes show the following approximate dependence on wavelength: 2 ergs cm^{-2} sec^{-1} between 20 and 100 A; 3×10^{-2} erg cm^{-2} sec^{-1} between 8 and 20 A; and 10^{-2} erg cm^{-2} sec^{-1} between 2 and 8 A. The total X-ray flux affecting the E-region during a class 2 + flare was roughly twice the quiet sun value.

In §4.5.5, experiments were described which indicated a background of X-rays at high altitudes with energies extending to about 50 kev. The flux observed was so small that it was not possible to make directional measurements which could identify the radiation with the sun. Theoretically, it was possible that such X-ray emission could originate in some celestial source or possibly as a secondary effect of the interaction of Van Allen belt electrons with the upper atmosphere. The latest series of measurements indicate that the observed X-rays are probably emitted by the sun at very low intensity even in the absence of solar flares. The intense excitation that accompanies a solar flare strongly enhances the X-ray emission over the entire spectral range.

12.4.3 *High Resolution Profile of Solar Lyman-α*

In § 4.7, mention was made of plans to study the profile of the solar Lyman-α line with high resolution, using the 13th order reflection from a concave grating. On July 21, 1959, J. D. Purcell and R. Tousey of the U.S. Naval Research Laboratory succeeded in obtaining several spectrograms between heights of 95 km and 200 km with sufficient resolution to reveal a narrow absorption core. Figure 2 shows a reproduction of one of their spectrograms and the corresponding microphotometer trace.

The absorption core removes 50–60 % of the intensity in the center of the line. This corresponds to an absorbing column of between 10^{12} and 10^{13}

neutral hydrogen atoms per cm². From the breadth of the core, the temperature of the hydrogen is estimated to be less than 3000 °C. Almost no measurable variation in depth of the core between 95 and 200 km was discernible.

The low temperature of the absorbing gas is compatible with the theory that the core is produced by hydrogen within the terrestrial atmosphere. The truncated shape of the emission line is probably associated with the structure of the solar atmosphere in the region where the line is formed. Any absorption contributed by interplanetary hydrogen would be difficult to separate from the wide absorption effect originating in the solar atmosphere and the narrow core produced by cold hydrogen near the earth.

12.8 Radar Studies of the Aurora

Recent results are reported in the following references.

1. J. S. Kim and B. W. Currie, "Horizontal movements of aurora," *Can. J. Phys.* **36**, (1958).
2. T. R. Hartz, "Auroral radiation at 500 Mc/s," *Can. J. Phys.* **36**, 677 (1958).
3. C. Collins, "Some observations of aurora using a low-power frequency-modulated radar," *Can. J. Phys.* **36**, 926 (1958).
4. G. F. Lyon and A. Kavadas, "Horizontal motions in radar echoes from aurora," *Can. J. Phys.* **36**, 1661 (1958).
5. B. Nichols, "Auroral ionization and magnetic disturbances," *Proc. IRE* **47**, 245 (1959).
6. J. H. Chapman, B. C. Blevis, F. D. Green, H. V. Serson and E. A. Cameron, "Preliminary data on radar returns from aurora at 488 Mc/s," Report No. 44.2.1, Radio Physics Laboratory, Defence Research Telecommunications Establishment, Ottawa, Canada, 1958.
7. B. C. Blevis and E. A Cameron, "Further data on radar returns from aurora at 488 Mc/s," Report No. 44.2.2, Communications Wing, Defence Research Telecommunications Establishment, Ottawa, Canada, 1958.
8. L. Harang and J. Troim, "Investigation of auroral echoes, Part I," Norwegian Defence Research Establishment, Kjeller-Lillestrom, Norway, 1959.

12.9 The Ionosphere

12.9.1 *The Polar Ionosphere*

Observations[1] made in the polar regions during the IGY have revealed some interesting features of both the "normal" and the "abnormal" ionosphere. Ionospheric soundings have been made at the south geographic pole, where, during winter, the sun's radiation does not strike the ionosphere, and during summer the angle of incidence is constant throughout the day. During winter it is found that the electron concentration at the peak of the $F2$ layer oscillates with a period of 24 hours, but that at midsummer it is much more nearly constant. A 12-hour oscillation is most marked at the equinox. These time variations would not have been expected on a simple theory. It has been suggested that they are evidence of important movements of electrons in winter with a 24-hour period, either compressing and expanding the layer, or carrying electrons from the illuminated parts of the ionosphere into the dark parts.

The two "abnormal" phenomena which have shown interesting behavior in polar regions are "polar blackouts"[2] (see §9.11.3.2) and "sporadic E (Es)"[3] (see §9.6.8). A study of the time of occurrence of either one of these phenomena at a number of places in the polar region shows that, at a given Universal time, there is a tendency for the phenomenon to occur at places near a line in the form of a spiral curling in towards the pole. This line is roughly stationary in space, so that, as the earth rotates beneath it, different places pass through it at different times.

It was suggested by Störmer,[4] some time ago, that charged particles approaching the earth would be guided, by its magnetic field, towards the polar regions and would arrive there along spiral lines curling in towards the poles. He also showed that the spiral would curl in opposite directions for positively and for negatively charged particles. Nikol'ski[5] showed that the morning maximum of magnetic activity observed in the polar region occurs along a spiral of this kind, with its direction corresponding to the arrival of positive charges.

It appears reasonable to suggest that the polar type of Es ionization and polar blackouts are also caused by particles incident on the earth. It is then found that the polar Es ionization corresponds to the incidence of negative charges.

When polar blackouts are studied, it is found, on the contrary, that the spirals are in the opposite sense, as if they were the result of positive charges arriving at the earth. The spirals are closely similar to those of maximum magnetic disturbance.

The above-mentioned investigations on polar blackout were made by observing the smallest frequency on which echoes could be recorded on an ionosonde. Although this procedure has proved useful for a study of the geographical distribution of the blackouts it is better to measure the absorption on a greater frequency if the details of different blackouts are to be compared. Measurements of this kind have been made by observing (a) the waves from radio stars[6,7] and (b) the waves used in commercial "forward-scatter" communication links.[8] These observations have shown that, in the polar regions, abnormal increases of absorption can be of different types.

Type I occurs at the same time as a solar flare, and only when the ionosphere is sun-lit. It is the same as the short wave fade out (S.W.F.) mentioned in § 9.11.2.1.

Type II is associated with aurora and local geomagnetic disturbance. It occurs mainly at night and, although it is more intense at higher latitudes, it is noticeable outside the auroral zone. It has been suggested that this type of abnormal absorption might result from an increase in the collision frequency of the electrons in the E region.

Type III starts a few hours after the occurrence of a major solar flare and usually persists for 2 or 3 days. During that time it is much more intense by day than by night. Although it is usually confined to high latitudes, the most intense occurrences spread to lower latitudes, and it is probable that the event of February 23, 1956 (see § 9.11.5) was accompanied by intense absorption of type III.

It appears that what is normally called polar blackout consists mainly of type III absorption. Measurements of cross modulation (see § 9.5.2.1.3), and of waves weakly reflected at vertical incidence (see § 9.5.2.2.1), have shown that there is appreciable electron concentration (100 or 200 cm^{-3}) down to 50 km at time of blackout.[9] It has been suggested that the electrons are produced by a stream of protons, with energies in the range 5–50 MeV, which would produce a peak of electrons at this level. Protons of slightly greater energy have been detected from balloons during periods when type III absorption was observed. The continued arrival of protons for some day after the solar flare could be explained if they were "trapped" by solar magnetic lines of force which had been extended, by the disturbance, to the distance of the earth.[10]

12.9.2 *Solar Flares and Ionosphere Storms*

It was mentioned in § 9.11.1 that solar flares are sometimes accompanied by S.I.D.'s and are sometimes followed, about 26 hours later, by an ionosphere storm, as might be expected if particles, ejected from the sun when the flare occurred, traveled to the earth with a velocity of the order of 2000 km sec^{-1}. It has long been known, however, that not all flares are associated with either S.I.D.'s or storms.

During the IGY it has been realized that the type of radio "noise" burst which accompanies a flare is apparently related to the type of ionospheric phenomenon to which it is related. It appears that those flares which will be associated with an S.I.D., but not with a storm, are frequently accompanied by an outburst of radio noise in which the power (in the frequency range 200–10,000 Mc/s) is greater on the lower frequencies, or in which the power measured on 200 Mc/s reaches a maximum after the peak of the flare. If, on the contrary, the power is greater on the higher frequency, or, when measured on 200 Mc/s, it reaches a maximum before the peak of the flare, an S.I.D., but not a storm is likely to occur. By observing the frequency at which there is maximum power in the burst, and the way in which this frequency varies with time, an attempt has been made to deduce the outwards acceleration of a region of disturbance in the sun, and to relate the resulting velocity to the probability that the corresponding ejected particles will reach the earth.[12]

References

1. R. W. Knecht, "Observations of the ionosphere over the south geographic pole," *J. Geophys. Res.* **64**, 1243 (1959).
2. W. H. Bellchambers and W. R. Piggott, "Ionospheric measurements made at Halley Bay," *Nature* **182**, 1596 (1958).
3. E. L. Hagg, D. Muldrew and E. Warren, *J. Atmos. Terr. Phys.* **14**, 345 (1959).
4. C. Störmer, *Terr. Magn. Atmos. Elec.* **22**, 23 and 97 (1917).
5. A. P. Nikol'ski, *Izvest. Akad. Nauk S.S.S.R.* **109** (1956); **112**, 628 (1957).
6. G. C. Reid and C. Collins, "Observations of abnormal VHF radio-wave absorption at medium and high latitudes," *J. Terr. Atmos. Phys.* **14**, 68 (1959).
7. G. C. Reid and H. Leinbach, "Low-energy cosmic-ray events associated with solar flares." *J. Geophys. Res.* **64**, 1801 (1959).
8. D. K. Bailey, "Abnormal ionisation in the lower ionosphere associated with cosmic-ray flux enhancements," *Proc. IRE* **47**, 255 (1959).
9. B. Bjelland, O. Hult, B. Landmark and F. Lied, "The *D* Region of the ionosphere," *Nature* **184**, 973 (1959).
10. T. Gold, "Plasma and magnetic fields in the solar system," *J. Geophys. Res.* **64**, 1665 (1959).
11. K. Sinno and Y. Hakura, "On the relation of solar eruptions to geomagnetic and ionosphere disturbances. I. On the power spectrum of solar radio outbursts; II. On the types of solar radio outbursts," *Rept. Ionosph. Res. Japan* **12**, 285 and 296 (1958).
12. M. B. Wood and C. S. Warwick, "Geomagnetic disturbance and velocity of slow-drift solar radio bursts," *Nature* **184**, 1471 (1959).

12.11 The Upper Atmosphere and Meteors

12.11.1 *The Initial Radii of Meteor Trails*

Recent experimental work has shown the existence of severe limitations in the use of radio echo methods for the observation of faint meteors. The variation of atmospheric pressure at the point of maximum light and ionization of a meteor, as a function of velocity and mass, is given by Eq. (11.3), and it is found that the photographic meteor observations agree quite well with the theoretical predictions for magnitudes between -3 and $+3$. An examination of the radio echo height measurements, on the other hand, show that $+6$ to $+7$ magnitude meteors apparently vaporize considerably lower than expected. This behavior is evident from a comparison of the radio and photographic meteor height distributions in Fig. 7 of Chapter 11. For a difference in brightness of 9 magnitudes, corresponding to a mass ratio of 4000, there is a difference in height of only 10 km instead of the 20 km predicted by Eq. (11.3).

Simultaneous meteor echo observations at wavelengths of 8 and 17 meters, by Greenhow and Hall,[1] have shown that this effect is due to the large initial radii of the ionized columns. The effect of a finite trail radius is to reduce the initial echo amplitude below the value A_0 given by Eq. (11.10), as the electrons in any cross section of the trail no longer scatter in phase. If a radial Gaussian distribution of electron density is assumed, and the initial radius r_i is defined as the standard deviation of this distribution, then the initial echo amplitude A_i is related to A_0 by the expression

$$A_i = A_0 \exp - \frac{(2\pi r_i)}{\lambda} \qquad (12.1)$$

where λ is the wavelength.

When r_i is equal to $\lambda/2\pi$, the initial amplitude is reduced to 0.37 of the expected value. Because of the squared term in the exponent in Eq. (12.1), however, a further increase of a factor 2 in r_i, or a reduction in wavelength by a factor 2, is sufficient to reduce the amplitude to only 2 % of A_0.

Large amplitude ratios of this order are found in the radio echoes for individual meteor trails, when observed simultaneously at wavelengths of 8 and 17 meters. Values of initial trail radius which increase from 100 cm at a height of 90 km, to 300 cm at a height of 115 km are deduced. Thus at any particular wavelength there is a height region above which the attenuation in echo amplitude is so great that the meteors are not detected. The magnitude of this effect is particularly severe at wavelengths of a few meters, at which many of the radio echo observations have been made. At a wavelength of 4 meters only about 1.5 % of + 6.5 magnitude meteors are detected. This proportion increases to 10 % and 40 % at wavelengths of 8 meters and 17 meters respectively.

12.11.2 *The Mass Distribution*

A result of this reduction in radio echo amplitudes is that the counts of meteor echoes do not give a true indication of the meteor mass distribution. A re-evaluation of the meteor echo data now shows that at magnitudes of + 6 to + 8, the numbers of sporadic meteors increase by approximately 3.8 per magnitude. This is considerably higher than the value 2.5 suggested previously.

A similar estimate of $x = 3.4$ (Eq. 11.12) has been obtained by Hawkins and Upton[2] for meteors brighter than + 2 magnitude. These workers used the photographic technique, instead of relying upon visual observations. The visual estimates also suggested a value of $x = 2.5$, and this difference is probably due to the variable cone of vision of an observer, together with the various physiological effects which arise in the visual observations of meteors.

The total mass in each magnitude range therefore increases, at least up to + 8 magnitude. If this increase is maintained up to micrometeorites of + 20 magnitude, it is found that the numbers of micrometeorites would be about three orders of magnitude greater than the previous estimates.

References

1. J. S. Greenhow and J. E. Hall, unpublished observations.
2. G. S. Hawkins and E. K. L. Upton, *Astrophys. J.* **128**, 727 (1958).

Author Index

Numbers in italics refer to the pages on which references are listed in bibliographies at end of each article. Numbers in brackets refer to reference numbers in the text against which no authors' names are shown.

Abadie, P., 237, *264*
Abbott, W. N., 283, *295*
Abe, S., 501, *512.*
Agy, V., 355(7), *374*
Ainsworth, J., 56(32, 37), 57(37), 63(37), 70, 91(16, 20, 21), *129, 130*
Aitchison, G. J., 435(1), *456*
Akasofu, S., 508, 509(68), *512*
Alfvén, H., 282, *295*, 343, *353*, 505, *512*
Allen, A. H., 456(2), *456*
Allen, C. W., 136(1), 138, 144, 150, *215*, 416(3, 4), 417(3, 4), 432(5), 433(3, 4), *456*
Allen, S. J. M., 184, *217*
Allis, W. P., 344(159), *353*
Al'pert, Y. L., 435(301), *469*
Anderson, K. A., 322(111a), *352*
Andrillat, Y., 225, *262*
Appleton, E. V., 196, *217*, 355, *374*, 379, 380(7, 8), 387(22), 388(22), 389(16), 397(7), 402(18), 403(6), 408(18), 409(18), 414(7, 280), 416(22), 417(10), 418(20, 21, 9), 419(11), 428(12, 17), 452(15, 19), 455(281), *456, 468*, 483, 486, *511*
Argence, E., 417(220), 442(23), *457, 466*
Arima, Y., 429(308), 435(309), 437(309), *469*
Armstrong, E. B., 226, 230, *263*, 340, *352*
Arnoldy, R., 288(676), *296*, 322(111), *351*
Arrhenius, 287, *296*
Aschenbrand, L. M., 119(85), *131*, 249(160), 250(162), *265*
Ashburn, E. V., 306, 315, *350, 351*
Aspinall, A., 356(12), *375*

Babcock, H. D., 221, *261*
Babcock, H. W., 220, 226, *261*
Bagariazky, B. A., 298, 300, *349*
Bagariazky, B. Y., 310, *350*
Bagaryatskii, B. A., *219*

Bailey, D. K., 404(26), 405(25), 428(24), 446(25), 452(25), 456(303), *457, 469*, 559(8), *561*
Baker, W. G., 392(28), 393(27), *457, 458*, 483(14), 484, 485, 488, 489, 506, *511*
Bandeen, W. R., 91(23), 93, 97(23), 98, *130*
Bannon, J., 429(29), *458*
Bappu, M. K. V., 220, *261*
Barber, D. R., 256, *267*
Barbier, D., 220, 222, 223, 224, 225, 226, 228, 229, 234, 235, 236, 237, 239, 240 (99, 102, 122b, 123, 126, 129, 130), 241, 253, 255, 257, 258, *261, 262, 263, 264, 266, 267*, 283, 289, *295*, 298, 300, 301, 304, 306, 313, 330, 339, *348, 350, 351*
Barnett, M. A. F., 483, *511*
Bartels, G., 456(153), *463*
Bartels, J., 272, 274, 283, 285, 286, 289(4), 290, 292(4), *294*, 434(30), *458*, 472(1), 477(15), 478(1), 480(1, 5), 481, 483, 486(1), 487(1), 489(1), 491(1), 492, 493(36), 494, 495, 498(1), 504(1), 505(1), 508(1), *511, 512*
Bartman, F. L., 91(23), 93, 97(23), 98, *130*
Bateman, R., 405(25), 446(25), 452(25), *457*
Bates, D. R., *16*, 28, 32(11), 48, 68(22), *69*, 70, 182, 183(45), 188, *216, 217*, 226 (79, 80), 227(80), 241, 245, 247, 248, (80, 157), 249, (80), 250, 251, 254(195), 255, 256(157), 258, 259(80, 211, 215a), 260, *263, 264, 265, 266, 267*, 307, 316, 318, 319, 321, 322, 323(89, 114, 115), 324(44, 89), 325(114), 327, 329(114), 330, 331(114), 334, 335, 337, 338(89, 135, 136), 339(135, 137), 343, *350, 351, 352, 353*, 383(31–35, 39, 131), 385(39, 40), *458*, 412(39), 413(36, 37), 435(40), 436, (38), *462*, 546(54), 549(55), *549*
Bauer, W., 274, *294*
Baum, W. A., 152, *216*

565

Baumbach, S., 145, *216*
Bawn, C. E. H., 250, 254, *265*
Bazzard, G. H., 417(307), 451(184a), *464*, *469*
Beckmann, B., 355(3), *374*
Bedinger, J. F., 118(84), *131*, 250(166, 166a), 253(184, 187), 260(216), *265*, *266*, *267*
Beeck, O., 533, *548*
Bellchambers, W. H., 559(2), *561*
Belon, A. E., 284(46), *295*, 302, 303, 336, *349*, *352*, 355(6), *374*
Belrose, J. S., 456(41), *458*
Benedict, W. S., 224, *262*
Benkova, N. P., 490, 499, *511*, *512*
Bennett, R. G., 259, *267*
Bennett, W. H., 505, *512*
Benson, O. O., 73(2), *129*
Berg, O. E., 110(56), 119(86), 121(91), *131*, *132*, 241(136), 260, *265*, *267*, 323(113), *352*
Berkner, L. V., 429(42, 44, 233), 450(43), 452(45), 455(282), *458*, *466*, *468*
Bernard, R., 221, 251, *261*, 300, 312, *349*, *350*
Berning, W. W., 104(46), 107, *130*, 435(304), *469*
Berthier, P., 230, 234, 236, 240, 260(103), *263*
Beynon, W. J. G., 408(46), 417(48), 418 (47, 317), *457*, *458*, *470*
Bibl, K., 404(50a), 414(50), 417(50), 437(51), *458*
Biermann, L., 144, *216*
Billam, E. R., 519(21), *548*
Billings, D. E., 147, *216*
Birkeland, Kr., 505, *512*
Bjelland, B., 560(9), *561*
Blackett, P. M. S., 243, *265*
Blagonravov, A. A., 111(64), *131*
Blamont, J. E., 252, *266*
Bless, R. C., 292, 293, *296*
Blevis, B. C., *558*
Boggess, A., 207(88), *217*
Boller, W., 283, *295*
Booker, H. G., 356(16), 366, 369, 373, *375*, 401(52), 447(53, 54), *459*
Bosanquet, C. H., 57(53), *71*
Boudart, M. J., 251(169), *266*
Bowe, P. W. A., 407(55, 56), *459*

Bowen, W. A., Jr., 109(51, 53), *130*, 483, *511*
Bowles, K. L., 356(20), 357, 364, 365, 374, *375*, 435(314), *469*
Boyd, R. L. F., 435(178), *464*
Boyd, T. J. M., 255, *266*, 327, *352*
Bracewell, R. N., 196(75), *217*, 406(58), 451(58), 452(57), 454(58), *217*, *459*
Bradbury, N. E., 187(55), *217*, 388, *459*
Bradley, J. E. S., 181(42), *216*
Bramhall, E. H., 272, *294*
Bramley, E. M., 406(199), *465*
Brandt, J. C., 260, *267*
Branscomb, L. M., 246, *265*, 332, 340, *352*
Breit, G., 483, *511*
Bricard, J., 226, 252, 253, *263*, *266*
Briggs, B. H., 422(62), 442(283), 445(60, 61, 63), 446(60, 61), 447(63), 450(64), *459*, *468*, 483, 486, *511*
Briggs, R. E., 57(48), 58(48), *70*
Broida, H. P., 222, 223, *262*
Brooks, C. F., 284, 286, *295*
Brown, G. M., 417(48, 49), 418(47, 317), *458*, *470*
Brown, J. N., 406(258), 418(258), *467*
Brown, R. A., 438(65), *459*
Browne, I. C., 519(21), 523(24), *548*
Bryam, E. T., 417(66), *459*
Buckingham, R. A., 245(145), *265*, 383(31), *458*, 546(54), *549*
Budden, K. G., 400(68), 401(67, 68), 406 (58), 451(58), 454(58), *459*
Bullough, K., 293, *296*, 360, 362, 364, 365(23), *375*, 523(24), *548*
Burch, D. E., 225(69), *262*
Bureau, R., 452(69), *459*
Burhop, E. H. S., 344, *353*
Burkard, O., 429(71), 432(73), 438(70), *459*
Burnight, T. R., 168(36), *216*
Byram, E. T., 29(8), 56(35, 38), *70*, 148(21), 154(21), *155*, *156*, *167*, 168(21), 169 (39), *183*, 188(21), 191(64), 198(39), 202(83), 207(87), 208(90), 209(90), 210(91), 214(90), *216*, *217*, *218*, 222, *261*
Byrne, E. C., 284(46), *295*, 355(6), *374*

Cabannes, J., 220, 221, 223, 224, 227, 235, 256, *261*, *262*, *263*, *264*, *267*
Cahill, L. J., Jr., 110(55), *130*

Cain, J. C., 366, *375*
Cameron, E. A., *558*
Campbell, W. W., 221, *261*
Cannon, C. G., 180, 181(42), *216*
Capron, J. R., 269(1), 272(2), *294*, 297(2), *348*
Carleton, N. P., 335, 340, *352*
Ceplecha, Z., 534(40), *548*
Chackett, K. F., 111(58–60), *131*
Chamberlain, J., 277, *294*
Chamberlain, J. W., 220, 222, 223, 224, 225, 227, 228, 239(121), 245, 252, 254, 255(192), 258, 259, 260, *261, 262, 263, 264, 265, 266, 267*, 285(54), 286, 287(54), 289(54), *295*, 298, 299(14), 302, 303, 304, 306, 308, 315, 318, 319, 322, 333, 334, 340(144), 342, 343, 344, 345, 346, *348, 349, 350, 351, 352, 353*
Chapman, J. H., 418(156), *463*
Chapman, S., *16*, 29, 36, 49, 50, *70*, 187, 212, 215, *217, 218*, 230, 242, 246, 250, 251, 254(163), 255(163), *264, 265*, 272, 274, 283–286, 289(4), 290, 292(4), 294, *294–296*, 305, 337, *349, 352*, 366, *375*, 380, 382, 387(74, 76), 393(77), 395, 455(78), *459, 460*, 472(1), 477, 478(1), 480(1, 7), 481, 482, 483(1, 9, 18), 486, 487(1), 488, 489(1), 491(1), 492–495, 498(38, 39), 501, 504, 505(1, 59), 508(1), *511, 512, 558*
Chatterjee, B., 422(79), *460*
Cherniev, V. I., 251, *266*
Chree, C., 284, 286, 287, 288, *295, 296*
Christiansen, W. N., 148, *216*
Chubb, T. A., 29(8), 56(35), *70*, 155, 156, 158, 159(30), 162, 163(30a), 167, 169(38, 39), 173, 191(64), 196, 198(39), 202(83), 207(87), 208(90), 209(90), 214(90), *216, 217, 218*, 222(28), *261*, 417(66), *459*
Chudakov, A. E., 121(93), 122(95), *132*, 202(82), *217, 554*
Chudesenko, E. F., 435(301), *469*
Clark, C., 422(80), *460*
Clark, K. C., 302, 303, 336, *349, 352*
Clayton, H. H., 285, 287, 288, *295*
Clegg, J. A., 518, 529, *548*
Clemmow, P. C., 448(81), *460*
Closs, R. L., 519, *548*
Coates, R. J., 140, *215*

Colgate, S. A., 321, *351*
Collins, C., 456(316), *470, 588*, 559(6), *561*
Cook, A. F., 516(10), *548*
Cook, M. A., 516(5), *548*
Cooper, C., 480(6), *511*
Cooper, C. D., 253, *266*
Costello, M., 259(215), *267*
Courtès, G., 221, 258, *261*
Cowling, T. G., 36, 50, *70*, 483, 484, 486, *511*
Cox, J. W., 416(253), *467*
Crombie, D. D., 456(2), *456*
Crompton, R. W., 443(133), 444(133), *462*
Croom, S. A., *433*
Cullington, E. H., 260(216), *267*, 270, *294*
Currie, B. W., 251, 256, *266*, 272, 278, 279, 284, 285, 289, 293, *294, 295, 296*, 356(15), 357, 358, 359(15), 360(15), 362, 363, 373, *375, 558*

Dagg, M., 446(82, 84, 85), 447(82, 83), 450(82–84), *460, 464*
Dahlstrom, C. E., 298, 303, 313, *349*
Dalby, F. W., 259, *267*
Dalgarno, A., 39, 47(18), *70*, 241, 242, 248, 256(157), 260, *264, 265*, 318, *351*
Das Gupta, N. N., 317, *351*
Dauvillier, A., 242, *265*
Davids, N., 406(284), *460, 468*
Davidson, I. A., 529, *548*
Davies, F. T., 283, 289, *295, 296*
Davies, J. G., 515, 522, *548*
Davies, K., 408(46), *458*
Davis, L. R., 110(56), 121(91), *131*, 323(113), *352*
Deal, O. E., 508, *512*
de Jager, C., 140, 145, 146, *215*, 243, *265*
Déjardin, G., 222, 223, 224, *261, 262*
Delannoy, J., 255, *266*
Dellinger, J. H., 451(87), *460*
Deming, L. S., 188, *217*
Devenport, M. H., 456(41), *458*
Dieminger, W., 355(3), *374*, 405(90), 408(89), 450(88), *460*
Ditchburn, R. W., 180, 181(42), *216*
Dixon, F. E., 287, *296*
Dogniaux, R., 303(31), *349*
Dolginov, S. Sh., 111(57), *131*, 511(73), *512*

Dolphin, L., 356(19), 359, 360(19), 361, 362, 366(19), 367(19), 368, 370(19), 371, *375*

Donahue, T. M., 256, 260, *266, 267*

Douglas, A. E., 304, *349*

Dufay, J., 220, 221, 222, 223(7, 62), 225, 227, 228, 234, 235(109), 236, 240, 251, 253, 257, 258, 259, *261, 262, 263, 264, 265, 266, 267,* 313, 348, *350*

Dufay, M., 220, 221, 224(7, 54, 225, 227), 234, 255, 258(208, 210), 259, *261, 262, 263, 266, 267,* 302, 313, *349, 350*

Duncan, R. A., 283, *295,* 313, *351,* 439(91), 441(92), *460*

Dungey, J. W., 390(93), 441(93), *460,* 509, *512*

Dyce, R. B., 359, 360, *375*

Edlen, B., 143, *216*

Edwards, H. D., 118(84), *131*

Edwards, H. W., 251, 256, *266,* 272, 278, 284, 289, *294, 296*

Egedal, J., 275, 277, 285, *294, 295*

Elder, J. S., 407(229), *466*

Elford, W. G., 448(94), *460,* 539, *549*

Ellison, M. A., 194(68), 197(77), 198, *217,* 288(66), *296,* 450(95), *460*

Ellyett, C. D., 405(95), *460,* 539, *549*

Elvey, C. T., 219(1), 221(1), 225, 229, 230, 257, *261, 262, 263, 267,* 292, *296,* 314, *351*

Elwert, G., 144, 145, *146, 148,* 189, 199, 200, *216*

Emhert, A., 456(97), *460*

Epstein, P. S., 39, *70*

Eshelman, V. R., 519, *548*

Evans, A. G., 250, 254, *265*

Evans, J. V., 435(98), *461*

Evans, S., 523(24), 530, *548*

Eyfrig, R., 355(3), *374*

Eyring, H., 516(5), *548*

Fan, C. Y., 298(9), 308(9), 313, 315, 321(102), 333(9), 340(144), 342(9), *349, 351, 352*

Farley, D. T., 447(315), *470*

Farnsworth, A. H., 229, 257, *263*

Federova, N. I., 225, *262,* 298, 300, 304, *349*

Fedynsky, V. V., 537, *548*

Fejer, J. A., 392(99), 397(99), 404(100), 409, 410, 439(99), 461(100), *461,* 483(17), 485, *511*

Ference, M., 91(14), 97(14), *129*

Ferraro, V. C., 47(19), *70,* 390(101), *461,* 499, *512*

Ferrell, O. P., 422(102), *461*

Fishbach, F. F., 56(33), *70*

Forbush, S. E., 488, 500, *511, 512*

Försterling, K., 401(103), *461*

Forsyth, P. A., 285, *295*

Forsyth, T. A., 356(15), 357(15), 358, 359(15), 360(15), 362(15), 363, 366, 373(15, 24), *375*

Fraser, P. A., 304(35), *349*

Fricker, S. J., 356(18), 362, 366, *375*

Friedman, H., 29, 56(35, 38), *70,* 148, 154 (21), 155(29), *155, 156, 158,* 159(30), *162,* 165(32), *167,* 168(21), 169(38, 39), *173,* 188(21), 189(63), 191(64), 196, 198(39), 201(81), 202(83), 207(87), 208(90), 209(90), 210(91), 214(90), *216, 217, 218,* 222(28), *261,* 383(119), *461*

Friedman, M., 417(66), *459*

Fritz, H., 280, 287, *295*

Frongia, G., 222, *261*

Fukushima, N., 501, 505(49), *512*

Fuller, V. R., 272, 284, *294*

Gadsen, M., 255, *266*

Gailar, N., *167*

Galbraith, W., 243, *265*

Gallet, R., 422(104), *461*

Galperin, G. I., 307, 310, 312, 314, 318, 320, *350*

Gardner, F. E., 452(106), *461*

Gardner, F. F., 405(96), 408(106, 207), 409, 140, *461, 465*

Garrigue, H., 256, *267*

Garstang, R. H., 256, 259, *267,* 300, *349*

Gartlein, C. W., 270, 283, 284, 286, 292 (46a, 72a), 293(85), *294, 295, 296,* 299, 303, 314, 334, *349, 351,* 356(16), 366(16), *375*

Garvin, D., 251(169), *266*

Gautier, T. N., 432(158, 159), 438(158, 159), *463*
Gauzit, J., 221, 258, *261, 267*, 313(71), *350*
Gaydon, A. G., 222, 223, *262*
Geddes, M., 272, 283, *294, 295*
Gehrels, E., 401(286), 435(286), *468*
Gerard, V. B., 292(72c), *296*, 422(107), *461*
Gerson, N. C., 285, *295, 296*, 390(108), *461*
Ghosh, S. K., 317, *351*
Ghosh, S. N., 250(166), 253(187), *265, 266*, 329(121), *352*
Gibbons, J. J., 403(285), *468*
Gill, J. C., 515, *548*
Gill, P. J., 292(72c), *296*
Gish, O. H., 292, *296*
Glaume, J., 239, 240, *264*
Glazer, H., 416(183), *464*
Gluckauf, E., 28(2, 5), *69*
Gnanalingam, S., 411(109), *461*
Götz, F. W. P., 225, 236, 237, 243, *262, 264*, 313, *350*
Gold, T., 237, *264*, 560(10), *561*
Goldberg, L., 138(5), *215*
Goodwin, G. L., 422(110), *461*.
Goody, R. M., 225(69), *262*
Gorchakov, E. V., 202(82), *217*
Gottlieb, M. B., 121(89), *131*, 215(94), *218*, 322(107), *351*
Goubau, G., 102, *130*, 355(3), *374*
Grawert, G., 402(111), *461*
Green, F. D., *558*
Greenhow, J. S., 448(112, 113), *461*, 517, 519, 529, 531, 539, 541, 543, 545, 546, 547(20), *548, 549*, 562, *563*
Gregory, J. B., 405(114, 116), 406(115), 452(117), *461*
Grew, K. E., *24*
Griffing, G. W., 318, 319, *351*
Grotrian, W., 143, *215*
Groves, G. V., 57(51, 54), *71*
Gush, H. P., 220, 224, 227, *261*

Hall, J. E., 529, 562, *563*
Hagg, E. L., 559(3), *561*
Harang, L., 272, 273, 274, 275, 277, 278, 279, *294, 295*, 310, 312, 314, 315, 318, 326, 339, *350, 351, 352*, 355(2), 356(11, 17), 358, 360, 361, 366, 373, *374, 375, 558*

Harnischmacher, E., 416(118), *461*
Harris, I., 57(44, 45), 59, 60, *70*, 95(25), *130*
Harrison, A. W., 240(124), 260(215d), *244, 267*, 298, 301, 304, 342, *349, 353*
Harrower, G. A., *48*
Harteck, P., 250, *265*
Hartz, T. R., *558*
Hasegawa, M., 488, *511*
Haselgrove, J., 400(251), 432(251), *467*
Havens, R. J., *16*, 54, 56, *70*, 189, *217*, 383(119), *461*
Hawkins, D., *133*
Hawkins, G. S., 356(12), *375*, 517, 520(22), *548*, 562, *563*
Heddle, D. W. O., 180, *216*
Hellgren, G., 356(14), 359, 360(14), *375*
Helliwell, R. A., 401(286, 287), 406(120), 435(286, 287), *461, 468*
Hendrix, W. C., 480(6), *511*
Hepburn, F., 407(121), *461*
Heppner, J. P., 110(54, 56), 112(73–75), 117, 120, 121(91), *130, 131*, 225, 263 (74), *263*, 284, 291, *295, 296*, 355(6), *374*
Herlofson, N., 516, 519, 545, *548*
Herman, R. C., 224, *262*
Herzberg, G., 222, 224, 247, 250, *262*, 265
Herzberg, M., 436(122), *461*
Hewish, A., 445(123), 446(123), 447(223), *462, 466*
Hibberd, F., *467*
Hines, C. O., 445(288), 446(124), *462, 468*
Hinteregger, H. E., 163, *216*
Hirono, M., 392(125), 397(126, 127), 439 (126, 127), *462*, 483(15), 485, 487(15), 488, 489, *511*
Hoeppner, J. P., 323(113), *352*
Hoffman, R., 288(676), *296*, 322(111), *351*
Hollingworth, J., 407, *462*
Holmes, J. C., 112(77, 81, 82), 117, *131*
Holzer, R. E., 508, *512*
Hooker, J. D., 283, *295*
Hornbeck, G. A., 224, *262*
Horowitz, R., 56(32, 34, 37), 57(37), 63(37), *70*, 91(19–22), *129, 130*
Houston, R. E., Jr., 108(49), *130*, 192, *217*, 410, 456(129), *462*
Hoyle, F., 188, *217*, 383(131), *462*
Hulburt, E. O., 188, 189(63), 214(93), *217, 218*, 285, *295*, 383(119), *461*

Hult, O., 560(9), *561*
Hultqvist, B., 282, 283, *295*
Humphreys, C. J., 224(58), *262*
Hunten, D. M., 239(121), 240(124a), 252, 253, 254(192, 194, 196), 255(192), 256, *264, 266, 267,* 298, 300, 303, 304, 305, 306, 307, 308, 309, 313, 314, 315, 334 (130), 336, 339, 341, 342(148), 343, *349, 352, 353*
Hunter, W. R., *153*
Huruhata, M., 240, *264*
Huxley, L. G. H., 404(132), 443(133), 444, *462, 470*

Ibbs, T. L., *24*
Ingalls, R. P., 356(18), 362(18), 366(18), *375*
Ingram, L. J., 355(1), *374,* 455(281), *468*
Inn, E. C. Y., *161, 180,* 184(49), *216*
Ireton, H. J. C., 221, *261,* 272(12), *294*
Istomin, V. G., 116(83), *131*

Jacchia, L. G., 57(46–48), 58(46, 48), 59, 60, 69, *70, 71,* 516(12), 529, 531, 533, 535, *548*
Jackson, J. E., 103(33, 34, 36–41, 44, 45), 104–108, *130,* 187(56), *217,* 379(134), 399(134, 234), 400(135), 422(136), 454 (234), *462, 466*
Jacobs, J. A., 499, 501, *512*
Janin, J., 224(59), *262*
Jarmain, W. R., 304, *349*
Jastrow, R., 57(44, 45), 59, 60, *70,* 95, *130*
Jelley, J. V., 243, *265*
Jensen, R. E., 279, *295*
Johnson, C. Y., 112(73–75, 77, 80–82), 113(72), *117, 131*
Johnson, F. S., 48, *70,* 111(66–69), 113, 114, *131,* 152(23), 153(26), 165(31), 167, 168(27), 193(27), 205, 214, *216, 218*
Johnson, M. A., 448(81), *460*
Johnston, H. F., 492, 493(36), *512*
Jones, A. V., 220, 225, 227, 233, 240(124), 254, 255, 256, 260(215d), *261, 264, 266, 267,* 298, 301, 304, 315, 339, 342, 343(136a, 150b), *349, 351, 352, 353*
Jones, C. K., 279, *295*

Jones, H. S., 230(107), 231, 232, 235, 237, *264*
Jones, I. L., 446(137), 448(138), *462*
Jones, L. M., 56, *70,* 111(61, 63), *131*
Jones, R. E., 195, *217,* 389(191, 192), 412(191), 416(139), *462, 465*
Jonsson, E., 184, *217*
Jursa, A., 119(85), *131,* 249(160), 250(162), *265*

Kaiser, T. R., 293, 294, *296,* 360, 362, 364, 365(23), *375,* 519, 523(24), 526, 530, 532, 545, 546, *548, 549*
Kallman, H. K., 91(17), *129,* 193, *217,* 417(140, 141), *462,* 484(29), *511*
Kane, J. A., 103(40), *130*
Kaplan, J., 223, *262*
Karandikar, J. V., 228, *263*
Kasper, J. E., 322, *351*
Kastler, A., 222, 226, 246(32), 252(175, 176), 253, *261, 263, 266*
Kato, S., 439(142, 143), 449(142, 143), 486, *511, 512*
Kato, Y., 500, 505, 508, 509(68), *512*
Kavadas, A., 293, *296, 558*
Kellog, W. W., 483, *511*
Kelso, J. M., 404(289), *468*
Kent, G. S., 446(144), *462*
Kestin, J., 51, *70*
Khvostikov, I. A., 226, *263*
Kiepenhauer, K. O., 288, *296,* 433(145), *462*
Kim, J. S., 293, *296, 558*
Kimball, D. S., 292(72a), 293(85), *296*
King-Hele, D. G., 57(52, 57), 69, *71*
Kirby, R. C., 405(25), 446(25), 447(25), *457*
Kirkpatrick, C. B., 439(146), *463*
Kitamura, T., 396(127), 439(127), *462*
Knecht, R. W., 355(8), *374,* 558(1), *561*
Koenig, H. J., 343(150b), *353*
Koll, R. T., *16,* 54(28), 56(28), *70*
Kononovitch, W. E., 140, *215*
Koomen, M., 119(86, 87), *131,* 241(136), 257, 258(204, 209), *265, 267*
Kopal, Z., 74, *129*
Korff, S. A., 155(28), *216*
Koster, J. R., 446(147), 450(147, 270), *463, 468*

Krassovsky, V. I., 106(48), 108(48), 123 (96), *130, 132,* 220, 223, 224, 249(158), 251, *261, 265, 266,* 312, *350*
Kreplin, R. W., 167, 169(38), *216*
Krogness, O., 272, 273, 274, 275, 277, 278, 279, 293, *294, 296*
Kron, G. E., 224, *262*
Kruse, F. W., 406(120), *461*
Kundu, M. R., 421(190), *464*
Kupperian, J. E., Jr., 56(38), *70,* 167, 168(35), 169(38), 201(81), 202(83), 204, 207(87, 88), 210(91), *216–218,* 222(28), *261*
Kvifte, G., 251(173), 256(199g), *266, 267,* 298, 301, 303, 304, 307, 308, 312, 319, 328, 334, 335, 341(98, 145), *348, 350, 351, 352*

La Gow, H. E., *16,* 54(28), 56(28, 32, 34, 37), 57(37), 63(37), *70,* 88, 91(16, 19–22), *95, 124, 129, 130, 132*
Lamar, E. S., 344(159), *353*
Landmark, B., 446(137), 454(148), *462, 463,* 560(9), *561*
Landmark, V., 356(17), 359, 360, 361, 366, 373, *375*
Lange, I., 473(2), 480(6), 497(2), 501(2), 509(2), 510(2), *511*
Lange-Hesse, G., 409(150), 455(149), *463*
Laporte, L., 473(2), 480(6), 497(2), 501(2), 509(2), 510(2), *511*
Lassen, H., 400(111), *461*
Lauter, E. A., 407(152, 154), 454(151), 456(153), *463*
Lawrence, T. R., 335, *352*
Lawrie, J. A., 292, *296*
Leadabrand, R. L., 355(9), 356(19), 359, 360, 361, 362, 366, 367, 368, 370, 371, *374, 375*
Lebedinsky, A. J., 343, *353*
Lee, A. W., 284, 285, 289, *295*
Lee, Po, 180, 181, *182,* 184, *216*
Leighauser, G., 355(3), *374*
Leinbach, H., 559(7), *561*
Leslie, D. C., 57(52), *71*
Lewis, R. P. W., 453(155), *463*
Lichtman, S. W., 148(21), 154(21), 167, 168(21), 188(21), *216*
Lied, F., 560(9), *561*

Liller, W., 537, *548*
Lindquist, R., 406(284), *468*
Link, F., 534(40), 535, *548*
Linke, W., 225(65), *262*
Little, C. G., 215, *218,* 337, *352,* 455(78), *460*
Littlewood, C. A., 418(156), *463*
Lock, C., 258(209), *267*
Loh, L. T., 111(61), *131*
Lovell, A. C. B., 514(1), 515, 518, 520, 522, 523(1), 524, 525, 526, 527, 546, *548*
Lowan, A. N., 49, *70,* 91(18), *129*
Logachev, Y. I., *554*
Lozachev, J. I., 202(82), *217*
Ludwig, G., 122(94), *132,* 322(109), *351,* 505(53), 506(53), *512*
Lung, H. L., 428(157), *463*
Lynn, N., 337, *352*
Lyon, A. J., 387(22), 388(22), 416(22), 418(20, 21), *457*
Lyon, G. F., 293, *296, 558*
Lytle, E. A., 256, *267,* 343(150a), *353*

McCaulley, J. W., 237(120a, 122a), *264*
Maccoll, J. W., 74, *129*
McCreedy, L. L., 408(207), *465*
McDowell, M. R. C., 322(106), *351,* 383(34), *458*
McEwen, D. J., 272, 275, *294*
McIlwain, C. E., 121(92), 122(94), *132,* 322(109), 323, *351, 352,* 505(53), 506(53), *512*
McIntosh, D. H., 453(155), *463*
Mack, J. E., 254, 255(192), *266*
McKinley, D. W. R., 517, *548*
McKinley, J. D., 251, *266,* 356(13), *375*
McLennan, J. C., 221, *261,* 272, *294*
McLeod, J. H., 221, *261*
McNamara, A. G., 373, *375*
McNish, A. G., 288(66), *296,* 432(158, 159), 438(158, 159), *463*
McPherson, D. H., 254, *266*
McQuarrie, W. C., 221, *261*
Maeda, H., 393(160), 397(126), 439(126, 161, 162), 449(161, 162), *462, 463,* 485, 486, 487, *511*
Maeda, K., 483(16), 485, *511*
Maeda, K. I., 452(290), *468*
Malitson, H. H., 152, 167, 168(27), 193(27), 214(27), *216*

Mallinckrodt, A. J., 406(120), *461*
Malville, J. M., 284, 285, 292, 294, *295*
Mange, P., *16*, 29, 31(9), 39, *70*, 166, 191, *216*, 258, *267*, 424(306), 436(204, 306), *465*, *469*
Manning, L. A., 422(255), 448(164), *463*, *467*, 539, *549*
Manring, E. R., 118(84), *131*, 228(97), 229, 230, 234, 238, 250(162, 166, 166a), 253(184, 187), *263*, *265*, *266*, 300, *349*
Maple, E., 109(51, 53), *130*, 483, *511*
Mariani, F., 429(166, 167), 433(165), *463*
Marmo, F. F., 119(85), *131*, 180, 181(44), 184(49), 191(44), *216*, 249(160), 250(162), *265*
Marovich, E., 240(122a, 131), *264*, 283, *295*
Martyn, D. F., 144, *216*, 236(112), *264*, 316, *351*, 390(175), 392(175), 393(27), 397(171, 172, 174), 404(26), 418(168, 293), 427(170, 173), 431, 432(172), 434(172, 173), 437(168, 291–294), 438(168, 292, 293), 439(171), 441(176), 446(295), 448(171), 449(171, 174), 450, 452(169), 455(169), *457*, *463*, *464*, *468*, *469*, 483(14), 484, 485, 488, 489, 494, 506, *511*, *512*
Mason, R. G., 292, *296*
Massey, H. S. W., 245(145, 146), *265*, 323(114), 325(114), 329(114), 331(114), 344, *352*, *353*, 383(31–33, 177), 385(33), 413(36, 37), 435(178), *458*, *464*, 546(54), 547(55), *549*
Matsushita, S., 292, *296*, 422(179–181), *464*
Maxwell, A., *464*
Mayaud, P. N., 252, *266*
Meadows, E. B., 29, 47, 57(39), *69*, *70*, 94, 112(71, 72, 76–79, 81, 82), 117, *131*
Meek, J. H., 283, 289, 290, 293, *295*, *296*, 355(4, 5), 374, *374*
Megill, L. R., 238(120d), 240(131), *264*
Meinel, A. B., 220, 221, 222, 223, 224, 225, 227, 240, 243, 259, 260(34), *261*, *262*, *263*, 277, 285, 286, 287, 289, 293, *294*, *295*, *296*, 298(7, 9), 299(14, 18), 300, 303(7, 9, 28), 304, 308(9), 309, 310, 311, 312, 313, 314, 315, 319, 321(102, 103), 330, 333(9), 334, 342(9), *349*, *350*, *351*
Menzel, D. H., 416(183, 305), *464*, *469*
Menzel, W., 355(3), *374*

Meos, J., 356(14), 359, 360(14), *375*
Meredith, L., 241(136), *265*
Meredith, L. H., 110(54, 56), 119(86, 88), 120, 121(89, 91), *130*, *131*, 215, *218*, 225, 241(74), *263*, 322, 323, *351*, *352*
Merson, R. M., 57(75), *71*
Michnevich, B. B., 241, *264*
Michnevich, V. V., 56(36), *70*, 96(28), 111(65), *130*, *131*
Miley, H. A., 260(216), *267*
Milligan, J. E., 207(88), *217*
Millman, P. M., 356(13), *375*, 517, *548*
Mills, B. Y., 148(18), *216*
Minnaert, M., 300, *349*
Minnett, H. C., 148, *216*
Minnis, C. M., 389(184), 407(307), 451 (184a), *464*, *469*
Mironov, A. V., 227, *263*, 300, 313, *349*
Mirtov, B. A., 111(62), *131*
Mitra, A. P., 195, *217*, 236(113), *264*, 386, 389(191, 192), 404(189), 410(188), 412(186, 191, 193, 194), 413, *464*, *465*, *469*
Mitra, S. K., 329(122), *352*, 380(187), 421 (190), *464*
Mitra, S. N., 447(185), *464*
Moffitt, W., 247, *265*
Mohler, F. L., 388(195), *465*
Mohr, E. I., 184, *216*
Moiseiwitsch, B. L., 251, *266*
Montalbetti, R., 259(215), *267*, 272, 275, *294*, 314, 315, 342, *351*, *353*
Moore, C. B., 250(166a), *265*
Moore, R. K., 286, *296*, 355(10), *375*
Moreau, G., 313, *350*
Morgan, M. G., 401(287), 435(287), *468*
Morozov, V. M., 260, *267*
Morse, P. M., 344, *353*
Muldrew, D., 559(3), *561*
Muller, H., 148, *216*
Mulyarchik, T. M., 340, *352*
Munday, G., 180, 181(42), *216*
Munro, G. H., 445(198), 446(196–198), 447, *465*
Murcray, W. B., 303, 313, *349*, *350*
Myamoto, S., 144, *216*

Nagata, T., 501, *512*
Naismith, R., 355(1), *374*, 417(10), 419(11), 421(200), 455(281), *457*, *465*, *468*

Nazarova, T. N., 125(99), *132*
Nearhoof, H. J., 404(289), *468*
Negaard, B. J., 285(54), 286, 287(54), 289(54), *295*
Neill, H. W., 111(61), *131*
Nertney, R. J., 404(289), 410, *465*, *468*
Netzer, Th., 355(3), *374*
Neufeld, E. L., 448(112, 113), *461*, 531, 541, 543, 545, *548*, *549*
Newell, H. E., 73(3, 4, 6), 91(13, 17), *129*, 417(40), *462*
Newman, P., 270, 292, *294*
Newton, H. W., 499, *512*
Nichols, B., 356(16, 21), 364, 365, 366(16), *375*, *558*
Nichols, M. H., 111(61), *131*
Nicholls, R. W., 223, 227, *262*, 304(35), 307, 308(47), 333, *349*, *350*
Nicolet, M., *16*, 26(1), 27(1), 31(9, 10), 32(11, 12), 38(14), 57(56), 67, *69–71*, *106*, 166, 191, 192, 208, 210, *216–218*, 225, 241, 243, 245, 249–252, 258, 259, *262*, *264–267*, 303 (30, 31), *349*, 382(202), 436(204), 443, *465*, *469*
Nidey, R. A., 153(24), *216*
Nikolsky, A. P., 508, *512*, 559, *561*
Nordberg, W., 55(31), *70*, 91(15, 23), 93(15), 97(15, 23), 98, *129*, *130*

Obayashi, T., 499, 501, *512*
Oberly, J. J., 152(23), *216*
Odishaw, H., 256, *257*, 288, *296*
Ogawa, M., 250, *265*
Oguti, T., 500, *512*
Oliver, N. J., 224, 225, 227, *262*, *263*, 298, *348*
Olivier, C. P., 537, *548*
Omholt, A., 298, 302, 305, 306, 308, 309, 310, 312, 313, 314, 315, 319, 320, 322 (106), 326, 327, 332, 334(129, 131), 335(12), 337, 346, *349*, *350*, *351*, *352*
Osborne, B. W., 449(205), *465*
Oster, L., 50, *70*
Otterman, J., 91(23), 93, 97(23), 98, *130*
Ozdogan, I., 47(19), *70*

Packer, D. M., *153*, 257(204), 258(204, 209), *267*

Paetzold, H. K., 57(50), *71*
Paneth, F. A., 28, *69*, 111(58–60, 62), *69*, *131*
Pant, P. S., 483, *511*
Parkinson, R. W., 410(206), *460*, *465*
Parkinson, W. C., 499(41), *512*
Paschen, F., 221, *261*
Paulsen, A., 287, *296*
Pavlova, E. N., 228(95), *263*
Pawsey, J. L., 405(105), 408(207), 409, 410, *461*, *465*
Pearse, R. W. B., 222, *261*, 323(114), 325(114), 329(114), 331(114), *352*
Pedersen, P. O., 483, *511*
Pekeris, C. L., 483, 490, *511*
Penndorf, R., 188, 191, *217*
Penton, W. A., 456(2), *456*
Percival, I. C., 310, 331, *350*, *352*
Peterson, A. M., 422(80, 255), 448(164), *460*, *463*, *467*, 539(46), *549*
Peterson, J. W., 56(33), *70*
Peterson, L., 200, *217*, 288(676), *296*, 322(111), *351*, 355(9), 356(19), 359, 360(19), 361, 362, 366(19), 367(19), 368, 370(19), 371, *374*, *375*
Petrie, W., 259(215), *267*, 298, 300, 301, 302, 303, 304, 309, 312, 314, 334, 335, 336, 342, *349*, *350*, *353*
Pettit, H. B., 228, 229, 230, 233, 234, 235(94), 237, 238(94, 100), 239, 240 (94, 127), 250(166a), *263*, *264*, *265*, 293(84), *296*, 300, 306, *349*, *350*
Peyron, M., 224(59), *262*
Pfister, W., 423(210), 444 (209), *465*
Phillips, G. J., 445(60, 61), 446(60, 61), *459*
Pickar, A. D., 103(34), *130*, 187(56), *217*, 399(234), 454(234), *466*
Piddington, J. H., 148, *216*
Pierce, J. A., 526, *548*
Pietenpol, W. A., 153(24), *216*
Piggot, W. R., 196, *217*, 402(18), 408(18, 211), 409(18), 418(212), 452(15, 19), *457*, *465*, 559(2), *561*
Pineo, V. C., 406(213), 446(213), *465*
Plendl, H., 355(3), *374*
Plimmer, R. N. A., 57(57), *71*
Plyler, E. K., 224(58), *262*
Porter, J. G., 529, *548*
Pressly, E. C., 29(6), *69*, 112(71), *131*

Pressman, J., 119(85), *131*, 181(44), *182*, 191(44), *216*, 249, 250(162), *265*
Pritchard, A. G., 418(20), *457*
Prokudina, V. S., 222, 227(88a), *261, 263*, 300(21a), 313(21a), *349*
Pulley, O. O., 236(112), *264*
Purcell, J. D., 111(66, 67, 69), 112–114, *131*, 152, 153(26), 165(31), 167, 168 (27, 37), 193(27), 214(27), *216*
Purdy, C. M., 237(120a), 240(120a), *264*
Pushkov, N. V., 511(73), *512*

Quenby, J. J., 510, *512*

Ramsauer, C., 533, *548*
Ranyard, A. C., 297, *348*
Ratcliffe, J. A., 392(217), 397(218), 404(132), 406(58), 425(217, 297), 432(214), 434(297, 299), 435(216, 217), 436(216), 440(217), 445(215, 296), 451(58), 454(58), *459, 462, 466, 469*
Rawer, K., 380(219), 404(50a), 417(220), 442(23), *457, 458, 466*
Ray, E. C., 322(109), *351*, 505(53), 506(53), *512*
Rayleigh, Lord, 221, 225, 230, 231, 232, 234, 235, 236, 237, 239, *261, 263, 264*, 313, *350*
Rdultovskaya, E. V., 228(95), *263*
Reasbeck, P., 111(60), *131*
Reber, G., 450(302), *469*
Rees, M. H., 240(131), *264*, 308, 323, *350*
Reid, G. C., 456(316), *470*, 559(6, 7), *561*
Reisig, G. H. R., 98–101, *130*
Rense, W. A., 151(22), 153, *167*, 206, *216*
Revello, K., 456(97), *460*
Richardson, R. S., 288, *296*
Roach, F. E., 225(73), 228(93, 94), 229, 233, 234(94), 235, 237, 238, 239(121), 240(73, 94, 120a, 122a, 127, 131), 253, *263, 264, 266*, 283, 293, *295, 296*
Roach, W. T., 225(69), *262*
Robbins, A. R., 400(250, 251), 427, 432 (250, 251), 433, 434(299), 439(250), *466, 467, 469*
Robertson, D. S., 448(94), *460*, 539, *549*
Robinson, B. J., 414(222), 416(222), *466*
Robley, R., 226, 252(176, 181), *263, 266*
Rodionov, S. F., 228(95), *263*

Roesler, F. L., 220, 224, *261*, 302, 340, *349*, *352*
Romick, G. J., 292, *296*, 314, *351*
Rooney, W. J., 292, *296*
Ross, W. J., 456(129), *462*
Rostad, A., 291, *296*
Rowland, J. P., 288, *296*
Ryle, M., 447(223), *466*
Rypdal, R., 334, *352*

Saito, T., 505(62), *512*
Salmon, K., 255, *266*
Sanford, R. F., 252, *266*
Sato, T., 452(290), 455(224–227), *466, 468*
Schaefer, D. H., 124(98), *132*
Schaffert, J. C., 124(98), *132*
Schilling, G. F., 57(43, 49), 59, 60, *70, 71*, 483, *511*
Schlapp, D. M., 442(228), *466*
Schmerling, E. R., 392(217), 400(230), 425 (217), 435(217), 440(217), 456(129), *462, 466*
Scholz, J., 292, *296*
Schonland, B. F. J., 407(229), *466*
Schulte, D. H., 293, *296*, 313, 315, *351*
Schuster, A., 477, 482, 490, *511*
Scolnik, R., 119(86, 87), *131*, 241(136), 258(209), *265, 267*
Scott, J. C. W., 433(232), *466*
Scott, W. E., 473(2), 497(2), 501(2), 509(2), 510(2), *511*
Scrimger, J. A., 254, *266*
Seaton, M. J., 183, 184(45), *216*, 241–243, 245, 246, 248, 255, 257, 259, *265, 266*, 302, 305, 307, 310, 312, 323, 325, 326(26), 327–331, 334, 337–339, 343, 347, *349, 350, 352*, 383(35), 429(42, 233), 452(45), *458, 466*
Seaton, S. L., 455(282), *458, 468*
Seddon, J. C., 103(32, 34–37, 41–45), *105, 106, 107, 130*, 187(56), *217*, 399(234), 407(235), 422(136), 442(235), 454(234), *462, 466*
Sedov, L. I., 96(29), 97(29), *130*
Sen, H. K., 483, 490, *511*
Serson, H., 259(215), *267, 558*
Setty, C. S. G. K., 392(217), 425(217), 435(217), 440(217), 446(137), *462, 466*
Severny, A. B., 201, *217*

Shain, C. A., 404(189), *464*
Shane, C. D., 253, *266*
Shapiro, B. S., 435(301), *469*
Shaw, I. J., 442(236), *466*
Shaw, J. H., 225(69), *262*
Shefov, N. N., 225, 227(88a), *263*, 300(21a), 313(21a), *349*
Shepherd, G. G., 253, *266*, 334(130), 341, 342(148), *352, 353*
Sheppard, P. A., 292, *296*
Sherman, D. F., 303, *349*
Sherman, K. L., 292, *296*
Shimazaki, T., 383(237), *466*
Shinn, D. H., 445(61), 446(61), *459*
Shklovski, J. S., 319, 335, *352*
Shklovsky, I. S., 140, 144, 204, *215, 216, 217*, 222, 260, *261, 267*, 316, 320, 335, *351*
Shrum, G. M., 221, *261*
Shull, H., 259, *267*
Shuyskaya, F. K., 227(88a), *263*
Shvidkovsky, E. G., 96(27), *130*
Sibley, W. L., 283, *295*
Silberstein, R., 379(298), *469*
Simpson, J. A., 510, *512*
Singer, S. F., 73(1), 109(51–53), *109, 129, 130*, 483, 505, *511*, 512
Siry, J. W., 57(55), 60, *71*, 73(3), *129*
Skeib, G., 456(153), *463*
Skellet, A. M., 526, *548*
Skinner, N. J., 404(238), 422(239), 450(270), *466, 468*
Slipher, V. M., 221, 259, *261, 267*, 313, *350*
Sloan, R., 225(69), *262*
Small, R., 298, 300, 303, 304, 309, 314, 334, 335, 336, *349*
Smit, J. A., 344, *353*
Smith, C. A., 225, *262*
Smith, E. K., 419(240, 300), 420, 421, *467, 469*
Smith, F. G., 435(241), *467*
Smith, H. J., 516(9), *548*
Smith, P. T., 320, 337, *351*
Smith, S. J., 246, *265*, 332, *352*
Snyder, E. J., 283, 287, *295*
Spencer, M., 445(63), 446(243), 447(63), *459, 467*, 483, 486, *511*
Spitzer, L., Jr., 12, *16*, 48, *70*, 226, *263*, 339, *352*
Sprague, G., 292(72a), *296*, 303, 334, *349*

Sprenger, K., 454(151), 456(153), *463*
Stacey, D. S., 153, *216*
Stagg, J. M., 272, 284, 289, *294*, 488, 508, *511, 512*
St. Amand, P., 228(94), 233, 234(94), 235(94), 236, 238(94), 239, 240(94), *263, 264*
Stebbins, J., 225(66), *262*
Stein, S., 355(9), *374*
Sterne, T. E., 57(40, 43), 59, 60, *70*
Stetson, H. T., 284, 286, 287, *295, 296*
Stewart, A. L., 318, *351*
Stewart, B., 482, *511*
Stewart, D. T., 249, *265*, 320, 337, *351*
Stibbs, D. W. N., 137(2), 140(2), *215*
Stith, G. A., 153(24), *216*
Störmer, C., 236, *264*, 272–277, 278(18), 279, 280, 285, 293, *294, 295*, 312(61, 64), 314, 325, 337, 338, *350, 351*, 505, *512*, 559, *561*
Stoffregen, W., 356, *375*, 454(245), *467*
Stolarik, J. D., 110(54), *110, 130*
Stone, A. H., 74, *129*
Stone, J. M., 226, *263*
Stone, M. L., 356(18), 362(18), 366(18), *375*
Storey, L. R. O., 401(246, 247), 435(246, 247), *467*
Strain, C. V., 152(23), *216*
Straker, T. W., 196(75), *217*, 406(58), 451(58), 452(57), 454(58), *459*
Stroud, W. G., 55(31), *70*, 91(14, 15, 23), 93(15), 97(14, 15, 23), 98, *129, 130*
Struve, O., 204, *217*
Sugiura, M., 500, *512*
Sutton, D. J., 443(133), 444(133), *462*
Svenson, A. C., *467*
Sverdrup, H. U., 281, 284, 287, *295*
Swings, P., 222, 225(65), 228, 252, 259, *262, 263, 266*, 312, 332, *350, 352*

Takahashi, H., 435(309), 437(309), *469*
Tamur, Y., 486, *511*
Tanaka, Y., 184, *216*, 330, *352*
Tandberg-Hanssen, E., 238(120d), *264*
Tate, J. T., 320, 337, *351*
Taubenheim, J., 419(248), 451(248), *467*
Taylor, G. I., 74, *129*, 483, 490, *511*

Tcheng Mao-Lin, 228, 234, 235(109), 236, 240, 253, 257, *263, 264, 266*, 313(71, 73), 348, *350*

Tereda, T., 508, *512*

Thomas, J. A., 419(300), *467*

Thomas, J. O., 392(217), 400(230, 250–252), 425(217), 432(250–252), 433, 434(299), 439(250), 440(217), *466, 469*

Thomas, R. N., 516(5–8), *548*

Thomson, J. H., 435(1), *456*

Titus, R., 91(23), 93, 97(23), 98, *130*

Tönsberg, E., 251(173), *266*, 272, 273, 293, *294, 296*, 308, 309, 310, 312, 341(48, 145), *350, 352*

Tousey, R., 111(67, 69), 112, 113, 114, 119(87), *131*, 152(23), 153(26), 165(31), 167, 168(27, 37), 193, 214(27), *216*, 241(136), 257(204), 258(204, 209), *265, 267*

Townsend, J. W., Jr., 29(6, 7), 47, 57(39, 58), *69, 70, 71, 94*, 113(70, 71, 76, 79), *115, 131*

Tremellen, K. W., 416(253), *467*

Troim, J., *558*

Troïtskaia, V. N., 508, *512*

Tromholt, S., 285, 293, *295, 296*

Turnbull, A. G., 418(21), *457*

Tuve, M. A., 483, *511*

Ulwick, J. C., 423(210), *465*

Unthank, H. W., 499, *512*

Unwin, J. J., 245(145), *265*, 383(31), *458*, 546(54), *549*

Unzicker, A., 56(38), *70*, 210(91), *218*

Upton, E. K. L., 562, *563*

Vacquier, V., 490, *512*

Vakulov, P. V., 202(82), *217, 554*

Van Allen, J. A., *49*, 110(55), 121(89, 90), 122(94), *130–132*, 138(3, 4), 215(94), *218*, 332(107–110), *351*, 505(53), 506, 511(72), *512*, 551, *554*

van Wyk, J. W., 407(229), *466*

Vassy, A., 237(118), 253, *264, 266*

Vassy, R., 237(118), 253, *264, 266*

Vawter, F. E., 285, *295*, 356(15), 357(15), 358, 359(15), 360(15), 362(15), 363, 373(15), *375*

Vegard, L., 186, *217*, 251, *266*, 272, 273, 274, 275, 277, 278(30, 31), 279, 284, 285, 287, *294, 295, 296*, 298, 299, 300, 301, 303, 304, 307, 308, 309, 310, 311, 312, 313, 314, 315, 316, 319, 324, 328, 334, 335, 339, 341, *348, 349, 350, 351, 352*

Veller, A. E., 315, *351*

Vernov, S. N., 122(95), *132*, 202(82), *217*, 505, *512*, 551, *554*

Vestine, E. H., 281, 282, 283, 287, 294, *295, 296*, 343, *353*, 473(2), 480(6), 488(34), 497(2), 500, 501(2), 505(61), 509, 510, *511, 512*

Victoreen, J. A., 184, *217*

Vilbig, F., 355(3), *374*

Villard, O. D., 422(255), 448(164), *463, 467*, 539(46), *549*

Villars, F., 424(256), 447(256), *467*

Vitousek, M. J., 292, *296*

Vogan, E. L., 366, 373, *375*

Vuks, M. F., 251, *266*

Waldemeier, M., 147, 194, *216, 217*

Wallace, L., 302, 303, *349*

Walsh, J. R., 55(31), *70*, 91(14, 15), 93(15), 97(14, 15), *129*

Wang, S. T., 356(18), 362(18), 366(18), *375*

Warburton, J. A., 148, *216*

Warfield, C. N., 78(11), *129*

Wark, D. Q., 226, 257, *263, 267*

Warren, E., 559(3), *561*

Warwick, C. S., 194(70), *217*, 561(12), *561*

Warwick, J., 194(69), *217*

Warwick, J. W., 404(257), *467*

Watanabe, K., 111(67), 114, *131, 161*, 163, 166, *167*, 168(37), *180*, 181, *182*, 194 (34, 49), 191, *216*

Watts, J. M., 406, 418(258, 259), *467*

Waynick, A. H., 403(260, 261, 285), 404(289), *467, 468*

Webber, W. R., 510, *512*

Weekes, K., 380(262), 406(58), 410(109), 418(9), 435(1, 263), 448(81, 264), 451(58), 454(58), 456(41), *456–461*, 486, *511*

Weill, G., 255, *266*
Weisner, A. G., 91(14), 97(14, 30), *129, 130*
Weiss, A. A., 439(265, 266), *467, 468*, 545, *549*
Weisskopf, V. F., 424(256), 447(256), *467*
Weissler, G. L., 184, *216*
Wells, H. W., 429(42, 44), 451(43), 452(45), *458*
Wenzel, E. A., 111(61), *131*
Whale, H. A., 414(267), *468*
Whipple, F. L., 54(30), *70*, 483, 486, *511*, 516, 518, 529, 533, 537, *548*
White, C. S., 73(2), *129*
White, F. W. G., 283, *295*
White, M. L., 483, 490, *511*
White, W. B., 91(17), *129*, 417(140), *462*
White, W. C., 516(8), *548*
Whitehead, J. D., 408(269), 446(268), *468*
Whitford, A. E., 225(66), *262*
Whitney, C. A., 57(49), 59, 60, *71*
Wiborg, B. S., 111(60), *131*
Wiechert, E., 221, *261*
Wilkes, M. V., 382(312), *469*, 483, 490, *511*
Williams, D., 225(69, 72), 239, *262, 263*
Williams, D. R., 127, 224, 228(94), 233, 234(94), 225(94), 238(94), 240(94), *262, 263, 264*, 293(84), *296*, 298, 300, 301, 304, 314, *348*
Wilson, E. J., 111(58, 59), *131*

Winckler, J. R., 200, *217*, 288, *296*, 322, *351*
Witherspoon, A. E., 339(137), *352*
Wolbach, J. G., 416(183), *464*
Wood, F., 429(29), *458*
Wood, M. B., 561(12), *561*
Woolley, R. v.d. R., 137(2), 138(3, 4), 140(2), 144, *215*
Worley, R. E., 184, *216*
Wright, R. W., 404(238), 422(239), 450(270), *466, 468*
Wulf, O. R., 188, *217*, 244, *265*, 343, *353*, 483, 490, 505(60), *511, 512*
Wynne-Edwards, H. S., 272(12), *294*

Yabsley, D. E., 148(18), *216*
Yerg, D. G., *468*
Yonezawa, T., 429(308), 435(272–276, 309, 310), 436(273–276), 437(309), 441(272–276, 310), *468, 469*
Yumura, T., 500, *512*

Zelikoff, M., 119(85), *131, 161, 180*, 249(160), 250(161), *265*
Zenneck, J., 355(3), *374*
Zirin, H., 404(257), *467*
Zschörner, H., 57(50), *71*

Subject Index

Absorption
  by earth's atmosphere, 134, 135, 185, 186
  cross section, 179
  linear coefficient, 178, 179
  mass coefficient, 173
  of radio waves, 355, 373, 402
    deviative, 403
    non-deviative, 403
    types I, II and III, 560
    winter anomaly, 408
Acceleration of gravity, 78, 83
  variation with altitude, 83
Aeronomy, 4
After-effect of ionosphere storm, 454
Airglow, 5, 202, 205, 207
  see also nightglow, twilightglow or dayglow
Albedo, 203, 205
Amateurs, radio, 355
Angle, off perpendicular, 367, 372
Anomaly
  in $F2$ layer, 428, 429, 430
  sudden phase (SPA), 412, 452
  winter, in absorption, 408
Arc, auroral, 271, 272
Argon, 27, 29, 44, 45, 47, 111, 113, 114, 115
"Argus" experiment, 554
Aspect-sensitivity of auroral echoes, 359, 369
Atmospherics, (radio), 407
Atom-atom interchange, 226, 247, 248, 250, 323, 334
Atomic, see Hydrogen, Oxygen, etc.
Attachment of electrons, 246, 332, 383, 546, 547
Attenuation of radio waves, 355, 373
Aurora, 6, 16, 128, 558, Chaps. 6, 7, 8
  altitude, 272-278
  appearance, 269-272
  artificial, 271, 292
  discharge theories, 322, 328, 343-348
  diurnal occurrence, 284-285
  divided, 274, 337-338
  D region, 291

earth currents, 292
E layer, 291
electron density, 121, 327, 337, 338, 344-348
Es associated with, 455
excitation processes, 316-339
F layer, 291
forms, 271-272
geographical distribution, 280-284, 285, 286
geomagnetic control, 276-286, 315, 316
geometry, 278-280
heating by, 343
intensity, absolute, 304-307
intensity-altitude distribution, 277, 278, 318-320
ionization, 121, 321, 337, 344-346
lower border, 273-277
low latitude, 283, 284, 300, 302, 313, 316, 339, 347, 348
lunar tidal effect, 277
magnetic disturbance, 282, 285, 287-292, 316, 322
motion along lines of latitude, 293, 294
nuclear reactions in, 321
particles in, 120, 121, 122
penetration of primary stream, 316, 317
polarization of light, 297, 313
primary processes, 128, 316-321
radio echoes, 285, 291, 355
recurrence relations, 287, 288
secondary and other processes, 322-324
solar cycle and sunspots, 283, 286-288
sound from, 274
sunlit, 278, 304, 312, 337-339
type A, 300, 302, 312, 314, 316
type B, 303, 304, 306, 307, 312, 314, 316, 342
ultraviolet radiation, effects of, 330, 332, 337
upper limit, 277-278
vertical potential gradient under, 292
X-rays in, 121, 214, 215
yearly occurrence, 285, 286

Auroral spectrum, 298-304
  altitude effects, 310-312
  correlations, 315
  identifications, table of, 298, 299
  individual features—*see under* atom or
    molecule concerned
  intensities, relative, 303, 305-310, 312-
    314, 318, 320, 321, 325-328, 330-332,
    334, 339, 344-348
  latitude effects, 312, 313, 315
  temporal variations, 314-316
  type effects, 313, 314
  vibrational levels, rates of population
    of, 333, 336, 338-339
Auroral zone, 280
  currents during initial phase of storm, 501
  currents during main phase of storm, 501
  electric fields generated by winds, 506
  electrojets, 501, 503, 505, 506
  interlinkages by lines of force, 510
  leakage of charges to particles, 504, 505,
    506
  predicted by cosmic ray theory, 510
  pulsations, 508
Auto-correlation function, 369
Axis, geomagnetic, 16

Back-scattering, radio from aurora, 355,
  366, 369, 373
Balmer lines, *see* Hydrogen
Bands, spectral, in aurora, 271, 272
Bay, magnetic, 495
  current system for, 503
  electrojet for, 505
  production of, 506
Black-out, polar radio, 337, 454, 559, 560

Calcium, 225, 255
Carbon, dioxide, 4
  monoxide, 4
    bands in nightglow, 222
Chapman, function, 382
  layer, 382, 387, 398
Charge transfer, 245, 299, 317, 318, 335,
  337, 384, 435
Chemiluminescence, 246-251
Chemistry of atmosphere, 4, 111-118
Cherenkov radiation, 243
Chromosphere, 8, 138, 139, 166
Coefficient, radio reflection, 402
Coherent pulse radar, 539, 543

Collision, frequency of electrons, 14, 106,
  441-444, 560
  cross section, 443, 533
Columns of ionization, 369
Commencement, sudden, magnetic, 453
Composition, of atmosphere, 2, 15, 112
Compression cap, meteor, 516, 518
Condensation, coronal, 147, 174
Conductivity, electrical
                of ionosphere, 394, 484
                of layer, 395, 485
  thermal, 8, 9, 10, 11, 12, 20, 48, 50, 68
    eddy, 9, 10
    molecular, 9
Constituents, major, 20, 22, 25, 37, 47, 54,
  57
Convection, 20, 48, 49
Corona, 7, 8, 140-144, 272
  condensation, 147, 174
  "constant", 11
  extent, 141
  polarization of light from, 143
  spectrum of, 142, 143, 169
  temperature of, 7-10, 172-176
Coronograph, 141
Correlation distance in radio echoes, 369,
  446
Cosmic rays, 16, 122, 123, 128, 207
  auroral soft radiation, 122
  latitude dependence, 120, 121, 510
  nightglow, 243
  satellite measurements, 122, 123
Counts, of meteors, 523
Coupling, of radio waves, 401
Crochet, magnetic, 197, 198, 450, 488
Cross-modulation, ionospheric, 404
Cross-section, atomic, 183, 184
  collision, 443
  molecular, 180-182
  resonance, 212-214
  X-ray, 185
Current ring, 128
Current system, atmospheric, calculation
  of, 479
  for bays, 503, 507
  initial phase of storm, 500
  L, 493
  main phase of storm, 502, 503, 505
  pulsation, 509
  S.C., 499
  S_q, 418, 481

Dayglow, 219, 260
Deactivation, 226, 227, 241, 245, 247, 248, 249, 251, 257, 259, 312, 315, 323, 325-329, 330, 331, 333, 334, 338, 346, 348
Density, atmospheric, 81, 82, 96, 125
  at high latitudes, 94
  at middle latitudes, 96
  by absorption of radiation, 172-175, 208-214
  height dependence, 81, 82, 90, 533, 534
  rocket measurement, 88, 89
  rocket panel, 185, 186, 211, 212
Detachment of electrons from ions, 246, 326, 332, 413
  collisional, 384
  photo, 384, 455
Diffraction, grating, 213
  by ionosphere, 445
  by meteor trail, 530
Diffusion, of molecules, 6, 20, 24, 29, 35ff, 65, 111, 127, 128, 532
  of electrons
    ambipolar, 391, 545, 547
    at night, 441
    in $F2$ layer, 437
    in ionosphere, 390
    in meteor trails, 532, 534, 544, 545, 547
Discharge, nightglow, 244
  aurora, 322, 328, 343-348
Dispersion, of "whistlers," 401
Dissociation, 4, 13, 30, 63
  of molecular oxygen, 165, 166, 178, 188, 189, 209, 210, 211
Distribution of electrons, in D region, 409
  in E region, 416
  in F region, 427-439
Disturbance, magnetic, 448, 495, 496, 497
  of Feb. 1946, 456, 560
  sudden ionospheric (S.I.D.)
  travelling, in ionosphere, 446
D layer, 379, 411
Doppler shift, optical, 141, 205, 212
  radio, 102, 103, 364, 374
Drag, effect of on meteors, 534
Drapery, auroral, 272
D region, 105, 107, 127, 379, 403, 450
  and aurora, 291, 337

and Lyα, 165, 192
and magnetic L, 494
and nightglow, 244
and X-rays, 186
recombination in, 196, 197
Drift, auroral, 365, 374
  in ionosphere, 447
  (see also Winds)
Dynamo, atmospheric, 392, 418, 439, 482, 485

Echo, radio, coupling, 401
  from aurora, 355, 357
  from meteor train, 529, 530, 532, 539, 544-547
Eclipse, and ionosphere, 389, 412, 414, 425, 434
  and X-rays and U.V., 178
E layer, 104, 105, 125, 126, 379, 399, 414, 526, 527
  and nightglow, 236, 244, 246
Electrojet, equatorial, 396, 424, 480, 499, 500
  polar, 506
Electron, 8, 369, 370, 373
  artificially produced, 119
  capture, 245, 299, 317, 318, 335, 337
  density, in corona, 145
  high energy, 322, 323
  in D region, 105, 107, 127, 409
  in E region, 416
  in F region, 427-439
  in ionosphere, 189-192, chap. 9
  in meteor trails, 517, 530, 545-547
  in space, 206
  in Van Allen belt, 552, 555
  loss processes, 383
    rocket measurements, 104, 105, 106
    satellite measurements, 108
Equation of state, 75
E region, Lyβ absorption in, 187, 192
  X-ray absorption in, 187-192
Escape, of gases from earth, 6, 7
Es layer, 419, 527
  auroral, 291, 424, 559
  meteoric, 421
Ethylene, release from rockets, 5, 119, 250

Evaporation, of meteors, 515-517, 528-530, 533, 534
Excitation potentials, table of, 301
Exosphere, 6
Extraordinary wave, 103, 399

Faculae, 149, 150, 417
Fade-out, short wave, 195, 199, 412
F-corona, 142
F-echo, spread, 450
Field, electric, in ionosphere, 374, 397, 484, 487-489
Filter, for radiation detector, 160, 161
Fireballs, 516, 518, 529
Flare, solar, 193-201, 450, 560
F1 layer, 379, 399, 436
F2 layer, 379, 399, 450
Flocculi, 149, 150, 417
Fragmentation, of meteors, 531
Fraunhofer lines, 136, 220, 225, 253
Free-path, of electrons, 370
F region, 104-107, 126, 127, 379, 484, 488, 489
    absorption of UV and X-rays, 187, 189-191
    airglow, 234, 236, 244-246, 258
    aurora, 291
Frequency, critical, 150, 398
    of E, 414, 416
    of F1, 425
    collision (of electrons) 398, 422
    penetration, 397, 398
    plasma resonance, 369, 398
Fresnel zone, in meteor trail analysis, 515

Gamma rays, 200-202
Gas equation, 75
Geocorona, 205
Geomagnetic
    axis, 16
    field, 473
    pole, 497
    time, 497
    variations, 5
Glow, auroral, 271
Granules, solar, 150
Gyro-frequency, 14
    radius, of electrons, 370

Hall, conductivity, 394
    currents, 484, 489
Height, equivalent, 126, 398, 400
Helium, 2, 24, 26, 28, 44, 45, 47
    emission line (304A), 556
    in aurora, 300, 321
    solar spectrum, 135, 144, 151, 154, 206
Heterosphere, 20, 35
$h'(f)$ curve, 398, 414
Hollingworth interference pattern, 407
Homosphere, 23, 25, 48, 55, 62
Hopfield, bands, 188
Hydrogen, 2, 557
    alpha line, 450
    atomic, 4, 6, 13
    Balmer lines, 221, 222, 299, 300, 306, 307, 312-316, 336
    geocoronal, 205, 212, 213
    incoming, 242, 243, 316
    interplanetary, 203, 204
    line profiles, 222, 299, 319-321
    Lyman lines, 222, 332
Hydroxyl (OH), 4, 119, 120, 221, 224, 225, 250, 251

Interference pattern, Hollingworth, radio wave, 407
Ion-atom interchange, 243, 343, 436
Ionization, 4, 5, 13
    auroral, 355, 369, 373
    chambers, 162, 166
    efficiency, 179, 526
    equilibrium, 144, 206
    meteor trails, 517, 519, 526, 527, 530, 531
    potentials, 142
    thermal, 14
Ion, negative, 246, 326, 327, 332, 413
    ratio to electrons, 384, 413
Ionogram, 398
Ionosphere, 5, 18, 21, 187, 195-197, 355, Chap. 9
    highest parts of, 115-118, 126, 127
    polar, 558
Irregularities of ionization, 369, 445
    in D region, 411
    in E region, 422
Isoaurorals, 284
Isochasms, 280

Kaplan-Meinel band, 223
K corona, 142, 143

Lambda (λ) ratio ions/electrons, 384, 413
Lapse, 2,
  rate, 2, 9
Layer, ionospheric, D, 105, 107, 111, 127,
    379, 411
  Bradbury, 388, 436
  Chapman, 381, 414, 425
  E, 125, 126, 379, 399, 414
  F, 107, 126, 127, 379, 399
  F1, 379, 399
  F2, 126, 379, 399, 426
  time varying, 388
L corona, 143, 144
Ledge, ionospheric F1, 425, 436
Light, from meteors, 523, 533
  of night sky, 219
Lithium, 255, 256
Lyman, alpha line, 410, 557
  absorption by O_2, 135, 165
  in flares, 196, 197
  in night sky, 203-208
  ionizing NO, 135, 166, 192
  profile, 206
  solar flux, 167, 193
  solar photograph, 177
  beta line, 186, 187, 192, 193, 205
  continuum, 136, 153, 154, 187, 192
  series, 153, 154, 207, 222, 332

Magnitude, visible, of meteors, 523-525,
    529
Mass, distribution, meteors, 522-525, 530
  spectrometer, 111-114, 116
  transport velocity, 35
Mean-free-path, 83
Mesopause, 3, 11, 19, 29, 35, 55
Mesosphere, 3, 4, 19, 28, 35, 210
Metapause, 14, 15, 16
Metasphere, 14, 15, 21
Meteor, 2
  bright, 529, 536, 537, 545
  daytime, 527
  distribution, 524
  echo, radio, 529, 530, 532, 544
  evaporation, 514, 515, 528-530, 534
  height, 528-530

ionization by, 208, 356, 365, 424, 448,
    515, 518, 519, 528, 530, 532
  mass, 515, 518, 522-524, 529, 532, 562
  nightglow, 242, 243, 255
  number of, 513, 520, 522, 524, 526
  orbits, 513, 514
  shower, 514, 520, 522, 524-526
  size, 513, 518
  sporadic, 514, 520, 522, 524-529, 531
  trail radius, 561
  velocity, 515-518, 528-534
  visual magnitude, 515, 519, 529
Methane, 28
Micrometeorites, 123-125, 514, 518, 524,
    563
Minauroral belt, 280
Mode, waveguide, 400
  Whistler, 40
Moon, and geomagnetism, 490-494
  and ionosphere, 418, 421, 432, 438
Motor, ionospheric, 382, 397, 439
Mount, 2
Movement, of electrons
  horizontal, 445
  irregular, 446
  vertical, 389, 418, 437
  term, in continuity equation, 391,
    437

Nebulosity, 207
N(h), curve, 398, 400, 414
Nightglow, 119, 120, 128, 219-251
  altitude, 128, 240, 242
  annual variation, 230-234, 237, 250
  artificial, 249, 250
  cells, 238, 239
  correlation of intensity with other pheno-
    mena, 234-236
  diurnal variation, 228-230
  E layer, 236, 244, 246
  excitation mechanisms, 242-251
  fluctuations, 230, 233, 234
  intensity, absolute, 239
  latitude dependence, 228, 237, 238
  magnetic disturbance, 236, 238
  morphology, 237, 239
  patchiness, 238
  polarization, 226, 243
  secular variation, 234-235
  sky surveys, 238-239

Nightglow spectrum, 219-226
  continuum, 225, 226, 246, 249
  correlations between features, 236, 237
  individual features, *see under* atom or
    molecule concerned
Nitric oxide, 4, 5, 112, 114, 166, 184, 192,
    410
  bands in aurora, 303
  bands in nightglow, 222
  released from rocket, 119, 249
Nitrogen, atomic, 4, 6, 48
  abundance, 250, 259, 324, 348
  atomic ion, deactivation, 331
    excitation, 331, 333
    lines in auroras, 302
    transition probabilities, 301
  deactivation, 259, 330, 331
  excitation, 259, 330, 331, 348
  lines in auroras, 300-303
  lines in nightglow, 221
  lines in twilightglow, 258, 259
  metastable, 118
  molecular, 2, 4, 6, 24-29, 33, 47, 54, 68
    absorption by, 134, 184
    bands in aurora, 303, 304
    bands in nightglow, 222, 223, 224
    deactivation, 334
    dissociative recombination, 189, 190
    excitation, 249, 333-335
  molecular ions, bands in aurora, 304
    bands in nightglow, 224
    bands in twilightglow, 259, 260
    excitation, 243, 259, 260, 335-339
  transition probabilities, 301
Nuclear explosion, effect of, 554

Ordinary wave, 103, 399
Oscillation, of atmosphere, 483, 490
Oxygen
  atomic, 4, 6, 16, 24, 28, 30, 47, 52, 54,
    58, 436
    deactivation, 241, 245, 248, 249, 257,
      315, 325-329, 346
    Doppler, widths of lines, 226, 227,
      243, 257, 339, 340
    excitation, 245, 246, 248, 256, 258,
      324, 325, 329-333, 344-348
    lines in auroras, 300, 302, 303
    lines in dayglow, 260
    lines in nightglow, 119, 120, 220, 221

  lines in twilightglow, 256-258
  transition probabilities, 301
  atomic ions
    deactivation, 331
    excitation, 331
    lines in auroras, 300, 301, 303
    transition probabilities, 301
  molecular, 2, 4, 24, 29, 30, 40, 56, 68, 436
    absorption by, 134, 180-184
    bands in auroras, 303
    bands in nightglow, 222, 223, 227
    bands in twilightglow, 260
    deactivation, 227, 247-249, 333
    dissociation, 137, 188-190, 209, 210
    excitation, 247, 249, 251, 260, 333
  molecular ion, bands in aurora, 303
    excitation, 333
Ozone, 4, 20, 35, 111-115, 134, 135, 151,
    225, 303

Peak, of electron production, 382
  of electron density, 387
Penetration, frequency, 397
Periodicity, 27-day, in *D* region, 409
  in *F*2 layer, 434
Phase, of LF radio wave, 406
Photocell, 163
Photodetachment, 165
Photodissociation, 19, 33, 40
Photoelectric threshold, 158, 159
Photoequilibrium, 24, 25, 30, 33, 35, 38,
    40
Photographic technique for meteor in-
    vestigation, 514, 515, 529, 533-537, 547
Photoionization, 48, 63, 159, 179
Photomultiplier, 163
Photon counter, 155-162
Photorecombination, 189, 190
Photosphere, 7, 136, 137, 165, 166
Plage, 149, 150
Pointing control of rocket, 153
Polarization, electrostatic in ionosphere,
    295
  of emerging radio wave, 404
Pole, geomagnetic, 497
Post-twilight effect, 229
Potassium, 256
Potential, in dynamo theory, 477
Predissociation, 179
Preionization, 179

Pressure, 1, 74, 78, 80-82, 90, 125
  rocket measurement, 84-87
  variation, diurnal, 125
    geographic, 94, 125
    height, 81, 82, 90
    seasonal, 90, 125
Pre-twilight effect, 229
Profile, electron, 400
Proton, 8, 455, 560
  flux, 318, 323
  in aurora, 320, 336, 339, 344, 373
  in Van Allen belt, 552
  precession magnetometer, 110
  speed, 299
  spiralling, 299, 319, 320
  travel time, 288
Protosphere, 14, 15, 21

Radiation, from ionosphere, 408
  belt (Van Allen), 122, 551-555
  producing the ionosphere, 186-193
  producing S.I.D.s, 195-204
Ray, radio, 400
Recombination, 144, 145, 178, 187, 245,
  255, 258, 259, 323, 324, 329, 330, 332,
  339, 383
  coefficient, 385, 413, 526, 527
  D region, 413
  dissociative, 189, 190, 385, 413, 435, 546
  E region, 414, 546
  F1 layer, 425
  in meteor trails, 545-547
  ionic, 384
  radiative, 384, 546
  three-body, 384
Recurrence-tendency, 27-day, 409, 434
Reflection, of radio waves, coefficient, 402
  from aurora, Chap, 8
  from meteor trails, Chap. 11
  partial, 405
Refractive index of ionosphere, 397
Region D, 379, 403, 450
  E, 379, 399, 414
  F, 379, 399, 436, 450
Resonance, absorption, 204, 212-214
  bands, 182, 183
  scattering, 203, 204, 222, 251-257, 259,
  260, 339
  transitions, 179
Rocket experiments, 16, 510

airglow, 222, 225, 241, 242, 245, 249,
  250, 253, 260
atmospheric contamination from, 118,
  119
aurora, 322, 323
density, 56, 57, 63
electron densities, 104, 105, 407
geomagnetism, 108-111, 483
pressure, 23, 54, 84-87
radiation belts, 551
temperature, 23, 54, 79-83, 90, 125
winds, 98-101, 250
yaw and precession, 151, 203, 214
Rocket panel, 185, 186, 211, 212
Rockoon, 198, 215

S.E.A. (sudden enhancement of atmospherics) 452
S.I.D. (sudden ionosphere disturbance)
  389, 408, 412, 450, 541, 560
Satellite, artificial earth, measurements,
  16, 163, 202, 514, 524
  air density, 57-60, 64
  ionosphere, 435, 446
  radiation belts, 551
S.C. (sudden commencement), 499
Scale height, 13, 22, 23, 39, 42, 53, 54, 59,
  61, 66, 79, 80, 83, 93, 126, 208, 209, 211,
  214, 382, 528, 531, 533
Scattering, of radio waves,
  from D region, 411
    forward, 405, 445, 559
    incoherent, from ionosphere, 435
  optical, fluorescent, 222, 227, 256, 258
Schumann, continuum, 135, 180, 209
Schumann-Runge bands, 180
Scintilation, counters, 201, 202
  radio star, 450
S.C.N.A. (sudden cosmic noise absorption),
  451
Sluggishness of ionosphere, 389, 434
Sodium, 5
  ab ndance, 252-254
  excitation, 250, 251
  ionization, 255
  lines in auroras, 300, 307, 314
  lines in dayglow, 260
  lines in nightglow, 119, 120, 221
  lines in twilightglow, 251
  origin of atmospheric, 255, 256
  release from rockets, 118, 119, 250, 253

Solar cycle, and D region, 409
  and E region, 417
  and $F2$ layer, 433
Sound waves, 2
S.P.A. (sudden phase anomaly), 412, 454
Space-charge, ionospheric, 396
Spectrograph, 152, 153
Sporadic E, see Es
Spicule, 140
Stratopause, 3, 19, 55
Stratosphere, 2, 19
Storm, geomagnetic, 495, 496
  and Van Allen belt, 553
  current systems, 498
  electrojets, 502
  peculiar, 503
  sudden commencement, 499
  ionosphere, 451, 452, 560
Subauroral, belt 280
Sun, aurora, 283, 286-288, 316
  chromosphere, 8
  corona, 7, 8
  flares, 8
  nightglow, 234-236, 243
  photosphere,
  radio emission, 417
  spots, 8, 149, 150, 193, 409, 417, 433
  storms, 8
  X-rays, 75
S.W.F., (short wave fade-out), 412, 451

Telemetery, 163, 164
Temperature, 1-3, 6, 7, 23, 54, 74, 78-83,
    90, 125, 533
  airglow, 226-228, 241, 246, 252, 257, 258
  aurora, 334, 339-343
  geographical variation, 94, 125
  height variation, 81-83, 90, 93
  of ionosphere, 390, 441
  seasonal variation, 94, 125
Thermopause, 11, 15, 17, 19
Thermosphere, 3, 11, 20, 28, 33, 47, 48, 50,
    59, 61, 68
Tide, 483
  lunar, 418, 438
Time delays, in ionosphere, 389, 412, 434
Transition probabilities, 301
Transmission characteristics, 160, 161
Tropopause, 2, 17, 19
Troposphere, 2, 17, 19, 48

Turbulence, 243, 369, 424, 447, 544
Twilightglow, 219, 251-260
  annual variation, 252, 253, 254
  artificial, 253
  individual features of spectrum, see
    under atom or molecule concerned
  magnetic disturbance, 252, 258, 259
  polarization, 252

Ultraviolet radiation, nightsky, 202-208.
  penetration, 134, 185, 186
  residual at eclipse, 178
  solar, 153, 154, 168

Van Allen belt, 122, 551
Van Rhijn method, 240
Velocity, auroral drift, 365, 373, 374
  group, of radio wave, 400
  of meteors, 530, 531

Water vapour, 4
Wave, characteristic (radio), 399
  lengths (optical), 221, 301
  propagation (radio), 397
Whistler, 16, 401
Wien's law, 146, 147
Winds (see also Drifts), 1, 2, 238, 244,
    250, 293, 324, 343
  and dynamo theory, 482, 487, 488, 490
  angle of attack method, 97
  direction, 97
  grenade method, 97, 98
  meteor method, 536-544
  nomenclature, 97
  speed, 91, 92, 365, 367

X-rays, 322, 337, 383, 450, 455
  absorption coefficients, 173, 185
  in aurora, 215
  in night sky, 202
  in solar flares, 195-201, 556
  penetration in atmosphere, 134, 185, 186.
  photon counters, 155-157
  residual at eclipse, 178
  solar spectrum, 144-147, 168-176
  transmission of thin films, 156, 157

Zodiacal light, 10
Zone, auroral, 359,